WSU

(Stolen fr

MW01097188

D
7D

Agricultural Buildings and Structures

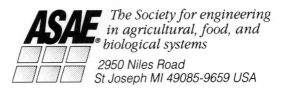

ASAE The Society for engineering
in agricultural, food, and
biological systems

2950 Niles Road
St Joseph MI 49085-9659 USA

Agricultural Buildings and Structures

Revised Edition

James A. Lindley

Associate Professor
Agricultural Engineering Department
North Dakota State University

James H. Whitaker

Professor Emeritus
Agricultural Engineering
University of Connecticut

The American Society of Agricultural Engineers is not responsible for statements and opinions advanced in its meetings or printed in its publications. They represent the views of the individual to whom they are credited and are not binding on the Society as a whole.

Copyright © 1996 by the American Society of Agricultural Engineers
All Rights Reserved

REVISED EDITION
LCCN 96-083566 ISBN 0-929355-73-3
ASAE Textbook 801M0296

This book may not be reproduced in whole or in part by any means (with the exception of short quotes for the purpose of review) without the permission of the publisher.

For information, contact:

ASAE® The Society for engineering in agricultural, food, and biological systems
2950 Niles Road
St. Joseph, MI 49085-9659, USA
voice: 616.429.0300   fax: 616.429.3852
World Wide Web: http://asae.org/   e-mail: hq@asae.org

Pamela DeVore-Hansen, Editor
Technical Books
Information Publishing Group

Manufactured in the United States of America

Contents

Part III: Housing Systems

Preface

In revising this text some of the material has been updated, some has been expanded, and some has been rearranged. The book has been divided into three parts instead of two to emphasize the importance of the environmental control considerations. Also, greater emphasis has been placed on the biological aspects of agricultural structures.

The practice of presenting both IP (customary) and SI units has continued in this volume. However, in some cases only one system of units is used. The readers, particularly those in the United States, should be familiar with both systems of units. Most consumer products in the U. S. are given in IP units—drinks and many foods may have dual units. While many manufacturers, especially those involved in international trade, do use SI units, the construction industry is quite devoid of SI units. Twenty years ago it seemed that the conversion to SI in the U. S. might be imminent, but at this time it seems unlikely that the U. S. will convert to a universal system of SI units within the next decade or two.

Significant revisions have been made relating to plywood based on the APA's Performance Standards. Updates to the section on wood fasteners are based on the 1991 National Design Specification for Wood Constructions. Revisions to information concerning building loads are based on the ASAE Standard S288.3. New developments in livestock housing systems have been incorporated as well.

Part I begins with the introductory historical perspective followed immediately by chapters on construction materials. Concepts of design and analysis are briefly introduced with wood fasteners and building loads. Framing and building components are discussed followed by a chapter on simple timber design. The first part concludes with a discussion of plans, cost estimating, and economics.

Environmental control in agricultural buildings emphasizes the physiological needs after providing an introduction to basic relationships. Chapters are also provided on systems for environmental control. Waste management is discussed at the end of part II.

Part III covers housing systems starting with planning the overall farmstead and then miscellaneous facilities. Separate chapters are provided on swine, dairy, and poultry because of the complexity of these housing systems.

Important contributions were made in preparing this revision. James Kirchhofer, Northco, Minn., devoted a great deal of effort to updating the material on poultry housing. New material on turkey housing was provided by Kevin Janni, Sally Noll, and David Halvorson, University of Minnesota. John Bartok, University of Connecticut, revised the chapter on greenhouses and the sections on apple storage and nursery stock storage. Larry Turner, University of Kentucky, revised the material on horse housing. Sheep housing was reviewed by Harvey Hirning; beef housing was reviewed by Dexter Johnson; and potato storage was reviewed by Ken Hellevang. Bynum Driggers made suggestions regarding the swine housing chapter.

A special thanks to my wife, Carol, for her encouragement, assistance, and criticism. We spent many hours separately in review and together in debate.

James A. Lindley

Preface to the First Edition

This text is designed to furnish the fundamental subject matter for a general course in farm structures for junior and senior students in agricultural mechanization or related agricultural curriculums.

It is intended to give a logical approach to structures planning and design in keeping with modern agriculture. While many design procedures are examined and illustrated, it is recognized that in some courses *method* rather than *theory* may be emphasized. For this reason, table material and standard practice designs are included. Although this text is not intended as a handbook, a considerable amount of data required for design parameters are included. The book should be of value as a reference to vocational agriculture teachers, extension workers, and others in agricultural building design.

In recognition of the use of the SI metric system in Canada and in anticipation of conversion to this system in the United States, customary and SI units are presented side by side throughout the book.

The book is organized in two parts. The first part begins with a brief review of the development of farm buildings in North America. After chapters devoted to the economic feasibility of buildings and farmstead planning, much of the balance of Part I deals with materials of construction and basic structural design. In addition, chapters covering heat transfer and solar energy, air-moisture relationships, and ventilation are included. And finally the subject of construction cost estimating is examined.

Part II is introduced with a discussion of a "systems approach" to planning and its importance in selecting, laying out, and designing buildings for specific farm enterprises. Housing requirements for dairy, poultry, and general livestock are included along with those for the storage of crops, and finally, greenhouses and several miscellaneous buildings are dealt with.

I am indebted to many people who have aided the progress of this book in its various stages. Appreciation and a sense of deep obligation are expressed to the authors of the numerous and varied resources used in the preparation of this volume. I extend my sincerest thanks to my colleagues at the University of Connecticut who have read parts of the manuscript and offered helpful suggestions and encouragement. I wish in particular to acknowledge the help of John W. Bartok Jr., George A. Ecker, James A. Lindley, Ralph P. Prince, and William C. Wheeler as well as Robert G. Light of the University of Massachusetts.

My appreciation is also extended to the following persons from across the United States and Canada who supplied regional information: Gerald R. Bodman, University of Nebraska; Kenneth G. Boyd, Lambton County, Ontario; Theodore J. Brevik, University of Wisconsin; Frank D. Ciambriello, Orange, Connecticut; Keith A. Clark, Vineland Station, Ontario; George A. Duncan, University of Kentucky; W. C. Fairbanks, University of California; George F. Grandle, University of Tennessee; Dexter W. Johnson, North Dakota State University; Franklin Kains, Regional Municipality of Waterloo, Ontario; Michael A. McNamee, University of Wyoming; Richard Phillips, University of Missouri; John Ed Ryan, National Forest Products Association; Frank H. Theakston, University of Guelph; and James F. Thompson, University of California.

And finally, I am deeply grateful to my daughter, Carol, for the illustrations in the first chapter and to my wife, Alice, for her loyal assistance and encouragement during this endeavor.

James H. Whitaker

PART I:

FARM BUILDING CONSTRUCTION

Part I presents basic principles relating to the characteristics and applications of building materials commonly used in agricultural construction. The design of structural components from foundation to rooftop is explored in detail. Inevitably, new building materials with superior characteristics will be introduced and new construction methods will be developed that will either reduce costs or improve the characteristics of the structure. Nevertheless, the fundamental principles discussed will remain useful in developing plans, selecting materials, and designing safe, efficient, and effective buildings for modern agricultural needs.

1 Introduction

Buildings are an integral part of modern agriculture and contribute greatly to the efficiency of operation, the quality of the products, and the health and comfort of workers and livestock. While buildings of today are no more functional than the barns of past generations, they tend to be much more specialized. Often a system is chosen for an agricultural enterprise and then a building is selected or designed to provide the necessary conditions for the system. These conditions may range from little more than protection from wind and rain to sophisticated control of the building's environment.

Terminology used must be understood to make the discussion meaningful. The following specific definitions may be useful:

Barn: large building for storage of farm products, for feed, and for the housing of farm animals or equipment.

Building: roofed and walled structure built for a permanent use.

Structure: (1) something constructed, (2) something made up of interdependent parts in a definite pattern of organization.

Eric Sloane (1966) accurately states, "The successful farmer has been transformed into a businessman and the barn has become a factory". Agricultural buildings have changed over the years as differing requirements have been imposed and new methods and materials have been developed. However, a close look at how the needs for crop and animal shelter were met by early farmers reveals a surprising number of ideas that are still valid today. A brief study of early barns should be interesting and worthwhile.

Early Barns

The design of the earliest barns was largely influenced by labor and materials at hand. At first, only the very minimal requirements were met. The first settlers probably provided only shelter for themselves and their families, waiting until the first crops were harvested to construct the necessary storage. As a quick and easy way of getting that first storage, *wattle* and *daub* were sometimes used. (*Wattle* refers to small branches woven together to form a wall, and *daub* is the mud or plaster used to seal the surface.)

However, in the forested areas of the East, barns were usually constructed of logs supported on low stone piers. As farmers prospered, more stone was used for the walls of the first floor. Eventually the ends, and finally the entire barn, were constructed of

Figure 1.1. An early log barn.

stone. Stone barns were popular in the Pennsylvania area in the late 18th century and throughout the 19th century.

The first roofs were usually covered with slabs of bark, although thatching was also employed to a limited extent, particularly in Canada. Some roofs were constructed with warped or scooped-out wooden slabs laid with the hollow sides alternately up and down and overlapped, much as tile is used today. This carried the rain water off with little leakage. However, shakes, which were thin slabs split from logs 3 ft or less in length, soon became the most common roofing material.

In the middle and southeastern areas of the country, corn was the predominant crop and the earliest buildings were log corn cribs. As hay became more important, a mow was constructed over two or more cribs. Frequently, the mows were cantilevered well beyond the crib walls.

Figure 1.2. Log corn cribs and cantilevered hay mow of Appalachia.

Figure 1.3. Dutch barn of eastern New York state.

As the pioneers pushed West in the mid-19th century, sod houses and barns became common on the treeless prairies. With characteristic ingenuity, the pioneer used wide strips of sod laid one upon another to build up a thick wall. Sod was also used in various ways to cover the roof. The "soddies", as these dwellings were called, were common until the early 20th century. As soddies were gradually replaced, it was common to see wood frame construction used first for the barn and later for the house. This sequence of change probably occurred because the sod houses were considerably warmer and required less heat during the bitter winters. But while the sod made an excellent wall for house and barn, leaky roofs were almost inevitable, and dust and debris from the roof filtered down into the rooms.

During the 18th and early 19th centuries, little or no winter production was expected from livestock. Therefore, buildings were constructed only for the protection of grain and equipment, while the forage was stacked in the yard and the stock was given minimal shelter. As the country's agriculture developed, larger barns were constructed with hay storage and threshing floors. Horses were the first to be given protection, while cows were provided only an open shed. Later, as barn design evolved, stables for cows were added as lean-tos, and these gradually became an integral part of the barn.

Although local materials were used, a distinct European influence reflecting the settler's origins began to appear at an early date. One of the earliest examples was the Dutch influence evidenced by low side walls and a steep-pitched roof which helped prevent damage from heavy snow and leaks from imperfect roof covering. These barns were common in eastern New York. The hewn timber frame provided a floor plan reminiscent of European basilicas with a center nave and narrower side aisles. Fitting with this was a single door in one end of the barn.

The English influence appeared in the form of both wooden and stone barns designed with higher walls and lower pitched roofs. These barns had doors near the middle of each side for drive-through access to the threshing floor. Bays on either side of the threshing floor were used to store unthreshed grain or hay. Mow storage for hay also may have been provided above the granary or cow stable at one end of the barn.

Figure 1.4. English-type barn with its drive-through threshing floor.

Frequently, barns and sheds of this period were built to form an "L" or "U" shape, providing more protection from the weather.

The Victorian influence appeared in the form of steep-pitched roofs, many gables and dormers, a cupola, and perhaps sash windows. There appears to have been a considerable prestige factor involved in owning one of these charming buildings.

The Pennsylvania barn was influenced by the heritage of settlers arriving from numerous European countries. However, it is generally conceded that the South German and North Swiss influence was predominant. Today this influence is popularly known

Figure 1.5. Victorian influence on the English-type barn.

Figure 1.6. Pennsylvania German barn.

as Pennsylvania Dutch, a corrupted form of Pennsylvania Deutsch (German).

The characteristic most often associated with the Pennsylvania barn is the cantilevered overhang that provided shelter for the stock. However, probably just as typical is the use of stone for much or all of the walls. Usually there is also a drive floor entrance above the stable reached from a bank or hill on one side. In many cases intricate ventilation openings were built into the stone end walls. The hex signs, appearing in the mid-19th century, were for decorative effect only.

Gambrel roof barns appeared late in the 19th century as farms increased in size and greater storage space was needed. With the increased use of balers and combines in the mid-20th century, many of these barns, still standing and in good condition, seemed unnecessarily large and high.

Examples of the connected barn can be seen in Quebec and northern New England, although they have a somewhat different origin in each area. Those found in Quebec probably relate to a European heritage where the living quarters are found in one end of

Figure 1.7. New England connected barn.

Figure 1.8. Prairie barn.

a single, large building. In contrast, the New England connected barn seems to have been born from the rugged winters and consists of a string of several small buildings connecting the house to the main barn. With this design one can walk from house to barn without trudging through the deep snow.

Prairie barns seem to rest near the earth, probably because stones for a foundation were scarce, and the low profile reduced the effect of strong winds. Typically, they had doors at the ends to allow wagons to be driven through and a hay door in the gable end through which the hay mow could be loaded from outside the barn. They often had a lean-to on one or both ends for sheltering the stock.

It would be negligent to overlook the round barns that were found in many areas of

Figure 1.9. Round barn with a central silo.

Figure 1.10. Flue-curing tobacco barn of the Southeast.

eastern Canada and the northeastern United States. Probably the earliest of these was built of stone in 1825 in Hancock, Massachusetts, by the Shakers, a religious community with an industrious and inventive spirit. The round barn was a pioneering example of functionalism in American architectural design. The efficiency of the building soon became obvious and many versions of the building, using a wide choice of materials, were erected by people outside the sect. Although years ahead of their time in moving hay and silage, the difficult and expensive construction undoubtedly prevented these barns from becoming more popular.

Eventually there were a number of specialized buildings that became common in the areas where they were needed. The root cellar for storing fruits and vegetables was usu-

Figure 1.11. Air-curing shed of Connecticut and Massachusetts.

ally built into a bank to take advantage of the uniformly cool soil temperature. It was undoubtedly the forerunner of the potato storages of New England.

Tobacco curing barns were of various designs necessary to meet the needs of the curing process. In the Southeast, they were rather small, high buildings with provisions for a fire to flue cure the bright leaf tobacco. A lean-to often covered the wood storage area. Air drying of cigar tobacco in the North called for a much longer curing period and therefore larger sheds. The vertical siding was designed so that alternate boards either swung out at the bottom or were hinged at the side to provide maximum ventilation.

Other small buildings, important to the business or the quality of farm life, included smoke and ice houses, corn cribs, spring houses, forges, and several others.

Changes in Building Design

There have been many changes in design and materials used in construction of all buildings. There has been an evolution from the wattle and daub, and large timber frame structures to light-weight, intricately designed buildings. Farm buildings today may use "frameless" steel structures, flexible fabric air-supported systems, or shells of foamed-in-place plastic foams. The buildings may be simple, low profile, one-story structures— or as in a recent patent proposal—an eight-story, rotary dairy barn.

Construction techniques have varied from high labor demands, such as hewing timber frames, to factory production of components for quick, on-site erection. For instance, a 36 × 120 ft barn was recently erected in two days including the footings. Of course, that is slow compared to the construction of a three bedroom house in 2 h, 52 min, and 31 s by a 350-man team of house builders in San Diego.

Buildings must be designed to achieve their desired functions. They must provide weather protection, withstand the environment, resist imposed loads, and provide the restraint or confinement desired.

Changes in Agriculture

The continued change in North American agriculture has influenced the design of farm buildings to a considerable extent. Mechanization and improved cultural practices have increased crop production. Improved breeding, feeding, and health care have similarly increased animal production. These developments have required larger buildings designed for the specific needs of the enterprise.

Competition for quality farm labor has boosted wages and fringe benefits while working conditions are influenced by new safety laws. This means that modern buildings must be designed for maximum efficiency, comfort, and safety.

The last few decades have witnessed the shift from the small multipurpose farm with a barn housing cows, horses, sheep, pigs, and chickens plus hay and grain, to large, single enterprise operations. The farmyard flock has been replaced by modern, cage laying units housing 40 to 100,000 birds; fruits and vegetables are harvested by machines to be handled in bulk and stored in modern environmentally controlled storages; and far greater use is being made of on-farm grain storage incorporating sophisticated drying and handling systems. These are just three examples of the influence that a changing agriculture has had on farm building requirements. However, that influence extends to the housing needs of practically every farm enterprise in the United States and Canada today.

There has been a growing concern in recent years about the environmental impact of large specialized agricultural enterprises. Interest has been increasing in "sustainable agricultural" practices where animal production and crop production are balanced and external inputs are minimized. Diversity into alternative enterprises such as deer, elk or rabbit production are often considered as a means of reducing economic valleys.

Planning Agricultural Buildings

The first task in planning a farm structure is to determine the specific purpose of the building: What is the building going to do? Two basic purposes of farm buildings are: (1) to provide protection from elements (environmental modification) for animals, products or equipment; (2) provide containment (confinement of livestock, storage of products, or security of equipment). The building design selected will be influenced by the needs, resources available, personal desires, technical knowledge, and construction skills.

Farm building planning decisions will be affected by the expected building life. The planned building life will be related to economics, materials, and expected changes in technology. Many buildings are found to still be in excellent physical condition long past the expiration of the expected life. However, buildings also may fail long before the end of their expected life. Building failures may occur because of improper design, poor construction or unexpected conditions. Building design is based on predicting conditions. Such predictions are based on probability and in some cases materials or conditions will not meet the expectations and failure will occur.

Real Value

It has been estimated that early barns had an average life of nearly 50 years. Actually, with a good foundation and proper roof maintenance, many barns have lasted much longer than that. But the real value of a barn built years ago needs to be determined. As a result of their long life, many old barns, though obsolete, have continued to be used simply because they seem "too good to be abandoned". These barns, designed in years past for far different conditions, are inflexible and inefficient for today's operations. While remodeling is a possibility, in many cases it would not only be expensive but would produce questionable results.

Thus it becomes necessary to assess the real value of an old building for the present enterprise and decide whether it is satisfactory in its current condition or whether it should be remodeled, added to, or abandoned and replaced. The following outlines will serve to systematically analyze a situation and help in making such a decision.

How Buildings Influence an Enterprise

Farm buildings represent a production or a storage cost. And just as a return from feed or labor costs is expected, a benefit from a building investment also should be anticipated. There are at least five benefits that a building should provide:

- Facilities for an efficient operation.
- An environment providing healthful and sanitary conditions.
- Comfortable surroundings for both stock and workers.
- Safe conditions for both stock and workers.
- Desirable conditions for production or storage.

Design Characteristics of Buildings

A number of factors must be considered in planning a building to obtain the greatest number of benefits at a reasonable cost. Some of these design factors are:

1. The functional requirements for the enterprise, such as space, temperature, light, physical protection, sanitation, and safety.
2. A structural design that is adequate for the loads to which the building will be subjected, one in which both original cost and maintenance costs are reasonable, and one which will provide the desired length of life.
3. The suitability of materials, including such characteristics as durability, fire resistance, cost, upkeep, ease of cleaning, insulating value, and appearance.
4. Economy of construction. Costs are reduced by choosing modular dimensions, standard size materials and components, and prefabricated subassemblies.

Problems

1.1. Make a list of the major changes in agriculture in your state over the past two decades and describe how those changes have affected farm building requirements and design.

1.2. Determine the five most important agricultural enterprises in your state based on total annual income. For each of these, list the major building requirements.

2 Structural Lumber and Plywood

Versatile and indispensable, wood has been used in structures since ancient times. Kept dry and protected from insects, wood is capable of very long-term service. The roof trusses in the Basilica of St. Paul in Rome have been in use for more than 1,000 years. Wood has been a popular building material in the United States and Canada from the time of the earliest settlers, and it has numerous applications in the construction of agricultural buildings today. When compared to other building materials, wood has both advantages and disadvantages. It is easy to work, has medium insulating value, and is light in weight in relation to its strength. On the other hand, wood is subject to damage by insects, moisture, and fire.

To make the correct choice for a particular job, the specific requirements must be determined. Then the appropriate lumber must be selected that has the combination of qualities to best meet those requirements. A wise selection requires an understanding of the general characteristics of wood including differences relating to species, moisture content, and quality, and the ability to relate those properties to a particular use. This chapter will deal with these characteristics as they relate to the use of wood for construction.

Wood Classifications

All woods native to the United States and Canada are classified as either hardwood or softwood. Hardwoods are obtained from angiosperms most of which are deciduous trees (those that lose their leaves in autumn). Examples of angiosperms include ash, elm, hickory, maple, oak, willow, cottonwood, basswood, and balsa. Softwoods are obtained from gymnosperms which are primarily evergreens and coniferous or needle-bearing trees. Cedars, pines, firs, hemlocks, and spruces are all classed as softwoods. The classification is not an indication of the physical characteristics of the lumber. For example, willow, a hardwood, is quite soft while yellow pine, a softwood, is very hard.

Wood Properties

The chemical composition of wood, about 60% cellulose, 28% lignin, and 12% sugar and extractives, is quite variable. Fibers in wood are arranged with long axes parallel to the axis of the trunk of the tree; this leads to an *anisotropic* material meaning that it has different properties in different directions. Variation is also found across the diameter of a log. A growing tree produces a layer of light-colored sapwood consisting of living cells each year. As the tree ages, the older cells cease to be active and darken; this wood is called heartwood. When dry, there is little difference in the weight or strength of the *sapwood* and *heartwood*. Heartwood may contain deposits which make it more decay resistant; however, sapwood is easier to treat with wood preservatives either by pressure or other methods.

The rate at which a tree grows varies with the season. Rapid, spring growth is followed by slower, summer growth and eventual dormancy in the winter. Wood formed early in the growing season normally has larger cell cavities and thinner cell walls and is known as *springwood*. Slower growth rate later in the season results in more dense and stronger wood which is called *summerwood*. The resulting growth rings of alternate low and high density produce the grain found in lumber. Since the dense summerwood is stronger, a visual evaluation may be used in such woods as Douglas fir and southern yellow pine to compare the ratio of summerwood to springwood and thus estimate the relative strength.

The specific gravity of solid wood substance is about 1.5 regardless of the species. However, variations in pore space and cell cavities result in dry wood specific gravities which range from about 0.33 for black cottonwood to 0.75 for hickory. Typical wood density is about 30 to 40 pcf (480 to 640 kg/m^3).

The moisture content of wood is usually expressed as percent of oven-dry weight (original sample weight minus the oven-dry weight divided by the oven-dry weight). The moisture content of "green" wood, that is freshly-cut trees, will vary with species, between sapwood and heartwood and from one part of the tree to another. Green heartwood in black locust, white ash, Douglas fir, and southern pine may have a moisture content of 30 to 40% while the sapwood of some conifers may exceed 200% (dry basis).

When either living or green trees are cut, they begin to lose water first from the cell cavities and later from the cell walls. The point at which the cell cavities are empty but the cell walls are still saturated is known as the *fiber-saturation point*. The fiber-saturation point for most woods occurs at about 25 to 35%. It has been found that above the fiber-saturation point there is little change in strength properties with changes in moisture content, but below the fiber-saturation point, strength generally increases with decreases in moisture content. The equilibrium moisture content of lumber will depend on the environment in which it is used, but normally will be in the range of 10 to 20%.

Wood Characteristics

Strength

The strength of wood is its ability to resist breaking when loaded. The strength in bending is particularly important for applications such as rafters, floor joists, and beams. The heavier, higher density species have the greatest strength. However, any member may have reduced strength because of knots, crossgrain or other defects. The strength of wood is indicated by its safe fiber stress in pounds per square inch (lb/in.^{2}; kPa). A high moisture content reduces strength thus requiring the use of lower design values.

Stiffness

The stiffness of wood is its ability to resist deflection or bending when loaded. Like strength, it is an important characteristic for such members as studs, joists, and beams. Stiffness is necessary to prevent a gradual deflection in members which are loaded continuously over long periods of time. In general, the strongest species are also the stiffest. However, there are exceptions such as western hemlock and Sitka spruce which are noted for their stiffness although they are only of medium strength. The stiffness of wood is indicated by its modulus of elasticity in pounds per square inch (lb/in.^{2}; MPa).

Hardness

Hardness is the property of wood that resists denting, scratching, and wear. Although hard species are difficult to work and are subject to splitting, they are desirable for flooring, stair treads, and bearing blocks used at the top of posts, which must be hard in order to avoid crushing. For such things as cabinets and furniture, hard wood is desirable because it will resist scratches and produce a high polish.

Toughness

The ability of wood to withstand shock-loading is spoken of as toughness. Even when loaded to the breaking point, members made from a tough species resist separation. Joists and beams under drive floors that will carry trucks and tractors need the property of toughness.

Dimensional Stability

All wood will shrink or swell with a change in moisture level. Most of the dimensional change occurs when the moisture content of the wood is below the fiber saturation point. Longitudinal shrinkage is quite small, with average values of 0.1 to 0.2% for wood going from green to oven dry. Typical maximum tangential shrinkage values are 4 to 5%. Radial shrinkage may be in the order of 2 to 3% when green wood is dried to 20%. The maximum radial shrinkage for softwoods ranges from 5 to 8%; values for hardwoods are typically 1 to 2% greater. Radial shrinkage of oak, from green to oven dry, may be as high as 12%.

Wood also exhibits dimensional changes in response to temperature. The longitudinal coefficient of thermal expansion ranges from 1.1E-6 to 3.3E-6 in./°F (2.0E-6 to 5.9E-6 mm/°C). The radial and tangential coefficients range from 14.6E-6 to 34.1E-6 in./°F (26.3E-6 to 61.4E-6 mm/°C).

Those species that show the greatest stability and least change are desirable for use with materials that are themselves stable. The frame for a plastered house should be stable to avoid cracks. The best quality flooring is made from woods that exhibit little shrinking and swelling.

Table 2-1. Woods classified for ease of working

Easy to Work	Relatively Easy to Work	Difficult to Work
Hardwood (Deciduous)		
Basswood	Birch (paper)	Ash, white
Butternut	Cottonwood	Beech
Chestnut	Magnolia	Cherry
Yellow poplar	Sycamore	Elm
	Walnut	Hickory
		Locust
		Maple
		Oak
Softwood (Evergreen)		
White pine	Balsam fir	Douglas fir
White cedar	Hemlock	Southern yellow pine
Ponderosa pine	Eastern red cedar	Western larch
Sugar pine	Eastern spruce	
Western red cedar	Lodgepole pine	
	Redwood	
	White fir	

Resistance to Warping

Warping is the characteristic bowing, twisting or cupping displayed by some woods. While warping is affected by the method of sawing, different species vary considerably in their natural tendency to warp. Warping is objectionable because it causes waste, poor fitting, and a generally undesirable appearance.

Nail Holding

The ability to hold nails is closely related to density. While harder woods hold nails better, they are also prone to splitting which can seriously reduce their holding value. Preboring a hole to 75% of the nail diameter, the use of smaller nails, or the use of blunt-pointed nails are methods used to reduce the incidence of splitting. Since nailing is the most commonly used fastening method for wood members, good nail holding properties are essential in wood used for agricultural construction.

Ease of Working

Softer species that have a uniform grain are easiest to work and generally are more resistant to splitting. Wood that is easy to work increases labor efficiency and helps ensure uniformity in the strength of nailed joints. Woods are grouped according to workability in table 2-1.

Paint-holding Ability

Species that have a uniform grain and exhibit little swelling and shrinking are likely to hold paint well. Edge grain ordinarily holds paint better than flat grain. Softwood species in particular should be free of knots and excessive pitch if they are to be painted. Regardless of species, paint holding properties are affected by moisture in the wood as well as exposure to sun and rain.

Table 2-2. Comparative decay resistance of the heartwood
of common native species

Very Resistant	Resistant	Moderately Resistant	Slight or No Resistance
Black locust	Cedars	Douglas fir	Ashes
Red mulberry	Black cherry	Honey locust	Aspens
Osage-orange	Chestnut	Western larch	Beech
Pacific yew	Post oak	Eastern white pine	Birches
	White oak	Slash pine	Cottonwood
	Redwood		Elms
	Sassafras		Hemlocks
	Black walnut		Hickories
			Maples
			Spruces
			Poplar
			Sycamore
			Willows

Decay Resistance

Some species have a high natural resistance to decay (table 2-2). However, for any given species, the heartwood (darker, center area of a tree) is likely to be much more decay resistant than the sapwood (lighter colored, outer area of the tree made up of active living cells). Almost any wood that is continuously below 20% or over 35% moisture content is not likely to decay. Moisture in the 21 to 25% range is likely to result in decay in any but the most resistant species. Construction members that come in contact with the ground should be selected for decay resistance, or better still, they should be made of pressure-preservative treated wood.

Grain

Some woods are chosen for a particular application because of the appearance of their grain. Naturally finished furniture, wall paneling, and siding are typical examples.

Odor

A few woods, such as cedar, may be selected for a particular application because they have a pronounced odor. Others may be selected because they are free of odor and taste. This would be a consideration in the construction of certain types of product storage buildings. Apples in storage, for example, may absorb odors and flavor from a wood that has a strong odor.

Wood Defects

Defects in wood may be either natural or caused by the type of milling and curing (table 2-3 and fig. 2.1).

Decay

Decay results from wood moisture contents of 21 to 25% in the presence of air. Obviously, decay reduces the strength of the wood and spoils its appearance.

Table 2-3. Imperfections that affect grading in stress-graded lumber
(from *Construction Materials* by Hornbostel, 1978)

Type of Imperfection	Description of Imperfection	Effects on Strength	Effects on Grading Structural Lumber
Slope of grain	Areas where the direction of the wood fiber is not parallel to the edges of the piece of lumber.	Tends to twist with changes in moisture content, the components of longitudinal, tensile and compressive stresses acting across the grain where wood is the least strong.	Cross-grained pieces are undesirable; reduction of strength due to cross grain in structure is taken as twice the reduction observed in tests of small clear specimens.
Knots	Knots interrupt the direction of grain and cause localized cross grain with steep slope.	Knots reduce the tensile strength more than compressive and shear strength and affect stiffness slightly.	The size, number and location of knots is restricted for structural lumber; cluster knots are prohibited.
Shakes	A separation of the wood between the annual growth rings.	In lumber subjected to bending, shakes reduce the resistance to shear; they do not affect the strength for longitudinal compression.	Shakes are restricted in those parts of a bending member where shearing stresses are highest.
Checks and splits	Actual split in the wood.	Same as for shakes.	Same as for shakes.
Wane	Bark or lack of wood on the edge or corner of the piece of lumber.	Affect nailing and bearing.	Limited in structural lumber requirements for fabrication, bearing, nailing and appearance and not for effect on strength.
Pitch pockets	Openings between annual growth rings containing pitch or bark.	Have little or no effect on strength.	Usually disregarded except if a large number occur; shake may be present or bond between annual growth rings may be weakened.
Holes	Either a knothole or a hole caused by some other means.	Same as for knots.	Same as for knots.

Knots

If tight and small, knots may be of little consequence. However, if they are large, loose or missing, they seriously reduce the strength and appearance value of the piece.

Checks

Checks are cracks across the growth rings that occur during curing. They reduce strength and increase the likelihood of splitting due to nailing near the end of a piece.

Shakes

Cracks along the growth rings are called shakes, but they produce the same results as checks.

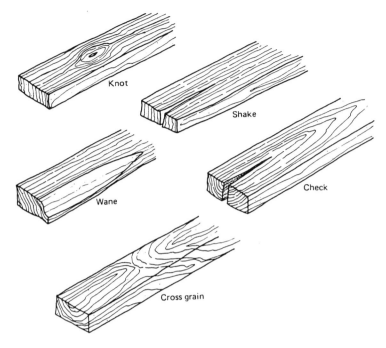

Figure 2.1. Defects in lumber.

Pitch Pockets

These are found in some softwood species. The pocket, hole or crack, with a pitch accumulation, is almost impossible to paint or varnish satisfactorily.

Crossgrain

Crossgrain results from sawing crooked logs. It may seriously reduce the strength of the piece.

Warping

This may not be classified always as a defect, but can certainly reduce the usefulness of lumber. Warping is caused by unequal shrinkage as the lumber is cured, and results in bowing, twisting, cupping, etc. (fig. 2.2). Warping is much more prevalent in some species than others and will be worse for a given species if the lumber has been slash sawn (fig. 2.3) and not "stuck" well while curing. To ensure uniform drying during air curing, a pile will have 1 in. strips "stuck" between each layer to let the air circulate freely.

Shrinking and Swelling

Besides its effect on warping, excessive shrinking and swelling can present other problems. It may result in paint failure, cause cracks in floors or paneling, and in some cases is severe enough in a roof deck to cause asphalt roof coverings to buckle and

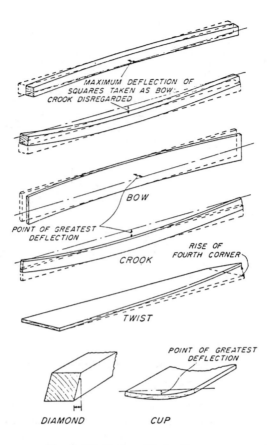

Figure 2.2. Various kinds of warp.

become uneven. Wood shrinks the most tangentially, that is parallel with the growth rings. It shrinks about a half to two-thirds as much radially, that is at right angles to the growth rings, and very little along its length.

Juvenile Wood

Young trees produce wider than normal growth rings and have a lower density and strength. This is called juvenile wood and may be produced for up to 30 years by Western species and for 4 to 10 years by southern pine. Longitudinal shrinkage with changes in moisture content may be greater in juvenile wood and this may result in excessive warp.

Reaction Wood

Abnormal wood may occur where the tree is under compressive or tensile stress because of branches or because tree is leaning from vertical. This is normally seen as compression wood in conifers and as tension wood in deciduous species. Reaction wood

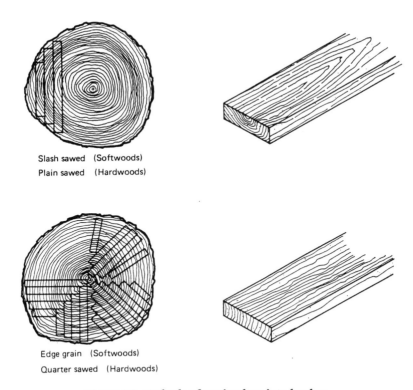

Slash sawed   (Softwoods)
Plain sawed   (Hardwoods)

Edge grain   (Softwoods)
Quarter sawed   (Hardwoods)

Figure 2.3. Methods of sawing logs into lumber.

is generally denser than normal wood and may have greater strength in compression. However, reaction wood tends to fail in a brash manner (with a clean snap rather than a fibrous tear). Longitudinal shrinkage properties are similar to juvenile wood. Because of these characteristics, reaction wood may be unsuitable for use as structural lumber.

Lumber from Logs

The appearance of the grain and its effect on warping, shrinkage and swelling, paint holding, and wear resistance are largely determined by the method in which the log is sawed into lumber. If the log is slash sawed (simply sawed from one side of the log to the other) there will be variations ranging from all flat grain to all edge grain with most pieces having some of each (fig. 2.3). This is the easiest, least wasteful, and least expensive method and produces the widest boards. However, the boards are very likely to warp as they dry. Quarter sawing refers to the two or three methods used to saw a log in such a way that a predominately edge grain is obtained throughout the width of the board. Quarter-sawed lumber is less likely to split, warp or shrink excessively. It also holds paint better and wears well if used for flooring.

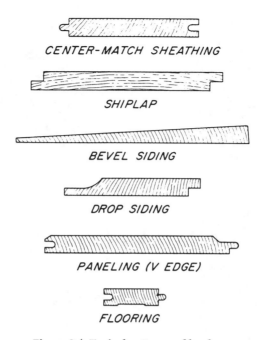

CENTER-MATCH SHEATHING

SHIPLAP

BEVEL SIDING

DROP SIDING

PANELING (V EDGE)

FLOORING

Figure 2.4. Typical patterns of lumber.

Lumber Finish

After sawing, and before further finishing, lumber is referred to as *rough-cut*. Most lumber is planed for better appearance and easier working. It is then referred to as dressed or surfaced. The degree of dressing is often indicated by abbreviations such as S2E if two edges are planed or S4S if all four surfaces are finished.

In addition, lumber may be worked. Lumber with a tongue and groove is referred to as *matched* or *T&G*. Lumber that is rabbeted on both edges to provide a close-fitting lapped joint is referred to as *shiplap*. If a shape or molded form is cut into the surface, it is referred to as *patterned lumber*. Some worked and molded cross-section shapes are shown in figure 2.4.

Lumber Size

Lumber is spoken of and sold on the basis of nominal size. However, the actual size of dressed lumber is appreciably smaller than the nominal size. Note that in SI measurements, lumber sizes are given in actual dimensions to the nearest millimeter (table 2-4). Specific rules are given by grading agencies. The difference between nominal and actual dimension varies depending on size and moisture content, but the following general guideline can be used for seasoned lumber. For example, a nominal 1 × 8 in. is actually 3/4 × 71/4 in. Table 2-4 gives the nominal and actual measurements for dressed boards and dimension lumber.

Table 2-4. Nominal and actual sizes of dressed lumber

Nominal Size		Minimum Dressed Size of S4S			
(in.)	(mm)	Dry (in.)	Green (mm)	Dry (in.)	Green (mm)
1	19	3/4	25/32	19.05	19.84
1 1/4		1	1 1/32		
2	38	1 1/2	1 9/16	38.10	39.69
3	64	2 1/2	2 9/16	63.50	65.09
4	89	3 1/2	3 9/16	88.90	90.49
6	140	5 1/2	5 5/8	139.70	142.87
8	184	7 1/4	7 1/2	184.15	190.50
10	235	9 1/4	9 1/2	234.98	241.03
12	286	11 1/4	11 1/2	285.75	292.10
14	337	13 1/4	13 1/2	336.55	342.90

In order to improve the standardization of actual sizes, the American Softwood Lumber Standard defines dry and green lumber and the minimum sizes for each category. Dry lumber has been dried or seasoned to 19% or less moisture content. Green lumber is that with a moisture content in excess of 19%.

Lumber Measurement

The unit of measure used for lumber is the board foot. One board foot is a volume of any shape that is equal to a piece 1 ft long, 1 ft wide, and 1 in. thick. Board measure is always calculated with nominal sizes.

A rule of thumb that is useful in calculating board feet starts with the number of pieces, the width in inches, the thickness in inches, and the length in feet. Look for the number 12, or a number readily divisible by 12, and divide by 12. The product of the remaining numbers is the board feet. For example:

$$24 \text{ pcs} - 2 \text{ in.} \times 8 \text{ in.} \times 10 \text{ ft}$$

$$= \left(\frac{24}{12}\right) \times 2 \times 8 \times 10$$

$$= 320 \text{ board feet}$$

In determining the quantity of lumber to cover a surface such as a roof deck or subfloor, the measurements will be in square feet. Because the actual size of the lumber is less than the nominal size, it is necessary to order more board feet than the square feet of surface to be covered. The following rules of thumb may be used:

• Rough-cut — Order 10% extra.
• Dressed, S4S — For sizes over 4 in., order 10% extra; for 4-in. width, order 15% extra.
• Tongue and groove — For sizes over 4 in., order 20% extra; for 4 in. width, order 30% extra.

Very little waste is assumed with these rules. Consequently an additional amount may need to be ordered to account for waste. An extra 5% in addition to the above quantities will be needed if the lumber is to be installed diagonally.

For example: an area, 16×32 ft, is to be covered with 1×8 in. T&G boards. The board feet required would be $16 \times 32 = 512$ ft^2 + 20%; $512 \times 1.20 = 615$ board feet to order.

Commercial versus Native Lumber

Most commercial lumber that is available in lumber yards is softwood from the western or southern part of the U.S. Table 2-5 indicates the usage of western lumber. Examples of softwood grades developed by the American Softwood Lumber Standard are given in table 2-6. Particularly in the eastern United States and Canada, a number of native woods may be purchased from local sawmills. The quality and seasoning vary greatly, and finish is to order. The cost of this lumber, often used rough-cut, is somewhat less than yard lumber. Many species are satisfactory for boards and some for light framing.

The National Hardwood Lumber Association has established five basic hardwood grades (table 2-7). Grading is based on the length and width of the boards as well as the percent of usable lumber in each piece. The parts of the boards free of defects are called clear face cuttings.

Lumber Grades

The U.S. Department of Commerce publishes voluntary standards for softwood lumber. The latest revision provides for standardization in terminology, classification, size, and grading provisions. The standard classifies lumber according to use:

Factory and Shop Lumber

This lumber is graded on the basis of what usable material can be cut from the piece.

Structural Lumber

Large-sized joists, beams, and posts are classified as structural lumber.

Yard Lumber

Most commonly found in retail lumber yards, yard lumber is graded on the basis of the use of the entire piece.

Boards

Boards are less than 2 in. thick and 2 in. or more in width.

Dimension lumber

Dimension lumber is 2 in. to 4 in. thick and 2 in. or more in width.

Timbers

These are 5 in. or more in their least dimension.

Grade Examples

The following agencies have developed grading rules which conform to the provisions of the American Softwood Lumber Standard:

Northeastern Lumber Manufacturers Association (NELMA), Maine

Northern Softwood Lumber Bureau (NSLB), Maine

Table 2-5. Wood characteristics and uses (taken from *Great Trees of the West* by Western Wood Products Association, Portland, Oreg.)

Species	Uses	Properties
Douglas fir	Heavy structural timbers, residential building, light & heavy construction, poles.	Straight grained, readily worked with machine tools.
Ponderosa pine	General industry and home building, architectural woodwork, furniture. Most versatile wood.	Soft-textured, relatively free of pitch and resin pockets.
True firs	Residential and light construction, particularly for framing. One of the nations most versatile softwoods.	
Western hemlock	Residential and commercial construction, paneling, flooring, doors, ladder stock.	Strong, free from pitch, works easily.
Redwood	Posts, fences, siding, doors, ties, bridge timbers.	Highly resistant to disease, natural termite repellent, straight grained, easy to work, little shrinkage or swelling.
Lodgepole pine	General purpose, studs, railroad ties, poles and timbers.	Straight grained, easily worked to smooth satin surface. Low shrinkage and swelling factor give it excellent stability.
Engelmann spruce	Rough construction to fine interior finish. Highway and snow fencing, signs, theater scenery.	Lightest of the commercially important softwoods and extremely strong in relation to its weight. Smooth, soft textured, straight grained, odorless, tasteless.
Western red cedar	Lumber for many building purposes, premium siding material, shakes, shingles, poles, ties.	Completely non-resinous, most decay resistant species in America, strong aromatic or spicy odor, one of the lightest softwoods. Long-lived, slow-growing, largest of all cedars.
Western white pine	Paneling, woodwork, siding, matches.	Free of any tendency to split or sliver, excellent workability across or with the grain.
Sugar pine	General industry and light commercial construction, paneling, windows, doors, molding. Excellent finish lumber.	Fine, even-grained texture, readily fashioned into smooth, straight surfaces.

Redwood Inspection Service (RIS), California
Southern Pine Inspection Bureau (SPIB), Florida
West Coast Lumber Inspection Bureau (WCLIB), Oregon
Western Wood Products Association (WWPA), Oregon
National Lumber Grades Authority (NLGA), British Columbia

Table 2-6. Grades of lumber (*Wood Handbook*, USDA-FS Handbook No. 72)

Lumber Classification	Grade Name	Strength Ratio* (%)
Light framing (2 to 4 in. thick, 2 to 4 in. wide)	Construction	34
	Standard	19
	Utility	9
Structural light framing (2 to 4 in. thick, 2 to 4 in. wide)	Select Structural	67
	1	55
	2	45
	3	26
Studs (2 to 4 in. thick, 2 to 6 in. wide, 10 ft or shorter)	Stud	26
Structural joists and planks (2 to 4 in. thick, 6 in. and wider)	Select Structural	65
	1	55
	2	45
	3	26
Appearance framing (2 to 4 in. thick, 2 in. and wider)	Appearance	55

* Percentage of clear specimen strength.

Table 2-7. Hardwood grades

Grade	Minimum Width	Length	Clear Face Cuttings*
Firsts	6 in.	8 to 16 ft	91 2/3%
Seconds	6 in.	8 to 16 ft	83 1/2%
Selects	4 in.	6 to 16 ft	91 2/3%
No. 1 common	3 in.	4 to 16 ft	66 2/3%
No. 2 common	3 in.	4 to 16 ft	50%

* Percentage of piece that must work into clear face cuttings (sizes of cuttings are specified by grading rules).

Historically, design strength values for all stress graded lumber were assigned based on strength properties of small clear specimens; this is still true for timbers, decking and some species and grades of dimension lumber. The clear specimen values are adjusted for the effects of knots, slope of grain, splits, checks, size, duration of load, moisture content, and other influencing factors.

When clear, essentially defect-free specimens are used they are tested to failure. The values measured are reduced by strength ratios (table 2-6) to account for visible defects. Full size specimens are now used for in-grade tests to determine design values for most species and grades of visually graded dimension lumber. Figure 2.5 shows the interpretation of a grade stamp and typical softwood stamps.

The yard lumber class may be broken down into finish lumber, boards, and framing (table 2.8). The first two are graded on the basis of appearance, while the framing is graded on the basis of strength. The most widely available grades of framing lumber, 4 × 4 in. and smaller, are **Standard & Better** and **Stud. Construction** and **Utility** are also commonly available. When greater strength is required **Select Structural, No. 1 & Better,**

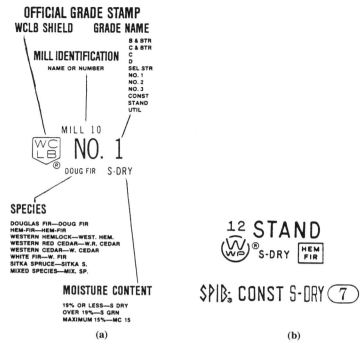

Figure 2.5. (a) Interpretation of a grade stamp. (b) Typical grade stamps.

No. 1, or **No. 2** should be selected. Where lumber wider than 4 in. is needed, e.g. for joists, rafters, beams, etc., **No. 2** is a good choice and is commonly available.

Machine Stress-rated Lumber

Most lumber is graded using only visual grading procedures. This procedure involves inspecting each piece for location, size and extent of knots, other defects and grain direction and downgrading from a clear piece in accordance with the established grading rules. With the visual inspection some defects may be hidden and not detected; therefore in order to reduce the possibility of failure, design strength values are set very conservatively.

An alternative to visual-only grading is to utilize a non-destructive machine test on each piece. Since strength properties can be generally related to elasticity, a flexure test can be used to estimate the other strength properties. Machine stress rating of lumber which is combined with visual inspection reduces the probability of failure due to hidden defects and allows the use of less conservative design values. This results in less overdesign and more efficient utilization of lumber resources.

Machine stress rating (MSR) is accomplished by passing each piece through a machine. The flatwise piece is bent first in one direction and then the other continuously along the length. The average force required for a preset deflection is determined.

Table 2-8. Yard lumber

Class	Grade	Description
Finish • Graded on appearance • < 4 in. thick • < 16 in. wide	A select	Free of most defects.
	B select	Very few imperfections.
	C select	More imperfections.
	D select	Increasingly more imperfections.
Boards • Graded on appearance • < 2 in. thick • 2 to 12 in. wide	No. 1 common (select merchantable)	Suitable for use without waste. Used for trim, cabinet work.
	No. 2 common (construction)	Defects limited. Used for subfloors, sheathing, and siding.
	No. 3 common (standard)	Graded to assure high degree of service.
	No. 4 common (utility)	Graded with less emphasis on appearance and more on utility.
	No. 5 common (economy)	All defects which do not interfere with use of full-length piece are permitted.

Dimension
• Graded on
  strength and
  stiffness
• 2 in. to 5 in.
  thick
• > 2 in. wide
	Construction
	(No. 1 dimension)
		General use where structural grade not required for strength.

	Standard (No. 2 dimension)	Lowest grade stocked by many lumber yards (may be standard & better).
	Utility (No. 3 dimension)	Contains many defects; not suitable for most building purposes.
	Economy (No. 4 dimension)	Admits all defects except broken ends.
Studs • 2 to 4 in. thick • 2 to 6 in. wide • 10 ft or shorter	Stud	Limited defects; strength sufficient for load bearing.
	Economy stud	Increased defects; lower strength.

The computerized machine can then calculate the strength properties and stamp the lumber with a grade stamp. Typical grades might be 1450f-1.3E, 1650f-1.5E, 2100f-1.8E or 2400f-2.0E. The first number is the allowable fiber bending stress and the second relates to the modulus of elasticity. A typical MSR machine might process lumber at the rate of 1,200 fpm.

Preserving Lumber

Insects or fungi may attack wood and destroy its strength. Biodecay is brought about by living organisms and requires the following conditions: oxygen, favorable moisture content (about 20 to 35%), favorable temperature range (45 to 100°F), and a suitable food supply. Wood is the food supply and making this unsuitable will prevent the decay. Powder post beetles and termites may attack seasoned lumber if they have access to moisture in the ground. Carpenter ants utilize damp decaying wood as shelter rather than a food supply.

The best way to preserve wood is to keep it dry, well ventilated and sufficiently above the ground to discourage termites. Where it is necessary to have wood exposed to the weather or have it in contact with the ground, preservative treatment is desired. The earliest known preservative method, charring, was carried out about 4,000 years ago. The French experimented with chemical preservatives in 1831 and a plant to treat railroad ties was built in 1836.

Today there are a number of effective commercial wood preservatives. Pressure treatment by a wood treating company insures deep penetration of the preservative and therefore the greatest protection. Some preservatives may be brushed on by the user with a 1/4 to 1/2 in. (6 to 13 mm) penetration. While this is helpful, it is not as satisfactory as the pressure process. Brushing is useful for cut ends, bored holes or any areas exposed during fabrication. Properly treated lumber or posts in the ground may last 20 to 30 times as long as untreated lumber. Some companies will guarantee the treated lumber for 40 years or more.

Moisture must be removed from the wood to make room for the preservative. The reduction of moisture may result in a reduction of the elasticity of the wood; other mechanical strength properties may be increased slightly. Creosote or oil-borne preservatives tend to return the natural elasticity to the wood which reduces potential damage or breakage of poles during handling.

The size and arrangement of pores and cells in wood affect its treatability. The sapwood of southern pine and Douglas fir is relatively easily penetrated with chemical preservatives. The heartwood of most species, except white fir and western hemlock, is difficult to treat. Both the sapwood and heartwood of red and white spruce are rather resistant to penetration. Lumber that is difficult to treat may be incised to increase the penetration. Three major types of wood preservatives are *creosote*, *pentachlorophenol*, and *inorganic arsenicals*. The preservative effectiveness depends on the type of chemical, method of application, depth of penetration, preservative retention, and treatability of the species of wood. Preservative retention or amount of preservative in the wood after treatment is expressed in pounds of chemical per cubic foot of wood (pcf). Recommended minimum preservative retention varies from 0.25 pcf ($4 kg/m^3$) of chromated copper arsenate for aboveground uses of lumber to 16.0 pcf ($245 kg/m^3$) of creosote for western red cedar farm building posts. A common recommendation is 0.40 pcf ($6 kg/m^3$) of waterborne arsenate compound. However, lumber or posts that are below or near the ground should have a minimum of 0.60 pcf ($9 kg/m^3$).

If misused, wood preservatives can be hazardous. Precautions are recommended to prevent undesirable effects from use of these chemicals. Wood preservatives should not be allowed to contaminate human or animal food. Treated wood should not be allowed to come in contact with drinking water. Wood treated with pentachlorophenol or creosote should not be used where animals might lick or chew on it. During construction, care should be taken to avoid frequent or prolonged inhalation of sawdust from treated wood.

Coal Tar Creosote

This is excellent for protecting lumber and poles that will be in continuous contact with the ground. Creosote is dark in color, produces unpleasant fumes that are harmful to plants, and the treated wood cannot be painted. Wood that is freshly treated with creosote is easily ignited and produces a dense smoke. Fortunately, this characteristic decreases with time. Wood pressure-treated with creosote is primarily used for railroad ties, utility poles, and piling. It may also be used for timbers in highway bridges and guard posts, as well as for marine use in bulkheads, docks, and seawalls.

Pentachlorophenol

Pentachlorophenol is a preservative that is dissolved in either volatile or heavier oils which may be applied by pressure treatment or by brush. The pressure treatment is much more effective. If volatile oils are used, the wood may be painted after several days. Pentachlorophenol is widely used for the treatment of utility poles. Vaulted ceilings over sports areas, swimming pools, churches, and shopping centers are sometimes made of glue-laminated beams treated with pentachlorophenol.

While penta-treated wood is less toxic to plants than creosote, there is still a possibility for damage from the carrier oil or from slight leaching. Other materials should be used if there is any chance of the treated wood coming in contact with the plants. It should be noted that plastic films may also be damaged.

There is some indication that wood treated with penta and still bleeding to any extent may present a health hazard to animals. While it may not be the penta itself, but minute quantities of dioxins that are produced in the manufacturing process, it seems advisable to avoid using penta-treated lumber in feed bunks, hay racks, or in any place where the feed is in direct contact with the treated wood. This would also apply to bunker silos unless they are lined with plastic before filling. Existing feed bunks or silos can be lined with plywood after thorough cleaning. Penta-treated poles, stall gutters, posts, and outside gates and posts probably do not present a hazard. It is unnecessary and undesirable to use penta-treated wood for stall dividers.

Copper Naphthenate

This is available in volatile oils at 2 to 10% concentrations. It will provide limited protection of plant growth structures when brushed on by the user. It is not commonly available as commercial pressure-treated lumber. There may be some plant damage during the first season.

Waterborne Salt-type Preservatives

These are essentially nontoxic to plants and are recommended for use on plant flats and greenhouse benches where plants will come in contact with the treated wood. These include chromated copper arsenate (CCA), ammoniacal copper arsenate (ACA), acid copper chromate (ACA), chromated zinc chloride (CZC), ammoniacal copper zinc arsenate (ACZA), and fluor chrome arsenate phenol (FCAP). The CCA Type II and

FCAP are most commonly used for pressure-treated material, although they may not be a stock item and may have to be ordered. The CCA which results in a green-tinted wood, is suitable for both aboveground and ground contact applications, while the FCAP is more subject to leaching and is most suitable for above ground use. All of the waterborne preservatives leave a suitable surface for painting or gluing. Wood treated with waterborne preservatives is widely used in decks, gazebos, trellises, railings, privacy fences, and playground equipment.

Fire Retardent Treatments

The pressure treatment of lumber or plywood with certain inorganic salts, such as polybrominated biphenyls, can greatly reduce the possibility for the wood to support combustion. In case of fire, noncombustible gases and water vapor that tend to reduce the flammability of the wood are released. Unfortunately, PBB presents a health hazard to livestock, people, and wildlife. The lumber should not be used in any location where animals can come in contact with it.

Fire retardant treatment reduces the lumber strength. Fiber stress design values (the allowable strength), for fire retardant treated material should be reduced by 10%.

Manufactured Wood

Manufactured wood panels include *plywood, composites,* and *reconstituted wood panels.* Plywood consists of multi-layers of cross-laminated wood veneers. Composites utilize veneer faces bonded to reconstituted wood cores. Reconstituted wood panels are made from wood pulp (fiberboard) or various sizes of wood particles (particleboard). Fiberboard may be low, medium, or high density. The high density board, known as hardboard, may be tempered with oil for outdoor use. Particleboard may be made from splinters, chips, flakes, strands or shavings. Waferboard and flakeboard are made from relatively large flakes or shavings. Oriented strand board (OSB) is manufactured with layers of oriented strands and has good structural strength.

Plywood is a useful building material manufactured by laminating wood veneers together under great pressure. Strength and rigidity are obtained by alternating the direction of the grain in each layer. Although the layers usually consist of single veneers which have been peeled from logs, they are also made by laminating two veneers with their grain parallel.

Most plywood is produced in 4 × 8 ft (1200 × 2400 mm) panels. However, other sizes are available on special order. From three to seven layers are used to produce panels ranging from 3/16 in. (4.8 mm) up to 11/8 in. (28.6 mm) in thickness. The common thicknesses used for sheathing grade panels are 3/8, 1/2, and 3/4 in. (9, 12, 18 mm).

Panels may be manufactured to meet the specifications of the U.S. Product Standard PS1-83 and/or the provisions of the American Plywood Association Performance Standards, PRP-108. American Plywood Association (APA) is a non-profit trade organization whose member mills produce nearly 80% of the structural wood panel products in the United States. The purpose of the standards is "to provide a basis for common understanding among producers, distributors and users". It covers such subjects as

wood species, grading, glue, construction, moisture content, dimensions, and tolerances. The Product Standard PS-1 establishes requirements for producing, marketing,
and specifying construction and industrial plywood. The Performance Standards PRP-
108 deal with how a product must perform in a designated application rather than from
what or how the product must be manufactured.

Plywood Classification

APA classifies plywood in four main categories: (1) Performance-Rated Panels, (2)
Sanded and Touch-sanded Plywood, (3) 303 Siding, and (4) Specialty Grades. A number of factors including moisture resistance, species strength, and veneer grade are
important in selecting the proper wood panel.

Grade

The term *grade* may refer to panel grade or to veneer grade. Panel grades are identified in terms of the veneer grade used on the face and back panels (e.g., A-B, B-C,
etc.) or by a name suggesting the intended use (e.g., Rated Sheathing, Underlayment,
etc.). Veneer grades define the veneer appearance, defects, and repairs made during
manufacture. The grades, with some but not all of their characteristics are discussed
below.

Veneer Grades

N   So free of defects and has so few repairs that it is suitable for a natural
     finish and is often used for cabinet work.

A   *Smooth, free of knots, and paintable*; not more than 18 neatly made
     repairs may be present. Patches may be of the "boat," "router" or
     "sled" type and small cracks may be repaired by filling.

B   Also *smooth and generally suitable for painting*. However, sound, tight
     knots may be found along with varying numbers of repairs. Minor sand-
     ing defects, holes up to 1/16 in. (1.5 mm) and splits up to 1/32 in. (1 mm)
     are also allowed in this grade.

C   Allows 1 1/2 in. (38 mm) tight knots, 1 in. (25 mm) knot holes and occa-
     sional 1 1/2 in. (38 mm) knot holes. Splits of up to 3/8 in. (9.5 mm) of any
     length are permitted if they taper to 1/16 in. (1.5 mm) or 1/2 in. (13 mm)
     for half the panel length. Repairs may be of either wood or synthetic
     material and are restricted in size but not in number. Sanding defects
     that do not impair strength or serviceability are permitted.

C   A repaired "C" grade that limits defects to 1/4 × 1/2 in. (6 × 13 mm) and
plugged splits to 1/8 in. (3 mm) so that the panel is suitable for use as underlay-
     ment for nonrigid floor covering materials.

D   May have any number of repairs, worm or bore holes, and sanding
     defects that do not seriously affect the strength or serviceability of the
     panel. Tight knots and knot holes up to 2 1/2 in. (64 mm) and an occa-
     sional 3 in. (76 mm) knot are allowed as long as the aggregate width

does not exceed 10 in. (250 mm) out of the 48 in. (1200 mm) panel. Up to 1 in. (25 mm) splits are allowed, but they must taper to 1/16 in. (1.5 mm) at one end. Limited quantities of "white pocket", a decay that occurs in living conifers, are allowed in veneers.

Almost any combination of the foregoing grades is available as face and back surfaces for panels. In buying plywood for appearance, attention should be paid to the surface veneer grade (A-A where both sides will show, A-D where only one side will show). If the plywood is to be used in any location where high moisture may occur, an exterior panel should be selected.

In contrast, by far the greatest quantity of plywood used in agriculture consists of grades engineered to the needs of construction applications.

Exposure Durability

Four exposure durability classifications have been established by APA: Exterior, Exposure 1, Exposure 2, and Interior. These classifications limit the type of adhesive and veneer grades that can be used in manufacture. Exterior panels are made with 100% waterproof bonding. Exposure 1 is also made with exterior adhesive but may utilize "D" veneers. These panels are highly moisture resistant and may be used in applications where there will be long, but not permanent exposure to severe weather or moisture. Exposure 2 panels are manufactured with intermediate adhesives and intended for protected construction applications where only moderate delays in providing protection from moisture may be expected. Interior panels are manufactured with interior adhesives and are intended for interior applications only.

Species Group Number

There are approximately 70 species of logs peeled for use as plywood. Since these vary considerably in strength and stiffness, they are divided into five groups for use in the engineered grades (table 2-9). The lower the group number the greater the strength.

Span Ratings

Performance rated panels carry numbers called span ratings which indicate the maximum recommended support spacing for the panel in construction applications (table 2-10). These ratings assume panel placement with the surface grain perpendicular to supports and that there are at least three supports. Rated sheathing panels will have two numbers separated by a slash, e.g., 32/16, 48/24, etc. The left number denotes the maximum spacing when the panel is used for roof sheathing and the long dimension crosses three or more supports. The right number relates to use of the panel for subflooring. For example, a 48/24 means that a 48 in. (1200 mm) span on a roof deck or a 24 in. (600 mm) span on a subfloor is acceptable. A 24/0 means a 24 in. (600 mm) roof span is satisfactory, but the panel is not recommended for subflooring. These values are based on a 30 psf (1440 Pa) roof snow load and an 85 psf (4070 Pa) floor load. The floor load limitation is a deflection of 1/360 of the span. Due to differences in strength of species in the groups, the same span rating may be found on panels of differing thicknesses.

Table 2-9. Plywood veneers species groups

Group 1	Group 2	Group 3	Group 4	Group 5
Apitong	Cedar, Port	Alder, Red	Aspen,	Basswood
Beech,	Cypress	Birch, Paper	Bigtooth	Poplar,
American	Douglas Fir	Cedar, Alaska	Quaking	Balsam
Birch,	Fir,	Fir, Subalpine	Cativo	
Sweet	Balsam	Hemlock, Eastern	Cedar,	
Yellow	California	Maple, Bigleaf	Incense	
Douglas Fir	Grand	Pine,	Western, Red	
Kapur	Noble	Jack	Cottonwood,	
Keruing	Pacific Silver	Lodgepole	Eastern	
Larch,	White	Ponderosa	Black	
Western	Hemlock,	Spruce	Pine,	
Maple, Sugar	Western	Redwood	Eastern White	
Pine, South,	Lauan,	Spruce,	Sugar	
Loblolly	Almon	Engelmann		
Longleaf	Bagtikan	White		
Shortleaf	Red			
Slash	Tangile			
	White			
	Maple, Black			
	Mengkulang			
	Meranti, Red			
	Pine,			
	Pond			
	Red			
	Virginia			
	Western White			
	Spruce,			
	Black			
	Red			
	Sitka			
	Sweetgum			
	Tamarack			
	Yellow Poplar			

When structural strength is critical such as for box beams, gusset plates or stressed-skin panels, Structural I or II Rated Sheathing may be required. Veneers in Structural I panels are limited to Group I species and Structural II panels are limited to Groups I or II.

Rated Sturd-I-Floor panels, designed for use as a combined subfloor and underlayment, will have a single span rating. This rating is based on the application of the panel across at least three supports.

APA 303 Sidings are produced with span ratings of 16 or 24 in. These ratings refer to stud spacing when the panels are applied vertically directly to the studs. If the panels are applied horizontally, blocking should be used at the horizontal joints. If these panels are applied over other structural panels or lumber sheathing, then the span rating provides the recommended spacing for vertical rows of nails. Figure 2.6 shows four typical APA grade trademarks along with an explanation of each term shown. Panel selection guidelines are given in table 2-11.

Table 2-10. Allowable live loads on manufactured wood panels (psf)

Span Rating	Minimum Panel Thickness (in.)	Maximum Span (in.)	Support Spacing Center-to-Center (in.)					
			12	16	20	24	32	48
Rated Sheathing								
12/0	5/16	12	30					
16/0	5/16	16	70	30				
20/0	5/16	20	120	50	30			
24/0	3/8	24	170	100	60	30		
24/16	7/16	24	190	100	65	40		
32/16	15/32	32	220	155	120	70	30	
42/20	19/32	42		200	165	125	60	
48/24	23/32	48			210	165	95	45
Rated Sturd-I-Floor								
16 oc	19/32	24	185	100	65	40		
20 oc	19/32	32	270	150	100	60	30	
24 oc	23/32	36		240	160	100	50	25
32 oc	7/8	40			250	185	100	40
48 oc	1 3/32	48				290	160	65

Specialty Panels

There are dozens of combinations of grade, size, type, thickness, and species group; many but not all of which are found in the marketplace. In addition, there are some specialty plywoods which are produced for specific applications. A brief description of several of these follows.

Plyform

Plyform is manufactured especially for use in building concrete forms. It is a sanded panel that has a "B" veneer on both sides and is edge-sealed and mill-oiled at the factory. It comes in Class I which is limited to Group 1 face veneers, or Class II which may have Group 1 or 2 face veneers.

MDO and HDO

These are the designations for medium density overlay and high density overlay. The surface is a hard, semi-opaque, resin-impregnated fiber overlay that is heat-fused to both panel faces. It is highly abrasion resistant. The MDO makes an excellent base for paint while the HDO ordinarily does not need to be painted. The amount of resin in HDO makes it difficult to paint unless the surface is roughened first. The overlays are suitable for cabinets, countertops, concrete forms, storage of corrosive materials and are often the base for reflective road signs.

Marine Plywood

Marine plywood is made only from Douglas fir or western larch and has solid-jointed core construction. Although it is made only with A, B, or overlay veneers, it is no more resistant to moisture damage than any other exterior-type plywood.

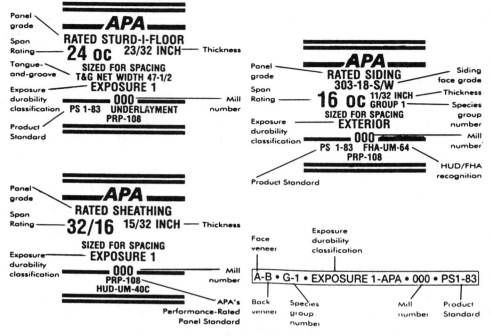

Figure 2.6. Typical plywood grade stamps.

303 Siding

This siding is available in many textures and finishes including MDO. The grade stamp indicates the species group as well as the recommended stud spacing. The 303 siding panels may be installed over sheathing or directly to studs for greater economy. Texture 1-11 panels, now included in the 303 category, are available as 5/8 in. (16 mm) exterior, sanded or unsanded, with 1/4 in. (6 mm) grooves giving the appearance of vertical siding. Texture 1-11 is also available with an MDO finish.

How to Order APA Panels

Sanded and Touch-sanded Panels

Designate thickness, grade, group number, exposure durability classification, dimensions and number of pieces. For example: 3/4 in.; A-A; Group 1; Exposure 1; 48 × 96 in.; 100 pcs.

Performance Rated Panels

Designate thickness, grade, span rating, and exposure durability. For example: 15/32 in.; RATED SHEATHING; 32/16, Exposure 1.

Rated Siding

Designate thickness, face grade, span rating, texture, pattern. For example: 19/32 in.; 303-18-W; 16 o.c.; rough-sawn Texture 1-11; grooves 4 in. o.c.

Table 2-11. Plywood selection guide

	Exposure Durability Classifications	Common Thicknesses	Uses
APA Performance-Rated Panels			
RATED SHEATHING	Exterior, Exp. 1, Exp. 2	5/16, 3/8, 7/16, 15/32, 1/2, 19/32, 23/32, 3/4	Designed for subflooring and wall and roof sheathing.
STRUCTURAL I RATED SHEATHING	Exterior, Exp. 1	5/16, 3/8, 7/16, 15/32, 1/2, 19/32, 23/32, 3/4	Unsanded grade for use where shear and cross-panel strength properties are of maximum importance, such as panelized roofs and diaphragms.
RATED STUR-I-FLOOR	Exterior, Exp. 1, Exp. 2	5/16, 3/8, 7/16, 15/32, 1/2, 19/32, 23/32, 3/4	Designed as combination subfloor-under-layment. Provides smooth surface for applica-tion of carpet and pad and possesses high concentrated impact load resistance.
RATED SIDING	Exterior	5/16, 3/8, 7/16, 15/32, 1/2, 19/32, 23/32, 3/4	For exterior siding, fencing, etc.
APA Sanded & Touch-Sanded Plywood Panels			
A-A	Exterior, Exp. 1, Interior	1/4, 11/32, 3/8, 15/32, 1/2, 19/32, 5/8, 23/32, 3/4	Use where appearance of both sides is important for applications such as built-ins, cabinets, furniture, fences, signs, shipping containers, tanks, ducts, etc.
A-B	Exterior, Exp. 1, Interior	1/4, 11/32, 3/8, 15/32, 1/2, 19/32, 5/8, 23/32, 3/4	For use where appearance of one side is less important but where two solid surfaces are necessary.
A-D	Exp. 1, Interior	1/4, 11/32, 3/8, 15/32, 1/2, 19/32, 5/8, 23/32, 3/4	For use where appearance of only one side is important such as paneling, shelving, partitions, flow racks, etc.
B-B	Exterior, Exp. 1, Interior	1/4, 11/32, 3/8, 15/32, 1/2, 19/32, 5/8, 23/32, 3/4	Utility panels with two solid sides.
B-C	Exterior	1/4, 11/32, 3/8, 15/32, 1/2, 19/32, 5/8, 23/32, 3/4	Utility panel for farm service and work buildings, boxcar, and truck linings, containers, tanks, agricultural equipment, as a base for exterior coatings and other exterior uses or applications subject to high or continuous moisture.
B-D	Exp. 1, Interior	1/4, 11/32, 3/8, 15/32, 1/2, 19/32, 5/8, 23/32, 3/4	Utility panel for backing, sides of built-ins, industry shelving, separator boards, bins and other interior or protected applications.
UNDER-LAYMENT	Interior	1/4, 11/32, 3/8, 15/32, 1/2, 19/32, 5/8, 23/32, 3/4	For application over structural subfloor. Provides smooth surface for application of carpet and pad and possess high concentrated and impact load resistance.
C-C PLUGGED	Exterior	1/4, 11/32, 3/8, 15/32, 1/2, 19/32, 5/8, 23/32, 3/4	For use as an underlayment over structural subfloor, refrigerated or controlled atmosphere storage rooms, pallet fruit bins, tanks, boxcar and truck floors and linings, open soffits, and other similar applications where continuous or severe moisture may be present.
APA Specialty Plywood Panels			
HDO	Exterior	1/4, 11/32, 3/8, 15/32, 1/2, 19/32, 5/8, 23/32, 3/4	Has a hard semiopaque resin-fiber overlay both sides. Abrasion resistant. For concrete forms, cabinets, countertops, signs, tanks.
MDO	Exterior	1/4, 11/32, 3/8, 15/32, 1/2, 19/32, 5/8, 23/32, 3/4	Smooth, opaque, resin-fiber overlay one or both sides. Ideal base for paint, both indoors and outdoors.
MARINE	Exterior	1/4, 11/32, 3/8, 15/32, 1/2, 19/32, 5/8, 23/32, 3/4	Ideal for boat hulls. Made only with Douglas fir or western larch. Special to special limitations on core gaps and face repairs.
B-B PLYFORM CLASS 1	Exterior	1/4, 11/32, 3/8, 15/32, 1/2, 19/32, 5/8, 23/32, 3/4	Concrete form grades with high reuse factor. Standard both sides and mill-oiled unless otherwise specified. Special restrictions on species.

For example:
  19/32 in.; 303-18-W; 16 o.c.; rough-sawn Texture 1-11; grooves 4 in. o.c.

Concrete Form
  Designate thickness and class.
    For example:
      5/8 in.; B-B PLYFORM Class I.

Application Recommendations

1. *Exterior-type plywood* (C-C is the minimum grade) should always be chosen
    if moisture levels are likely to exceed 16% either continuously or intermit-
    tently. In continuously dry applications, the less expensive C-D structural
    grades with exterior glue are satisfactory.

2. For greatest strength and stiffness, plywood should be installed with the face
    grain perpendicular to the framing.

3. *Plywood Rated Sheathing* may be installed as roof decking with an unsup-
    ported edge equal to the roof portion of the span rating up to 20 in. (500 mm).
    Spans of 24 to 60 in. (600 to 1500 mm) require an intermediate edge support;
    this may be provided by tongue-and-groove edges, panel edge clips (plyclip)
    or blocking between supports. Spans of more than 48 in. (1200 mm) require
    two plyclips.

4. Texture 1-11 or other panels applied vertically on studs spaced as much as
    48 in. (1200 mm) apart should be supported with cross blocks at 32 in.
    (800 mm) intervals (fig. 2.7).

5. When plywood siding is used on post-frame buildings, nailing-girts may be
    spaced 32 in. (800 mm) o.c. However, if the building is to be insulated, a
    24 in. (600 mm) spacing will usually be more convenient.

6. When ceiling joists are spaced up to 24 in. (600 mm) o.c., 3/8 in. (9 mm) ply-
    wood may be installed, face grain perpendicular to the joists, without notice-
    able sag if nothing more than insulation is supported. However, blocking at
    the edges will provide a more dust-free installation and should be used on
    spans of more than 24 in. (600 mm).

7. Panels are very dry when manufactured and expected to expand in use.
    Therefore, they should be installed with a space between panels. Panels are
    actually undersized to allow modular spacing. It is recommended that 1/16 in.
    (1.5 mm) spaces be left between the ends of the panels and 1/8 in. (3 mm)
    spaces between the edges. These values should be doubled under high mois-
    ture conditions. Panel size tolerances are from zero to minus 1/16 in. (1.5 mm),
    which helps to facilitate the end and edge spacing during installation. Joint
    details are shown in figure 2.8.

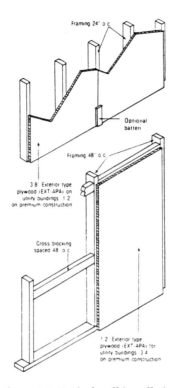

Framing 24" o c

Optional
batten

Framing 48" o c

3 8' Exterior type
plywood (EXT-APA) on
utility buildings 1 2
on premium construction

Cross blocking
spaced 48 o c

1 2 Exterior type
plywood (EXT-APA) for
utility buildings 3 4
on premium construction

Figure 2.7. Typical wall installation.

8. The general recommendation for nail spacing is 6 in. (150 mm) along the edge and 12 in. (300 mm) at intermediate supports except that with spans of 48 in. (1200 mm), spacing is 6 in. (150 mm) at all supports. Common, galvanized or ring-shank nails may be used. Recommended nail sizes are:

    • Panels up to 1/2 in. (12 mm) 6d nails.
    • 5/8 to 7/8 in. (15 to 21 mm) 8d nails.
    • 1 in. (25 mm) 10d nails.

Engineered Lumber

An increasing number of engineered lumber products (ELP) are being used for floor joists, rafters, columns, and headers. Engineered lumber products can span greater distances than solid lumber joists and stringers and are lighter and easier to handle. Also, they arrive at the job site without the bows, twist, and warps that make working with traditional dimension lumber frustrating. The ELP consume less wood and can be made from second- and third-growth trees.

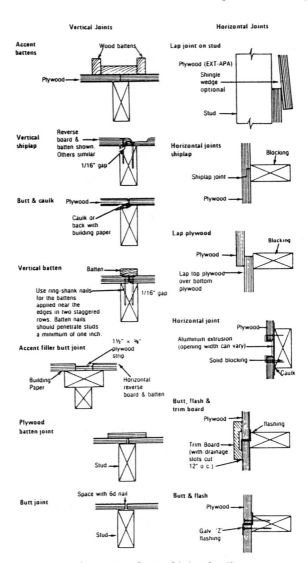

Figure 2.8. Plywood joint details.

Clear, strong 2 × 10s, 2 × 12s, and other large structural components are scarce and expensive. Manufactured I-joists provide a uniformity of size and quality that can't be matched by dimension lumber. Wood I-joists were first made in the 1920s, but were first mass produced in 1969. I-joist production was pegged at 170 million linear feet in 1988 and this is expected to grow to 318 million linear feet by the turn of the century.

It is estimated that by the year 2000, the annual production of ELP will exceed 1.5 billion linear feet. The biggest gain is predicted for laminated veneer lumber (LVL) which is manufactured in thicknesses of 1 to 3 in. (38 to 89 mm), widths of 5 to 18 in. (140 to 457 mm), and lengths of up to 80 ft (24 m). Individual plys are 1/8 or 1/10 in. thick and slightly over 4 ft (1.2 m) wide and 8 ft (2.4 m) long. Unlike plywood, LVL has veneers oriented with parallel wood grain.

Just over 100 million linear feet of LVL (about 18% of the ELP market) was produced in 1988. The production of LVL is expected to reach 371 million linear feet (23% of the market) by the turn of the century. Parallel chord trusses (PCT) are expected to increase from 211 million linear feet (in 1988) to 436 million linear feet (in 2000). Similarly glued laminated lumber production was estimated at 130 million linear feet in 1988 and might reach 338 linear feet by the year 2000.

Engineered wood products still cost more than the lumber being replaced; however, the gap is narrowing and there are advantages to the ELP. For instance, I-joists don't require bridging that is required by 2 × 10s and often they can be set 24 in. o.c. compared to 16 in. o.c. for the 2 × 10s. I-joists typically cost 10 to 15% more than dimension lumber. One lumber yard priced 9 in. I-joist about 40% higher than 2 × 10s.

Parallam, a parallel strand lumber product, is manufactured by peeling southern pine or Douglas fir logs and clipping the veneer into strands up to 8 ft (2.5 m) long and 1/10 to 1/8 in. (2.5 to 3.2 mm) thick. Defects are removed and then the oriented strands are coated with waterproof adhesive, pressed, and cured using microwave energy. Emerging as a continuous billet, Parallam can be cut into almost any dimension, but is typically cut to fit with standard framing. Standard thicknesses are from 1 to 7 in. (44 to 178 mm). Widths varying from 7 to 11 in. (178 to 280 mm) and lengths up to 66 ft (20 m) are available.

An offshoot of Parallam is a product called PSL 300. PSL 300 is similar to Parallam but is manufactured from aspen and uses strands that are about 300 mm in length. This product is expected to be used as a substrate for doors and windows. Typical strength properties are as follows:

Design value (psi)	LVL Products	Parallam PSL
Modulus of elasticity, E	2.0e6	2.0e6
Bending fiber stress, F_b	2900	2925
Tensile fiber stress, F_t	1800	2400
Horizontal shear stress, F_v	190	210
Parallel compressive stress, F_c	3035	2900

Pressure-treated Plywood

Plywood may be pressure-treated with wood preservatives to increase the resistance to decay and insect attack. Oil-borne creosote, oil- or gas-borne pentachlorophenol or water-borne salts are all satisfactory for agricultural purposes. Salt-preservative-treated plywood is readily paintable after drying. As there may be some roughening of the surface during treatment, the MDO panels give the best results when painting is required. Ordinarily the painting of creosote or oil-borne penta-treated plywood is not recommended.

Finishing Plywood

Special primers are available for plywood. They are recommended to help prevent the hairline checking that often develops in plywood over long periods of time. The MDO surface on plywood is an excellent base for painting and avoids the checking completely.

Exterior plywood, used outside, can be stained, painted or left to weather. Painting or staining does not materially increase the life of the plywood but is used instead to produce a more desirable appearance. A penetrating stain will leave no surface film and will weather gradually. When paint is to be applied, it is very important to prime and paint the edge of the panels, as any moisture entering the end grain moves along readily and can cause paint failure and checking. Edge priming and painting may be most easily accomplished while the plywood is still in the pile.

Fire-retardent Plywood

Fire-retardant treated plywood is available and has a flame spread of 25 or less. The material used as a retardant tends to be toxic to animals and humans.

Grain Bins

Plywood is an excellent material from which to construct grain storages. The floor load may be determined by multiplying the depth times the weight per unit volume, as given in table 6-3.

The pressure on bin walls, however, is more difficult to obtain. Nevertheless, a good estimate may be made by using figure 2.9. The equivalent bin diameter needed in figure 2.9 is one of the following:

- Diameter of a round bin
- Width of a bin more than 1.5 times as long as wide
- Equivalent diameter = 4×4 floor area/perimeter when length is less than 1.5 times width.

Using the grain depth and the equivalent diameter, find the pressure zone on figure 2.9. Using that pressure zone, the identification index of a suitable plywood and the maximum support spacing may be found.

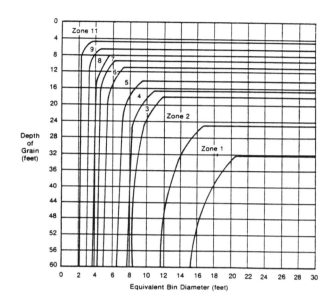

Figure 2.9. Bin wall pressure zones for shelled corn, wheat, flaxseed, and rye.

Problems

2.1. Prepare a list of the species of wood that are available from local lumber yards or that are grown and sawed locally. Note the particular applications or uses for each species.

2.2. Using a detailed plan for a small building, develop a bill of materials for all of the lumber needed, including the size of lumber for each part, the length and number of pieces required for each part, and a summary showing the order and the total board measure. Save this information for related problems in later chapters.

2.3. A single-pitch shed roof 26 × 36 ft (8 × 11 m) is to be covered with 8 in. (184 mm) tongue and groove roofers. Determine the size of the order assuming minimal waste.

2.4. Calculate the total board measure for the following:

> 30, 2 × 4 in. × 12 ft (38 × 89 × 3658 mm)
>
> 16, 2 × 6 in. × 10 ft (38 × 140 × 3048 mm)
>
> 12, 2 × 8 in. × 14 ft (38 × 184 × 4267 mm)

2.5. A deck 20 × 24 ft is to be covered by 2 in. thick (rough-cut) planking with a density of 40 lbs/ft^3. Calculate the following:

> (a) Surface area
>
> (b) Actual board feet
>
> (c) Actual weight

2.6. If the above 20 × 24 ft deck is to be covered by 2 × 8 in. T&G (Tongue and Grooved) boards, estimate:

> (a) Required board feet
>
> (b) Actual weight

2.7. Give the actual dimensions of a 2 × 4 in. S4S STUD.

2.8. Give the specifications for plywood panels that would be appropriate for each of the following applications:

> (a) Sheathing for a home
>
> (b) Cupboard doors for a home
>
> (c) Underlayment for vinyl tiles
>
> (d) Fruit pallet boxes
>
> (e) Roof deck for a barn
>
> (f) Siding for a barn
>
> (g) Wall panelling for a home
>
> (h) Walls in a CA storage

Figure 2.10. Five plywood grade stamps.

2.9. Five grade stamps are shown in figure 2.10. List the items shown on each stamp and explain briefly but explicitly what information is indicated by each.

2.10. Trusses are to be spaced 48 in. (1200 mm) o.c. on a shed. Give the specifications for a suitable panel to use for the roof deck.

2.11. A grain bin is to be built 12 ft^2 (3600 mm) to store dry, shelled corn to a maximum depth of 10 ft (3000 mm). Determine a suitable plywood panel and safe support spacing for the plywood floor of the bin.

3 Concrete and Masonry Construction

Concrete has several properties that make it eminently suited for a wide variety of agricultural uses. When first mixed it is plastic, and may be formed into almost any shape required. When properly cured, it provides a hard, sanitary surface with an attractive appearance. It is durable, noncombustible, resistant to termites and rodents, and is nearly maintenance free. When made with a rich mixture it can be virtually waterproof. Concrete is strong in compression and, with the incorporation of steel reinforcing, can withstand bending and tensile forces as well. Concrete is very heavy and will add significant weight to buildings. Alterations in concrete structures cannot be made as easily as in wood structures. Also, concrete has a high thermal conductivity and thus has very little insulation value.

Important factors in concrete quality are compressive strength, water-tightness, and durability or abrasion resistance. Concrete strength changes with time, but a 28-day test is the normal standard. Useful concrete can have a 28-day compressive strength as low as 2,000 psi (14 MPa). At the other extreme, the ultimate limit of concrete strength at 90 days may be as high as 20,000 psi (138 MPa). With a strength above 6,000 psi (41 MPa), concrete is generally classed as high strength. Ultrahigh strength concrete, greater than 10,000 psi (70 MPa) strength, has been developed by using superplasticizers (high-range, water-reducing substances). Agricultural applications such as livestock feeding floors should use concrete with a minimum of 3,500 psi (24 MPa) 28-day strength.

Concrete is composed of two components: *paste* and *aggregate*. The paste is made by mixing portland cement and entrained air with water. Aggregates are generally divided into two groups (1) a fine aggregate (sand) and (2) a coarse aggregate (gravel, crushed rock, crushed slag, etc.). The cement and water form a paste which, during mixing, coats the aggregate. Within two to three hours a chemical reaction known as *hydration* causes the paste to harden, binding the sand and rock particles into a dense, homogeneous, rock-like mass.

The name *portland* refers to the type of cement which is universally produced by all manufacturers. Natural cements have been used since the time of the Roman Empire. However, in the mid-18th century, it was found that burning and grinding impure limestone produced a superior natural cement. In 1824 Joseph Aspdin, an

Englishman, patented a process in which he calcined a mixture of limestone and clay. He called the resulting powder "portland cement" because when it hardened in water it resembled the stone found in quarries on the Isle of Portland.

About the same time natural cement rocks were discovered and used in a similar way in the eastern United States. However, it was 50 years before true portland cement was being manufactured in a plant near Allentown, Pennsylvania. Today portland cement is a carefully controlled mixture of lime, silica, alumina, and iron oxide burned and ground into a fine powder. Tremendous quantities are used in all phases of the construction industry.

Portland cements are made by blending a mixture of calcareous (lime-containing) and argillaceous (clayey) materials. These materials are ground, burned, cooled, and reground to provide a very fine powder. Gypsum controls the rate of set of the concrete and is added during the regrinding. The type of cement produced depends on the ratios of tricalcium silicate, dicalcium silicate, tricalcium aluminate, and tetracalcium alumi-noferrite in the final mixture. Portland cement is available in five types as designated by the American Society for Testing and Materials (ASTM) (Portland Cement Association, 1952).

Type I – Normal portland cement is a general purpose cement suitable for most farm and general construction work.

Type II – Modified portland cement is a low heat-producing cement that may be specified for very large concrete structures.

Type III – This is spoken of as high-early-strength cement. Because of extremely fine grinding, it hydrates more rapidly and gains strength sooner. It may be specified for cold weather application or when a load must be supported as early as possible.

Type IV – Low-heat portland cement has a still lower heat of hydration than Type II and is intended for use only in large masses of concrete such as large gravity dams.

Type V – Sulfate-resistant portland cement is a special cement that resists damage due to the high sulfate content of water. It is also used in construction that is subjected to severe sulfate action.

In addition to the basic five types of cement, each may have air-entraining agents added and be designated as, for example, Type IA.

Making Quality Concrete

Although much of the concrete used in agricultural construction is delivered to the site "ready-mixed" or "transit-mixed," ready to be placed in the forms, it is important to understand what makes good quality concrete. This will help in ordering and using ready-mixed material or, when necessary, mixing on the job. No other building material depends so much on the user for its success. The use of good quality materials, accurate proportioning, and careful control in all operations are essential to the production of good quality concrete. Any lapse in quality control during any phase of these operations can destroy the inherent performance of quality concrete.

Selecting Proper Ingredients

Quality control begins with the careful selection of cement, water, and aggregates.

Cement. Normal portland cement is suitable for most farm and general construction work. For on-the-job mixing, cement is sold in sacks, each sack containing 94 lb or 1 ft³. Where SI units are used, sacks weigh 40 kg. Cement tends to absorb moisture which gradually reduces its strength, but if kept dry, it will retain its quality indefinitely. Therefore, dry storage is essential. Cement containing lumps that cannot be easily broken up should not be used.

Water. Water for making concrete should be clear, free of acids, alkalies, oil, and organic matter. In short, it should be fit to drink. In some areas, the sulfate content of the water may make it unsuitable for use with normal cement, in which case sulphate-resistant cement should be used.

Aggregates. Both the cost and quality of the concrete are affected by the kind of aggregate selected. Small aggregate is that which will pass through a 1/4 in. (6 mm) mesh screen. Larger material is referred to as coarse aggregate. Aggregates used for concrete should be clean, hard, and strong. Sharp, rough or flat aggregates make excellent concrete, but require more cement-water paste. Concrete can be no stronger than the aggregate used. Easily fractured material or any flaky surface layers will severely reduce the strength of the final product. Excessive amounts of silt will prevent a secure bond between the paste and aggregate and will likewise reduce the durability of the concrete.

Bank-run gravel is a natural mixture of sand and stones. The character of bank-run gravel varies widely depending on the locality in which it is found and often contains an excessive amount of silt and organic matter. If concrete is mixed from unwashed and ungraded materials such as bank-run gravel, the following two tests may be used to check the suitability of the material.

Silt test. Two inches (50 mm) of aggregate and 6 in. (150 mm) of water are shaken vigorously in a glass jar. If, after standing for an hour, more than 1/8 in. (3 mm) of silt has settled at the top of the aggregate, the aggregate should either be abandoned or washed.

Organic matter test. One-half pint (250 mL) of water and 1/2 pint (250 mL) of aggregate are stirred with 1 tsp (6 g) of lye (sodium hydroxide). If the water is clear after three to four hours, the aggregate is suitable. Even if the water is a light straw color, it is suitable for all but those jobs requiring great durability. A dark straw color indicates too much organic matter for most jobs. (Note: Lye is injurious to the skin and eyes. Use it with caution.)

Admixtures are ingredients other than portland cement, water and aggregate that are added to the concrete mixture immediately before or after mixing. Admixtures may be classified as follows:

a. Air-entraining
b. Water-reducing
c. Retarding
d. Accelerating
e. Pozzolans
f. Workability agents, including superplasticizers

g. Miscellaneous agents such as bonding, damp-proofing, permeability-reducing, grouting, and gas-forming.

An air-entraining additive causes millions of microscopic air bubbles (diameters of 0.003 to 0.05 in.) to form throughout the cement mixture. Providing an air to concrete volume ratio of from 2 to 8% will increase the resistance of the concrete to scaling due to freezing and thawing and to the action of de-icing salt. The amount of air required increases with increasing cement composition in the concrete and with decreasing aggregate size. For instance, 5% air might be used with 1 in. aggregate, but 7% with 1/2 in. maximum size aggregate. The entrained air also increases the workability of concrete during placing. Although the strength of concrete made with air-entraining cement is somewhat less than that made with standard cement, it should be used for all yards, drives, and structures exposed to freezing and thawing because of its resistance to weather.

Water-reducing and workability agents allow concrete to be handled with a lower water-cement ratio. Retarding agents are used to give more time to place and consolidate the concrete. Accelerating agents are used to increase the rate of set. Calcium chloride is a common accelerating agent.

Pozzolans are siliceous or siliceous and aluminous materials which are not cementitious except in a finely divided form and in the presence of moisture and calcium hydroxide. Pozzolans include natural materials such as diatomaceous earth, opaline chert and shales, and artificial materials such as fly ash. As a supplement or partial replacement for portland cement, pozzolans are used to improve workability and plasticity or to help reduce internal temperatures. Cements with pozzolan contents of 15 to 40%, are designated with a "P", e.g., "IP". Cements which include the "S" designation contain 25 to 65% blast-furnace slag.

White portland cement is used for producing white concrete or tinted concrete when color pigment is added. Color may be added to normal portland cement, but the full coloring value of pigments can be obtained only with white portland cement.

Proportioning Materials

The considerations governing the design of concrete mixes are strength and durability, economy of materials, and workability during placing. Correct proportioning of materials will achieve a proper balance among these essentials. The strength of concrete is directly proportional to the amount of cement used. The following sections will show how the water-cement ratio and the aggregates that are used influence the amount of cement required and the characteristics of the concrete obtained.

Designing a concrete mix consists of selecting the water-cement ratio which will produce concrete of the required strength and durability, and finding the most suitable combination of aggregates which will give proper workability when mixed with the cement and water in this ratio.

Water-cement ratio. The key element in producing good concrete is the ratio of water to cement. This is commonly expressed as the ratio of the volume of water to a sack of cement. The strength of concrete is directly proportionate to the amount of

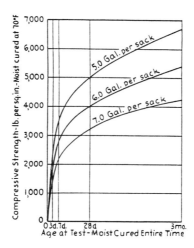

**Figure 3.1. The effect of the quantity of water
on the strength of concrete.**

cement used. For given materials and handling, the lower the water-cement ratio, the stronger the concrete. Figure 3.1 shows that the strength of concrete develops over a long period of time, but the relative strength at any one time is always related to this water-cement ratio as long as the cement-aggregate ratio remains the same. Durability, water-tightness, and resistance to freeze-thaw action are all controlled by the amount of water used per sack of cement in forming the paste.

Figure 3.2 illustrates two factors. First, as the maximum size of coarse aggregate used increases, the yield of concrete per sack of cement also increases. Within the limits of the thickness of section of the finished concrete, the use of larger aggregate will reduce costs. Secondly, for any one maximum size of coarse aggregate used, increasing the water per sack of cement allows the use of more aggregate. While this reduces the strength and durability of the concrete, it also increases the yield. For construction in which lower strength and less durable concrete is satisfactory, more sand and gravel may be used with the same quantity of cement with a resulting saving in cost.

It is important to bear these facts in mind when selecting a concrete mix for a specific job. For example, footings and below-grade walls are not exposed to severe weather conditions. Structural strength is the sole requirement in selecting the mix. On the other hand, exterior walls, floors, and partitions are exposed to abrasion, animal manure, corrosive moisture, and freezing and thawing. Exposure and durability are the prime concerns. Table 3-1 gives the suggested ratios for various jobs. Concrete structures that must be waterproof should be made with a mixture not exceeding 6 gal (21.2 L) of water per sack of cement. Care should be taken not to use too much aggregate, as a fully plastic and workable mixture that can be placed without any voids is essential. Six gallons of

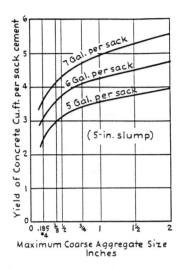

Maximum Coarse Aggregate Size
Inches

**Figure 3.2. Volume of concrete (ft³) produced
from one sack of portland cement.**

Table 3-1. Trial mixes made with separate aggregates

Kind of Work	Water: Cement Ratio	Maximum Size of Aggregate	Suggested Mass Ratio*	Percent to Reduce Water if Sand is:		
				Damp Sand	Wet Sand	Very Wet Sand
Concrete subjected to severe wear, weather, or weak acid and alkali solutions	5 gal/sack (0.45 L/kg)	3/4 in. (19 mm) 1 1/2 in. (38 mm)	1:1.9:2.3 1:1.7:3.1	10%	20%	30%
Floors (such as home, basement, dairy barn), driveways, walks, septic tanks, storage tanks, structural beams, columns and slabs	6 gal/sack (0.53 L/kg)	3/4 in. (19 mm) 1 1/2 in. (38 mm)	1:2.5:2.8 1:2.2:3.7	10%	20%	30%
Foundation walls, footings, mass concrete, etc.	7 gal/sack (0.62 L/kg)	3/4 in. (19 mm) 1 1/2 in. (38 mm)	1:3.1:3.3 1:2.8:4.2	11%	21%	32%

* Cement:sand:gravel.

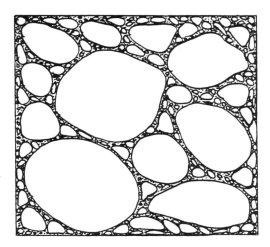

Figure 3.3. Well-graded aggregate fit together so perfectly that a minimum of cement-water paste is required.

water per sack is also recommended for resistance to freeze-thaw action.

Combination of aggregates. The use of well-graded aggregates will produce an economical mixture requiring the least amount of cement for the job. "Well-graded" in this case means a variety of materials ranging from fine sand, to coarse sand, small stones, and aggregate as large as is suitable for the particular job. The economy and quality results from each succeedingly smaller size filling in the voids between the larger particles as shown in figure 3.3. It is necessary for good quality concrete to have the cement-water paste coat all the surfaces and to fill all the voids not occupied by fine sand. If only coarse aggregate were used, the cement-water paste would have to fill in all the large voids. If only fine aggregate were used, the cement-water paste would have to coat much more surface area. Since the cement is the most expensive ingredient in the mix, the importance of the proper ratio of sizes cannot be overemphasized.

The mixture of fine and coarse aggregates as taken from a gravel bank does not usually make good quality concrete unless it is first screened to separate the fine aggregate from the coarse. Once this is done, it is recombined in the correct proportions. Most gravel banks contain an excess of sand in proportion to coarse material. Use of this ungraded bank-run gravel does not result in the most economical concrete, because the excess of fines requires more cement paste than would otherwise be necessary to produce concrete of a given quality.

For the sake of economy, coarse aggregate should be graded up to the largest size suitable for the job. This may be illustrated by thinking of an apple. Whole, it has a certain volume and surface. Cut into quarters, it will have the same total volume but considerably more surface. Large-size aggregate will fill more volume in relation to the amount of surface area that must be covered with cement-water paste. The maxi-

Table 3-2. Desirable range of sand particle size

Sieve Size	Percent Retained (Cumulative)
No. 4	0-5
No. 8	10-20
No. 16	20-40
No. 30	40-70
No. 50	70-88
No. 100	92-98

mum size of aggregate that can be used depends on the shape and size of the concrete structure and the distribution of reinforcing steel. The maximum size should not exceed one-fifth the minimum dimension of the member, or three-fourths of the clear spacing between reinforcing rods.

Not only does the coarse aggregate affect quality and economy of concrete, but grading of sand particles also influences workability, quality, and economy. The suitability of sand for concrete may be determined with a sieve analysis. The standard sieves used are numbered 4, 8, 16, 30, 50, and 100, each with square openings. The recommended range of particle size for well-graded sand to be used for concrete is given in table 3-2. Where washed materials are used, it may be found that much of the very fine material has been undesirably removed.

Suggested ratios may need to be adjusted to obtain the best concrete. Too much coarse aggregate will be difficult to work and result in a rough, porous concrete. Too little coarse aggregate will be easy to work, but the low yield of concrete makes it uneconomical. Figures 3.4 (a), (b), and (c) illustrate these characteristics.

Slump test. Mixtures of plastic consistency are required for most concrete. However, a much stiffer mix will be suitable for a flat surface such as a floor or driveway than for a thin, heavily reinforced member. The consistency of a trial batch may be measured with a slump test.

An open-ended cone, 12 in. (305 mm) high, 4 in. (102 mm) in diameter at the top and 8 in. (203 mm) at the bottom, is dampened and placed on a flat, moist, nonabsorbent surface and filled with concrete. The concrete is added in three layers and each layer is rodded with strokes uniformly distributed over the cross-section. The top layer should be heaped and then screeded level after the final rodding. The cone is then lifted off and set next to the concrete. The rod is laid across the top of the cone and the distance down to the concrete is measured. A 2 to 4 in. (51 to 102 mm) slump is satisfactory for most agricultural construction. Figures 3.5 (a) and (b) show the extremes that might be found with a slump test.

(a)

(b)

(c)

Figure 3.4. Proportioning aggregates for economy and working ease.

(a)

(b)

Figure 3.5. Extremes found in slump test.

Table 3-1 provides suggested ratios of water, cement, and aggregate. Note that the water used is reduced when sand is damp, wet or very wet. To determine the amount of water in the sand, a small amount of sand is squeezed in the hand as shown in figure 3.6, and then the hand is opened, palm up. Damp sand will fall apart; wet sand will form a ball; very wet sand will glisten and leave the hand wet.

Calculating the Amount of Materials Required

The grading and size of the aggregate as well as the moisture content of the sand will affect the proportions and amounts required. Consequently, the most accurate way to determine the volume of concrete from a mixture of ingredients is with a trial batch. However, when a trial mix ratio by mass (weight) is given, as in table 3-1, the volume to be expected from a trial batch may be calculated with the absolute volume method.

The specific gravity for cement may be taken as 3.15 and for aggregate as 2.65. The sum of the absolute volumes of cement, sand, and coarse aggregate, plus the water, will equal the volume of the concrete. As an example of the use of this method,

(a)

(b)

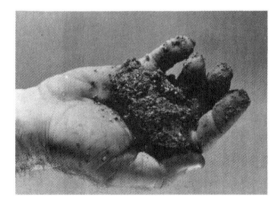

(c)

Figure 3.6. Moisture test for sand.

take the first ratio listed in table 3.1: Water — 5 gal/sack of cement and cement, sand, and gravel 1:1.9:2.3 by mass (weight). To determine the volume of a one-sack batch:

$$\text{Water: 5 gal/(7.5 gal/ft}^3) = 0.67 \text{ ft}^3$$

$$\text{Cement: } \frac{94 \text{ lb}}{(3.15 \times 62.4 \text{ pcf})} = 0.48 \text{ ft}^3$$

$$\text{Sand: } \frac{94 \text{ lb} \times 1.9}{(2.65 \times 62.4 \text{ pcf})} = 1.08 \text{ ft}^3$$

$$\text{Gravel: } \frac{94 \text{ lb} \times 2.3}{(2.65 \times 62.4 \text{ pcf})} = 1.31 \text{ ft}^3$$

$$\text{Total} = 3.45 \text{ ft}^3$$

Thus, 3.54 ft^3 of volume would be filled by each sack-batch of concrete. To make 1 yd^3 of concrete would require 27 ft^3/yd^3/3.54 ft^3/sack or 7.63 sack-batches consisting of:

$$\text{Cement} = 7.63 \text{ sacks}$$

$$\text{Sand: } 7.63 \times 1.9 \times 94 = 1,363 \text{ lb}$$

$$\text{Gravel: } 7.63 \times 2.3 \times 94 = 1,650 \text{ lb}$$

$$\text{Water: } 7.63 \times 5 \text{ gal} = 38 \text{ gal}$$

A satisfactory estimate for the volume of the materials required for a job may be made with the following formula (Note that the factor 40 is a conversion from cubic feet to cubic yards adjusted to compensate for pore space in the aggregate.):

$$C = \frac{40^*}{(c + s + g)} \; ; \; S = \frac{C \times s}{27^\dagger} \; ; \; G = \frac{C \times g}{27^\dagger}$$

$$(3.1)$$

(*Use 56 with SI units. †Use 38 with SI units.)

where

C = sacks of cement per yd^3 (m^3) of concrete
c = proportion of cement in mix
s = proportion of sand in mix
g = proportion of gravel in mix
S = yd^3 (m^3) of sand per yd^3 (m^3) of concrete
G = yd^3 (m^3) of gravel per yd^3 (m^3) of concrete

For example, suppose a job will require 5 yd^3 of concrete. Determine the quantity of materials to order when a 1:2:3 ratio by volume of cement, sand, and gravel will be used.

$$C = \frac{40}{(1 + 2 + 3)} = 6.67 \text{ sacks of cement} / yd^3 \text{ concrete}$$

$$S = \frac{6.67 \times 2}{27} = 0.49 \text{ yd}^3 \text{ sand} / yd^3 \text{ concrete}$$

$$G = \frac{6.67 \times 3}{27} = 0.74 \text{ yd}^3 \text{ gravel} / yd^3 \text{ concrete}$$

For the job:

$$5 \times 6.67 = 33.4 \text{ or } 34 \text{ sacks of cement}$$

$$5 \times 0.49 = 2.45 \text{ or } 3 \text{ yd}^3 \text{ of sand}$$

$$5 \times 0.74 = 3.7 \text{ or } 4 \text{ yd}^3 \text{ of gravel}$$

Inasmuch as they are inexpensive, the aggregates are rounded up to the nearest cubic yard. Leftover cement that is undamaged and not opened may be returned.

In measuring the materials during the mixing operation, nothing is as accurate as weighing. This is particularly true with sand where a change of 2% in moisture causes a similar change in weight required. However, that same 2% change might result in a 10% change in the volume required because of the bulking characteristic of damp sand.

Mixing

The purpose of mixing is to achieve a uniform distribution of the ingredients. Thorough mixing of concrete is essential to obtain a plastic and workable mixture. Normally a sufficiently uniform mixture is achieved in a minute or less with batches of 1 yd^3 or smaller. Larger batches should be mixed an additional 15 s/yd^3. In using a power mixer at the site, it is desirable to put the materials in the mixer in the following order: the measured quantity of water, a little aggregate, the measured amount of cement, and then the balance of the aggregate for the desired consistency. More water should not be added at any time.

Excessive mixing can result in loss of concrete strength, a rise in temperature, excessive loss of entrained air, and rapid loss of slump. When truck mixers are used, the ASTM guidelines call for 70 to 100 revolutions at mixing speed and a maximum of 300 revolutions at mixing and agitating speeds. Mixing speeds are generally 6 to 18 rpm and agitating speeds are 2 to 6 rpm. The concrete should be delivered and discharged within 1 1/2 h.

If a small amount of concrete for an odd job must be mixed by hand, the usual procedure is as follows: spread the measured amount of sand on a flat, watertight surface and distribute the required amount of cement over it evenly. Use a shovel to turn the cement and sand over until a uniform color indicates they are thoroughly mixed. Spread out this mixture and add the measured coarse aggregate in a layer over the top. Again turn with a shovel until the coarse aggregate is evenly distributed. At least three turnings are necessary. Form a hollow in the center of this mixture and slowly add the measured water, while at the same time turning the material towards the center. Continue mixing in this manner until all ingredients are thoroughly and uniformly combined and the desired workability and smoothness are obtained.

Forms

Forms should be ready and in place before the concrete is mixed or before the ready-mix arrives. They may be made of any of several materials including plywood, steel or sheathing to be used on the building. The forms should be clean, tight, and rigid, and tied together with form ties to prevent bulging. They must also be tied down to prevent floating. It should be remembered that concrete has a density of nearly three times that of water. Thus, wood forms will readily float unless they are well anchored.

Forms must support the weight of concrete and construction live loads. Concrete density is normally between 140 and 150 pcf. The construction live load is commonly assumed to be 75 pcf. Lateral pressure imposed on wall or column forms is influenced by the density of concrete, rate of placement, method of placing, and the temperature. Variations in mixture, size, and shape of forms, and the amount and location of reinforcing also affect lateral pressure, but except for special aggregate these effects are small. When concrete is placed by hand, the effective pressure increases with depth until by compaction and/or hardening the concrete tends to support itself. High frequency vibration causes the concrete to act as a fluid for its full depth. The American Concrete Institute recommends that the following formula be used for vibrated concrete in vertical forms:

$$p = 150 + \frac{9,000 \ R}{T} \qquad (3.2)$$

where
  p = maximum lateral pressure (psf)
  R = rate of placement (ft/h)
  T = temperature of concrete in forms (°F)
  (Maximum values: 3,000 psf for columns and 2,000 psf for walls)

To facilitate removal and to give a better surface to the concrete, wood forms should be oiled with form oil or used, crankcase oil prior to placement of the concrete. Earth forms should be firm and smooth.

In warm weather, forms may be removed from footings or foundations in 24 h. However, concrete which is fully supported by forms, such as floor slabs or beams, may need four to five days of curing before it is safe to remove the forms.

Placing the Concrete

Before placing the concrete, the job site must be properly prepared. Subgrades should be uniformly graded and compacted. If the supporting earth is extremely dry, it should be dampened to prevent absorption of the mixing water from the concrete. Steel reinforcement rods, if needed, should be in place.

Concrete placement should be done when the plastic mixture has a mushy, not soupy, texture. To prevent segregation of the aggregates, it is important not to "flow" the concrete any more than necessary. It is equally important not to drop the concrete more than 3 ft (1 m). Chutes are recommended when concrete must be dropped more than 3 to 4 ft. In deep forms, it is desirable to place the concrete in 6 to 12 in. (150 to 300 mm) layers. Spading and tamping, or vibrating with a mechanical vibrator, to remove all entrapped air pockets is essential for a dense, smooth job. But again, too much will cause segregation.

Finishing

Immediately after the concrete is in place, it is struck off with a straight edge, usually a 2 × 4 in. (38 × 89 mm) or 2 × 6 in. (38 × 140 mm) board. This action is called *screeding* and it removes all humps and hollows, leaving an even surface. In screeding, the use of short strokes avoids tearing the surface. Soon after screeding, the surface may be floated, that is, smoothed somewhat, with a *darby* or a *bullfloat*. A darby is a flat wooden float about 6 in. × 3 ft (150 mm × 1 m), and a bullfloat is a large, flat rectangular piece of wood, aluminum or magnesium about 8 in. × 2 to 5 ft (200 mm × 0.6 to 1.5 m) long equipped with a long handle. The surface should not be worked again until the concrete has begun to set and the free water has disappeared from the surface.

The type of finish depends on the tool used. A wood or magnesium float will leave a sand finish. Brooming or scoring will produce an anti-skid surface. Aluminum oxide grit may be added at this time to give an anti-skid surface. A steel trowel leaves a smooth, dense surface. The timing of steel troweling is critical. If done prematurely, it brings a mixture of water, cement, and fine sand to the surface, resulting in a surface that will flake or develop numerous fine cracks. Regardless of the type of finish, the surface should not be overworked, and dry cement or water should never be added to the surface during working.

Slabs poured over polyethylene film are slow to reach working condition. It is desirable to pour the concrete in the afternoon for finishing the following morning. Unvented oil heaters in rooms where concrete is being poured should be avoided as the CO_2 will cause the surface to powder.

Exposed concrete walls may be improved in appearance by first saturating the surface and then brushing on a grout made of one part cement to one and one-half to two parts of sand. The surface is then vigorously scoured with a wood or cork float. A rubber float may then be used to remove excess grout, and after drying, the surface is rubbed with burlap to remove all signs of the grout. Moist curing is continued for at least two days.

Curing

Fresh concrete develops 70% of its potential strength and durability during the first seven days of curing. During this critical period, the concrete must be protected from freezing and excessive heat, and kept continually damp. Cured in this way, concrete will be as much as 50% stronger than that which is allowed to dry out quickly. Damp sand or moist straw is commonly used to protect the newly placed concrete and should be kept wet by sprinkling. Covering the concrete with plastic film or other watertight material to seal in the moisture is another satisfactory method.

Curing at 70 to 80°F (20 to 30°C) is optimum but not essential. As temperatures decrease, hardening takes place more and more slowly until at 32°F (0°C) it ceases altogether. If freezing takes place during the first 24 h, permanent injury to the concrete is almost certain.

Cold weather curing. If concrete must be placed in cold weather, the ground must first be thawed. The freshly mixed concrete should be between 50 and 70°F (10 and 20°C) when it is placed in the forms. To achieve this, the mix water can be heated as high as 150°F (65°C) and when air temperatures are below 30°F (–1°C) it may be necessary to heat the aggregate as well. As soon as the concrete is placed, it should be covered and maintained at 50°F (10°C) for seven days.

Type III, high-early-strength cement is often used for winter concrete work because it sets more rapidly than Type I portland cement. When Type I portland cement is used in cold weather, replacing 2 to 4% of the cement with calcium chloride will hasten setting but will have little effect on the freezing point. Calcium chloride should not be used in concrete that will have aluminum conduit imbedded within it.

Hot weather curing. During hot, dry weather special precautions must be taken to keep the concrete moist and cool. Concrete placed in the late afternoon takes advantage of the cooler evening temperatures. The subgrade and wood forms should be dampened so they will not absorb water from the mix. After placing, the concrete must be kept constantly wet to avoid alternate wetting and drying during the curing period. Water not only acts as a curing agent, but also cools the cement. Satisfactory curing conditions can also be maintained by directing a fine spray of water directly on the concrete as soon as it has set firmly enough to avoid damage from the spray.

Joints

Three types of joints may be used when pouring floors or slabs: isolation, control, and construction. Joints relieve stresses that might occur because of shrinkage or movement of the slab.

Isolation joints are used to separate floors from points of abutment with walls, columns or building footings. The floor is then permitted to move independently. A resilient or flexible material can be placed in the joint.

Control joints are used to determine where shrinkage cracks will occur. These joints are sometimes called contraction joints and should be spaced every 10 to 15 ft (3 to 5 m) in slabs or every 3 to 4 ft (1.0 to 1.3 m) in sidewalks. A groover can be used to make grooves about 1 in. deep soon after the concrete has been placed. A saw may be used to cut the grooves to a depth of 1/5 to 1/3 of the slab thickness. The joints may be cut 6 h or more after the concrete is placed.

Construction joints in slabs are used where concrete placing is discontinued and then resumed later. A keyway should be formed in the edge of the slab using a wooden or metal key on the form. When the keyway form is removed, the next pour will conform to the keyway to provide a vertical load transfer. The keyway can be coated with form oil to prevent the second pour from bonding, thus allowing horizontal movement.

Using Ready-mix Concrete

Fresh concrete mixed and ready to use is commonly available at competitive prices from ready-mix plants. These plants have the expertise and design aids to provide high quality concrete of the desired characteristics. However, it is necessary to provide them with information regarding the needed strength, workability, aggregate size, quantity, and any special needs. Concrete strength should be specified as to the 28-day compressive strength. The amount of cement used per cubic yard of concrete will strongly influence the concrete strength, but it is not the sole determining factor and thus not an adequate specification. Many agricultural applications do not necessarily require a high strength concrete; however, higher strength concrete is more resistant to freeze-thaw action and thus may be desirable. Table 3-3 provides a guide for ordering ready-mixed concrete for various types of work. Remember that concrete strength is greatly affected by water-cement ratio and adding water to concrete will reduce its strength. The driver should not be asked or allowed to dilute the mix with water to get it to flow more easily.

Ready-mixed concrete is almost always well-mixed when it arrives on the job. Over-mixing can be detrimental because small bonds which are formed as the water and cement come into contact will be broken. ASTM Standard C94 specifies that concrete be mixed for no more than 100 revolutions at mixing speed (6 to 18 rpm). Additional drum rotation at agitating speed (2 to 6 rpm) up to a total of 300 revolutions is allowed. Also, concrete should be delivered and discharged within 1 1/2 h after introduction of water to the cement.

Reinforced Concrete

Although concrete has a high compressive strength, it has relatively low tensile strength. To compensate for this weakness, steel reinforcing rods are imbedded in the area of concrete subject to tensile stress. Reinforced concrete structures are more rigid than steel and are virtually fireproof. Reinforcement of floor slabs poured on grade also reduces the chance of cracking due to changes in temperature. The design of reinforced structures is a complex subject and will not be covered here. Proper selection and placement of steel are essential to the performance of reinforced concrete.

Reinforcing steel is deformed to improve the bonding with the concrete. Steel rods or bars (rebars) are available with a minimum yield strength of 40,000 psi (276 MPa) (Type 40) or 60,000 psi (414 MPa) (Type 60). The bar number indicates the diameter in eighths of an inch, i.e., a no. 5 bar has a diameter of 5/8 in. (Metric rebars are sized in multiples of 100 mm^2 and designated with a number close to the diameter in mil-

Table 3-3. Guide for ordering ready-mixed concrete
(Specifications for medium consistency concrete — 3 in. slump)

Kind of Job	Approx. Strength (psi)	Minimum Bags of Cement per Cubic Yard	Gallons Water/Bag of Cement	Water-cement Ratio (lb Water per lb Cement)
Flatwork (maximum aggregate size 1 1/2 in.)				
Severe exposure: (above-ground bunker silos, floors in dairy plant)	4500	7	5	0.44
Normal exposure: (feedlots, floors, drives, sidewalks)	3500	6	6	0.53
Mild exposure: (building footings)	2500	5	7	0.62
Formed work: (maximum aggregate size 3/4 in.)				
Severe exposure: (feedbunks, slat, manure storage tanks)	4500	7-3/4	5	0.44
Normal exposure: (reinforced walls, open top or ventilated manure tanks)	3500	6-1/2	6	0.53
Mild exposure: (foundations)	2500	5-1/2	7	0.62

limeters (mm). A no. 10 bar has a diameter of 11.3 mm and a cross-section of 100 mm^2. A no. 15 bar is 16.0 mm diameter and 200 mm^2 in area). Properties of steel reinforcing bars are shown in table 3-4.

Welded wire fabric or mesh is an alternative means of reinforcing (see table 3-5). It may be difficult or impossible to get sufficient steel area with wire mesh to provide for significant bending stresses; however wire may economically improve the performance of flat slabs. Mesh is typically available in rolls of 100 ft (30 m) × 4 or 5 ft (1.2 to 1.5 m) widths.

Reinforcing steel must be clean and relatively rust-free to allow good bonding with the concrete. For full strength development, the steel must be completely surrounded by concrete—normally a minimum of 1 to 11/2 in. (25 to 38 mm) of concrete should cover the steel.

Cracks in concrete which expose the rebar to corrosive conditions can lead to premature failure. Rust on steel bars causes expansion and further cracking. If such a problem is anticipated, rebars can be epoxy coated, or glass-fiber reinforced plastic bars are available.

Tensile strength of concrete may be improved by using steel fibers which are 1 to 2 in. (25 to 50 mm) long with a diameter of 0.01 to 0.02 in. (0.25 to 0.50 mm) at the rate of 1 to 2% by volume. Such fibers have been used to allow forming sandwich panels of concrete and foam insulation with 1/2 in. thick concrete. Polypropylene fibers have been used at the rate of 1.5 lb/yd^3 (0.9 kg/m^3 (0.1% v/v). Polymer spheres (0.000008 in. [200 nm] diameter) have been used in thin concrete to provide light weight concrete with low water absorption and low thermal conductivity.

Table 3-4. (a) Properties of steel reinforcing bars (IP)

Bar Size	Diameter (in.)	Weight (lbs/ft)	Cross-sectional Area (in.^{2})
3	0.375	0.376	0.11
4	0.500	0.668	0.20
5	0.625	1.043	0.31
6	0.750	1.502	0.44
7	0.875	2.044	0.60
8	1.000	2.670	0.79

Table 3-4. (b) Properties of steel reinforcing bars (SI)

Bar Size	Diameter (mm)	Cross-sectional Area (mm^2)
10	11.3	100
15	16.0	200
20	19.5	300
25	25.2	500
30	29.9	700
35	35.7	1,000

Table 3-5. Properties of steel reinforcing mesh

Style Size Wire Gauge	Wire Spacing (in.)	Wire Diameter (in.)	Weight (lbs/100 ft.^{2})
6 × 6 - 10 × 10	6 × 6	0.135	21
6 × 6 - 8 × 8	6 × 6	0.162	30
6 × 6 - 6 × 6	6 × 6	0.192	42
4 × 4 - 10 × 10	4 × 4	0.135	31
4 × 4 - 8 × 8	4 × 4	0.162	44
4 × 4 - 6 × 6	4 × 4	0.192	62

Concrete Masonry

Walls constructed with stones, bricks, tile or concrete blocks bonded together with cement mortar are described as masonry construction. This type of construction is popular because it is durable, fire resistant, low in maintenance, and attractive in appearance. It is not affected by high humidity, termites or most agricultural products and wastes. However, because masonry construction is more porous and more subject to cracking than concrete, it is difficult to make watertight.

Concrete Masonry Units

Of the previously mentioned masonry units, the concrete block is by far the most common for agricultural use, resulting no doubt from the fact that it is the least expensive "in place". These blocks come in a number of different shapes and sizes (fig. 3.7). Some of the more common types along with their nominal sizes and typical uses are shown in table 3-6.

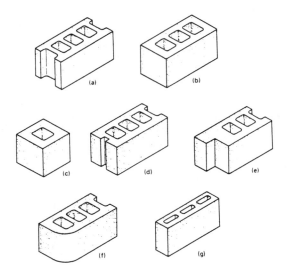

Figure 3.7. Shapes of concrete masonry units.

Actual sizes are 3/8 in. (10 mm) less than nominal in each dimension. However, when laid in place with mortar, the length and height should equal the nominal dimensions.

Several of the blocks are also available in 12 in. (300 mm) widths when greater wall loads are expected or where greater lateral stability is required. Although less common, 6 in. (150 mm) and 10 in. (250 mm) blocks are available in some localities. Lightweight aggregate blocks are available in several of these sizes. They are not quite as strong and are likely to be slightly more expensive.

Table 3-6. Masonry units

Key to Figures 3-7	Block	(in.)	(mm)	Typical Units
a	Stretcher	8 × 8 × 16	200 × 200 × 400	For the bulk of the wall
b	Corner block	8 × 8 × 16	200 × 200 × 400	Has square end for corner
c	Half block	8 × 8 × 8	200 × 200 × 200	Used in alternate rows at openings
d	Sash block	8 × 8 × 16	200 × 200 × 400	Has vertical groove in end for metal sash
e	Jamb block	8 × 8 × 16	200 × 200 × 400	Has 2 in. × 4 in. piece cut out at one end for a door jamb or wooden window sash
f	Bull nose	8 × 8 × 16	200 × 200 × 400	Has one rounded corner for smooth wall openings
g	Partition	4 × 8 × 16	100 × 200 × 400	For inside walls subject to small loads

Dimensioning Block Walls

In designing a building to be constructed of concrete masonry units, it is desirable to make all dimensions multiples of 1/2 block length. This will allow construction without the need to cut blocks, an economy of both materials and labor. Cut pieces of block also detract from the appearance of the wall.

Block walls have limited lateral strength which determines the recommended unsupported length and height. Eight inch (200 mm) blocks may be used in walls up to 12 ft (3.6 m) high, if no more than 7 ft (2 m) is below grade in well-drained soil. Higher walls should be constructed with 12 in. (300 mm) blocks, although the top 12 ft (3.6 m) may be of 8 in. units. No block wall should be more than 35 ft (10 m) high.

Lateral Support and Control Joints

Because high-roof barns cause large, horizontal thrusts to the walls, long barn walls should be stiffened at regular intervals. Lateral bracing, either with cross walls or pilasters should be provided each 12 ft (3.6 m) or less in an 8 in. (200 mm) block wall and each 18 ft (5.6 m) or less in a 12 in. (300 mm) wall. A pilaster is built as an integral part of the wall by turning two, 8 in. blocks crosswise to the wall on alternate courses as illustrated in figure 3.8. The pilaster should be built on the side opposite the expected lateral force, e.g., inside of basement walls, on the outside of storage buildings.

In the side walls of long barns, stresses may develop that tend to cause cracks near doors and windows. To relieve the stresses due to expansion and contraction, control joints should be placed in above-grade walls at major openings and, on unbroken sections, at intervals no more than 21/2 times the wall height. The wall must be keyed together at the control joint so that lateral strength is not sacrificed. The vertical joints are filled with a non-hardening mastic to allow for expansion and contraction and to make it watertight. Figure 3.9 shows three methods of constructing control joints to maintain stiffness in the wall.

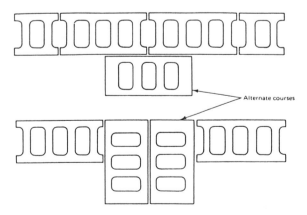

Alternate courses

Figure 3.8. Pilaster formed by turning two blocks in alternate courses.

(a)

(b)

Figure 3.9. Three methods of constructing control joints.

Lintels and Sills

Lintels are reinforced concrete beams used over doors, windows, and other openings. Precast units are available from block suppliers in lengths to bear 8 in. (200 mm) into the wall on each side of the opening. They may be split into two, 35/8 in. (90 mm) wide units for easier handling.

(c)

Figure 3.9. *(continued)*

Concrete sills below windows prevent water from seeping into the cores of the block. Water running off the windows is directed away from the wall to prevent streaking. Sills may be precast or cast on the site.

Roof Anchorage

A farm building is no stronger than its weakest connection. Often this is where the roof is anchored to the wall. This joint is subject to severe strain during high winds. A rigid connection between the roof and the wall furnishes lateral support to the walls and prevents high winds from lifting the roof off.

To anchor the roof, 1/2 in. (12 mm) × 18 in. (450 mm) bolts are inserted into the core of every third block, extending down through two courses. The core area containing the bolts should be filled with concrete to insure good anchorage. After the concrete has hardened, the roof plate is placed and fastened securely to the wall. Rafters and trusses can then be attached to the plate with framing anchors. In high wind areas, local codes may require anchorage to more layers of the wall or even all the way to the footing.

Mortar

Mortar bonds the concrete blocks together to form a wall, and the quality of a masonry wall can be no better than that of the mortar with which it is laid. Therefore, the selection and mixing of the ingredients is of prime importance.

Masonry cement is widely used for preparing mortar. It contains lime or an air-entraining agent that helps to make the mortar plastic and workable and reduces the possibility of weather damage. However, if a wall is likely to be subjected to extremely heavy loads or water pressure, violent winds or severe frost action, it is advisable to

1 SET BATTER BOARDS AT SAME ELEVATION –

A hose with glass tubes in each end may be used to do this.

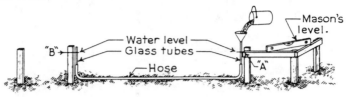

1. Set batter boards at one corner as at right.
2. Place hose as shown.
3. Fill with water until water level is at top of batter board "A".
4. Mark water level at opposite end "B" and set board to mark.

2 LAY OUT BUILDING FIRST

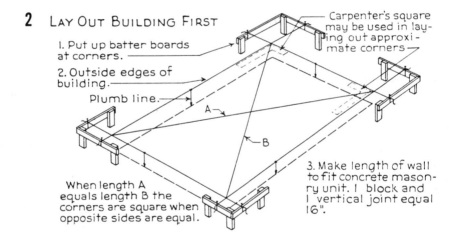

1. Put up batter boards at corners.

2. Outside edges of building.

Plumb line.

When length A equals length B the corners are square when opposite sides are equal.

Carpenter's square may be used in laying out approximate corners

3. Make length of wall to fit concrete masonry unit. I block and I vertical joint equal 16".

Figure 3.10. Steps in masonry construction.

substitute 50% portland cement in the mix.

Usual proportions are:

Normal conditions. 1:2¼ to 3 of masonry cement to loose damp sand.

Conditions requiring extra strength. 1:1:4½ to 6 of masonry cement to portland cement to sand.

Sufficient water is added to obtain a workable mortar. For face shell joints, of either 8 or 12 in. (200 to 300 mm) blocks, approximately 2.3 ft^3 (0.064 m^3) of mortar will be needed for 100 blocks. A cubic foot of mortar requires one-third sack of mortar cement and 1 ft^3 of sand. Several steps in masonry construction are shown in figure 3.10.

3 ADEQUATE FOOTINGS ESSENTIAL

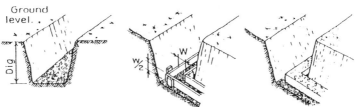

1. Dig trench down to firm soil below frost.

2. Make bottom of trench flat and level.

3. Forms to make footings proper size.

W = Twice masonry wall thickness.

4. Fill with 1:2¾:4 concrete.

5. Remove form after concrete hardens.

6. Sweep off top of footing before laying concrete masonry.

4 START LAYING BLOCK AT CORNERS

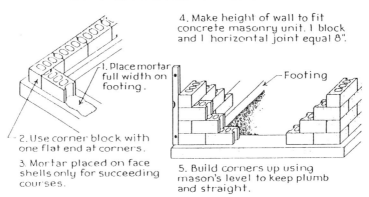

4. Make height of wall to fit concrete masonry unit. 1 block and 1 horizontal joint equal 8".

1. Place mortar full width on footing.

2. Use corner block with one flat end at corners.

3. Mortar placed on face shells only for succeeding courses.

5. Build corners up using mason's level to keep plumb and straight.

5 BUILD WALL BETWEEN CORNERS

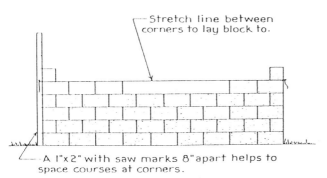

Stretch line between corners to lay block to.

A 1"x 2" with saw marks 8" apart helps to space courses at corners.

Mortar joints are ⅜" thick.

Block should be dry when laid in wall.

Figure 3.10. *continued.*

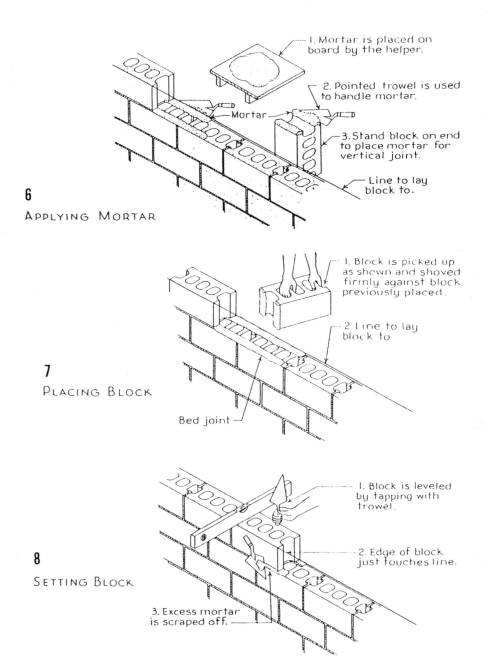

1. Mortar is placed on board by the helper.

2. Pointed trowel is used to handle mortar.

—Mortar

3. Stand block on end to place mortar for vertical joint.

Line to lay block to.

6

APPLYING MORTAR

1. Block is picked up as shown and shoved firmly against block previously placed.

2. Line to lay block to

7

PLACING BLOCK

Bed joint

1. Block is leveled by tapping with trowel.

2. Edge of block just touches line.

8

SETTING BLOCK

3. Excess mortar is scraped off.

Figure 3.10. *continued.*

9 JOINTS ARE TOOLED AFTER MORTAR HAS BECOME QUITE STIFF

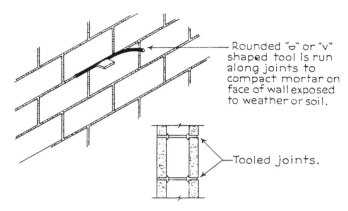

Rounded "o" or "v" shaped tool is run along joints to compact mortar on face of wall exposed to weather or soil.

Tooled joints.

Figure 3.10. *continued.*

Laying Block Walls

Blocks should be well cured and dry before use. After delivery on the job, the blocks should be stored on a dry base, covered and not wetted prior to laying them in a wall. Cracking in the wall results from the shrinkage that occurs when damp blocks dry out. The wall should be started on a good concrete footing installed on firm, undisturbed, well-compacted soil (fig.3.10). In laying masonry walls, mortar is placed between the ends of adjoining blocks (bed joints). The first course of blocks is laid in a full mortar bedding placed on the footing. Succeeding courses are laid with face shell joints (mortar along the edges of the blocks only). All the joints should be tooled to compress the mortar, leaving it neat and compact. Tooling the joints on both sides of the wall enhances its appearance and improves its water-tightness. Improperly filled and tooled joints are often the cause of water leakage through a masonry wall.

Surface Bonding

Surface bonding is a system of constructing masonry walls without the use of mortar joints. The blocks are simply stacked up on a carefully leveled first course and then the surface bonding material is applied to both sides of the wall. The finished wall is generally stronger than a wall laid up with mortar in the usual way and less skilled labor is needed for the construction. The hard double surface is virtually waterproof. Either smooth or textured surfaces are possible and color may be added if desired, thus eliminating any further finishing.

The most important requirement before starting the first course of blocks is a concrete foundation that is level and smooth. The base layer of blocks is laid in a bed of mortar using great care so that the succeeding courses can be built accurately and rapidly into a straight, plumb, and level wall. To avoid settling, the mortar should be allowed to set up before stacking additional courses.

Inasmuch as there are no mortar joints, it is desirable to use special full-size blocks with ground surfaces. Where these are not available, it must be remembered that standard blocks are 3/8 in. (10 mm) undersize in each direction and produce walls with nonmodular dimensions that make it difficult to install windows and doors. The full-size ground surface blocks are not only more convenient to work with but also produce a wall with considerably more compressive strength.

It is also important to have high quality blocks of uniform size. If the units vary in size, they must be shimmed with sheet metal or mortar (never wood) to make them plumb. Rough blocks should be smoothed at the top and bottom by scraping two units together to remove excess materials and burrs. Once the wall is in place the bonding mix is applied to both sides of the wall with a trowel or with specialized spray equipment.

The ingredients for home-mixed surface bonding are portland cement (preferably white portland cement), hydrated lime, calcium chloride, calcium stearate, and fiberglass. These can be purchased from building materials dealers, agricultural chemical dealers, and chemical distributors.

Commercial premixes are also available in bags ranging from 25 to 80 lb (11 to 36 kg) and offer several advantages. While the commercial premixes may cost as much as three times the ingredients for home mixing, they are accurately proportioned and eliminate most of the labor of mixing. They also eliminate the need to locate ingredients, some of which are sold only in large quantities.

Tilt-up Concrete

Tilt-up concrete is a system of constructing durable, maintenance-free buildings that can be erected quickly with little labor and equipment. Concrete panels are cast in a horizontal position and then raised to a vertical position. After carefully plumbing and bracing, columns are cast between the panels to stabilize them and form the wall of the building.

Simple pier foundations are used for some low-cost buildings, but a continuous foundation is preferred. This allows the wall panels to bear uniformly on the footing. It also helps to control rodents and undermining caused by erosion.

Tilt-up panels may be cast either on a previously placed concrete floor or on a carefully prepared bed of sand; the methods work equally well. In either case, a sheet of 4 mil polyethylene film is spread over the surface before casting is begun to prevent bonding with the wall panel.

To form the panels, 2 × 4s are set on edge and fastened together to the desired panel size. The panels need reinforcement to withstand the stresses of tilting into place. A typical design is shown in figure 3.11 in which five, no. 3 bars are spaced equally in each direction starting 3 in. (75 mm) from the edge. The horizontal bars are allowed to extend 2 in. (50 mm) so that they may anchor the panel to the column. Bolts must also be cast in the panel in such a way that the tilting frame may be attached for the erecting operation. Reinforcing bars are cast in the footings that extend up through the columns. Three, no. 4 bars are used with 8 × 8 ft (2.4 × 2.4 m) panels or three, no. 6 bars with 10 × 10 ft (3 × 3 m) panels. The three bars are spaced 6 in. (150 mm) apart in a triangular position as shown in figure 3.11.

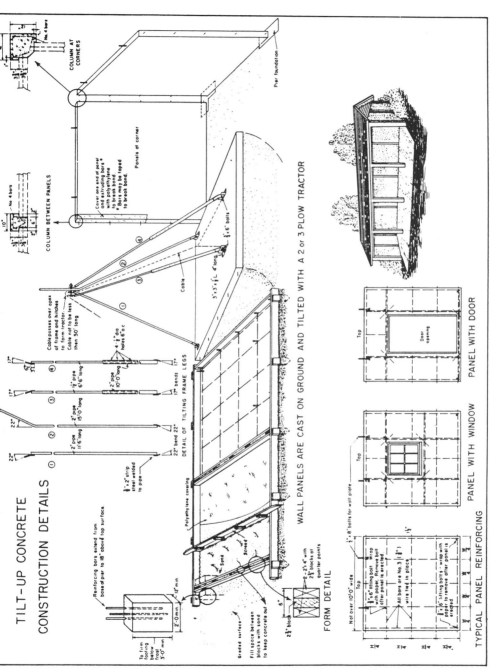

Figure 3.11. Tilt-up concrete construction details.

Once the panels have been cast to size and cured for five days, a tilting frame is attached and a tractor used to tilt the panel into position.

Tilt-up concrete is especially suitable in construction where temperature control is not essential, as in a machinery shed. However, insulated panels may be cast for tilting up where it is necessary to maintain a more uniform temperature. Perhaps the most practical application of tilt-up concrete is in the construction of horizontal silos, either above or below grade. It is also an ideal way to construct windbreaks for feedlots and barnyards.

Problems

3.1. If possible mix, weigh, and cast three trial batches of concrete. Cure in water for a week and then compare their relative strength. Suggested ratios by weight.

Batch 1		Batch 2		Batch 3	
Water	1.25	Water	0.9	Water	0.9
Cement	2	Cement	2	Cement	2
Sand	6.2	Sand	3.8	Sand	6.2
Pea gravel	5.8	Pea gravel	4.3	Pea gravel	—

(a) What is the effect of using more water per sack of cement on the amount of concrete obtained per sack?

(b) What is the effect of using only sand and very small aggregate on the amount of concrete obtained per sack of cement?

(c) Why is it sometimes more expensive to use free, bank-run gravel to make concrete instead of purchased sand and gravel?

(d) What is the comparative strength of the three samples? What factor causes the greatest difference in these samples?

3.2. Using the same plan assigned for problem 2.2, determine the total amount of concrete to be ordered for a monolithic foundation. Calculate separately the amounts required for the footings, foundations, and any piers needed. List the specifications for the concrete to be ordered and indicate the total amount to be ordered from the ready-mix company.

3.3. For the same plan used in the previous problem, plan a masonry block wall. Determine the amount of concrete required for footings and for piers. Also determine the number of blocks of suitable width needed to construct the foundation walls.

3.4. Compare the cost of materials required in problems 3.2 and 3.3. Compare the labor and other materials costs to put each of the two alternatives in place.

3.5. Determine the cement, sand, gravel, and water required to form a 4 in. × 40 × 90 ft concrete floor. Use a 1:2:21/2, 5 gal mix.

4 Manufactured Building Materials and Paints

Building Materials

There is an ever increasing number of manufactured building materials available, most with characteristics that make them suitable for a few rather specific applications. They may be superior in insulating value, fire resistance, ease of cleaning, and resistance to weathering, or they may be prefinished to provide an attractive and durable appearance.

Building Boards

Gypsum Boards

Gypsum boards consist of a noncombustible core of gypsum with paper facings on front, back, and along edges. They may be used to construct durable, fire resistant, and economical walls and ceilings in buildings. With proper design they also contribute to the isolation of sound. They are not particularly resistant to rupture from heavy blows. Gypsum board is commonly used to finish interiors of houses, offices, and may be used for attic firewalls in farm buildings.

Although gypsum boards do not have a low coefficient of heat transfer, they have a high resistance to the spread of fire. This results from the fact that gypsum ($CaSO_4 \cdot 2H_2O$) contains about 21% water in combined form. In the presence of high temperature due to fire, the gypsum is subjected to very slow calcination as the moisture is driven off in vapor form. Since the temperature beyond the plane of calcination does not rise much above 212°F (100°C), there is little chance for the fire to spread until the calcination process is complete. With 21% of the substance being driven off, there is a tendency for the board to shrink and crack. Type X gypsum board, available in 1/2 and 5/8 in. (13 and 16 mm) thicknesses, has improved fire resistance due to additives that reduce the shrinking and cracking. When Type X board is applied to a partition in a single layer on each face of load-bearing, wood framing members, the 5/8 in. (16 mm) thickness provides at least a 1-h fire rating and the 1/2 in. (13 mm) thickness a 3/4 h rating.

Regular gypsum board is available in thicknesses ranging from 1/4 in. (6.3 mm) to 1 in. (25 mm). However, the three most commonly available are 3/8 in. (9.5 mm), used as a single layer in economy construction, or more commonly, double layer for quali-

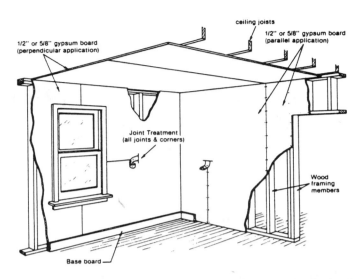

Figure 4.1. Wood stud framing should provide a firm, level, plumb, and even base for single-ply gypsum board application.

ty construction; 1/2 in. (13 mm), generally used as a single layer; 5/8 in. (16 mm), used either as a single or double layer where additional fire or sound resistance is required (figs. 4.1, 4.2, and 4.3).

Standard sizes are 4 ft (1200 mm) wide and 8, 10, 12 or 14 ft (2400, 3000, 3600 or 4200 mm) long. Other sizes may be ordered from the manufacturer.

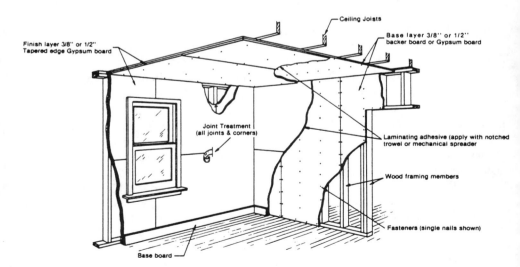

Figure 4.2. Double-layer, multi-ply system has laminated surface of gypsum boards and base layer of gypsum backing board for greater fire resistance.

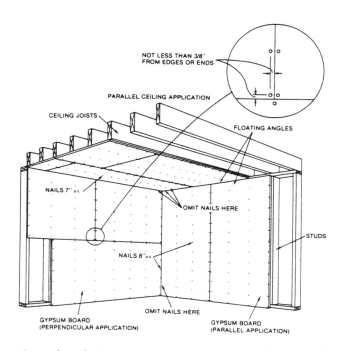

NOT LESS THAN 3/8"
FROM EDGES OR ENDS

PARALLEL CEILING APPLICATION

CEILING JOISTS

FLOATING ANGLES

NAILS 7" o c

OMIT NAILS HERE

STUDS

NAILS 8" o c

OMIT NAILS HERE

GYPSUM BOARD
(PERPENDICULAR APPLICATION)

GYPSUM BOARD
(PARALLEL APPLICATION)

Figure 4.3. Floating angle construction helps eliminate nail popping and corner cracking.

A number of other types of gypsum board are available. The water-resistant type has both a water-resistant core and a water-repellent paper facing. It is used as a base for various finished surfaces in bath, kitchen, and laundry areas. It is available as regular and Type X in 1/2 and 5/8 in. (13 and 16 mm) thicknesses. Gypsum sheathing is available in 2 and 4 ft (600 and 1200 mm) widths and 1/2 and 5/8 in. (13 and 16 mm) thicknesses. A water-repellent facing paper is used. It has a bracing effect and can be used under various surface materials that may be attached through the sheathing directly to the framing members.

By far the greatest quantity of gypsum board is used for interior walls in homes and public buildings. The side edges are commonly tapered to allow the installation of reinforcing tape and joint treatment compound, producing a nearly invisible, permanent joint between adjoining boards (fig. 4.4). The boards may be installed either vertically or horizontally on wood or metal studs (table 4-1). The horizontal position usually results in the shortest and least noticeable joints. Specially designed ring shank nails or screws are used for wood studs and self-tapping screws for metal studs.

The use of adhesives can reduce the number of nails or screws by 50%. The adhesive alone may be used to attach the boards to above-grade masonry or concrete that is dry, smooth, clean, and flat. When panels are nailed only, the nails should be spaced 7 in. (175 mm) along ceiling supports or 8 in. (200 mm) along studs. Nailing, started

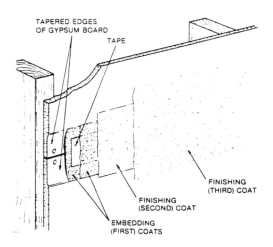

Figure 4.4. Reinforcing joints with tape prevents cracks from appearing at filled gypsum board joints.

Table 4–1. Maximum frame spacing for single-ply gypsum board

Location	Thickness in. (mm)	Application	Spacing in. (mm)
Ceiling	3/8 (9.5)	Perpendicular	16 (400)
	1/2 (12.7)	Perpendicular	16 (400)
	5/8* (16.0)	Parallel	16 (400)
	1/2* (12.7)	Perpendicular	24 (600)
	5/8 (16.0)	Perpendicular	24 (600)
Walls	3/8 (9.5)	Either	16 (400)
	1/2 (12.7)	Either	24 (600)
	5/8 (16.0)	Either	24 (600)

* Only 5/8 in. boards should be used, and then perpendicular to joists, when a water based texture finish is to be sprayed on.

near the center of a board, progresses outward to the edges. Nails that miss the support should be removed and those that are accidentally driven too deeply should be supplemented with another nail 2 in. (50 mm) away.

Fiberbond

A high-strength panel is made by blending cellulose fiber and gypsum. The durable fire-resistant panel can be used as an underlayment, wallboard or exterior sheathing. Fiberbond, which does not have a paper facing, resists surface abrasion, impact, and indentation damage. It is reported that Fiberbond is more dimensionally stable than plywood or oriented strand board.

The panels are available in thicknesses of from 1/4 to 5/8 in. (6 to 16 mm) and in lengths from 8 to 12 ft (2.5 to 4 m). Underlayment and wallboard comes in widths of 4 ft (1.3 m); sheathing is available in 2 or 4 ft (0.6 to 1.3 m) widths. The 1/4 in. (6 mm) thick underlayment has a density of 75 lb/ft^3 (1200 kg/m^3) and the 3/8 in. thick panels which incorporate perlite in the core have a density of 65 lb/ft^3 (1040 kg/m^3).

Particleboard

Particleboard is formed of wood particles or small chips bonded together with synthetic resin to produce a uniform, smooth, and dimensionally stable panel with excellent glue-bond characteristics. Although particleboard may be used as subflooring or underlayment, much of it is used as core stock by manufacturers of furniture, cabinets, countertops, and wall paneling. Most particleboard is intended for interior use, although a phenolic bonded type is available for exterior use. There is a wide range of densities, thicknesses, and panel sizes. For building purposes, the 4 × 8 ft (1200 × 2400 mm) size in either 3/8 or 3/4 in. (9.5 or 19 mm) thickness is most common.

Waferboard, Chipboard or Flakeboard

Several names have been used to describe this product. Waferboard is a versatile wood product made of larger chips. *Oriented strand board* is a special type of waferboard which is formed of layers of chips. The direction of orientation is altered with adjacent layers to form a structurally strong panel. When manufactured to required specification, these panels can be substituted for plywood performance rated panels.

Plastic Laminates

Surfaced with melamine, these are available in numerous patterns, both smooth and textured. They are commonly used in homes for surfaces of countertops and tables and for cabinet facings. Because of their hard, smooth, waterproof finish, they are also suitable for wall or work surfaces in agricultural buildings where ease of cleaning is a primary factor.

Fiberglass Reinforced Plastic (FRP) Paneling

This paneling, used in the food processing industries for years, is also popular on the farm for surfaces that are subject to impact, wear, and frequent cleaning. It is available either laminated to plywood or as a flat panel for installation on walls or ceiling. The laminated version is available in 4 × 8 ft (1200 × 2400 mm) and 4 × 10 ft (1200 × 3000 mm) panels from 1/4 to 3/4 in. (6 to 19 mm) thick. Using a carbide-tip saw for cutting, the material is installed in the same manner as ordinary plywood. Either a good quality caulking compound or fiberglass batten strips are used to seal the joints.

The flat panel material comes in thicknesses of 0.09 to 0.17 in. (2.3 to 4.3 mm) in regular sheets of 4 × 8 ft (1200 × 2400 mm) and 4 × 10 ft (1200 × 3000 mm). In addition, panels are available in widths up to 81/3 ft (2542 mm) and 40 ft (12 m) or longer in length. This is of particular advantage in milking parlors or milk rooms where a minimum number of joints is desirable. A silicone sealant is recommended for the joints in this type of installation. Finally, a fire-retardant version with a Class A flame spread rating of 15 may be obtained where required.

Solid Plastic Panels

Solid plastic panels that meet U.S. Food and Drug Administration and Public Health standards for clean room applications are available. The 4 × 8 ft (1200 ×

Figure 4.5. Polyethylene-coated fiberboard provides an easily cleaned surface.

2400 mm) size in 1/4 in. (6 mm) thickness may be installed directly on studs 16 in. (400 mm) on center. Although first cost is high, it should offer a long life and an easily cleaned surface.

Insulating Fiberboards

Sometimes called softboard, these materials are usually too thin to be of much value as insulation and too soft to have very much strength or resistance to rupture. However, when used as sheathing and nailed as directed, there is a good bracing effect and some insulating value. The finish siding material must be fastened through the board directly to the framing.

One manufacturer is producing an insulating board from recycled wood-fiber material which is resistant to weathering and is suitable for either exterior or interior wall and ceiling surfaces. It is available with a natural gray surface or prime-coated, ready for finish-painting. The material is easily cut and handled. However, due to considerable dimensional change with changing moisture conditions, it must be installed with edge gaps as specified by the manufacturer. For exposed exterior applications, the gaps should be caulked and covered with a batten. Instructions call for spacing nails 6 in. (150 mm) along all edges and 10 in. (250 mm) along intermediate supports which are spaced 16 in. (400 mm) on center. Insulating boards are available in thicknesses of 15/32 to 29/32 in. (12 to 24 mm) and in sizes ranging from ceiling tiles up to 4 × 14 ft (1200 × 4200 mm) panels.

Medium Density Fiberboard

Medium density fiberboard is a uniform material often used for furniture, cabinets or signs. It is sometimes used for interior wall finish. Thicknesses of 3/16 to 11/2 in. (4.8 to 38 mm) are available.

Hardboard

These are produced by pressing wood fiber mats at high pressure and temperature until the natural lignin in the fibers binds them together into a hard permanent board that is more dense than the wood from which it was made. Hardboards are available as either standard or tempered. The tempered is coated with oil and baked to increase the hardness, strength, and water resistance.

A major use of hardboard is as decorative panels for finishing walls. Panels that are at least 1/4 in. (6 mm) thick may be placed directly on studs that are 16 in. (400 mm) o.c. Thinner panels should be backed up with plywood, gypsum board or rigid insulation. Contact adhesives, with a minimum of nailing, provide a rapid method of application with few nailheads to mar the appearance. While it is unnecessary, the blemish-free surface of the unfinished hardboards may be readily painted. The boards are east to cut and nail, but a carbide saw is advisable. Hardboards are commonly available in thicknesses of 1/8, 1/4, and 3/8 in. (3, 6, 9.5 mm) and in sheets 4 ft (1.2 m) wide × 6 to 16 ft (1.8 to 4.8 m) long. The sheets are more flexible than plywood and may be used to form curved surfaces with as little as a 12 in. (300 mm) radius. Manufacturer's recommendations should be followed both in procedure and in the minimum radius attempted. Hardboard underlayment is sanded on one side to aid in obtaining a good bond with the finish material. It is often used to bring finish floors level where different floor covering materials are used in the same area. When nailed to the recommended specifications of 4 in. (100 mm) along the edges and 8 in. (200 mm) along intermediate supports, considerable bracing effect is obtained.

Plastic-coated Insulation Boards

As shown in figure 4.5, plastic-coated insulation boards provide a smooth, easily cleaned surface with very low permeability. If the surface is to be hosed down, the joints must be sealed with tape. These panels may only be installed in areas where they are not subject to physical damage. The core may be of low-cost fiber material or of polyurethane. While the polyurethane is a considerably better thermal insulator, because of its burning characteristics local code restrictions may require that it be covered with some other surface material.

Siding Materials

There is a wide range of siding materials available for farm buildings and homes. They vary in appearance, initial cost, frequency and cost of maintenance, resistance to physical damage, vapor permeability, and bracing effect. Because of the expected long life of most of the materials, it is essential to consider all factors carefully before making a choice.

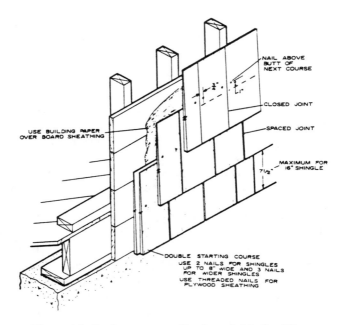

Figure 4.6. Single course application of shingle siding.

Wood Shingles and Shakes

Whether painted, stained or left natural, these provide an attractive and durable siding. They may be dipped in paint before installation to provide increased protection from moisture. Shingles are usually sawed from either cedar or redwood. Shakes are split or made to appear split from the log. Shingle grades include no. 1, which will be 100% heartwood, edge grain and clear; no. 2, which will be clear for 12 in. (300 mm) from the butt; and no. 3 and 4, which will have some flat grain and sapwood as well as increasing numbers of defects. Any amount up to just under half the length of the shingle may be exposed to the weather. Shingles may be applied with an uneven butt line and a noticeable side gap, giving a patterned appearance, or they may be lined up carefully and installed with a minimal side gap, giving almost the same appearance as beveled wood siding. Shingles may be squared and rebutted, that is, cut so the sides are parallel with each other and perpendicular to the butt when they are to be installed with a minimal side gap (fig. 4.6).

Bevel Siding or Clapboards

Milled from pine, redwood or cedar, these have been used as an attractive siding for generations. They may be left natural, stained or painted. Although failure to install a good vapor seal and to properly caulk around windows and doors has often caused premature paint failure, with proper attention to moisture control, paint life can be satisfactory. Figure 4.7 illustrates the proper layout of the siding around a window. A minimum of 1 in. of overlap should be allowed.

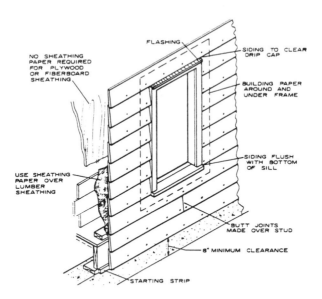

Figure 4.7. Application of bevel siding to coincide with window sill and drip cap.

Vertical Wood Siding

Left natural, stained or painted, vertical wood siding can provide good service and an attractive appearance. Moisture is less likely to be a problem than with horizontal siding. There are examples of unpainted vertical siding that are in excess of 150 years old, weathered very thin, but still with no signs of rot. Figure 4.8 shows three styles of vertical siding. It is important to nail the boards and battens as shown in the figure so that shrinking and swelling will not split the boards.

Plywood Siding

Designated as 303 siding by the American Plywood Association, plywood siding is available in many different patterns. Plywood provides a siding that is durable, gives good bracing effect, and requires little maintenance. One of the 303 sidings, Texture 1-11, has vertical grooves cut in either sanded or unsanded panels. One of the least expensive siding materials, it is suitable for many farm buildings as well as homes. The APA 303 grade stamp indicates the maximum stud-spacing for panels installed with the face grain vertical. This applies both for panels installed over sheathing or directly to the studs. The suggested nail size is 6d for 1/2 in. (13 mm) or less and 8d for thicker panels, with the nails spaced 6 in. (150 mm) along the edges and 12 in. (300 mm) along intermediate supports. Use Z flashing between sheets when using more than one horizontal row.

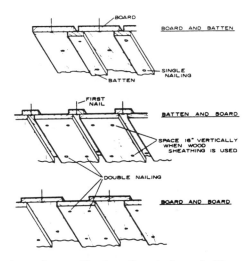

Figure 4.8. Application of vertical wood siding.

Metal Siding

This siding, made from aluminum or galvanized steel, provides an attractive finish for agricultural buildings with either wood or steel frames. Either material is available in painted or unpainted sheets with a variety of rib designs and widths. Typically, aluminum, as well as some steel sidings, carries a 20 to 30 year guarantee against leaking due to corrosion. The steel has the advantage of greater strength and dent resistance along with a lower coefficient of expansion which helps to reduce hole enlargement around the nails. Aluminum is available in 0.016 to 0.024 in. (0.4 to 0.6 mm) thicknesses while steel comes in 26 (the heaviest), 28, and 29 gauge. The thickness does not appreciably affect the life of either material, but it does influence the spacing of supports. Figure 4.9 provides some typical procedures used in installing metal siding and roofing. Panels are easily handled and may be rapidly installed.

Manufactured Sidings

Using a variety of prefinished materials, these sidings are rapidly gaining in popularity. Painted aluminum, solid vinyl, vinyl-coated hardboard, and plywood are among the most common. They are not only attractive, but the promise of little or no maintenance tends to offset any greater initial cost. It is significant that most of them are excellent vapor barriers. Therefore the vapor barrier near the inside surface of the wall must have a very low vapor permeability and must be installed very carefully if moisture is to be prevented from accumulating within the wall cavity.

Masonry Construction

Although usually more costly to build, masonry is popular in some areas of the country. It is attractive, low in maintenance, and not subject to rot or termite damage. Frame construction with masonry veneer is much more common in colder climates because of the ease of installing the necessary insulation.

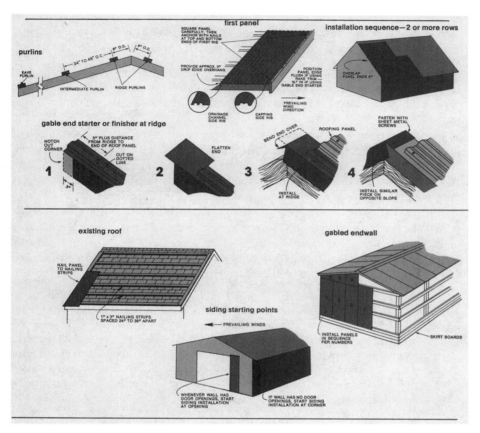

Figure 4.9. Installing metal roofing and siding.

Roofing Materials

A roofing material should be carefully chosen to ensure a type suitable for the roof pitch, the type of roof deck, and for the desired life. The lowest first cost may not necessarily be the most economical over the life of the building. Most roofing materials are sold by the square. One square covers 100 ft^2 of roof surface.

For a gable roof, the pitch of a roof is equal to the rise divided by twice the run (fig. 9.3). On even-pitch buildings, the rise divided by the span would be equally satisfactory. A 24 ft (7.3 m) building with a 6 ft (1800 mm) rise has a one-quarter pitch. This same pitch is often indicated by an inverted triangle dimensioned as 6:12 (50:100).

Wood Shingles

Wood shingles produce an attractive roof with a long life. They may be installed on a tight roof deck (fig. 4.10). However, it is more economical to install them on a slatted deck with the slats spaced equal to the shingle exposure. Providing the attic is well ventilated, the slatted deck will increase shingle life. For 16 in. (400 mm) shingles, the exposure of the butt to the weather is usually 5 in. (125 mm). As mentioned under the section on siding, shingles come in four grades. Because of the high labor costs involved, it is not practical to use anything but the no. 1 grade for a permanent building.

Asphalt Materials

These require a solid roof deck in all cases except the corrugated type. The weight per square of the saturated roofing is a reasonable measure of the durability of the material.

Felts are used to construct a built-up covering on a flat roof deck. A roof slope of 0.5 to 0.75:12 is desirable to provide adequate drainage, but it is also the maximum pitch. On greater pitches the roof tends to creep in hot weather. Felts are available in 15 and 30 lb/square (6.8 and 13.6 kg) weights. They are installed three to five layers thick with hot asphalt as a binding material.

Roll roofing is the least expensive asphalt material, but it also has the shortest life. It is available in rolls of 45 to 105 lb covering one square (2.2 to 4.8 kg/m^2). Roll roofing is suitable for a minimum roof slope of 3:12 when a 2 in. (50 mm) overlap is secured with exposed nails. A 2:12 slope is satisfactory when the nails are concealed and the overlap is sealed down with asphalt cement.

Double coverage roll roofing has a considerably longer life than ordinary roll roofing. It may be used on a roof slope as low as 1:12. Available in weights of 55 to 70 lb/square (2.7 to 3.4 kg/m^2), it combines blind nailing with cementing to provide the double coverage. A square requires two rolls plus 2 gal (0.8 L/m^2) of asphalt cement.

Shingles are available in many styles and colors (fig.4.11). They are the most pop-

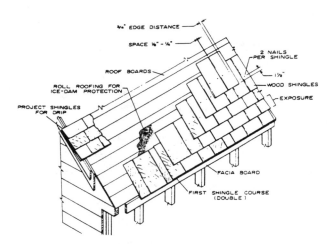

Figure 4.10. Installing wood shingles on a solid roof deck.

ular roofing for homes in much of the temperate areas of the United States and Canada. Qualities weighing from 205 to 390 lb/square (10 to 19 kg/m^2) are common, and depending on the weight, there are usually two to four bundles per square. Shingles are satisfactory for use on a roof with at least a 4:12 slope. However, if it becomes necessary to use shingles on a lower pitch, roll roofing should be installed first.

Asphalt shingles carry an Underwriters Laboratories' label indicating the degree of resistance to fire. Most carry a Class C rating which is effective against light exposure to fire, but a few carry a Class A label indicating effectiveness against a severe fire exposure. The Underwriters Laboratories' label for wind resistance indicates the ability to withstand a 60 mph (100 km/h) wind for 2 h. Strip shingles carrying the UL label have factory applied adhesive which is activated by the sun's heat to form a wind resistant bond. Methods of application of asphalt shingles are shown in figures 4.12, 4.13, and 4.14.

Corrugated asphalt roofing is available in several colors either with or without a mineral surface. The material is not affected by dust or fumes from fertilizers or animal wastes, and it may be installed on an open roof deck of at least 3:12 slope in the same manner as metal roofing. It is probably a little less subject to condensation on the underside of an open roof deck than are metals. In addition, it is flexible enough to be curved around a 15 ft (4.5 m) radius. Like most asphalt products, it carries the UL Class C fire rating. It also carries a 25-year guarantee against leaks. The necessary accessories, including translucent PVC panels, are available.

Figure 4.11. One of many textures available in asphalt shingles.

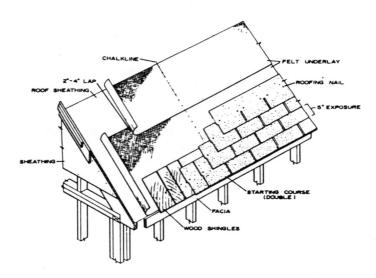

Figure 4.12. Application of asphalt shingles on a plywood roof deck.

Steel Roofing

Steel roofing is a popular material for farm buildings but is considered too noisy to be desirable for homes. It is suitable for use on open roof decks with at least a 3:12 slope. Steel is available in three gauges: 26 (the heaviest), 28, and 29. The gauge has little effect on durability and a high-tensile 29 gauge provides as strong a sheet as an annealed 26 gauge. Sheets are available in several rib designs, each of which will affect the panel strength. Consequently, it is important to follow the manufacturer's specifications on purlin spacing.

Steel roofing is galvanized to reduce corrosion by coating the surface with a thin layer of zinc. The thickness of the zinc in the coating is determined by the quantity of zinc applied. American Society for Testing and Materials designations of G30, G60, G90, G115, G140, 165, G185, G210 or G235 may be available. The number, i.e., 90 in G90, includes the total coating in (0.90) ounces per square foot on both sides. A minimum of G165 is recommended for rural applications. If paint is to be applied over the galvanizing, G90 is appropriate. Metallic zinc dust in an oil, alkyd or phenolic base is recommended as a prime coat when painting steel roofing. Galvanized roofing is also available with factory applied coatings that improve appearance and durability.

Steel roofing is installed with galvanized ring shank nails or screws that come with either a neoprene or lead washer. For metal framing, self-tapping screws with a sealing washer are used. Aluminum nails or paint should never be used with galvanized roofing as the resulting electrolytic action will soon cause corrosion. Roofing panels should be installed with the upper panels lapped over lower panels. Side laps should be away from the prevailing wind direction (fig. 4.15).

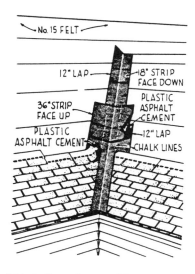

Figure 4.13. Roll roofing used for an open valley.

Figure 4.14. A woven valley.

Aluminum Roofing

Aluminum roofing is lightweight, naturally corrosion resistant, and easy to install on open roof decks of at least 3:12 slope. It is available in sheets similar to galvanized

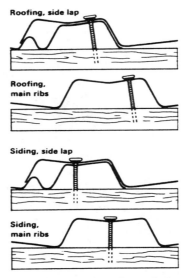

Figure 4.15. Metal roofing side lap showing anti-siphon design and proper nailing.

steel roofing except that the sheets are typically wider and come in lengths up to 30 ft (9.2 m). It also comes in rolls and in 4 ft (1.2 m) wide sheets backed with foam insulation. Although long sheets speed installation and reduce the number of joints, the high coefficient of expansion of aluminum may cause the enlargement of nail holes. A 24 ft (7.5 m) sheet of aluminum expands 1/4 in. (6 mm) with a temperature rise of 80°F (45°C). Aluminum roofing generally carries a 20- to 30-year guarantee against corrosion. Aluminum nails with neoprene washers are used for installing the sheets on purlins. Approximately 100 nails per square are required (table 4-2). Although the span between purlins is related to the thickness of the sheets chosen, which may range from 0.016 to 0.032 in. (0.4 to 0.8 mm), the alloy and temper of the metal greatly influence the strength and stiffness. Consequently, it is important to follow the manufacturer's instructions in matching the type of sheet to the purlin spacing. Embossing the sheets not only reduces glare from sunshine but also slightly increases the stiffness. If there is a possibility that the aluminum roofing or siding will come in direct contact with a steel frame, it must be protected from electrolytic action by paint or a layer of heavy builder's felt. Stainless steel self-tapping screws should be used to be compatible with both metals.

Corrugated roofing, whether asphalt, steel or aluminum, may be installed on an open deck. The savings in materials and labor partially offset the extra cost of these materials over some other types. In most cases the supplier will have fiberglass-reinforced PVC panels with the same rib design allowing a few of the regular roofing panels to be replaced by the translucent panels to provide light for the building.

Table 4-2. Nails required for roofing

Roofing Materials	Type of Nail	Length		Lb/Square	
		New	Over Old	New	Over Old
Wood shingles	Galvanized	1 1/2 in.	2 in.	3 1/2-4 1/2	4 1/2-6 1/2
Asphalt shingles	Galvanized	1 1/4 in.	1 3/4 in.	1 7/8	2 1/4
Galvanized steel	Galvanized	1 3/4 in.	2-2 1/2 in.	1 1/2	
Aluminum	Aluminum	1 3/4 in.	2-2 1/2 in.	100 nails/square	

Slate or Tile Roofing

These materials are seldom used on agricultural buildings. Although very durable and attractive, their extra weight requires a stronger roof frame and they may be difficult to repair or replace. In addition, the original cost is likely to be substantially higher than for most other materials. Additional roofing materials are discussed in the chapter on greenhouses.

Paints and Caulks for Agricultural Use

Paints and stains are applied to exterior wood surfaces primarily for the attractive appearance they provide. Although there are differences of opinion about the economic value of painting the exterior of farm buildings, most people will agree that there is an aesthetic value to a neat appearing, well-painted farmstead. Although paint offers wood surfaces limited protection against moisture and sunshine, there is no guarantee that moisture will not penetrate through cracks and other defects in the paint or permeate from within the building and cause considerable deterioration.

On the other hand, corrosion-prone metal surfaces can be provided considerable protection with quality paint carefully applied. Some factory-applied finishes last for up to 20 years or more while painting surfaces in place offers protection for a shorter period.

There are many types of surface coverings manufactured from an even greater number of ingredients and formulated in an infinite number of ways. A brief description of some of the more common coverings and the materials from which they are made follows. Table 4-3 can be used for selecting a suitable material for a specific application.

Caulking and Sealing Materials

The success of a paint job is often related to how well cracks and joints are sealed prior to painting. In turn, the quality of the sealing is often determined largely by the kind and quality of the materials used. Table 4-4 lists some of the more common caulking and sealing compounds with some of their characteristics and applications.

Types of Surface Coatings

Paints

Paints consist of an opaque pigment and a resin which serves as a binder to hold the pigment together and to form a protective surface. The binder may be a vegetable oil or a synthetic resin. Paint may be thinned with an organic solvent, in which case it is called a solvent or reduced paint, or with water, in which case it is called a latex paint.

Most solvent type paints harden by oxidation while the latex paints harden, as the water evaporates, by the coalescing of the resins in the binder.

A third type of paint hardens by the curing action of its resins. This type usually comes in two parts that must be mixed immediately before using. The "pot life" for this type of paint may be just a few hours.

Varnish

Varnish is a single-element coating consisting only of the resin and, unlike paint, contains little or no pigments. Its sole purpose is to protect a surface without hiding its natural beauty. Varnishes provide a treatment of protective finish that is used for either interior or exterior surfaces. However, varnishes are not always suitable for exterior use since they are usually subject to deterioration from the ultraviolet rays of the sun. A number of different resins are used and both solvent- and water-thinned varnishes are available.

Stains

Stains are intermediate between paints and varnishes. They contain coloring pigments, often transparent rather than opaque, but not enough to hide the wood grain in most cases. Some stains penetrate more deeply into the wood than paint or varnish. Most do not leave a surface film and therefore are not subject to peeling or cracking.

Lacquers

Lacquers are rapidly-drying coatings that harden by the evaporation of the solvent. They produce a glossy surface that is somewhat less durable than varnish. Lacquers are commonly used in factory-coated building materials.

Primers and Topcoats

Most paint systems consist of a primer coat and one or more top or finish coats. The primer seals the original surface and provides a uniform, nonporous, dull surface on which to apply the top coat.

The top coat provides most of the protection against weathering, chemicals, dirt, and staining. Top coats are available in three different finishes: gloss, semigloss, and flat. The gloss finish has the least pigment and does not cover imperfections well, but usually has the hardest, smoothest, and most easily cleaned surface. Flat finish paints contain the highest pigment-to-binder ratio and provide the most opaque covering. They have the best surface for repainting. Semigloss paints fall between the other two in most characteristics.

Binders Used in Paints

Oil

Oil-based paints have largely been replaced by alkyd-based or latex-based paints which are superior in most characteristics. However, linseed oil paints continue to be sold for use on houses and barns.

Table 4-3. Paint and stain selection chart

Type of Paint	Applications	Advantages	Disadvantages
Linseed oil paint	Wood buildings Exterior metal	Easy to apply Flexible Adhesive	Slow drying Soft Low water resistance
Alkyd-base paint	Interior or exterior wood and metal	Easy to apply Low cost Durable	Low water resistance
Latex, exterior paint	Wood, masonry, primed metal	Easy to use Water cleanup Blister resistant	Freezes (in can) Low heat resistance
Latex, trim paint	Door and window trim	Less chalking	Higher cost
Latex, interior paint	Interior wood, plaster, drywall, and masonry	Easy to use Water cleanup Nonflammable	Freezes (in can) Low heat resistance
Epoxy paint	Interior wood, masonry	Water resistant Easy to clean Smooth	Difficult to apply Expensive
Aluminum paint	New metal Old metal over primer	Weather resistant	
Zinc primer	Rust inhibitive	Durable Sacrificial corrosion inhibiting	High cost Must be top coated
Barn paint	Smooth or rough wood	Durable Inexpensive Covers well	
Asphalt coating	Roof coating	Heavy cover Low cost	Hot unless aluminum pigmented
Water-repellent preservative	Exterior wood	Penetrates Preserves Repels moisture	
Urethane varnish	Interior wood floors Exterior wood floors	Hard, durable inside	Only fair ultraviolet tolerance
Silicone sealer	Masonry	Repels water for several years	Can't be painted for several years
Stains, semi-transparent (latex or oil)	Unfinished wood	No failure except normal wear	Won't cover other finishes
Stains, opaque (latex or oil)	Finished or unfinished wood	Resist peeling	May not cover old finishes well

Table 4-4. Caulks and sealers

Type	Applications	Ease of Use	Surface Preparation	Life Expectancy	Can be Painted	Cost Comparison	Comments
Oil-based	Interior or exterior No movement	Easy	Primed	1-7 yrs	Yes	Low	Hardens and cracks
Acrylic-latex	Interior or exterior No movement	Very easy	Clean and dry Best primed	5-10 yrs	Yes	Low-med.	Dries rapidly
Butyl rubber	Interior or exterior	Easy	Clean and dry	10 yrs +	After 7 days	Low-med.	Adheres well Shrinks
Polysulfide rubber	Interior or exterior Tolerates movement	Difficult	Primed	20 yrs +	1-2 weeks	High	May be toxic
Silicone rubber	Interior or exterior Tolerates movement	Medium	Primed	20 yrs +	Read directions	High	Good on metal
Polybu-tylene	Temporary sealing	Easy	Best primed	20 yrs +	Yes	Med.	Low adhesion Never hardens
Neoprene rubber	Sealing metal outdoors	Difficult	Clean and dry	15-20 yrs	Yes	Med.	Slow curing
Urethane	Interior or exterior	Easy	Clean and dry	20 yrs +	Yes	Med.	Available in pour form for horizontal cracks

Alkyds

Alkyds are produced by the reaction of plant oils with certain alcohols. They have a wide range of desirable characteristics and have largely replaced oil paints. Alkyds are classified as long-oil, medium-oil, and short-oil. Long-oil alkyds are used extensively as house paints because they are easy to spread and they penetrate sufficiently to adhere well. Medium-oils are the base for gloss and semigloss enamels. The short-oil alkyds are used primarily for factory-applied finishes.

Alkyd-based paints are used for both interior and exterior wood surfaces as well as for metal. They are not recommended for fresh plaster or concrete surfaces as they do not tolerate the alkaline conditions.

Epoxies

Although epoxy paints offer a wide range of surface characteristics, the types used in agriculture produce a hard, smooth, easily cleaned surface. The high cost of epoxy paints is balanced by the durability and superior performance under adverse conditions such as those existing on milking parlor walls and the inside walls of concrete silos. When used for exterior application, there is apt to be considerable chalking which may or may not be desirable.

Latex (Acrylics and Vinyls)

Polyvinyl acetate and acrylics are the most important of the resins thinned with water. Paints manufactured with these resins are used extensively for both interior and exterior application. They are easy to apply because of thixotropic additives which give enough body to cause the paint to adhere to the brush without dripping and to the painted surface without sagging. At the same time, the pressure of the brush causes it to thin out for easy spreading. Latex paints offer good color retention and resistance to blistering, the latter resulting from a rather high permeability to water vapor. They may be applied on damp, but not wet, surfaces and are easily cleaned from brushes and rollers with soap and water.

Inorganic Vehicles

These binders are used primarily with zinc dust as a metal primer.

Phenolic Resins

Phenolics were among the first synthetic resins used. Originally based on tung oil, their prices became excessive until other sources were developed. Phenolic resins are used in exterior varnishes and as a base for aluminum paint.

Rubber-based Resins

These are distinguished from rubber-based latex in that they are solvent rather than water-reduced binders. They are used extensively on masonry surfaces, particularly swimming pools, because of their very low permeability to water and water vapor.

Silicone Resins

Silicone resins are used in high temperature paints which will withstand more than 1,000°F (540°C). Furthermore, they are very resistant to oxidation and are mixed with other resins to produce long-lasting, weather resistant paints. Many of the silicone mixtures are used by manufacturers in finishes guaranteed for up to 20 years. They are not widely available to the public.

Urethanes

Urethanes are similar to, but more complex than, alkyds and often exhibit superior wear, hardness, and solvent-resistant characteristics. They are used in both pigmented and clear finishes for both interior and exterior applications.

Pigments

Pigments are used to hide or color an underlying surface or to serve some chemical purpose such as corrosion resistance or ultraviolet absorption.

Titanium Dioxide

Titanium dioxide has such superior hiding power that, although its cost per pound is high, it offers the least expensive hiding power per unit area.

Zinc Oxide

Zinc oxide is used to provide a harder, and more chalk-resistant film. It is also mildew resistant, adds brilliance to white paints, and helps retain color integrity in colored paints by absorbing ultraviolet rays.

Lead Pigments

These have been banned by law from use in either interior or exterior house paint. Even though they were useful pigments, the danger they pose to health has resulted in a nationwide ban.

Extender Pigments

Extender pigments, such as calcium carbonate, clay, and talc, do not add significant hiding power, but they do add necessary bulk and other desirable characteristics that improve coating performance. They also reduce cost as compared to using the hiding pigments alone.

Colored Pigments

These are almost always used in very small quantities and are too numerous to cover individually. It is significant that tinted or colored paints almost invariably outlast the same formulation in white.

Solvents and Additives

Solvents are necessary to thin the resins so they can be spread or sprayed on a surface. Manufactured hydrocarbons such as benzene, toluene, and xylene along with derivatives of petroleum such as naphtha and mineral spirits are used as solvents for oil- and alkyd-based paints and varnishes. High cost and strong odor have reduced the use of turpentine. Esters and glycols are used primarily as lacquer solvents. However, they are also used to some extent in urethanes and in small quantities in most latex paints to improve coalescence of the resins at the instant the water evaporates. Alcohol is used for thinning shellac and glycol ethers are used to a limited extent for epoxies. Lastly, water is the solvent for latex paints, and its low cost, safety, and freedom from odor have all contributed to the great popularity of latex paints.

A number of additives are used in small percentages to improve spreading properties and the storing and mixing qualities of paints. Table 4-3 lists a number of more common paints that have application in agriculture along with information concerning their use.

Painting New Wood Surfaces

In addition to the composition and quality of the paint used, the appearance and durability of the paint applied to a building are influenced by the care taken during application. The following steps are recommended:

1. Seal all joints and around all door and window trim. Nailheads should be primed with an alkyd primer if latex paint is used as a first coat.
2. The use of a water-repellent wood preservative (WRP) will help to repel water and prevent damage to wood that paint by itself cannot prevent. It is essential that the WRP dries for two days or more in good drying weather before proceeding with painting.
3. Apply the primer recommended for the paint used. This is usually an alkyd-based paint. When latex paint is used, the wood may be damp. In all other cases, the wood should be dry before painting begins.
4. Apply two top coats as directed by the manufacturer for maximum durability. Latex paint should not be applied in direct sunlight, on a windy day, or when the temperature will drop below 50°F (10°C) before the paint is dry.

Repainting Old Wood Surfaces

1. Repaint after original paint has weathered considerably and has worn thin, but if possible, before there is excessive failure due to cracking and peeling.
2. All loose paint should be removed with a scraper and the edges sanded to blend or eliminate the delineating edges of the paint failure.
3. Bare spots are treated as new wood by first using a WRP and then spot priming.
4. If there are signs of mildew or excessive chalking, the surface should be thoroughly washed with trisodium phosphate or a strong detergent mixed with 8 oz (1/4 L) of bleach in 1 gal (4 L) of water. After washing, the surface should be thoroughly rinsed and painted immediately with a latex paint or as soon as the surface is completely dry if an alkyd paint is used.
5. Latex paint does not adhere well to a chalky surface. An alkyd primer may be necessary if the surface cannot be cleaned of all loose material.
6. Two coats of finish paint will increase paint life considerably.

Painting Metal Surfaces

1. The surface must be cleaned and free of any oil, wax, loose paint or corrosion.
2. A metal primer should be applied before the top coat. If corrosion is present or if the surface is galvanized, a metallic zinc powder primer is advisable. Paint adheres to galvanized surfaces best after three to four years of weathering.

Problems

4.1. Following is a list of locations where surfacing materials are required. Choose one or more materials that would be satisfactory for each and give supporting reasons.

    (a) Milk room walls and ceiling

    (b) Milking parlor walls

    (c) Siding for a cold free-stall barn

    (d) Greenhouse covering for bedding plants

    (e) Inside walls of apple storage

    (f) Walls and ceiling in a cage laying-house

    (g) Walls for a roadside produce market

    (h) Inside walls for a home

    (i) Outside wall covering for a home

    (j) Inside walls for a ski lodge

    (k) Outside wall covering for a ski lodge

    (l) Wall covering for a machinery shed

4.2. Choose a finishing material for each of the following situations. Give brief reasons for your choice.

    (a) Plywood siding on a barn

    (b) Galvanized steel roof just starting to rust

    (c) Smooth-finish roll roofing on a poultry house

    (d) A home sided with wood shingles

    (e) Wood trim on a brick home

    (f) Plywood walls in a milking parlor

5 Wood Fasteners

A primary objective in fabricating wood structures is to design joints that approximate the strength of the members to be joined. When this is accomplished, a safe, economical structure results. The failure to always achieve this is shown by the fact that a large proportion of wooden-building failures result from inadequate joint design or assembly. Member breakage often results from the crash rather than being the cause of the failure.

Farm buildings still stand today in which the framing timbers were fastened together without a nail. The wall frames were assembled on the ground with a mortise-and-tenon joint (an extension of one piece of wood fitted into the socket of another) and secured with a wooden peg. Then with the help of neighboring farmers using metal tipped poles, the "broadside" was pushed to an upright position. The strength and durability of this type of fastening is demonstrated by the survival of these early buildings. But the time required to construct and fit such a joint became prohibitive in the early 19th century when cut iron nails came into use followed by steel wire nails around 1875. Bolts were introduced about the same time as the early nails but have never been used as extensively since they are not as simple to use. Timber connectors that significantly increase structural strength were introduced in 1930, and more recently glue has been developed to make prefabricated joints readily available.

Mechanical connectors used to join wood structural members include nails, bolts, lag screws, wood screws, split ring connectors, shear plates, and metal plate connectors. Some of these may be used in combination and all have their own characteristics. The load may be transferred from one main member to another directly by use of fasteners or through intermediate members such as side plates or gussets. The potential mode of failure will vary depending on the system used and the design approach must recognize this potential failure. Design formulas and tables have been developed based on research and analysis. The nominal design value calculated or found in the tables is for "normal" conditions; if other than normal conditions exist then the value should be adjusted.

A word of caution to the reader is in order. This chapter and several of the following chapters are intended to provide some insight into the factors involved in structural analysis. While the procedures and equations given may seem somewhat complex and difficult to understand by some, they are in some cases generalized and based on simplifying assumptions. The knowledge gained should be useful in understanding the design process and with proper caution might even be used to plan simple structures. However, the information given here is not adequate to prepare the reader to be a structural designer or analyst.

Nails

Nails are the most frequently used connector for wood construction. In addition to the common wire nail, there are literally dozens of special purpose nails, including the hardened-steel threaded-shank nails used in heavy construction, and various types used to secure wall panels, roofing, flooring, and trim. Figure 5.1(a) illustrates the wide variety. The most frequently used nails for frame construction and wood trim include the following:

- Common wire nails are used for framing where there will be considerable lateral load.
- Spikes parallel the length of a number of the sizes of common nails. However, their larger diameter gives them greater holding power where they can be used without splitting the wood.
- Box nails are smaller in diameter than common nails and are used for installing sheathing or roof decks. Although their holding power is less, they also reduce the danger of splitting.
- Casing and finishing nails are smaller in both diameter and head size than common nails of the same pennyweight. The small head may be countersunk and covered for a neat appearance.

Some other variations are (1) type of point: diamond, needle, blunt or pointless; (2) type of head: flat, set, checkered, oval or duplex; (3) type of shank: smooth, helically grooved, annular threads or barbed; and (4) type of finish. Finishes available are: electrogalvanized (smooth, shiny) which has average holding power and tends to rust; hot-dip galvanized which are zinc-coated to reduce corrosion; cement-coated nails are dipped in a resin to increase the holding power; (5) blued nails are free of residues and have an improved appearance. Nails may also be heat-treated to provide hardened or annealed characteristics. Stainless steel nails are available for use in high corrosive areas.

Nail Size

Nails are sized in pennyweight (d) which is related to their length. Nail sizes and a suggested nailing schedule are shown in figure 5.1b. Diameters for each size vary with the type of nail (table 5-1).

Safe Withdrawal Loads for Nails

When nails are used such that the force tends to act in the direction of the nail and tends to cause it to pull out, it is said to be loaded in withdrawal. An example of this type of loading would be grain inside sheathing, and pushing it away from the framing or roofing which is subjected to uplift from wind.

The following formula may be used to obtain the safe withdrawal load for common nails:

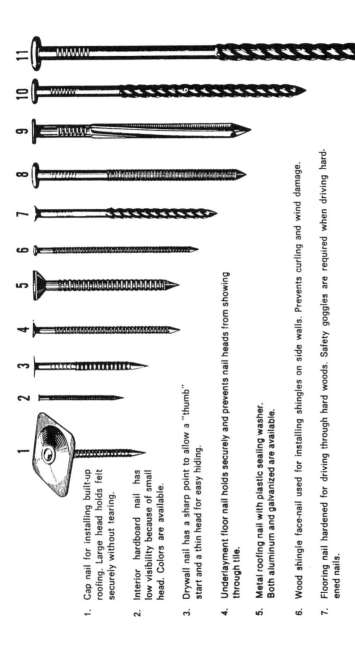

1. Cap nail for installing built-up roofing. Large head holds felt securely without tearing.

2. Interior hardboard nail has low visibility because of small head. Colors are available.

3. Drywall nail has a sharp point to allow a "thumb" start and a thin head for easy hiding.

4. Underlayment floor nail holds securely and prevents nail heads from showing through tile.

5. Metal roofing nail with plastic sealing washer. Both aluminum and galvanized are available.

6. Wood shingle face-nail used for installing shingles on side walls. Prevents curling and wind damage.

7. Flooring nail hardened for driving through hard woods. Safety goggles are required when driving hardened nails.

8. Common nail with annular thread for general use.

9. Masonry nail hardened for driving into bricks and concrete blocks. Goggles are required.

10. Trussed rafter nail hardened and especially designed for truss construction. Goggles required.

11. Pole type construction nail hardened and of slimmer gauge to reduce splitting while increasing structural strength.

Figure 5.1. (a) Special purpose nails. All of these nails are designed to have superior holding strength in addition to their other features.

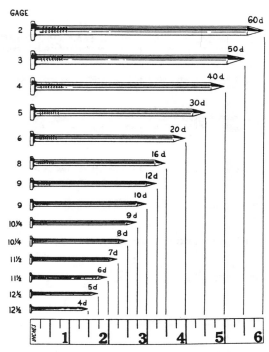

Recommended Nailing Schedule
Using Common Nails

Joist to sill or girder, toe nail	3-8d
Bridging to joist, toe nail each end	2-8d
Ledger strip	3-16d at each joist
1" x 6" subfloor or less to each joist, face nail	2-8d
Over 1" x 6" subfloor to each joist, face nail	3-8d
2" subfloor to joist or girder, blind and face nail	2-16d
Sole plate to joist or blocking, face nail	16d @ 16" oc
Top plate to stud, end nail	2-16d
Stud to sole plate, toe nail	4-8d
Doubled studs, face nail	16d @ 24" oc
Doubled top plates, face nail	16d @ 16" oc
Top plates, laps and intersections, face nail	2-16d
Continuous header, two pieces	16d @ 16" oc along each edge
Ceiling joists to plate, toe nail	3-8d
Continuous header to stud, toe nail	4-8d
Ceiling joists, laps over partitions, face nail	3-16d
Ceiling joists to parallel rafters, face nail	3-16d
Rafter to plate, toe nail	3-8d
1-inch brace to each stud and plate, face nail	2-8d
1" x 8" sheathing or less to each bearing, face nail	2-8d
Over 1" x 8" sheathing to each bearing, face nail	3-8d
Built-up corner studs	16d @ 24" oc
Built-up girders and beams	20d @ 32" oc along each edge

Figure 5.1. (b) Sizes of common wire nails.

Table 5-1. Nail sizes

Size	Length (in.)	Nail diameter (in.)*				
		COMMON	BOX	STEEL	SPIKE	FINISH
2d	1.00	0.072				
3d	1.25	0.083	0.076			0.067
4d	1.50	0.105	0.080			0.072
5d	1.75	0.105	0.080			
6d	2.00	0.113	0.099	0.120		0.092
7d	2.25	0.113	0.099	0.120		
8d	2.50	0.131	0.113	0.120		0.099
9d	2.75	0.131	0.113	0.120		
10d	3.00	0.148	0.128	0.135	0.192	0.113
12d	3.25	0.148	0.128	0.135	0.192	
16d	3.50	0.162	0.135	0.148	0.207	
20d	4.00	0.192	0.148	0.177	0.225	
30d	4.50	0.207	0.148	0.177	0.244	
40d	5.00	0.225	0.162	0.177	0.263	
50d	5.50	0.244		0.177	0.283	
60d	6.00	0.263		0.177	0.283	
70d	7.00			0.207		
80d	8.00			0.207		
90d	9.00			0.207		
5/16	7.00				0.312	
3/8	8.50				0.375	

* Multiply inches by 25.4 to obtain millimeters.

$$W = K_W \, G_5^2 D p \qquad (5.1)$$

where

W $=$ the safe withdrawal load (lb/nail)

K_w $=$ 1,380 for common wire nails, box nails or spikes

$=$ 1,500 for threaded nails

G $=$ the specific gravity of member receiving the nail point (see table 5-2)

D $=$ the diameter of the nail (in.)

p $=$ depth of penetration in members receiving the point (in.)

Table 5-3 gives safe withdrawal design values for various sized common and threaded steel nails. These values apply when used under "normal" conditions; under other conditions the safe load values should be adjusted.

- Values apply to nails driven into side grain for either seasoned or unseasoned wood.
- When a nail is driven into wood parallel to the grain, the holding power may be reduced as much as 50%. For this reason nails driven into end grain should not be loaded in withdrawal.
- Values for toe-nailed joints may be reduced by 33%.

Table 5-2. Dowel bearing strength for nail or spike connections

Species	Specific Gravity G	Dowel Bearing Strength (psi) F_e
Aspen	0.39	2950
Beech-Birch-Hickory	0.71	8850
Cottonwood	0.41	3200
Douglas fir-Larch	0.50	4650
Eastern hemlock	0.41	3200
Eastern spruce	0.41	3200
Eastern white pine	0.36	2550
Englemann spruce-Lodgepole pine (MSR 1650f and higher)	0.46	4000
Englemann spruce-Lodgepole pine (MSR 1500f and lower)	0.38	2800
Hem-fir	0.43	3500
Mixed maple	0.55	5550
Mountain hemlock	0.47	4150
Northern pine	0.42	3350
Ponderosa pine	0.43	3500
Red maple	0.58	6100
Red oak	0.67	7950
Red pine	0.44	3650
Sitka spruce	0.43	3500
Southern pine	0.55	5550
Spruce-Pine-Fir	0.42	3350
Western white pine	0.40	3100
Western woods	0.36	2550
White oak	0.73	9300
Yellow poplar	0.43	3500

• If the wood is wet at time of fabrication but dry in service, or it is dry at time of fabrication but subjected to wetting and drying in service, then the allowable load should be reduced by 75%.

Safe Lateral Loads for Nails

When structural members with forces acting along their length are joined by using sideplates, the forces will act laterally to the fasteners—nails, bolts or screws. With this type of joint, failure may occur in one of several different modes as illustrated in figure 5.2. The Type I failure represents bearing yielding or crushing. When the bearing yields in the main member the failure is classified as Type I_m; Type I_s failure occurs when the sideplate bearing yields. Type II failure occurs when the fastener rotates as the members slip with respect to one another; this type of failure does not occur in single shear nail connections. In failure modes III and IV, the fasteners also bend. The type of failure will influence the load that can be supported.

Formulas have been developed for each failure mode. The equation used to calcu-

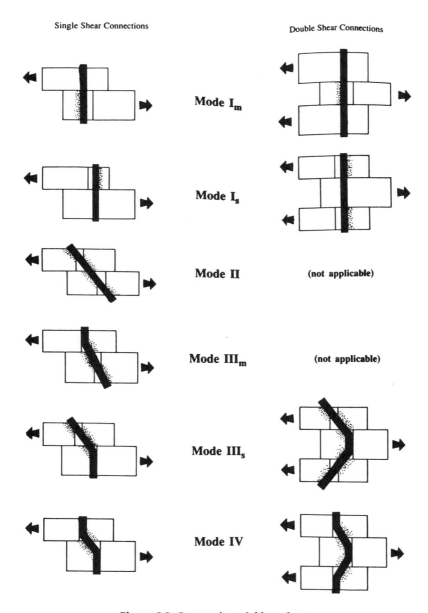

Single Shear Connections   Double Shear Connections

Mode I_m

Mode I_s

Mode II   (not applicable)

Mode III_m (not applicable)

Mode III_s

Mode IV

Figure 5.2. Connection yield modes.*

* There are four possible primary connection yield modes. Modes I_m and I_s represent bearing-dominated yield of the wood fibers in contact with the fasteners in either the main (m) or side member (s). Mode II represents pivoting of the fastener at the shear plane of a single shear connection with limited localized crushing of wood fibers near the wood faces. Modes III_m and III_s occur when the fastener yields in bending at one plastic hinge point per shear plane. Mode IV represents yield in bending at two plastic hinge points per shear plane, with limited localized crushing of wood fibers near the shear plane. (Taken from National Design Specification for Wood Construction, 1991 edition, National Forest Products Association, Washington, D.C.)

Table 5-3. Nail and spike withdrawal design values (W, lb/in. of penetration)

Nail Diameter (in.)	Wood Specific Gravity							
	0.73	0.68	0.55	0.50	0.44	0.40	0.36	0.31
Common wire nails, box nails and common wire spikes								
0.099	62	52	31	24	18	14	11	7
0.113	71	59	35	28	20	16	12	8
0.128	80	67	40	31	23	18	14	9
0.131	82	69	41	32	23	18	14	10
0.135	85	71	42	33	24	19	14	10
0.148	93	78	46	36	26	21	16	11
0.162	102	85	50	40	29	23	17	12
0.192	121	101	59	47	34	27	21	14
0.207	130	109	64	50	37	29	22	15
0.225	141	118	70	55	40	31	24	17
0.244	153	128	76	60	43	34	29	18
0.263	165	138	81	64	47	37	28	19
0.283	178	149	88	69	50	40	30	21
0.312	196	164	97	76	55	44	33	23
0.375	236	197	116	91	66	52	40	28
Threaded nails								
0.120	82	69	41	32	23	18	14	10
0.135	93	78	46	36	26	21	16	11
0.148	102	85	50	40	29	23	17	12
0.177	121	101	59	47	34	27	21	14
0.207	141	118	70	55	40	31	24	17

late the safe lateral load for a common wire nail which has a Type I_s yield mode illustrates some of the factors:

$$Z = D \, t_s \frac{F_e}{K_D} \qquad (5.2)$$

where

Z	=	the safe load (lb/nail)
D	=	diameter of the nail (in.)
t_s	=	thickness of side plate (in.)
F_e	=	dowel bearing strength (psi, table 5-2)
K_D	=	2.2 (for D = <0.17 in.)
K_D	=	$10D + 0.5$ (for 0.17 in. < D < 0.25 in.)
K_D	=	3.0 (for D > 0.25 in.)

The allowable nail loads for the other yield modes are determined by similar formulas. Safe loads for single shear lateral joints using various sizes of common nails are given in table 5-4. There are a number of conditions associated with the use of the formula and the values given in table 5-4.

•   Values assume that the nails are driven at approximately right angles into the side grain of seasoned wood with 19% or less moisture content. Toe-

Table 5-4. Lateral loaded nail design values (z) for single shear (two member) connections with both members of identical species

Side Member Thickness t_s (in.)*	Nail Length L (in.)	Nail Diameter D (in.)	Penny-Weight	Red Oak Z (lb)†	Mixed Maple, Southern Pine Z (lb)	Douglas Fir Larch Z (lb)	Spruce Pine-Fir Z (lb)
Box							
1/2	2	0.099	6d	73	55	48	38
	2 1/2	0.113	8d	88	67	59	47
	3	0.128	10d	106	82	73	59
	3 1/4	0.128	12d	106	82	73	59
	3 1/2	0.135	16d	115	89	79	65
	4	0.148	20d	129	101	90	73
	4 1/2	0.148	30d	129	101	90	73
	5	0.162	40d	149	117	105	87
1	2	0.099	6d	94	79	72	61
	2 1/2	0.113	8d	121	101	93	79
	3	0.128	10d	121	101	93	79
	3 1/4	0.128	12d	135	113	103	86
	3 1/2	0.135	16d	154	128	118	96
	4	0.148	20d	154	128	118	96
	4 1/2	0.148	30d	184	154	141	109
	5	0.162	40d				
1 1/2	3 1/4	0.128	12d	121	101	93	79
	3 1/2	0.135	16d	135	113	103	88
	4	0.148	20d	154	128	118	100
	4 1/2	0.148	30d	154	128	118	100
	5	0.162	40d	184	154	141	120
Common							
1/2	2	0.113	6d	88	67	59	47
	2 1/2	0.131	8d	110	85	76	61
	3	0.148	10d	129	101	90	73
	3 1/4	0.148	12d	129	101	90	73
	3 1/2	0.162	16d	149	117	105	87
	4	0.192	20d	172	137	124	103
	4 1/2	0.207	30d	185	148	134	112
	5	0.225	40d	200	162	147	123
	5 1/2	0.244	50d	205	166	151	127
	6	0.263	60d	230	188	171	144
1	3	0.148	10d	154	128	118	96
	3 1/4	0.148	12d	154	128	118	96
	3 1/2	0.162	16d	184	154	141	109
	4	0.192	20d	222	183	159	124
	4 1/2	0.207	30d	243	192	167	131
	5	0.225	40d	268	202	177	140
	5 1/2	0.244	50d	274	207	181	143
	6	0.263	60d	298	227	199	159
1 1/2	3 1/2	0.162	16d	184	154	141	120
	4	0.192	20d	222	185	170	144
	4 1/2	0.207	30d	243	203	186	158
	5	0.225	40d	268	224	205	172
	5 1/2	0.244	50d	276	230	211	175
6		0.263	60d	314	262	240	191

*Multiply inches by 25.4 to obtain millimeters.
†Multiply lb by 4.448 to obtain newtons.

nails should be started at a point approximately one-third the length of the nail from the end of the piece and be driven at an angle of approximately 30° with the piece.

- The values given in the table assume that the nail penetration into the main member is at least 12D. If the penetration, p, is less than 12D, the Z-value should be multiplied by:

$$C_d = \frac{p}{12D} \qquad (5.3)$$

but in no case should p be less than 6D.
- When more than one nail is used, the full sum of the value for single nails may be used if the following factors are observed: 1 in. (38 mm) edge distance, spacings of 1 in. (25 mm) across grain, 2 in. (64 mm) parallel to the grain, 2 in. (57 mm) end distance in tension members.
- For lateral loads on end-nailed joints, reduce the values in table 5-4 by 33%.
- For lateral loads on unseasoned wood that will remain wet or will be loaded before seasoning, reduce by 25%.
- For double shear joints (three members), if $t_m > 6D$, the Z-value is two times the lesser of the smallest nominal design value (t_m = thickness of the main member). The penetration depth factor, C_d, is based on nail penetration into the third member except that $C_d = 1.0$ if nail < 12d and is clinched by at least 3 diameters.
- Values for nails used to install large panels for sheathing, flooring, or roof decks may be increased 30%.
- Lateral load design values for toe-nailed joints should not exceed 83% of the table value.
- When using prebored guide holes of up to 90% of the diameter of the nail for wood with G > 0.6, or 75% of the nail diameter for wood with G < 0.6, do not reduce values.
- Values for nails used with kiln-dried, fire-retardant-treated woods should be reduced by 10%.
- With properly designed metal side plates, add 25%.

Research has shown that a 1/2 in. (12 mm) plywood side-plate will develop the full bearing strength of a 10d nail assuming the holding member is of adequate thickness and approximately equal density to that of the plywood. The following list provides the minimum plywood thickness needed to develop approximately the full bearing strength for the given nails.

Plywood thickness	Nail size
5/16 (8 mm)	6d
1/2 (9.5 mm)	8d
1/2 (12 mm)	10d
1/2 (16 mm)	16d

Fastener Example 5.1

Determine the number of common nails required to attach roof decking on rafters which are 2 ft o.c. Assume: uplift = 20 psf; SPF rafters; and 1/2 in. plywood deck.

Solution

Load = 2 ft × 20 psf = 40 plf

Use table 5.3, S.G. = 0.42, find for 6d nail allowable load = 18 lb/in.

Penetration = 2 in. − 1/2 in. = 11/2 in.

Number nail/ft = 40 plf / 18 lb/in. × 11/2 in. = 1.5

Required nail spacing 12 in./ft / 1.5 nail/ft = 8 in. o.c.

For 8d nail, allowable load = 20.5 lb/in., thus:

Penetration = 21/2 in. − 1/2 in. = 2 in.

Number nail/ft = 40 plf / 20.5 lb/in. × 2 ιv. = 0.98

Required nail spacing = 12 in. o.c.

Staples

Staples are often used in place of nails. Design values for staples are not provided in the 1991 National Design Specifications for Wood Construction, but the following table may provide guidance for their usage. These values are for 16 gauge staples with 7/16 in. (11 mm) crowns driven into Douglas fir lumber. The allowable load values are given in pounds per staple.

Penetration into lumber	Lateral load lb (N)	Withdrawal load lb (N)
3/4 in. (18 mm)	160 (712)	100 (445)
1 in. (25 mm)	180 (800)	150 (667)
13/4 in. (32 mm)	200 (890)	200 (890)
11/2 in. (38 mm)	220 (918)	

Wood Screws

The design procedure for screws is similar to that used for nails. Lead holes should be bored and the screw inserted by turning, not by driving with a hammer. Soap or other lubricant may be used to prevent damage to the screw in hard woods. Nominal withdrawal designs for a single wood screw inserted in side grain, with the screw axis perpendicular to the wood fibers are given in table 5-5. Wood screws should not be loaded in withdrawal from end grain of wood.

Table 5-5. Wood screw withdrawal design values (lb/in. of thread penetration)

Gauge	Diameter	Specific Gravity											
		0.75	0.66	0.62	0.55	0.51	0.46	0.44	0.42	0.40	0.38	0.36	0.31
6	0.138	220	171	151	119	102	83	76	69	63	57	51	38
7	0.151	241	187	165	130	112	91	83	76	69	62	56	41
8	0.164	262	203	179	141	121	99	90	82	75	67	60	45
9	0.177	283	219	193	152	131	106	97	89	80	73	65	48
10	0.190	304	235	207	163	140	114	104	95	86	78	70	52
12	0.216	345	267	236	186	160	130	119	108	98	89	80	59
14	0.242	387	299	264	208	179	145	133	121	110	99	89	66
16	0.268	428	332	293	230	198	161	147	134	122	110	99	73
18	0.294	470	364	321	253	217	177	162	147	134	121	108	80
20	0.320	511	396	349	275	236	192	176	160	145	131	118	87
24	0.372	594	460	406	320	275	224	205	186	169	153	137	102

Table 5-6. Wood screw lateral load design values (lb/screw)*

Side Member Thickness (t_s) (in.)	Wood Screw Diameter (D) (in.)	Wood Screw Gage	Member Specific Gravity				
			0.67	0.55	0.50	0.43	0.35
1/2	0.138	6g	111	85	75	62	49
	0.151	7g	123	95	84	70	56
	0.164	8g	140	108	96	81	65
	0.177	9g	152	119	107	90	72
	0.190	10g	156	122	109	92	74
	0.216	12g	173	138	124	105	86
	0.242	14g	183	146	132	112	92
	0.268	16g	212	171	155	133	107
	0.294	18g	235	190	172	148	118
1	0.164	8g	177	148	135	108	80
	0.177	9g	199	167	147	117	87
	0.190	10g	205	171	150	119	89
	0.216	12g	239	186	161	129	99
	0.242	14g	256	193	168	135	104
	0.268	16g	290	217	190	154	120
	0.294	18g	305	240	210	171	133
	0.320	20g	340	272	239	196	154
	0.372	24g	471	317	279	229	179
1 1/2	0.164	8g	177	148	135	117	97
	0.190	10g	205	171	157	136	113
	0.216	12g	239	200	183	159	121
	0.242	14g	256	213	195	170	126
	0.268	16g	290	255	233	192	142
	0.294	18g	305	284	260	212	157
	0.320	20g	340	336	300	238	178
	0.372	24g	471	394	349	277	207

* Assumes penetration $\geq$ 7D; use linear reduction down to 4D.

Table 5-7. Lateral loads on wood screws with ASTM A446, grade A steel side plates (lb/screw)*

Steel Side Plate	Wood Screw Diameter (D) (in.)	Wood Screw Gage	Member Specific Gravity				
			0.67	0.55	0.50	0.43	0.35
No. 3 gage	0.242	14g	276	241	225	200	171
$t_s = 0.239$ in.	0.268	16g	315	275	256	228	194
	0.294	18g	349	304	283	252	215
	0.320	20g	400	348	325	289	246
	0.372	24g	467	407	379	337	287
No. 10 gage	0.138	6g	131	114	107	95	81
$t_s = 0.134$ in.	0.151	7g	147	128	119	106	90
	0.164	8g	169	147	137	122	103
	0.177	9g	187	162	151	134	114
	0.190	10g	192	166	155	137	117
	0.216	12g	217	188	175	155	131
	0.242	14g	230	199	185	164	139
	0.268	16g	271	234	217	192	163
	0.294	18g	301	260	241	213	181
	0.320	20g	353	304	282	250	211
	0.372	24g	413	356	330	292	247
No. 16 gage	0.138	6g	114	98	90	80	67
$t_s = 0.06$ in.	0.151	7g	129	111	103	90	76
	0.164	8g	151	130	120	106	89
	0.177	9g	171	146	135	119	100
	0.190	10g	175	150	139	122	103

* Assumes penetration $\geq$ 7D; use linear reduction down to 4D.

The values given in tables 5-6 and 5-7 for lateral loading of wood screws apply under normal conditions and assume the screw is in side grain perpendicular to the wood fibers and the depth of screw penetration in the main member is greater than or equal to seven times the shank diameter, p = 7D. If the penetration p < 7D, then the design value shall be reduced using the following penetration depth factor:

$$C_d = \frac{p}{7\,D} \leq 1.0 \qquad (5.4)$$

However, the minimum allowable penetration is four times the shank diameter, $p_{min} = 4D$.

Bolts

When loads on wood connections are particularly heavy, bolted joints may be advisable. Tables 5-8, 5-9, and 5-10 provide data for designing bolted joints. When using the tables, it is important to determine which member is limiting and select the smaller allowable load. When multiple bolts are used, the table values should be reduced. For a 2 × 4 in. (38 × 89 mm) sideplate, the reduction factor is approximately 5% for each bolt in a row. For double 2 × 4 in. (38 × 89 mm) sideplates or a 2 × 6 in. (38 × 140 mm) sideplate, use a reduction of 4% per bolt in the row. Spacing criteria are given in the following table ['D' = bolt diameter and 'l' = the lesser of the (1) the length of the bolt in the main member or (2) the total length of bolt in the side plate(s)]. For end distances less

Table 5-8. Bolt design values for double shear joints with 1 1/2 in. sideplates (lb/bolt)

Specific Gravity	Bolt dia. (in.)	Main Member Thickness (in.)								
		1 1/2			3			4 1/2		
		Z_{ll}	Z_{sp}	Z_{mp}	Z_{ll}	Z_{sp}	Z_{mp}	Z_{ll}	Z_{sp}	Z_{mp}
0.55	1/2	1150	800	550	1320	800	940			
	5/8	1440	1130	610	1870	1130	1220	1870	1130	1290
	3/4	1730	1330	660	2550	1330	1330	2550	1330	1690
	7/8	2020	1440	720	3360	1440	1440	3360	1440	2170
	1	2310	1530	770	4310	1530	1530	4310	1530	2300
0.46	1/2	970	680	420	1160	680	810			
	5/8	1210	940	470	1660	940	940	1660	940	1110
	3/4	1450	1040	520	2280	1040	1040	2280	1040	1480
	7/8	1690	1100	550	3030	1100	1100	3030	1100	1650
	1	1930	1200	600	3860	1200	1200	3860	1200	1800
0.42	1/2	880	640	370	1080	640	740			
	5/8	1100	830	410	1570	830	830	1570	830	1040
	3/4	1320	900	450	2160	900	900	2160	900	1350
	7/8	1540	970	490	2880	970	970	2880	970	1460
	1	1760	1050	530	3530	1050	1050	3530	1050	1580
0.36	1/2	760	560	290	980	560	590			
	5/8	950	660	330	1430	660	660	1430	660	920
	3/4	1140	720	360	1990	720	720	1990	720	1080
	7/8	1330	790	390	2660	790	790	2660	790	1180
	1	1520	840	420	3040	840	840	3040	840	1260

Z_{ll} = load parallel to grain in both members; Z_{sp} = load perpendicular to grain in sideplate; Z_{mp} = load perpendicular to grain in main member.

than the recommended minimum but no less than one-half that value, the design value should be multiplied by a factor equal to the ratio of the actual distance to the recommended distance. More complete information may be found in National Design Specification for Wood Construction, 1991.

Minimum edge distance:
    loading parallel to grain   1.5D
    loading perpendicular to grain
        loaded edge   4D
        unloaded edge   1.5D

Minimum end distance:
    loading perpendicular to grain   4D
    loading parallel to grain
        softwoods   7D
        hardwoods   5D

Minimum spacing between bolts in a row   4D*
    * for loading perpendicular to grain if l/D ≥ 6 use 5D

Table 5-9. Bolt design values for single shear joints with 1 1/2 in. sideplates (lb/bolt)

Specific Gravity	Bolt dia. (in.)	Main Member Thickness (in.)								
		1 1/2			3			4 1/2		
		Z_{ll}	Z_{sp}	Z_{mp}	Z_{ll}	Z_{sp}	Z_{mp}	Z_{ll}	Z_{sp}	Z_{mp}
0.55	1/2	530	330	330	660	400	470			
	5/8	660	400	400	940	560	550	940	560	640
	3/4	800	460	460	1270	660	620	1270	660	840
	7/8	930	520	520	1520	720	690	1680	720	930
	1	1060	580	580	1740	770	750	2150	770	1000
0.46	1/2	440	270	270	580	340	380			
	5/8	560	320	320	830	470	440	830	470	560
	3/4	670	380	380	1090	520	500	1140	520	670
	7/8	780	420	420	1280	550	540	1520	550	730
	1	890	480	480	1460	600	600	1930	600	800
0.42	1/2	410	240	240	540	320	330			
	5/8	510	290	290	780	410	390	780	410	520
	3/4	610	340	340	1000	450	440	1080	450	590
	7/8	710	380	380	1160	490	490	1440	490	640
	1	810	430	430	1330	530	540	1760	530	710
0.36	1/2	350	200	200	490	280	270			
	5/8	440	240	240	710	330	320	710	330	430
	3/4	520	280	280	860	360	360	990	360	480
	7/8	610	320	320	1000	390	400	1330	390	530
	1	700	360	360	1150	420	440	1520	420	570

Minimum spacing between rows:
   loading parallel to grain   1.5D
   loading perpendicular to grain   5D

Ring Connectors and Shear Plates

A steel ring connector installed concentrically with a bolt in a wood-to-wood joint can increase the strength of that joint considerably over the bolt alone. A tool is used to cut an accurate groove into each of the wood surfaces to be joined, spreading the shear forces over a greater area of the wood. Steel or malleable iron shear plates are also available that transfer the force from wood to bolt and back to the wood again.

Tables 5-11 and 5-12 provides some design values for single, split-ring connections for single-shear joints in seasoned wood that will remain dry in service. These values require that the center of the connector be at least 13/4 in. (44 mm) from the edge of the member. The distance from the center of the connector to the end of a member loaded in tension should be at least 51/2 in. (140 mm), or for compression loading the distance should be not less than 4 in. (100 mm). If multiple connectors are used they should be spaced at least 63/4 in. (170 mm) parallel to the grain and 31/2 in. (90 mm) perpendicular to the grain.

Table 5-10. Bolt design values for double shear joints
with 1/4 in. ASTM A36 steel sideplates (lb/bolt)

Specific Gravity	Bolt dia. (in.)	Main Member Thickness (in.)					
		1 1/2		3		4 1/2	
		$Z_{\parallel}$	Z_p	$Z_{\parallel}$	Z_p	$Z_{\parallel}$	Z_p
0.55	1/2	1150	550	1570	1000		
	5/8	1440	610	2350	1220	2350	1420
	3/4	1730	660	3300	1330	3300	1910
	7/8	2020	720	4040	1440	4440	2170
	1	2310	770	4610	1530	5750	2300
0.46	1/2	970	420	1460	840		
	5/8	1210	470	2170	940	2170	1260
	3/4	1450	520	2900	1040	3060	1550
	7/8	1690	550	3380	1100	4100	1650
	1	1930	600	3860	1200	5320	1800
0.42	1/2	880	370	1400	740		
	5/8	1100	410	2090	830	2090	1190
	3/4	1320	450	2640	900	2940	1350
	7/8	1540	490	3080	970	3940	1460
	1	1760	530	3530	1050	5110	1580
0.36	1/2	760	290	1310	590		
	5/8	950	330	1900	660	1960	980
	3/4	1140	360	2280	720	2750	1080
	7/8	1330	390	2660	790	3690	1180
	1	1520	420	3040	840	4560	1260

Example 5.2

Two, 2 × 6 in. (89 × 140 mm) Douglas fir tension members are to be joined using 21/2 (64 mm) in. split rings on each side of the main member. The end distance is limited to 4 in. (100 mm).

Solution

The value for Douglas fir is found in table 5-11 to be 2,430 lb/ring or 4,860 lb for the two rings. However, the full value cannot be used because of the limited end distance. Based on table 5-12, the geometry factor is calculated as:

$$\frac{0.625 + (1.0 - 0.625)\left[\frac{(5.5 \text{ in} - 4.0 \text{ in.})}{(5.5 \text{ in.} - 2.75 \text{ in.})}\right]} = 0.83$$

The allowable load is thus: 4,860 lb × 0.83 = 4,032 lb.

Table 5-11. (a) Safe load design values for split-ring connectors (lb)

Ring Diameter	Load Direction*	Number Member Faces	Minimum Net Thickness of Member	Group A Species	Group B Species	Group C Species	Group D Species
2 1/2 in.	P	1	1 in.	2630	2270	1900	1640
			1 1/2 in.	3160	2730	2290	1960
		2	1 1/2 in.	2430	2100	1760	1510
			2 in.	3160	2730	2290	1960
	Q	1	1 in.	1900	1620	1350	1160
			1 1/2 in.	2280	1940	1620	1390
		2	1 1/2 in.	1750	1500	1250	1070
			2 in.	2280	1940	1620	1390
4 in.	P	1	1 in.	4090	3510	2920	2520
			1 1/2 in.	6020	5160	4280	3710
		2	1 1/2 in.	4110	3520	2940	2540
			2 in.	4950	4250	3540	3050
	Q	1	1 in.	2840	2440	2040	1760
			1 1/2 in.	4180	3590	2990	2580
		2	1 1/2 in.	2980	2450	2040	1760
			2 in.	3440	2960	2460	2120

* P = load parallel to grain; Q = load perpendicular to grain.
Note: a 1/2 in. diameter. bolt is to be used with the 2 1/2 in. ring and a 3/4 in. bolt with the 4 in. ring.

Table 5-11. (b) Species groups for split ring connectors

Group A	Group B	Group C	Group D
Beech - Birch - Hickory	Douglas fir-larch	Douglas fir - south	Aspen
Douglas fir-larch (dense)	Mixed maple	Eastern hemlock	Coast sitka spruce
Mixed oak	Mixed southern pine	Hem-fir	Cottonwood
Red oak	Red maple	Mountain hemlock	Eastern hemlock
Southern pine (dense)		Northern pine	Eastern softwoods
White oak		Ponderosa pine	Eastern spruce
		Red pine	Eastern white pine
		Redwood (close grain)	Redwood (open grain)
		Sitka spruce	Spruce-Pine-Fir (south)
		Spruce-Pine-Fir	Western white pine
		Western hemlock	Western woods
		Yellow poplar	

Stresses at an Angle to the Grain

When bolted or ring connector joints are loaded at an angle between 0 and 90° to the grain, a corrected safe compression stress value may be obtained by the use of Hankinson formula (fig. 5.3).

$$N = \frac{PQ}{P\sin^2\theta + Q\cos^2\theta} \qquad (5.5)$$

Table 5-12. Geometry adjustment factors for split rings

	Ring Diameter	Load Direction	Minimum for Full Design Value (in.)	Minimum for Reduced Design Value (in.)	Geometry Factor, C_Δ
Unloaded edge	2 1/2 in.	P	1 3/4	1 3/4	1.0
		Q	1 3/4	1 3/4	1.0
	4 in.	P	2 3/4	2 3/4	1.0
		Q	2 3/4	2 3/4	1.0
Loaded edge	2 1/2 in.	P	1 3/4	1 3/4	1.0
		Q	2 3/4	1 3/4	0.83
	4 in.	P	2 3/4	2 3/4	1.0
		Q	3 3/4	2 3/4	0.83
Tension end	2 1/2 in.	P	5 1/2	2 3/4	0.625
		Q	5 1/2	2 3/4	0.625
	4 in.	P	7	3 1/2	0.625
		Q	7	3 1/2	0.625
Compression end	2 1/2 in.	P	4	2 1/2	0.625
		Q	5 1/2	2 3/4	0.625
	4 in.	P	5 1/2	3 1/4	0.625
		Q	7	3 1/2	0.625
Spacing, parallel to grain	2 1/2 in.	P	6 3/4	3 1/2	0.5
		Q	3 1/2	3 1/2	1.0
	4 in.	P	9	5	0.5
		Q	5	5	1.0
Spacing, perpendicular to grain	2 1/2 in.	P	3 1/2	3 1/2	1.0
		Q	4 1/4	3 1/2	0.5
	4 in.	P	5	5	1.0
		Q	6	5	0.5

where
  N = allowable design value at angle with the grain
  P = allowable lateral design value parallel to grain
  Q = allowable lateral design value perpendicular to grain
  θ = angle of stress with grain

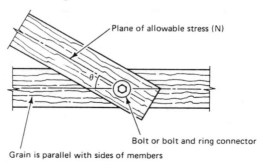

Figure 5.3. Stresses at an angle to the grain.

Example 5.3

From table 5-11(a), a $2^{1/2}$ in. (64 mm) ring in a two-member joint made with 1 in. (89 mm) thick Type A wood shows values for P = 3,160 lb (1435 kg) and Q = 2,280 lb (1035 kg). The safe load value may be found for a 45° angle as follows:

$$\sin 45° = \cos 45° = 0.707$$

$$N = \frac{3,160 \times 2,280}{3,160 \times 0.707^2 + 2,280 \times 0.707^2}$$

$$N = 2,650 \text{ lb } (1200 \text{ kg})$$

This procedure is discussed in more detail, along with more complete design tables, in National Design Specification for Wood Construction 1991.

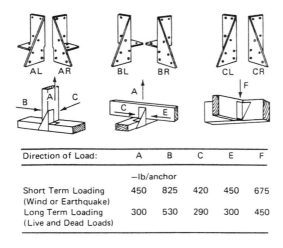

Direction of Load:	A	B	C	E	F
	—lb/anchor				
Short Term Loading (Wind or Earthquake)	450	825	420	450	675
Long Term Loading (Live and Dead Loads)	300	530	290	300	450

Figure 5.4. Safe working values for framing anchors.

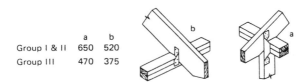

	a	b
Group I & II	650	520
Group III	470	375

Figure 5.5. Safe uplift values for rafter anchors.

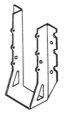

Recommended Joist or Beam Size	Steel Ga.	Height	Seat Width	Seat Depth	Recommended Safe Working Values
2x4	18	3-1/4"	1-5/8"	2"	400 lbs.
2x6-8	18	5-1/4"	1-5/8"	2"	900 lbs.
2x8-10-12	18	7"	1-5/8"	2"	1000 lbs.
2x10-12-14	18	8-1/2"	1-5/8"	2-3/4"	1200 lbs.
(2) 2x6-8	16	5-1/4"	3-1/4"	2-3/4"	1700 lbs.
(2) 2x8-10-12	16	7"	3-1/4"	2-3/4"	2200 lbs.
(2) 2x10-12-14	16	8-1/2"	3-1/4"	2-3/4"	2800 lbs.
3x6-8	16	5-1/4"	2-5/8"	2-3/4"	1700 lbs.
2x10-12-14	16	8-1/2"	2-5/8"	2-3/4"	2800 lbs.
4x6-8	16	5-1/4"	3-5/8"	2-3/4"	1700 lbs.
4x10-12-14	16	8-1/2"	3-5/8"	2-3/4"	2800 lbs.

Figure 5.6. Safe working values for joist hangers.

Framing Anchors

Framing anchors are available in a wide variety of configurations to aid in increasing the strength of connections of structural members in building frames. Several applications are shown in figures 5.4, 5.5, and 5.6 along with safe working loads in the direction indicated on the diagrams. The special nails supplied with the anchors are required.

Plywood and other panel sheathing materials offer an alternative to anchors in some locations. Properly nailed to sill, stud, and plate, panels provide excellent strength and bracing.

Gusset Plates

Gusset plates are used to transfer loads from one member to another at joints; this may be from a truss web to a chord or from one part of a chord to another. While nailed or nailed and glued joints using plywood gussets are still used, there is an increasing use of predrilled flat and deformed metal plate connectors. They are available in a large number of sizes and configurations. Most of them speed up the prefabrication of trusses and other structural components to a considerable extent.

Allowable design stresses for plate connectors are determined by tests with seasoned lumber. The value used is the smaller of the load at which a wood-to-wood slip of 0.03 in. occurs divided by 1.6 or, the ultimate load divided by 3.

Table 5-13. Adjustment factors for connectors

	Nominal Design Value*	Load Duration	Wet Service	Temperature	Group Action	Geometry	Penetration Depth	End Grain
Bolts	Z**	C_D	C_M	C_t	C_g	C_Δ	•	•
Lag Screws	W	C_D	C_M	C_t	•	•	•	C_{eg}
	Z	C_D	C_M	C_t	C_g	C_Δ	C_d	C_{eg}
Split Ring & Shear Connectors	P	C_D	C_M	C_t	C_g	C_Δ	C_d	•
	Q	C_D	C_M	C_t	C_g	C_Δ	C_d	•
Wood Screws	W	C_D	C_M	C_t	•	•	•	•
	Z	C_D	C_M	C_t	•	•	C_d	C_{eg}
Nails & Spikes	W	C_D	C_M	C_t	•	•	•	•
	Z	C_D	C_M	C_t	•	•	C_d	C_{eg}
Metal Plate Connectors	Z	C_D	C_M	C_t	•	•	•	•

* Value used for design is the nominal design value multiplied by the appropriate adjustment factor.
** Z refers to a lateral load.
  W refers to a withdrawal load.
  P refers to a lateral load parallel to grain.
  Q refers to a lateral load perpendicular to grain.

The value obtained from these tests is subject to adjustment for load duration, unseasoned wood (reduced 20%) and fire-retardant treated wood (reduced 10% if kiln dried). Since there is a great variety of plate connectors available, the design value for a specific connector should be obtained from the manufacturer.

Connector Adjustment Factors

All of the design values for nails, bolts, and connectors have been based on normal conditions. When conditions are not normal, the design values should be modified by multiplying by appropriate adjustment factors. The factors that need to be considered for each fastener are given in table 5-13.

Normal duration of loading is a period of 10 years. As shown in figure 5.7, permanent design loads should be reduced to 90% while loads with a duration of less than 10 years may be increased in relation to time. The load duration factor, C_D, for impact loads is 2.0.

The wet service factor, C_M, for connection systems that are fabricated using dry lumber and used in dry conditions is 1.0. Assemblies using bolts or screws which are fabricated using wet lumber or used under wet conditions should use $C_M = 0.67$. (This is more conservative than required by NDS for some applications.) For nail (except for threaded, hardened steel nails) connections that are fabricated using wet lumber or used in wet conditions, $C_{M\text{-withdrawal}} = 0.25$ and $C_{M\text{-lateral}} = 0.75$. No load reduction is required for threaded steel nails.

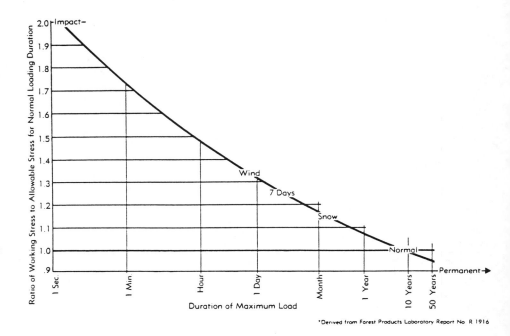

*Derived from Forest Products Laboratory Report No R 1916

Figure 5.7. Adjustments of working stress to duration of load.

Table 5-14. Temperature factors, C_t, for connections

In Service Moisture Conditions	$t \leq 100°F$	$100°F < t \leq 125°F$	$100°F < t \leq 125°F$
Dry	1.0	0.8	0.7
Wet	1.0	0.7	0.5

Nominal design values should be multiplied by the temperature factors, C_t, given in table 5-14 for connections that will be exposed to sustained elevated temperatures.

Glued Joints

Arched rafters, trusses, beams, posts, and other prefabricated parts of buildings can be made particularly strong and rigid by the use of glue. Properly selected and applied adhesives can provide joints that are about as good as the wood. Failure of such joints is likely to be shear in the wood thus the load transfer capacity of the joint will be related to the contact area and the shear capacity of the wood.

However, glue is best applied in the controlled conditions of a factory. Surfaces must fit together with close tolerances. In most cases, only a limited temperature range is permitted for applying and curing the glue and the spread must be accurate. Finally, the proper pressure must be applied to the joint during curing. Poor procedures cause serious weaknesses to occur. Joints designed for adequate strength when nailed alone may be given additional rigidity by using glue with the nails.

If it is decided to perform gluing operations at the construction site, there are several factors to consider. Wood should be clean and free of oily deposits and both surfaces to be glued should be dry (15% moisture or less) and equal in moisture level. Surfaces should be milled accurately to insure a close fit. Preservative-treated wood may need to be resurfaced before gluing to remove any surface coating.

Directions supplied by the manufacturer should be followed in all cases. When working with glue, the room temperature should be approximately 70°F (21°C). Assuming a butt joint with a plywood gusset, coat both surfaces with a uniform layer of glue; align the pieces carefully and then apply pressure with nails spaced to give a nail for each 8 to 9 in.^{2} (5000 to 5800 mm^2).

One of three types of adhesive is usually chosen for construction work. Casein (milk protein) glue, with a mold inhibitor, is highly moisture resistant and fills well in imperfectly fitting joints. It is workable at temperatures as low as 40°F, but with a considerably extended curing time. Woods that tend to be naturally oily may be sponged with a dilute solution of caustic soda an hour before gluing. This treatment, plus the naturally alkaline characteristics of the casein glue, provides the most satisfactory bond for naturally oily woods.

Synthetic adhesives include resorcinol and urea-formaldehyde. Resorcinol glue is waterproof and should be used when moisture levels may be high. It is relatively expensive, has a short working life, and needs close-fitting surfaces since the glue does not fill well. Plastic resin (urea-formaldehyde) glue provides strong, moisture resistant joints with a light-colored glue line. The glue has a working life in excess of 8 h.

Contact cement, used to apply plastic laminates to wood; panel adhesives, used for installing wall panels to masonry, rigid insulation or wood framing; and epoxies that adhere to a wide range of materials, including metal, are also used in home construction. The epoxies are too expensive for more than limited use. White polyvinyl glue is a frequently used household glue. Yellow aliphatic glue is called carpenter's glue. The last two glues mentioned have low moisture resistance and are suitable only for uses in dry interior applications.

Problems

5.1. The lower chord (tension member) of a truss is subjected to a maximum tension load of 500 lb (2224 N). The 2 × 4 in. (38 × 89 mm) chord is spliced together using 1 in. (19 mm) splice plates on each side of the chord. If spruce lumber is used for all members, determine the size and number of nails required to make the joint structurally sound.

5.2. Assuming the same loading and materials, how many bolts would be needed if one 2 × 4 in. (38 × 89 mm) plate were used on just one side?

5.3. A 2 × 12 in. (38 × 286 mm) joist is attached to a 2 × 6 in. (38 × 140 mm) stud with one 2 1/2 in. (63.5 mm) ring connector. What is the maximum safe load on the joint if both members are Douglas fir?

5.4. Two members in the supporting structure for a feed bin are connected with a 2 1/2 in. (63.5 mm) ring connector. The maximum angle of the stress with the grain is 30°. Assuming that a lap joint and Group B lumber are used, what is the maximum safe load that may be imposed on the joint?

5.5. If a 2 × 8 in. (38 × 184 mm) joist is to be attached to the side of a dry Douglas fir 2 × 6 in. (38 × 140 mm) stud (consider common nails):

(a) What would be the minimum size of nail that could be used?

(b) What would be the allowable load for a 10d and a 16d nail?

5.6. Evaluate the load capacity for a truss chord splice. The truss chord is 2 in. (38 mm) thick Southern pine.

(a) Consider use of 1/2 in. (12.7 mm) plywood sideplates.

(b) Consider 1 in. (nom.) (19 mm) spruce sideplates.

(c) Consider 6, 8, 10, and 12d nails.

5.7. (a) A bracket (3 ga., 0.239 in. [6 mm]) is to be mounted on the bottom of a Southern pine 4 × 4 in. (89 × 89 mm) and must support a 1,000 lb (455 kg) suspended load. How many screws are required?

(b) What if the bracket is mounted on the side?

5.8. Estimate the safe load, W, for the following. Nail is 8d box (2.50 × 0.113 in. [64 × 2.9 mm]) and wood block is 8 × 8 in. (203 × 203 mm) Douglas fir (S.G. = 0.50).

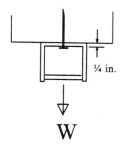

¼ in.

W

5.9. What is the allowable load on the following joint? All members are spruce 2 × 4 in. (38 × 89 mm). Assume 2 to 20d box nails each side.

½ Z

½ Z

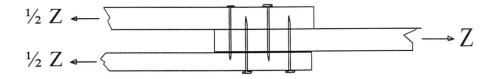

Z

6 Loads on Buildings

The purpose of a building is to provide a desired environment. Structural design of a building begins after it has been decided that a specific environment is to be provided. Design means the selection of members and materials that will accomplish the desired task in a reasonable and efficient manner. Structural components must be selected that are strong enough to withstand the forces or loads that will be imposed on them, thus satisfying the following equation:

$$\text{Load} \leq \text{Resistance.}$$

If the load effect exceeds the resistance, then the structure will fail. Neither side of the above equation can be determined with absolute certainty, therefore the designer must be willing to assign a risk factor to the solution. The nature and significance of the various types of loads that act on farm buildings must be assessed and this information related to decisions on design, materials, and construction methods. Risks are minimized by use of the most accurate estimates available.

Forces are imposed on building members by nature (wind, snow, earthquake) and by man's activities. Loads relating to climate and geography are difficult to predict. The maximum weather-related load may be many times the normal. Providing sufficient strength to resist the average or normal loading might allow failure to occur about one-half the time. To minimize the risk of failure, some extreme must be used. Economically we cannot justify designing buildings to resist loadings with an infinitesimally small chance of occurrence. It should be noted that even if the attempt was made to design for the ultimate loading, failure still might occur because of a construction error, a hidden defect or even a mistake in design.

Classification of Buildings

Buildings are classified based on the nature of occupancy for the purposes of applying wind and snow loads. Category I buildings are those that represent low hazard to human life in case of failure, and include agricultural buildings. Buildings not listed as category I, III or IV are assigned category II. Category III buildings, such as schools, represent a substantial hazard to human life in the event of failure. Essential structures, such as hospitals or fire stations, are category IV. The category is taken into consideration by the value of an importance factor which will be discussed later.

Types of Loads

The forces (loads) acting on structural members are grouped as follows:

Dead Loads are vertical, unchanging loads, and include the weights of the materials used in constructing the building, such as the concrete in the footings and foundations, and the lumber and other materials used in the frame, floors, roof deck, and permanently installed plumbing, heating, and electrical equipment. Dead loads are an integral part of the structure—they are permanent and stationary.

Live Loads include both static and dynamic loads resulting from the use or occupancy of the building. Static loads result from the weight and/or pressure from stationary equipment, livestock, and stored products. Dynamic loads result from the dynamic effect of tractors, farm equipment, vehicles, cranes, hoists, and materials handling equipment. The distribution of these loads must be considered in designing the building.

Environmental Loads such as wind, snow, and earthquakes must be estimated on the basis of meteorological records for the area. The weight of snow imposes vertical forces which must be applied to the horizontal projection of a roof. Wind loads act perpendicular to the surface and earthquakes impose major loads on member connectors.

The ability to accurately estimate maximum loads varies with the type of load. Dead loads can be predicted relatively accurately, thus there should be a small risk of failure and a small factor of safety can be used. On the other hand, there is considerable uncertainty in predicting the maximum wind load that might be imposed on a structure. Therefore, a designer may want to assign a large factor of safety to wind loads in order to reduce the risk.

Dead Loads

Estimated dead loads should be based on the actual members to be used; however, this requires an analysis to first determine the member sizes. Thus, it is often convenient to make an initial approximation. Structural support members may be estimated to represent 10% of the load to be supported. Roofs may weigh from 3 to 10 psf depending on span, load to be supported, and roofing material. Once actual materials and member sizes have been selected, the weight should be calculated to insure that the design is adequate. Table 6-1 gives weights for several building materials; additional information is found in many publications.

Example 6.1

Calculate the dead load of a 10 × 16 ft (3.1 × 5 m) roof section made of 290 lb (0.13 kg/m^2) asphalt singles on 1/2 in. (12.7 mm) plywood supported by 2 × 4 in. (38 × 89 mm) rafters 16 in. (406 mm) o.c.

Solution

roofing: $\dfrac{10 \times 16 \text{ ft} \times 290 \text{ lb}}{100 \text{ ft}^2} = 464 \text{ lb}$

sheathing: $10 \times 16 \text{ ft} \times 1.5 \text{ psf} = 240 \text{ lb}$

rafters: $16 \text{ ft} \times 12 \text{ in./ft} / 16 \text{ in.} \times 10 \text{ ft} \times 1.5 \text{ plf} = 180 \text{ lb}$

Total = 884 lb (400 kg)

Live Loads

Live loads are estimated based on the expected use of the building. Live loads may be concentrated, uniform, stationary, moving or impacting. The loads may act on the floor and/or the walls. General area loading values may be suitable for some cases, but for many agricultural applications more specific loading should be considered. Design loads may be found in standards published by the American Society of Agricultural Engineers.

The design load may vary depending on the structural component being considered, e.g., floor load for cattle in a tie stall barn is 70 psf (3.35 kPa), but on a slotted floor the value is 100 psf (4.8 kPa) and on an individual slat it is 250 lb/ft (3.65 kN/m). Loads resulting from livestock are given in ASAE Standard EP378.3. The effect of moving machinery is greater than an equal stationary load. A dynamic load may be estimated by adding a factor to the dead weight. For light machinery, either shaft or motor driven, the design load may be taken as the dead weight plus 20%. For reciprocating equipment add 50%, and for elevators add 100%. Table 6-2 lists several other live loads for agricultural buildings.

The floor load imposed by stored grains or other agricultural products is determined by multiplying the volume by the density (see table 6-3). ASAE Standard D241.3 gives densities of grains and seeds. Loads imposed by grains in storage are similar to fluids and will be discussed in a later section.

Table 6-1. Weights of building materials

Materials	Customary (pcf)	SI (kg/m^3)	Customary (psf)	SI (kg/m^2)	Customary (lb/ft)
Concrete	150	2432			
Steel	490	7943			
Oak 1 in. (19 mm)	45	729	3.5	17.1	
Yellow pine 1 in. (19 mm)	39	632	3.0	14.6	
Douglas fir 1 in. (19 mm)	34	551	2.5	12.2	
Soft pine 1 in. (19 mm)	30	486	2.2	11	
"Average wood"	40				
2 in. × 4 in. softwood					1.5
2 in. × 8 in.					3.0
2 in. × 12 in.					4.7
6 in. × 6 in.					8.4
(general 2.5 lb/bd ft)					
Plywood 3/8 in.			1.1	5.4	
1/2 in.			1.5	7.3	
5/8 in.			1.8	8.8	
Aluminum roofing (0.024)			0.4	1.9	
Galvanized roofing (28 ga.)			0.8	3.9	
Asphalt shingles			2.2–3.2	11–16	
Asphalt selvage roll			1.5	7.3	
Asphalt roll roofing			0.5–1	2.4–4.8	
Wood shingles			2.0	9.8	
Concrete block wall 4 in. (100 mm)			30	145	
8 in. (200 mm)			57	275	
12 in. (300 mm)			80	390	
Brick walls 4 in. (100 mm)			37	180	
8 in. (200 mm)			79	385	
Glass blocks			20	98	

Table 6-2. Live design loads

	Solid Floors		Slatted Floors	
	(psf)	(kg/m^2)	(lb/ft)	(kg/m)
Beef cattle				
Calves to 135 kg (300 lb)	50	245	150	225
Feeders, breeders	100	490	250	370
Dairy cattle				
Calves to 135 kg (300 lb)	50	245	150	225
Mature	100	490	250	370
Stall area	60	295	250	370
Maternity or hospital	50	245	250	370
Swine				
to 25 kg (50 lb)	35	170	50	75
90 kg (200 lb)	50	245	100	150
180 kg (400 lb)	65	315	150	225
225 kg (500 lb)	70	340	170	225
Sheep				
Feeders	40	195	100	150
Ewes, rams	50	245	120	180
Horses	100	490	250	370
Turkeys	30	145	25	37
Chickens				
Floor houses	20	100	15	22
Chickens, suspended cages per length of cage row:				
Full stair step (double deck, no dropping boards)			75	100
Modified stair step (double-deck, with dropping boards)			110	165
Modified stair step (triple deck, with dropping boards)			150	225
Greenhouses	50	245		
Manure	65*	1040†		
Maintenance shops	70			
Shops, storage, vehicles	150	730		
Dwelling	40			
Moving vehicle, < 3 t	100			
3-10 t	150			
> 10 t	200			

* Per foot of depth.
† Per meter of depth.

Example 6.2

Consider wheat in a bin 20 × 40 × 10 ft deep. The estimated load imposed on the floor would be found as 20 × 40 × 10 ft × 48 pcf = 384,000 lb or 480 psf.

Example 6.3

A confinement beef barn has a 16 ft wide slotted floor over a manure storage pit. The 8 ft slats, with an average width of 5 in. and a depth of 6 in., are supported by concrete girders on posts. There is a 1 in. slot between each slat. Estimate the load on the slats and on the posts which are spaced 10 ft o.c. The concrete girder has a cross-sectional area of 8 × 12 in.

Solution

The loading from table 6-2 is given as 100 psf on the floor and 250 plf on the slats. Total load to be supported by the post will be the sum of the live load plus the dead load. Each post must support a floor area of 8 × 10 ft = 80 ft^2, thus the total live load is 80 ft^2 × 100 psf = 8,000 lb. Each slat will weigh 150 psf × 8 ft × 5 in. × 6 in./144 in.^{2}/ft^2 = 250 lb. The girder weighs 150 pcf × 10 ft × 8 in. × 12 in./144 in.^{2}/ft^2 = 1,000 lb. The total dead load on each post will be: 2 × 250 lb/slat × 10 slats + 1,000 lb = 6,000 lb; thus, the total weight would be 14,000 lb.

Environmental Loads

Weather and natural occurrences often result in loads or stresses on buildings. Snow, wind, earthquake, and hydrostatic soil pressure are examples of these loads. Since there is a large uncertainty involved in predicting snow and wind loads on structures, it is necessary to use probability analysis for estimation. For design purposes, these values are modified to account for risk and other design factors.

The structure is then designed to withstand loadings that are not expected to be exceeded except infrequently. Weather-related loads are estimated based on the probability of occurrence of an extreme weather event. Several points should be kept in mind.

First, the weather data used to determine the probable extreme events are measured only at specific locations. The snowfall 1/2 mile from the weather station could be quite different. If a 40 in. (1.0 m) snow accumulation is predicted in southeast North Dakota with a 50-year recurrence interval, such an event may never actually occur on a given farmstead. However, it could occur several times during the period.

Second, the actual occurrence of the event does not necessarily mean the building will fail. There will be a factor of safety used in the design and the variability of materials may mean that the building is much stronger than the design specifies. On the other hand, because of variability, or unknown defects, the building could fail at a lesser load.

Thirdly, the recurrence intervals associated with risk classes are in no way related to expected building life. The expected or useful building life is related to longevity of materials, maintenance, and usage. However, buildings should be designed to provide an expected life at least as long as there might be an expected need and is economically feasible. The structural design should not result in a risk of premature failure. It would make no sense to do a feasibility analysis using a 50-year life and use materials expected to last 50 years, but base the structural design on loads that might be expected to occur once every two years.

Procedures for determining wind and snow loads have been published in ASAE Standard, ASAE EP288, "Agricultural Building Snow and Wind Loads". The provisions of the ASCE

Table 6-3. Density of agricultural products

Product		Angle of Repose		Bulk Density		EFD*
		Emptying	Filling	(pcf)	(lb/bu)	(pcf)
Barley		28	16	39	48	18
Corn,	ear			28	35	
	shelled	27	16	45	56	23
Flaxseed				45		22
Oats		32	18	26	32	13
Wheat,	soft red winter	27	16	49	60	23
	hard red spring	28	17	52	65	24
	hard red winter	27	16	51	64	24
	durum	26	17	52	65	26
Rye		26	17	45	56	23
Rice		36	20	36	45	14
Soybeans		29	16	48	60	21
Beans,	dry			48	60	
Peanuts, unshelled				13.6	17	
Potatoes				40-48	60	
Apples				48		
Fertilizer				60		
Lime				60		
Hay,	loose			4-5		
	baled			12-15		
	pelleted			40		
Silage				30-40		
Sunflower				19		

* Equivalent fluid density (assumes pile sloped at filling angle of repose).

7 Standard, "Minimum Design Loads in Buildings and Other Structures" are incorporated in EP288.

Snow Loads

The basic formula for snow loads on structures is:

$$P_s = R*C_e*I_s*C_s*P_g \qquad (6.1)$$

where

P_s = balance roof snow load (psf; kPa)

R = roof snow factor (ratio snow on roof/ground)

= 1.0 for ground snowpack of 15 psf (0.72 kPa) or less

= 0.7 for ground snowpack of 20 psf (0.96 Kpa) or more

= 0.6 in Alaska

C_e = exposure factor

= 0.8 in windy area, roof exposed with no shelter by terrain, higher structures or trees

= 1.0 where wind cannot be relied on to reduce roof loads

= 1.1 where terrain, higher structures, or trees will shelter the building increasing the potential for drifting

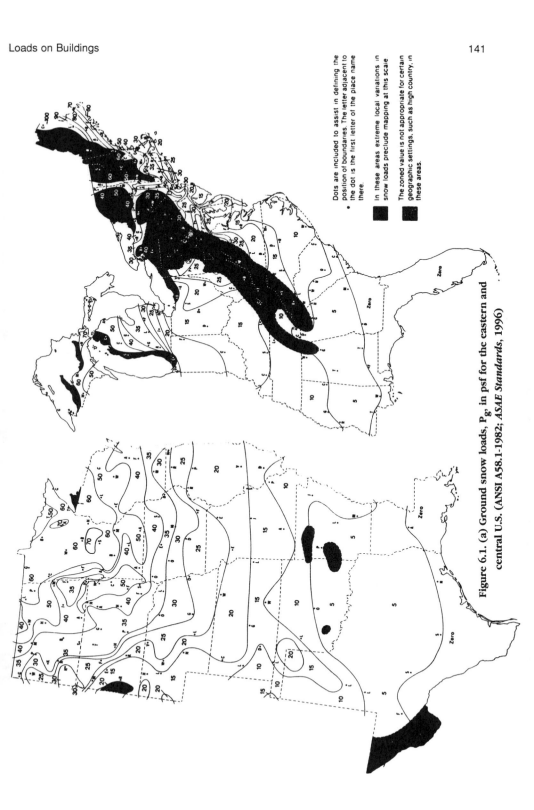

Dots are included to assist in defining the position of boundaries. The letter adjacent to the dot is the first letter of the place name there.

In these areas extreme local variations in snow loads preclude mapping at this scale

The zoned value is not appropriate for certain geographic settings, such as high country, in these areas.

Figure 6.1. (a) Ground snow loads, P g, in psf for the eastern and central U.S. (ANSI A58.1-1982; *ASAE Standards*, 1996)

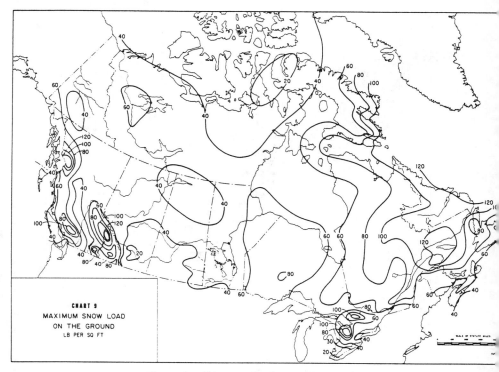

Figure 6.1. (b) Snow load map for Canada.

I_s = importance factor

   = 1.0 (0.02 probability) for agricultural buildings that require high reliability of design to protect property or people

   = 0.8 (0.04 probability) for agricultural buildings that present a low risk to property or people

C_s = slope factor

   = 1.0 for 0° to 15°

   = 1.0 − (slope − 15°)/55° for 15° − 70°

   = 0 for > 70° slopes

P_g = ground snow load from figs. 6.1 or 6.2

Example 6.4

Snow load on a low-risk agricultural building located in the southwest corner of Iowa with a 4:12 slope roof (18.4°) in a highly sheltered area:

$$P_s = 0.7 \times 1.1 \times 0.8 \times 0.94 \times 25 \text{ psf} = 14.5 \text{ psf}$$

$$P_s = 0.7 \times 1.1 \times 0.8 \times 0.94 \times 0.048 \times 25 \text{ kPa} = 0.69 \text{ kPa}$$

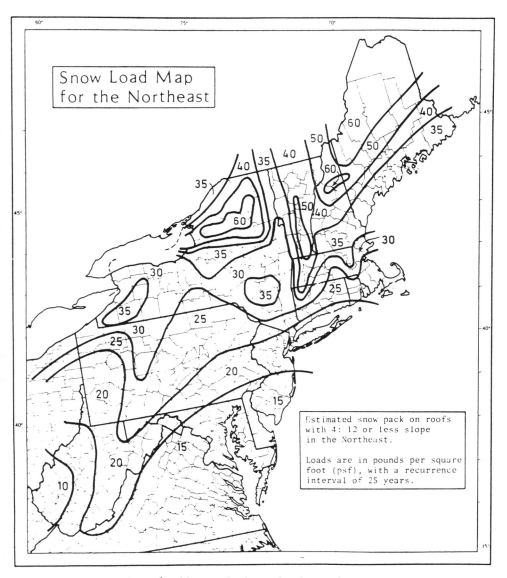

Figure 6.2. (a) Snow load map for the Northeast.

Design values must be increased to account for drift because of valleys or dual level roofs. Roofs that are in aerodynamic shade of an upper structure must be designed to support drifts. The geometry and magnitude of the drift load (fig. 6.3) shall be determined as follows, except that drifting shall not be considered, when $(H_r - H_b)/H_b < 0.2$ or in regions where ground snow load, P_g, is less than 10 psf (0.48 kPa).

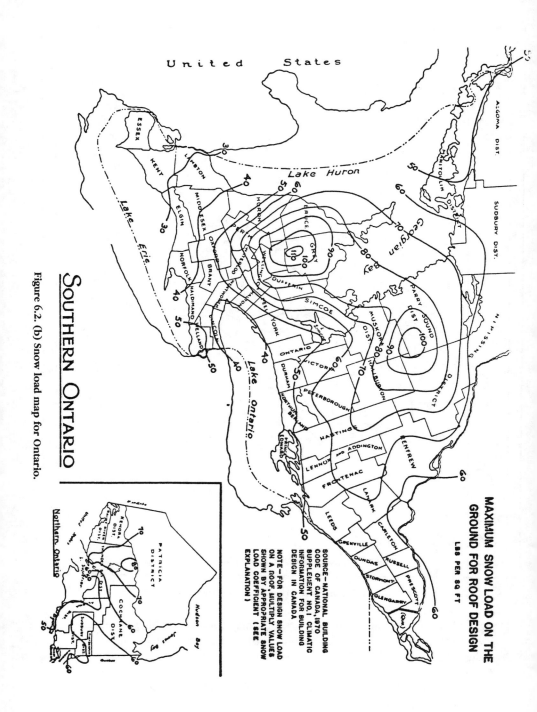

SOUTHERN ONTARIO

Figure 6.2. (b) Snow load map for Ontario.

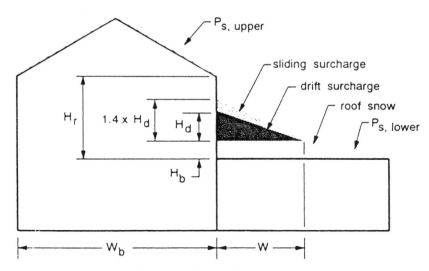

Figure 6.3. Snow drifts on roofs.

$$H_d = 0.195 \left(W_b\right)^{1/3} \left(20.9 \, P_g + 10\right)^{1/4} - 0.457 \; (m)$$

$$H_d = 0.43 \left(W_b\right)^{1/3} \left(P_g + 10\right)^{1/4} - 1.5 \; (ft) \tag{6.2}$$

where

H_d =   drift height (ft, m)

W_b =   horizontal dimension of upper roof normal to the line of the change in the roof level (ft, m)

P_g =   ground snow load (psf, kPa)

H_r =   height difference between the upper and lower roofs (ft, m)

H_b =   lower roof balance snow load height (ft, m) = $P_s/(g_{cd})$

P_s =   balance snow load on lower roof (psf, kPa)

d =   density of snow (pcf, kg/m^3) (table 6-4)

g_c =   conversion factor = 0.00981 km/s^2 for P_s (kPa) = 1.0 for P_s (psf)

$H_d + H_b \le H_r$

$W/4$ = H_d or $(H_r - H_b)$ whichever is less.

Table 6-4. Snow densities for establishing drift loads
(from ASAE EP288.5)

Ground Snow Load (Pg)		Snow Density (d)	
(psf)	(kPa)	(pcf)	(kg/m^3)
11 - 30	0.5 - 1.4	15	240
31 - 60	1.5 - 2.9	20	320
> 60	3.0 +	25	400

Example 6.5
What would be the design snow load on a 28 ft (8.8 m) wide milking parlor located 50 miles (80 km) east of Crookston, Minnesota, and what would be the
total load on a truss if spaced 4 ft (1.25 m) o.c.? The parlor has a 6:12 roof
slope and is nestled in a grove of tall pines.

Solution
The basic snow load formula is:

$$P_s = R * C_e * I_s * C_s * P_g$$

From figure 6.1(a), the snow pack on the ground near Crookston is found to be
60 psf (2.7 kg/m^2), therefore, $R = 0.7$. C_e = is taken as 1.1 and I_s for a high-value
building is taken as 1.0. The roof slope is found to be $q = \tan^{-1}(6/12) = 26.6°$.
Thus,

$$c_s = 1.0 - \frac{(26.6 - 15)}{55} = 0.79$$

$$p_s = 0.7 \times 1.1 \times 1.0 \times 0.79 \times 60 \text{ psf}$$

$$= 36.5 \text{ psf} (1.62 \text{ kg/m}^2)$$

The total load on a truss would be:

$$36.5 \text{ psf} \times 4 \text{ ft} \times 28 \text{ ft} = 4,088 \text{ lb} (1855 \text{ kg})$$

Wind Loads

The wind velocity pressure on a flat vertical surface is given by the formula:

$$q = 0.00256 \ K_z \ K_{zt}V^2 \ I \text{ (psf)}$$
$$q = 0.00061 \ K_z \ K_{zt}V^2 \ I \text{ (kPa)}$$

(6.3)

where
V   =   basic wind at a height of 10 m (33 ft) for 0.02 annual probability
        (50-yr recurrence interval)
K_z =   velocity pressure exposure coefficient at height z (table 6-5)
K_{zt} =   topographic factor
I   =   importance factor
    =   0.87, 1.00, 1.15, 1.15 for building categories I, II, III, and
        IV, respectively

The velocity pressure exposure coefficient is a function of height and exposure. Exposure
categories are based on topography, vegetation, and constructed features. Exposure A is large
city centers—buildings greater than 70 ft tall for at least 1/2 mile upwind. Wooded or urban

Table 6-5. (a) Velocity pressure exposure coefficients, K_z

Height (z)		Exposure Category			
(ft)	(m)	A	B	C	D
0-15	0-5	0.32	0.57	0.85	1.03
20	6	0.36	0.62	0.90	1.08
30	9	0.42	0.70	0.98	1.16
50	15	0.52	0.81	1.09	1.27
80	18	0.62	0.93	1.21	1.38

Table 6-5. (b) Combined exposure and gust factors, $K_z G$
(from ASAE EP288.5)

Mean Roof Height (z)			
(m)	(ft)	$K_z G$ Exposed	$K_z G$ Sheltered
4-5	15	1.07	0.62
6	20	1.14	0.68
9	30	1.24	0.77
12	40	1.32	0.84
15	50	1.39	0.91
18	60	1.45	0.96
24	80	1.54	1.06
30	100	1.62	1.14

areas with single family dwellings are considered exposure B. Category C is for open terrain with scattered obstruction with heights generally less than 30 ft. Unobstructed areas exposed to wind from open water of at least 1 mile are category D.

The minimum basic wind speed specified by ASCE 7-95 is 85 mph. The basic wind speed for most of the continental United States is 90 mph (40 m/s). The 85 mph (38 m/s) can be used for California, Oregon, and Washington except for the Pacific shore areas of Oregon, and Washington where speeds of 90 and 100 mph (40 and 45 m/s) are reported. Areas along the Gulf and east coast, including all of Florida, experience considerably higher wind speeds. The basic wind speed for the southern tip of Florida is 150 mph (67 m/s). Basic wind speed should be based on local data where sufficient information is available and special studies are needed in mountainous terrain, in gorges or where there are unusual wind conditions.

The topographic factor will be 1.0, except where wind speed is increased due to local terrain such as hills. Wind velocity will generally be maximum at hill crest and K_{zt} will be increased for this.

The wind load on buildings and structural components is found by multiplying the design wind pressure by the appropriate area. The design wind pressure, p, is basic wind pressure times a dimensionless pressure coefficient; however, a minimum value of 10 psf will be used:

$$p = q\ GC_p - q_h(GC_{pi}) \qquad (6.4)$$

where

GC_p = external pressure coefficient and gust factor
GC_{pi} = internal pressure coefficient and gust factor
q = q_z for the windward wall and q_h otherwise
q_h = velocity pressure at the mean roof height

For partially enclosed buildings, GC_{pi} = +0.80 or –0.30; for other buildings, the factor is +0.18 or –0.18. A positive coefficient means the pressure acts toward the surface and a negative pressure acts away from the surface. Values of external and internal pressures should be combined algebraically to determine the critical load. For most external surfaces, two different coefficients are given since the wind can blow in opposite directions. Localized effects may result in considerably higher forces on small areas compared to the complete building. Thus, different coefficients are given for components and cladding—such as purlins, studs, girts, sheathing, roofing, and siding—than for main structural members such as frames, trusses, posts, and girders. Pressure coefficients for main structural

Table 6-6. (a) External pressure coefficient, GC_p, for loads on main frame systems for buildings with mean roof heights of less than 60 ft

Roof Angle	Building Surface*					
	1	2	3	4	5	6
	Wind Primarily Perpendicular to Ridge					
0-5	0.40	-0.69	-0.37	-0.29		
20	0.53	-0.69	-0.48	-0.43		
30-45	0.56	0.21	-0.43	-0.37		
90	0.56	0.56	-0.37	-0.37		
Edge area:†						
0-5	0.61	-1.07	-0.53	-0.43		
20	0.80	-1.07	-0.69	-0.64		
30-45	0.69	0.27	-0.53	-0.48		
90	0.69	0.69	-0.48	-0.48		
	Wind Primarily Parallel to Ridge					
0-90	-0.45	-0.69	-0.37	-0.45	0.40	-0.29
Edge area:						
0-90	-0.48	-1.07	-0.53	-0.48	0.61	-0.43

* Definition of building surfaces:
  1 — windward sidewall
  2 — windward roof
  3 — leeward roof
  4 — leeward sidewall
  5 — windward endwall
  6 — leeward endwall
† Edge area means the area at the edge of the surface and extends for 20% of the length or a distance equal to 80% of the height whichever is smaller. For the endwall surface the area extends from the corner for a distance of 10% of the width or 40% of the height whichever is smaller.

members are given in table 6-6(a) and for components and cladding in table 6-6(b). The pressure coefficient for a round tank or silo is 0.6.

In addition to using the wind load information in component design, the potential for overturning and sliding should be evaluated. Only 2/3 of the dead load should be considered to resist overturning moment.

Example 6.6

What would be the design wind load on a steel roofing panel at the edge of a 30 ft high hay storage building in Wahpeton, North Dakota? What would be the total load on the 30 in. × 8 ft panel?

Solution

The basic wind pressure is calculated from the formula:

$$q = 0.00256 \ K_z \ K_{zt} \ V^2 \ I \ (psf)$$

Assume the wind speed, V, is 90 mph; I for a low risk building is 0.87; K_z for an exposed 30 ft building is 0.98. Therefore,

$$q = 0.00256 \times 0.98 \times 1.0 \times 90^2 \times 0.87$$

$$= 17.7 \ psf$$

Assuming the roof is 4:12, the external pressure coefficient, GC_p, is found in table 6-6(b) to be –2.1 or 0.5. This means there would be an uplift pressure of:

$$2.1 \times 17.7 = 37.2 \ psf$$

Table 6-6. (b) External pressure coefficient, GC_p for loads on components and cladding for buildings with mean roof heights of less than 60 ft

Area	< 10 ft²	> 500 ft²
Walls except at corners	-1.1, 1.0	-0.8, 0.7
Wall corners (edge, E, as defined in table 6-6a)	-1.4, 1.0	-0.8, 0.7
Area	< 10 ft²	> 100 ft²
Roof angle < 10°		
Roof except at edge	-1.0, 0.3	-0.9, 0.2
Roof edge, eave & gable	-1.8, 0.3	-1.1, 0.2
Roof corners	-2.8, 0.3	-1.1, 0.2
Roof overhang except at corners	-1.7	-1.1, 0.2
Roof overhang at corners	-2.8	-0.8, 0.2
Roof angle 10° < ω < 30°		
Roof except at edge	-0.9, 0.5	-0.8, 0.3
Roof edge, eave, gable & ridge	-2.1, 0.5	-1.4, 0.3
Roof overhang at except at corners	-2.2	-2.2
Roof overhang at corners	-3.7	-2.5
Roof angle 30° < ω < 45°:		
Roof except at edge	-1.0, 0.9	-0.8, 0.8
Roof edge, eave, gable & ridge	-1.2, 0.9	-1.0, 0.8
Roof overhang	-2.0, 0.9	-1.8, 0.8

or the force on the panel would be:

$$\left(\frac{30 \text{ in.}}{12 \text{ in./ft}}\right) \times 8 \text{ ft} \times 37.2 \text{ psf} = 743 \text{ lb}$$

Combination of Loads

Only dead loads will always be imposed on the building; however, several of the loading types may act simultaneously. The design analysis should consider the combinations of load types and select structural members which can withstand the most adverse conditions. Since various loads may act in different directions and at different places on a structure, it is the combination of these loads that results in the maximum stress on a structural member or group of members. It will not necessarily be the same combination that produces the maximum on other members. ANSI Standard A58.1-1982 recommends investigating the following load combinations:
1. Dead
2. Dead + [Live + (Roof live or snow or wind)] × 0.75
3. Dead + [Live or Earthquake] × 0.75
4. Dead + [Live + (Roof live or snow or rain) + (Wind or Earthquake)] × 0.75.

Pressures Exerted by Fluids and Hydrostatic Loads

A liquid exerts a force against any surface with which it is in contact. The force exerted per unit area is defined as pressure. In an open tank, the pressure increases uniformly from the top of the liquid to the bottom. The pressure exerted at a given level will be equal in all directions and normal to all surfaces. The pressure exerted by a liquid at any depth may be found by the formula:

$$p = \rho h \qquad (6.5)$$

where

p = pressure (psf, kg/m^2)
ρ = density (pcf, kg/m^3)
h = depth (ft, m)
Note: Pa = kg/m^2 × 9.8; ρ for water = 62.4 pcf = 1000 kg/m^3

The lateral force of fluids on a surface at any depth may be found by the formula:

$$F = pA \qquad (6.6)$$

where

F = force (lb, kg)
p = pressure (psf, kg/m^2)
A = area, ft^2 (m^2)
Note: N = 9.8 × kg

Example 6.7

A drum 2 ft (0.6 m) in diameter and 3 ft (0.9 m) high is filled with water. The pressure at the bottom is:

$$p = \rho h$$

p = 62.4 pcf (1.0 Mg/m³) × 3 ft (0.9 m)
p = 187.2 psf (914 kg/m²)

The force on the bottom of the drum is:

$$F = pA$$

F = 187.2 psf × 12 ft² × 3.14
F = 588 lb (227 kg)

Note that if a 10 ft length of 1 in. pipe is installed vertically on top of the drum and filled with water, the pressure becomes:

p = 62.4 pcf × 13 ft
p = 811.2 psf (3960 kg/m²)

The force would now be 2,548 lb (1150 kg).

This leads to the next assertion: Neither the cross-sectional area of the column nor the volume of the liquid affects the pressure; only the depth and density have an effect. The lateral force of a liquid against a vertical section of wall may be found by the formula:

$$P = \frac{\rho h^2}{2} \qquad (6.7)$$

where
P = horizontal force against a unit section of wall (lb/ft, kg/m)
ρ = density (pcf, kg/m³)
h = depth from free surface of liquid (ft, m)

As shown in figure 6.4 the centroid of this force is two-thirds of the depth below the surface of the fluid. The horizontal dimension (the distance it extends from the wall) of the liquid has no effect on the pressure on the wall.

The pressure of soil against walls varies greatly with depth, types of soil and moisture content. It is always desirable to provide drainage behind retaining walls, underground

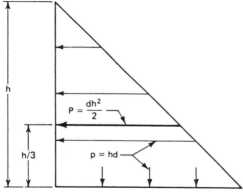

Figure 6.4. Distribution of forces by a fluid.

Table 6-7. Loads against walls—equivalent fluid density

		(pcf)	(kg/m³)
Manure	Outward, if above ground	60	960
Manure	Either direction on partition	60	960
Soil	Inward, well drained	15	240
Soil	Inward, fair drainage	30	480
Soil	Inward, high water table	60	960
Soil	Inward, saturated fine sand	110	1760

tanks, and building foundations that are below grade. The reason for this is illustrated by the values in table 6-7 which lists fluid equivalent values for liquid manure and soils with differing degrees of drainage.

Example 6.8
Durum wheat is stored to a depth of 14 ft (4.4 m) in a 16 × 24 ft (5 × 7.5 m) bin. What would be the maximum lateral (wall) pressure and the total force on a stud [spacing 18 in. (455 m) o.c.]? What would be the floor loading?

Solution
First determine if the bin is shallow or deep by comparing the equivalent diameter to the depth.

D = 1.6 * 16 ft > 14 ft, therefore the bin is shallow. From table 6-3 the density of durum is 52 pcf (0.7 kg/m³) and EFD is 26 pcf (0.36 kg/m³). The maximum wall pressure (at the bottom of the wall) will be: 14 × 26 = 364 psf. The total force on a stud will be: 14 ft × (14 ft/2) × 26 pcf × 18 in./12 in./ft = 3,822 lb (1735 kg). The floor loading will be 52 pcf × 14 ft = 728 psf (330 kg).

For example, assume a storage tank extends 5 ft into the ground that is moderately well drained. Find the total force on each foot of length of the wall.

$$P = \frac{\rho h^2}{2}$$

$$P = \frac{30 \text{ pcf} \times 5 \text{ ft} \times 5 \text{ ft}}{2}$$

$$P = 375 \text{ lb/ft}$$

Grain Pressures

The design of grain storages must consider not only a vertical force on the floor but also lateral forces. The pressures exerted by granular materials, such as grain or soil, are more complex than those exerted by fluids because of the friction of the particles moving against one another. These materials may be referred to as semifluid. Most grains are non-cohesive or free flowing and thus act similarly to fluids in creating forces on containing structures. Equivalent fluid densities (EFD) have been calculated for many grains (table 6-3) and, in some cases, these can be treated as if they were fluids.

Table 6-8. Lateral pressures on bin walls* (psf)

Depth from Top, Downward (ft)	Width or Diameter of Bin (ft)				
	4	6	8	10	12
12	109	150	179	207	220
10	106	137	168	187	192
8	100	127	140	162	168
6	87	113	124	132	141
4	72	85	94	96	98

* Values are for wheat (48 pcf), pressures from other grains are in proportion to their weights. Multiplying the above values by 1.67 will give the uniform vertical load (psf) on the floor. However, it must not be forgotten that the total weight must be supported by posts and by joists that extend beyond the bin walls.

This approach is valid as long as the grain forces acting on a wall are independent of any other wall. This is true as long as the rupture plane in the granular material does not intersect more than one wall. The rupture plane has been found to form an angle equal to $45° + \phi/2$). A bin that satisfies the above is called a shallow bin. The depth of a shallow bin, h, cannot exceed $D \times \tan(45° + \phi/2)$, where D is the distance between walls (or diameter of a circular bin) and ϕ is the emptying angle of repose. The emptying angle of repose for grains varies from 25 to 36° which means that the maximum depth for shallow bins cannot exceed from 1.6 to 2.0 times D. Analysis of forces on deep bins using Janssen's equation is more complicated and will not be discussed (ASAE EP433).

The EFD values may be used to find the lateral force (P) against a bin wall with a depth of grain (h) using $P = (EFD)h^2/2$. Table 6-8 illustrates lateral loads on bin walls. The loads on bin walls given for wheat are at least as great as for mixed feed and may be used to design any type of grain storage. Loads on potato storage bins are determined by using equivalent fluid densities which are found in ASAE D446.

Problems

6.1 Apple boxes are 17 in. long, 13 in. wide, and 11 in. high ($432 \times 330 \times 279$ mm). What is the load per unit area on the floor when boxes are piled 12 high? The mass of each box is 54 lb (24.5 kg).

6.2. A barn was originally designed to support a depth of 16 ft (5 m) of loose hay. What depth of baled hay would impose a similar load?

6.3. A farm pond has been constructed with a deep spillway 6.5 ft (2 m) wide which is closed off with planks dropped into guides cast in the concrete at either end. What is the total uniform load on the 12 in. (300 mm) plank in the lowest position when the water is 5 ft (1.5 m) deep at the bottom of the spillway (bottom edge of the plank)?

6.4. Estimate the total floor load and maximum lateral pressure on an 8×16 ft (2.5×5 m) grain bin if it contains:

(a) barley 4 ft (1.3 m) deep, (b) wheat 10 ft (3.1 m) deep.

6.5. Estimate the uplift force on a 30 in. × 16 ft roof panel in a 90 mph wind (assume a coefficient = 1.25).

6.6. A 16 × 40 ft (5 × 12.5 m) shed roof is constructed using 2 × 12 in. (38 × 286 mm) rafters 16 in. (406 mm) o.c., 1/2 in. (12.7 mm) plywood sheathing and 290 lb (0.13 kg/m²) asphalt shingles.

(a) Estimate the total dead load.

(b) What design snow load should be used, if the roof slope is 3:12?

(c) What is the total weight to be supported by the walls.?

6.7. A 40 ft wide building has trusses (2 × 6 in. top and 2 × 4 in. bottom chords) spaced 4 ft o.c. Purlins (2 × 6 in.) are located 2 ft o.c. to support steel roofing. The ceiling is 3/8 in. plywood attached to 2 × 4 in. nailers, 2 o.c., and supports 12 in. insulation.

(a) Estimate the total load on each truss support (i.e., each end).

(b) What design snow load should be used if the roof slope is 20.5° and the building is a general agricultural building located in a sheltered area near Fargo, North Dakota?

(c) What is the design wind load on the walls and roof if the building has an open front and is 20 ft high?

7 Foundations, Footings, and Floors

FOUNDATIONS

A well-designed and well-constructed foundation is essential for the structural integrity of a building. The foundation must resist and distribute the forces acting on it so that any movement will be small and uniform. Properly built footings and foundations keep buildings plumb, free of cracks, and in the case of a below-grade basement, free of leaks.

The most important loads acting on a foundation are:

1. The dead weight of the building, the contents of the building, and the snow load—all acting in a vertical direction.
2. Wind loads that impose lateral or lifting forces.
3. Horizontal forces from soil, water or stored products.
4. Uneven soil forces caused by nonuniform and variable moisture levels as well as frost action.

Each of these forces must be considered in footing and foundation design.

Footings

A footing is the enlarged base of a foundation. It increases the bearing area between the foundation and the underlying soil, thus reducing the unit pressure to a safe level. The size of the footing will depend on the weight imposed by the building and the safe bearing capacity of the soil.

Soil Bearing

The soil on which a footing is installed should be undisturbed, level, and smooth. When construction in a filled area is unavoidable, special precautions are required. The best solution is to extend the foundation so that the footing is on undisturbed soil. Alternatives are to let the filled soil settle for a year or to compact the soil thoroughly and then use larger footings to reduce the unit pressure on the soil. The bearing capacity of soils varies with type and moisture. Typical load capacities are shown in table 7-1.

If there are doubts about the bearing capacity of the soil, it is good policy and inexpensive to simply assume a lower safe-bearing value and increase the footing size. In

Table 7-1. Soil load-carrying capacities*

Sand Texture	Clay Consistency	Estimated Bearing Capacity (psf)	(Kpa)
	Very soft	< 500	< 24
Very loose	Soft	500 to 1,000	24 to 48
Loose	Medium	1,000 to 2,000	48 to 96
Medium	Stiff	2,000 to 4,000	96 to 192
Dense	Very stiff	4,000 to 8,000	192 to 384
Very dense	Hard	> 8000	> 384

Sands:†
Very loose	Penetrated easily by a bar pushed by hand
Loose	Penetrated with difficulty by a bar pushed by hand
Medium	Penetrated easily by a bar driven by a 5 lb (2.3 kg) hammer
Dense	Penetrated about 1 ft (305 mm) by a bar driven by a 5 lb (2.3 kg) hammer
Very Dense	Penetrated about 3 in (76 mm) by a bar driven by a 5 lb (2.3 kg) hammer

Clays:
Very soft	Penetrated several inches by fist
Soft	Easily penetrated several inches by thumb
Medium	Penetrated several inches by thumb with moderate effort
Stiff	Readily indented by thumb, but penetrated only with great effort
Very stiff	Easily indented by thumbnail
Hard	Indented with difficulty by thumbnail

* From Walker, J. N. and F. E. Woeste, eds. 1992. *Post-Frame Building Design*. St. Joseph, Mich.: ASAE. (description of clay taken from Peck, R. B., W. E. Hanson and T. H. Thornburn. 1953. *Foundation Engineering*. New York, N.Y.: John Wiley & Sons.
† Use 0.5 in (12.5 mm) reinforcing bar.

the design of a large building that will impose a heavy load on a foundation, soil-bearing tests are required before the footing size is determined.

It should be recognized that some settlement will occur on all but very light buildings. If this settlement is not uniform around the building, problems may result such as misaligned feeders, nonuniform slope on trough waterers or worse. Non-uniform settlement of silos and grain bins have resulted in failure because of tipping. Note that the bearing capacity of a soft clay which may be less than 500 psf will be exceeded by a grain depth of 12 ft (3.7 m). If half of a bin base is resting on a soft clay and the other half on a sand and gravel, failure is likely to occur.

Frost Action

A combination of below freezing temperature and moisture can cause the soil to heave or expand, only to settle again as the temperature rises. This situation is unsatisfactory for supporting a building foundation because the freezing is seldom uniform in all areas. The result will be uneven lifting and settling, cracking of the foundation, and a building that is out of plumb.

Ice layers may form if (1) soil temperatures are below freezing, (2) there is groundwater close to the frost line, and (3) the soil supports rapid movement of capillary water upward from the water table. As the frost line penetrates the soil, water freezes

Table 7-2. Suggested footing depths

Average January Temperature		Depth for Light Buildings		Depth for Heavy Buildings	
°F	°C	(in.)	(mm)	(in.)	(mm)
< 25	-4	24 to 48	600-1200	36-60	900-1500
25-35	-4 to 2	18 to 36	450-900	30-48	750-1200
35-50	2 to 10	12 to 24	300-600	18-36	450-900

in the soil pores. Freezing dries the soil, creates a capillary potential and brings water upward to the frost line causing the ice particles to increase in thickness. The ice lens can lift a foundation, but is more likely to result in saturated soil and low bearing strength upon melting.

To avoid frost heave problems, the footing for the foundation should be located below the maximum penetration of frost. The potential for frost damage of slabs or shallow foundations may be reduced by lowering the water table on sites with drain-able subsoil, using coarse granular fill, or providing a layer of non-swelling clayey material with low capillary conductivity. Table 7-2 provides recommended footing depths for various temperature zones. Local conditions and the inside temperature of the building will influence the depth actually chosen.

If an appreciably deeper foundation is required for considerations other than to avoid frost damage, a column-and-beam design may be more economical. In that case, the column footings extend below frost level, while a beam rests on the columns just above the soil surface. If the use of the building requires a rodent-proof joining of the wall and ground, the beam may be designed at least 12 in. (300 mm) below and 8 in. (200 mm) above grade. There should be 6 to 8 in. (150 to 200 mm) of uniform size gravel below the beam to prevent frost heaving.

Foundation Footings

Regardless of the material used for a foundation, a continuous footing cast of concrete is desirable. The width of the footing depends on the soil-bearing capacity and the load that it must carry. Having determined the width of the footing by dividing the load per unit of length by the soil-bearing capacity, the thickness of the footing for a wall or pier can be found (fig. 7.1). Wall footings should have a depth equal to two

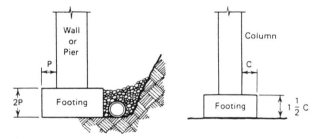

Figure 7.1. Footing proportions.

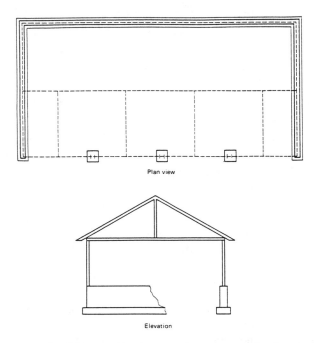

Plan view

Elevation

Figure 7.2. The division of loads on various areas of the foundation.

times the distance from the wall to the edge of the footing, while a wood or metal column footing depth should equal one and one-half times the distance from the column to the edge of the footing.

It is good practice to install a footing even for a lightly loaded building that does not appear to need one, because it provides a level surface on which to install the foundation forms and helps to insure a plumb wall. When the loading is not a factor, a rule of thumb that is frequently used calls for making the footing as deep as the wall is thick and twice as wide.

Figure 7.2 illustrates the distribution of dead loads and snow loads on various portions of the building footings. Each of the piers will carry 1/8 of the total load. The half load on the foundation at the rear of the building will be distributed uniformly.

If a wall footing is to be installed that has appreciably more area than is required to support the load, it is desirable to design any column footing to have approximately the same area per unit load. Any settling that occurs should then be equal in all locations. For the same reason, if a foundation is partly on bedrock and partly on soil, the part on soil should be twice as wide as would otherwise be indicated.

All foundations, piers, and columns should be loaded as nearly as possible along their central axis to prevent any tipping action. If a building is constructed on sloping land, the footing may need to be stepped down with the grade. In such a situation, the

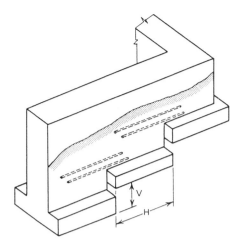

Figure 7.3. Stepped footing showing location of reinforcing rod.

horizontal length of each step should be at least double the height of the step and each section of footing should be tied to the adjacent wall with reinforcing rods. It should be emphasized that each section of the footing should be bearing on ground that has been carefully leveled. Figure 7.3 illustrates a stepped footing.

Lateral Pressure on Foundations

While it may be desirable to estimate the soil pressure more accurately, it can be assumed to be about 60 psf/ft of depth (9.2 kPa/m) for a wall without drainage and 30 psf/ft of depth (4.6 kPa/m) for a wall with drainage.

Example 7.1

The following will illustrate the finding of a safe footing size. Assume a gable roof building 24 × 48 ft is supported by a foundation in the rear and three piers in the front. The total load above the piers and foundation is 60,000 lb. The soil at the building site is medium clay. The foundation wall is 4 ft high and 8 in. thick. The piers are 1 ft^2 and 4 ft high.

Solution
1. From table 6-1, the weight of concrete is 150 pcf.
2. Figure 7.2 shows that the rear foundation supports 1/2 of the load, or 60,000 lb/2 = 30,000 lb.
3. The wall weighs 4 × 0.67 × 48 ft × 150 pcf = 19,300 lb.
4. The total weight/foot of length is:

$$\frac{(30,000 \text{ lb} + 19,300 \text{ lb})}{48 \text{ ft}} = 1,027 \text{ plf}$$

5. Table 7-1 lists medium clay with a bearing capacity of 2,000 psf.
6. The required footing width is 1,027 plf/2,000 psf = 0.51 ft.
7. While this value indicates that no footing is required to support the load, it is recommended that one be used as a desirable construction practice. Use the rule of thumb: Choose a thickness equal to the wall width and a width that is double the wall, 8 in. thick, 16 in. wide.
8. Figure 7.2 shows that each pier supports 1/8 of the building load: 60,000 lb/8 = 7,500 lb.
9. A pier weighs $1 \times 1 \times 4$ ft $\times 150$ pcf = 600 lb.
10. Arbitrarily try a pier footing of $2 \times 2 \times 1$ ft $\times 150$ pcf = 600 lb.
11. The required footing area is:

$$\frac{(7,500 \text{ lb} + 600 \text{ lb} + 600 \text{ lb})}{2,000 \text{ psf}} = 4.35 \text{ ft}^2$$

12. The estimated size of 2×2 ft is too small. Try 2.25 ft^2.
13. The new footing weight is $2.25 \times 2.25 \times 2.25$ ft $\times 150$ pcf = 949 lb.
14. The new required footing area is:

$$\frac{(7,500 \text{ lb} + 600 \text{ lb} + 949 \text{ lb})}{2,000 \text{ psf}} = 4.5 \text{ ft}^2$$

15. Somewhat under the 5 ft^2 actual size, it is satisfactory.
The end foundations, while supporting only a minimal load, should be constructed with the same dimensions as the rear foundation.

Types of Foundation

In areas that are subject to little or no ground frost, a floating slab foundation consisting of a concrete floor, in which the outer 6 in. (150 mm) is thickened to at least 12 in. (300 mm) below grade, is simple and economical to construct for small buildings.

A curtain wall foundation (fig. 7.4) with soil filled against both sides to within a foot or two of its top is commonly used for agricultural buildings which have their first floor at just above grade level. The typical wall is built 8 to 10 in. (200 to 250 mm) thick without reinforcing. A much thinner wall could easily support the vertical load but would need to be reinforced near the top and bottom with no. 4 ReBars. The additional labor in placing the bars and concrete, plus the possibly higher cost for concrete with smaller-sized aggregate that would be needed, tend to make the cost for either wall about the same. If a minimum-thickness curtain wall is installed where the grade is different on the two sides, it may need to be supported by buttresses or by being tied into the floor.

Masonry blocks of 8, 10 or 12 in. (200, 250 or 300 mm) width may be used for a foundation (fig. 7.5). However, they are neither as strong nor as watertight as poured concrete foundations. While the labor and materials for form work are saved, the cost of blocks and the labor of placing them often equals or even exceeds the cost of a concrete wall. When a block foundation is chosen, the first course should be set in a full

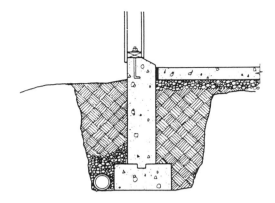

Figure 7.4. Concrete curtain wall.

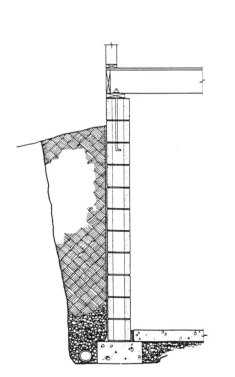

Figure 7.5. Concrete-block basement wall.

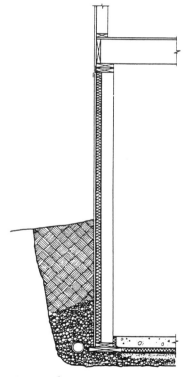

Figure 7.6. Preservative-treated wood foundation.

bed of mortar on a concrete footing. A block wall can be made quite watertight by:

1. Using a rich mortar and tooling it carefully.
2. Plastering the surface and then applying a commercial sealer.
3. Installing a footing drain with a foot of gravel over it.
4. Backfilling carefully and sloping the fill away from the wall.

For lightweight construction, piers may be used in place of a continuous foundation with resulting cost savings in materials and labor. However, it is difficult to get a tight fit between the ground and the side of the building. It may also be necessary to design sills as weight-bearing beams.

Treated wood and plywood may be used for a foundation as shown in figure 7.6. Crushed stone, with an assumed safe-bearing strength of 3,000 lb/ft^2 (144 kPa) may be used as a base on which to install a footing plate of pressure-treated wood. A treated sill and studs are installed above the footing plate and treated plywood is nailed to the outside of the studs. The foundation is made waterproof by the installation of a mastic and polyethylene barrier on the outside of the plywood below grade. This type of construction may be used for curtain walls, low walls with a crawl space or full basement walls. The principal advantages include the reduced labor required for installation and the ease with which insulation may be installed.

Pressure-treated Post and Lumber Foundations

The flexibility of post foundation and the convenience of stud wall framing can be combined by the use of pressure-treated post and lumber foundations. With this approach, short treated posts are set in the ground and cut off a foot or so above the ground. Pressure-treated planks are then nailed to both sides and the top of the post as a sill (see fig. 7.7). Conventional stud framing can then be constructed on the sill. Concrete footings may be required by soil and load conditions or by local building codes.

Footing Drains

High water levels on the outside of a wall can produce lateral pressures that endanger the wall and greatly increase the possibility of water leaks into a basement. In areas where there is sufficient slope so that a drainage line can be brought to grade in a reasonable distance, it is desirable to install a continuous drain around the outside of the foundation footing. This will help to maintain stable conditions in the soil that supports the building and to reduce the possibility of frost damage. Perhaps most importantly, in buildings with basements, it will help to prevent leakage problems.

The drain should be at a level below the concrete floor but not below the level of the bottom of the footing. In some soils that are subject to easy separation, it is best to place the drain 4 in. (100 mm) above the bottom of the footing to prevent ground water from washing out the fine material under the footings. In most cases, 4 in. (100 mm) land tile or perforated plastic or asphalt-fiber drainage pipe should be satisfactory. In a few cases where gravelly soils are known to carry large quantities of groundwater, 6 in. (150 mm) drains may be required (see fig. 7.1).

Drains should be installed with little or no gradient. This will help maintain a level

Foundations, Footings, and Floors   163

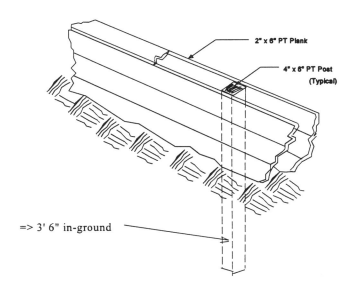

2" x 6" PT Plank

4" x 6" PT Post
(Typical)

=> 3' 6" in-ground

Figure 7.7. Post and plank foundation.

groundwater table at all points along the foundation footing while still keeping the drain line below the floor and above the bottom of the footing.

In areas of flat topography, the construction of a basement foundation may leave little choice but to end the footing and floor drain in a sump that can be pumped automatically.

In back-filling around a foundation wall, 1 to 2 ft (300 to 600 mm) of fine stone should be placed over the drain followed by soil that is graded to slope away from the foundation. The cost of footing drains is small in comparison to the total cost of the building, and they should not be omitted even when the location appears to be quite dry.

Post-frame Building Support

Footings for the base of the posts in post-frame buildings are important for stability and reasonable life. Concrete pads under each post should be sized to adequately support both the dead load of the building as well as the expected snow load. Inasmuch as post-frame buildings are comparatively light and do not have a heavy foundation, it is important to protect the building from wind damage by anchoring the base of each post. This may be done by running a rod through the post a few inches above the base and then pouring a concrete collar at least 12 in. (300 mm) in diameter around the base of the post. Another method is to drive eight to sixteen 20d nails half their length into the base of the post before pouring the concrete collar. A third, but much less effective alternative is spiking pieces of treated wood to the sides of the post near the base. The length of the blocks should be twice the thickness of the post. The soil is then well compacted above the wooden crosspieces to securely anchor the post. The three alternatives suggested are shown in figure 7.8.

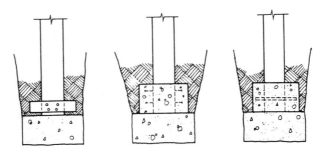

Figure 7.8. Methods of anchoring poles.

CONCRETE FLOORS

Concrete floors are used in many farm buildings. They are hard, strong, and durable and make an effective barrier against rodents. Concrete floors are especially valuable in buildings housing livestock and poultry because they are easy to clean and can be readily sanitized.

The type of construction varies with the use of the building. The floors of some buildings, such as grain storages, need to be protected from ground moisture only, while other floors need to be well insulated. For example, insulation helps to prevent heat loss in a farrowing house or freezing of the soil under a low-temperature storage building. Other buildings, such as machinery sheds, need only a smooth, durable surface.

The subgrade is prepared by removing all top soil and debris and then filling with at least 6 in. (150 mm) of gravel. If the area is well-drained, bank-run gravel should be satisfactory. However, if the subgrade is damp a single size of graded stones between 1/2 and 2 in. (13 and 50 mm) should be used in order to break any capillary action. When a high water table is present, there is the possibility for groundwater to accumulate under the floor. In this case, it is advisable to install drain tile in the fill to remove any free water. The fill should be placed in 6 in. (150 mm) layers and each layer thoroughly compacted with tampers, rollers or vibrators.

If it is particularly important to have a dry floor, such as with a grain storage, a vapor seal of 4 to 6 mil polyethylene plastic with well-lapped joints should be installed on top of the fill. A thin layer of stiff concrete or grout spread evenly under the plastic sheet will help avoid puncturing the plastic during placement of the concrete. Figure 7.9 illustrates this type of construction.

For a warm, dry floor, such as is required in a farm home, more complete insulation is necessary to reduce heat loss to the ground. A 1 in. (25 mm) thick layer of rigid waterproof insulation, such as extruded polystyrene, is placed on top of the grout. Details of this construction are shown in figure 7.9 (c).

Floors usually have a slab thickness of 4 in. (100 mm) for ordinary usage, and 6 in. (150 mm) when subjected to heavy loads such as tractors and trucks. Depending on the load requirements of the building, 2 × 4 in. (38 × 89 mm) or 2 × 6 in. (38 × 140 mm) forms are used. The forms should be securely staked and oiled for easy removal.

A strip of rigid insulating material should be placed along the base of the wall before placing the concrete. This serves as a heat barrier and also allows the concrete to expand and contract with temperature changes. In the case of large areas, the concrete should be cast in 10 to 15 ft (3 to 5 m) strips to allow for expansion joints. A tapered 1 × 2 in. (19 × 38 mm) wood strip along one side of the form provides a "key" to keep adjacent slabs in alignment. However, it is best to put a piece of asphalt paper or polyethylene in the joint to prevent bonding. A groover may be used to cut control joints across the strips. These grooves should be about one-fifth of the thickness of the slab and spaced 10 to 15 ft apart (3 to 5 m).

Concrete used for floors should have relatively small-sized coarse aggregate, 1 to 1 1/2 in. (25 to 40 mm), and be mixed relatively stiff (5 to 6 gal/sack of cement). Once in place and thoroughly spaded to eliminate cavities, it may be struck off with a screed board. A non-slip surface for livestock may be obtained by dragging a stable broom over the wet concrete. Using a wood float leaves the surface level but gritty. A smooth surface is possible by using a steel trowel after the watery sheen has disappeared from the surface of the concrete.

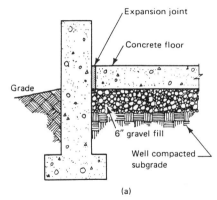

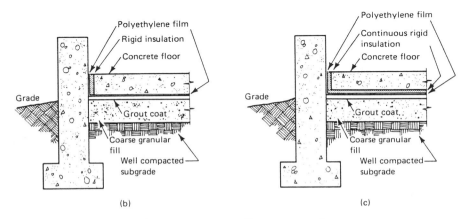

Figure 7.9. Concrete floor construction.

As soon as the concrete has set, provisions should be made to keep it wet for several days. A good method is to spread a layer of sand over the concrete and then wet it down well. A film of polyethylene is also effective and labor efficient.

Slotted Floors

Slotted floors may be used in livestock housing to allow manure to fall into a storage or collection pit below the animals. These systems reduce labor and can improve the environment by providing a relatively manure-free floor for the animal. The manure may be stored, drained or scraped away below the slats. There are several advantages of a slotted floor. It permits greater animal density and at the same time the animals remain cleaner. There is less moisture to be removed by the ventilation system and, where supplemental heat is needed, the amount of heat required is less than in buildings with conventional floor construction. In solid-floor barns, free-stall or bedded rest areas have commonly been used to provide clean resting areas for the animals. The slotted floor, on the other hand, will usually remain clean enough to make stalls unnecessary.

Slotted floors have some drawbacks too. The original cost is high when compared with a solid floor. However, this added cost eventually can be recouped by the greater number of animals housed and by the labor savings. In the past, slotted floors have tended to cause some problems with animals slipping, but there have been recent improvements in surface textures that promise to alleviate the difficulty.

Concrete has been far and away the most popular material for making slats. Concrete slats are hard, durable, easy to clean, and relatively free of slipping problems, but they are the heaviest to handle and require the strongest supports.

Wood slats are inexpensive and lighter to handle, but they are less durable and subject to warping which in turn leaves unequal spacing. Swine also tend to chew on wood decreasing the useful life of the floor.

Expanded metal and woven wire may be satisfactory for small animals up to 50 lb (22 kg), but has failed when subjected to the weight of larger animals.

Steel slats must be protected from corrosion to insure a satisfactory life. Aluminum slats are much more corrosion resistant, lighter in weight, and easier to install, but they are also considerably more expensive. Some metal floor units are formed so that short slots are staggered and spaced between the supports, a design that resists plugging and keeps the floor drier and cleaner. Extruded plastic and fiberglass slats also show promise although some tend to be slippery.

Table 7-3. Concrete specifications for slats

Air entrainment	7%	7%
Cement	7 3/4 sack/yd^3	11 sack/m^3
Water	5 gal/sack	17.7 L/sack
Aggregate	3/4 in. max. diameter	20 mm max. diameter
Slump	2 to 3 in.	50 to 75 mm
28 day strength	3600 psi	25 MPa

Table 7-4. Design loads and slat dimensions

Animal	Length (lb/ft)	Length (kg/m)	Area (psf)	Area (kg/m²)	4 ft (1.2 m) B&D* (in.) Bar No.	4 ft (1.2 m) B&D* (mm) Bar No.	6 ft (1.8 m) B&D* (in.) Bar No.	6 ft (1.8 m) B&D* (mm) Bar No.	8 ft (2.4 m) B&D* (in.) Bar No.	8 ft (2.4 m) B&D* (mm) Bar No.
Dairy cow	250	373	100	489	4 × 4 No. 4	100 × 100 15M	4 × 5 No. 5	100 × 125 15M	4 × 7 No. 5	100 × 175 15M
Calves and swine to 400 lb (180 kg)	150	224	50	245	4 × 4 No. 3	100 × 100 10M	4 × 5 No. 4	100 × 125 10M	4 × 6 No. 5	100 × 150 15M
Sheep and swine to 200 lb (90 kg)	120	179	50	245	4 × 4 No. 3	100 × 100 10M	4 × 5 No. 4	100 × 100 15M	4 × 5 No. 5	100 × 125 15M
Swine 50 lb (23 kg)	50	75	35	171	4 × 4 No. 3	100 × 100 10M	4 × 4 No. 3	100 × 100 10M	4 × 4 No. 4	100 × 100 15M
All slats to be lifted — top bar					No. 3	10M	No. 3	10M	No. 3	10M

Concrete Slat Design

Concrete slats can be purchased precast or they may be cast on the job either in forms on the ground or in place. Precast slats are less trouble and normally are a uniform high quality. While form construction is more difficult in place, the problem of lifting the heavy slats during installation is avoided and the top reinforcing bar may be eliminated. The specifications for concrete to be used in casting slats are given in table 7-3.

Design loads and slat dimensions are given in table 7-4. The reinforcing bar recommended in the table is placed 1 1/4 in. (32 mm) above the bottom of the slat. If the slat will be handled after casting, a no. 3 reinforcing bar is placed 3/4 in. (19 mm) below the top surface. Recommendations for finishing and curing include:

1. Finish the surface with a wooden float in all cases except for a farrowing house where a steel float should be used.
2. Leave a slight crown for good drainage.
3. Use an edging tool to produce a slightly rounded edge.
4. Keep the slats wet for at least 1 week for proper curing.

Retaining Walls

The cross-section for gravity retaining walls is depicted in figure 7.10. Dimensions recommended for several heights are given in table 7-5. The soil that slopes up and

Table 7-5. Recommended dimensions for retaining walls
(see fig 7-10)

Height of Wall (ft)	Height of Wall (m)	Without Surcharge (ft)	Without Surcharge (m)	With Surcharge (ft)	With Surcharge (m)
3	0.9	2 1/4	0.7	2 1/2	0.8
4	1.2	2 1/2	0.8	3	0.9
6	1.8	3 1/3	1.0	4	1.2
8	2.4	4 1/4	1.3	5 1/2	1.7
10	3.0	5 1/4	1.6	7	2.1

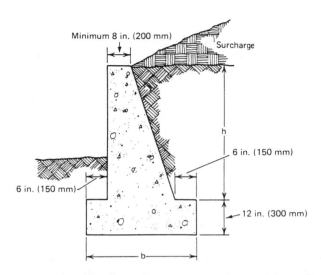

Figure 7.10. Dimensions of a concrete gravity retaining wall.

away from the back of the wall is referred to as the surcharge. It causes an additional force on the wall and requires a larger footing for stability.

Problems

7.1. A 20 × 30 ft (6 × 9 m) post-frame shed is supported by 8 posts. The total dead load of the building is 3,960 lb (1800 kg). Assume the building is located in the central Middlesex District of Ontario. The 5:12 pitch gable roof has a total area of 720 ft² (67 m²). Determine the design snow load. Combine the snow and dead loads and then determine the size of pad that should be installed under each post.

7.2. Using the total load value found for problem 6.7, design safe footings for the building using local soil conditions.

7.3. Design the slotted floor for a dairy herd replacement barn which has a slotted area 12 ft (3.66 m) wide and 100 ft (30 m) long. Give specifications for the slats and indicate the load per foot (m) on the central supporting member.

8 Building, Framing, and Bracing

A building framework is the backbone providing support and integrity. The structural members of the main frame must support all of the loads that may be imposed on the building. The frame must not only be strong enough to support vertical loads, but it must be anchored, braced, and securely fastened together to withstand forces from any direction. Many building failures occur because of inadequate bracing or joint strength. Rather than being the cause of the structural failure, members frequently fail as a result of a building collapse due to inadequate bracing or joints. It is important that the system of structural members be thoroughly tied together including sufficient ground anchorage.

Types of Frames

The type of frame chosen for a building will depend on floor and wall loads, the clear span required, and the type of interior and exterior wall coverings desired. In some cases, it is difficult to distinguish between the main wall frame and the roof frame. In other cases, there is a distinct separation.

Framing systems have evolved from the usage of a few very large members to many smaller members. In the case of timber framing, this occurred to some extent because of the limited availability of large timbers. A frame design which places the small members in a manner that causes them to carry near their maximum loads will generally use materials more efficiently.

The early post and beam framing (see fig. 8.1) provided strong, and with proper protection, long lasting buildings; however, the individual members were frequently loaded far less than their capacity.

Timber frames constructed of heavy structural members, spaced well apart, were popular in the 19th century, primarily because much less sawing of timbers was necessary. That they were well-designed and durable is evident today by the number of old barns still standing. They usually required vertical siding. More efficient methods of using wood are employed in most present-day frames.

Balloon frames (fig. 8.2), developed in the early 1800s due to a lack of available lumber in the Chicago area, have vertical members that extend from base to roof—tying the building together from base to roof and making it more wind resistant. Since

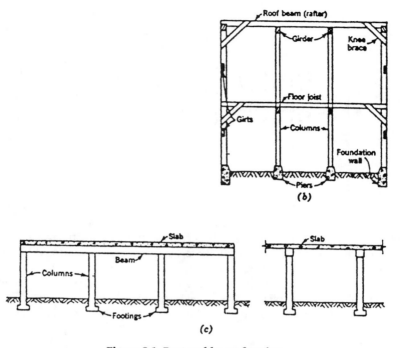

Figure 8.1. Post and beam framing.

some weight-bearing members are supported by ribbons attached to the sides of vertical members, the weight-bearing capacity is usually less than with a platform frame. Fire stops may need to be installed between the wall studs.

Platform or western frames (fig. 8.3) are used extensively in home building and in farm buildings subjected to heavy floor loads. In general, each succeeding group of members rests on top of the previous one. There are no open flues or passages within the walls from floor to floor through which fire may travel. This is a commonly used form of wood frame construction. Typically, sections of wall frames are put together on the floor and then erected into place.

Post-frames (figs. 8.4, 8.5) are simple, fast to construct, and usually less expensive because of little or no foundation cost. Frame members are often overlapped which reduces cutting and improves the strength of joints. One or more sides may be left open. Post-frame buildings are usually limited to a single story.

Rigid frames (figs. 8.6, 8.7) may be fabricated from either steel or wood. Many manufacturers of steel buildings make use of either solid-web or open-web rigid frames to produce a simple, low-pitch building with maximum interior clearance. Rigid frames fabricated from wood include glued laminated rafters for gothic arch roofs and medium-pitch frames with dimension lumber and nailed and glued plywood gussets. The cost of these frames is comparable to other types offering clear spans of equal length.

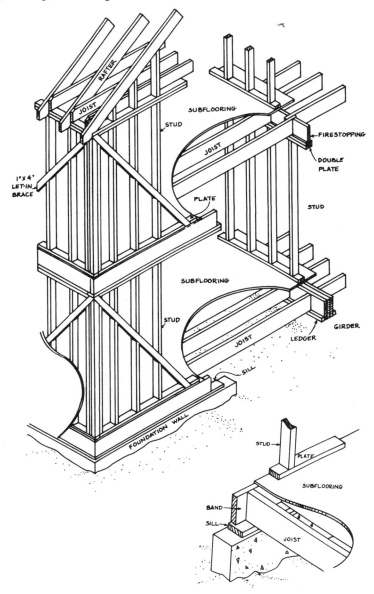

Figure 8.2. Balloon frame construction.

Frameless building types have no separate framing structure. Curvette buildings are formed of light-gauge, curved steel panels which serve as both wall and roof and are self supporting. Although agricultural applications have been limited, plastic films can be air supported to provide low-cost storage structures, however operating costs detract from their usefulness. Dome-shaped structures using foamed-in-place plastics

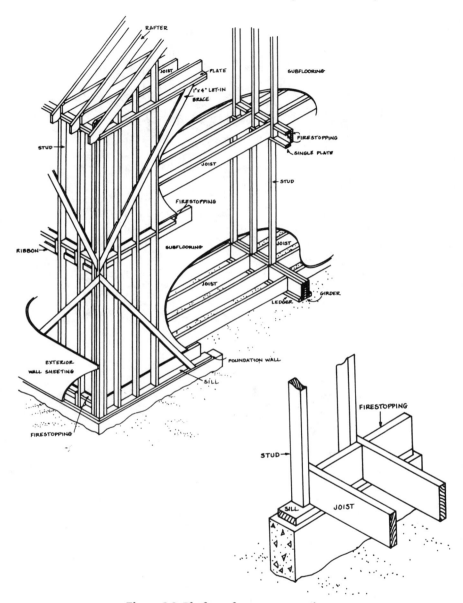

Figure 8.3. Platform frame construction.

that do not require a frame support system are also available. Many concrete block buildings have been used for agricultural applications. These buildings normally require only a roof frame. Monolithic concrete and tilt-up concrete panels may be used in place of blocks.

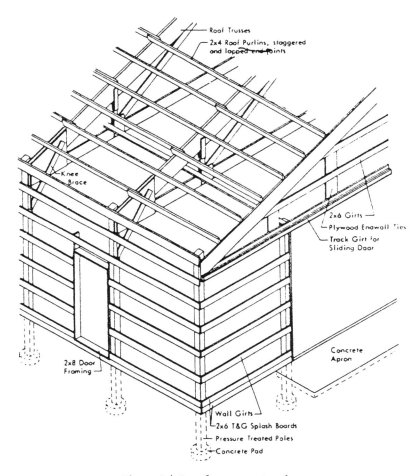

Figure 8.4. Post-frame construction.

Framing Components

Sills, horizontal wood members attached to the foundation, are usually 2 in. (38 mm) thick and from 4 to 12 in. (89 to 286 mm) wide depending on stud size and whether joists rest on the sill. If joist loads are heavy, a wide sill may be necessary in order to get adequate bearing surface between the joist and sill.

Sills should be anchored to the foundation to adequately resist wind forces. The following anchor design is recommended:

- Single story buildings - 1/2 in. bolts, 6 ft (2 m) o.c. or 5/8 in. bolts, 8 ft (2.5 m) o.c.
- Two or three stories - 5/8 in. bolts, 6 ft (2 m) o.c.

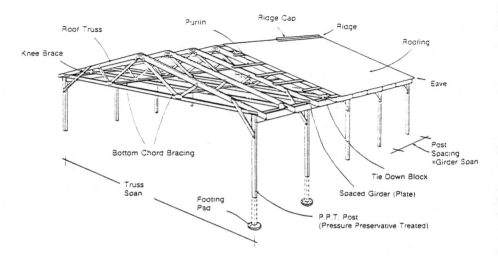

Figure 8.5. Clear-span post-frame construction.

All bolts should reach at least 12 in. (300 mm) into concrete walls, 16 to 18 in. (400 to 450 mm) into piers and from 2 blocks to 2 ft (600 mm) in masonry walls. In high wind areas, masonry walls should be avoided altogether or should be tied all the way to the footing. In all cases, large washers should be used on the bolts. Sills that are used on piers must be designed for beam loads.

Joists are horizontal members that are subjected to vertical loads. They are supported by the sill or intermediate girders on the first floor and by plates on subsequent floors. They are usually made of 2 in. (38 mm) dimension lumber with the depth and spacing determined by the load. Flat, open, web wood trusses or wood I-beams may be used, particularly for the first floor of homes. This reduces the number of support posts required and increases the usefulness of the basement area.

In homes, the choice of joist type and size, might be made on the basis of deflection in order to keep vibration to a minimum. In most agricultural buildings, the design would be based on strength. With platform frames, the sub-floor will be installed on the joists and a shoe or bottom plate to which the studs are attached placed on top of the subfloor.

Bridging consists of wood or metal bracing between joists as shown in figures 8.8, 8.9, and 8.10. Installed at the center of the joist span, bridging helps distribute concentrated loads and reduces vibration by increasing the rigidity of the joist.

Girders are large horizontal members which may be used to support the interior ends of first floor joists. When made of wood, they are frequently "built up" of two or more pieces (fig. 8.9). The joists may be lapped over the top of wood or steel girders (figs. 8.9, 8.10) or attached by metal framing anchors (fig. 8.11), or supported on a ledger attached to the side of the girder (fig. 8.2).

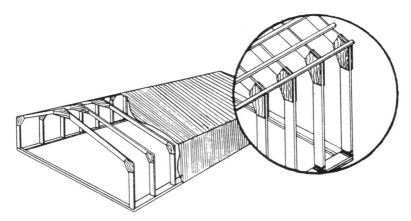

Figure 8.6. Rigid frame of wood and plywood.

Figure 8.7. Rigid frame of steel.

Studs are the upright wall members, usually spaced 16 in. (400 mm) or 24 in. (600 mm) to provide a modular spacing, that conforms well with common building materials. While the smaller spacing has been most common in home construction, with slightly thicker wall coverings, the larger spacing is satisfactory.

The width of the stud used depends on the height of the building and floor loads supported by the studs, along with wind and product loads that impose forces perpendicular to the wall. While 2 × 4 in. (38 × 89 mm) studs are common in single-story buildings, 2 × 6 in. (38 × 140 mm) studs are often required for multi-story buildings. A wider stud used with the larger spacing also allows additional insulation to be

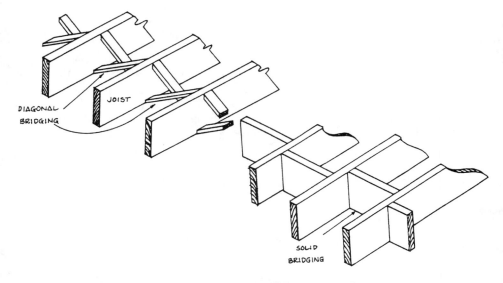

Figure 8.8. Bridging.

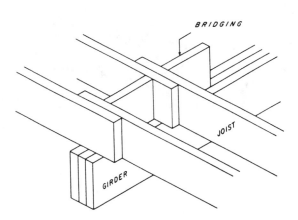

Figure 8.9. A built-up girder.

installed. The desire to conserve energy has led to the common use of 2 × 6 studs or double 2 × 4 stud walls. The double wall not only allows installation of more insulation, but also provides a space for electrical wiring and plumbing.

Plates, the horizontal members on top of the studs, provide rigidity and strength to the wall, particularly in resisting loads perpendicular to the wall. In addition, the plate must be wide enough to provide adequate bearing surface for joists or rafters.

Headers or lintels are required to span openings such as doors and windows (fig. 8.12). They are often used in addition to the regular horizontal plates which are still needed to resist horizontal forces.

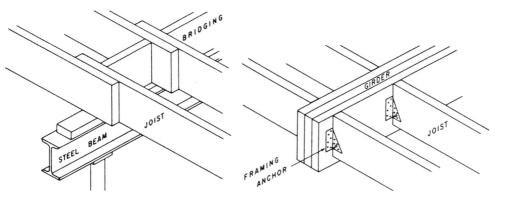

Figure 8.10. Joists on a steel beam.   **Figure 8.11. Joist connections.**

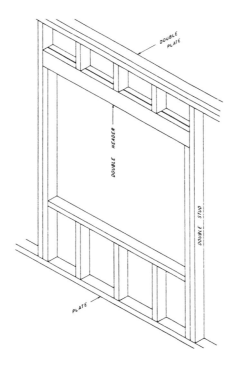

Figure 8.12. A header spanning an opening.

Rafters are roof framing members and are usually spaced to modular dimensions of 16 in., 2 ft or 4 ft (400, 600 or 1200 mm) on center. Rafter size is influenced by length, intermediate supports, spacing, and expected roof and ceiling loads. Intermediate supports are called purlins.

Framing Connections

The traditional method of fastening studs to sills, plate to studs, and rafters or joists to plate is by toe nailing or end nailing. These provide satisfactory rigidity, in most cases, but do not give very high ultimate strength. The use of metal straps and gussets in addition to the toe nailing will improve the strength. Commercial fasteners, used according to recommendations, provide both adequate rigidity and strength.

One of the easiest ways to obtain superior strength, rigidity, and bracing effect is to use plywood or large-size building boards nailed according to the manufacturer's recommendations.

Rafters and trusses may be anchored by nailing them to the side of studs, using wooden or metal ties to the studs or commercial fasteners. Toe nailing alone is risky, particularly where spans are long, rafter spacing is 2 ft or more, and significant wind uplift forces may occur.

Bracing

The importance of adequate bracing in a building cannot be over-emphasized. Along with inadequate fastening at joints, the lack of bracing is a major cause of structural failure. While it is impossible to generalize all bracing requirements, the important locations for bracing can be suggested.

Lateral bracing in a wall may be obtained by a brace that is "let" into notches in the studs, in both directions, at each corner as shown in figure 8.2. However, diagonal wood sheathing or fiberboard sheathing will provide better bracing. Properly nailed plywood sheathing is still better, and if glue is also used, an extremely rigid unit will be developed. When plastic insulation board is used in place of wood sheathing, metal straps may be used diagonally at corners to provide rigidity.

Knee braces between columns and beams or joists may be needed at each column for resistance to lateral wind forces. If interior walls are over 14 to 16 ft apart, it is desirable to install knee braces between the side wall and joists or rafters. Knee braces should be a minimum of 4 ft (1.2 m) long and made of 2 × 4 in. (38 × 89 mm) or 2 × 6 in. (38 × 140 mm) lumber.

In post-frame construction, knee braces may be installed in both directions at every weight bearing post. Roof decks and walls designed to provide diaphragm action may allow the omission of knee braces. Knee braces can induce significant stresses in truss members and should be subjected to a careful engineering analysis in modern design.

Truss bracing is used to provide stability during and after construction. Intermittent cross bracing between adjacent trusses prevents a "domino" type of collapse. Lower chord stiffeners will be needed, if there is no ceiling attached or the ceiling provides inadequate stiffness. Long web members will also require lateral bracing.

End bracing of buildings that are over 18 ft (6 m) wide without an inner partition or 8 ft (2.4 m) height without a floor is desirable. In connection with this bracing, horizontal plate members are desirable in order to withstand the wind loads against the end of the building.

Post-frame Building Systems

Pole frame construction was found to provide versatile, economical structures for livestock housing and agricultural product storage in the 1940s and 1950s. Early pole buildings used red cedar poles to resist decay. A shortage of red cedar prompted E. G. Perkins to propose the use of preservative-treated poles as the primary structural support members. Mr. Perkins also pioneered the idea of 2 × 4 in. lumber placed on edge for purlins to replace 1 in. lumber for roofing support. A patent application based on the "pole building concept" was completed in August 1949 and issued as Patent #2641988 in 1953.

Although early pole buildings used simple rafters with interior support poles, today these structures normally use trusses to provide a clear span interior. Round poles are seldom used now, and the term post-frame is preferred for the square or rectangular posts. Post-frame systems use fewer structural members than conventional framing systems. A single member serves as the foundation and as the vertical structural member. The three key elements of post design include (1) selecting the proper post size, (2) determining the required depth of embedment, and (3) sizing the footing pad. The size of post required will depend on the loading and spacing. Required depth of embedment is based on resisting uplift and overturning forces as well as frost depth. Footing size depends on the gravity loads and the soil bearing capacity.

Although post spacing is influenced by post size, building height, wind load, and diaphragm action, it should not ordinarily be more than 16 ft (5 m) on center (table 8-1). Wind loads may be calculated from information in chapter 6.

Post embedment should be at least 4 ft (1.2 m) in firm soil and 5 ft (1.5 m) in soft soil, but often needs to be deeper based on engineering design. The post should extend below the frost line. Pads and anchors for posts are discussed in chapter 7.

The simplest approach to setting posts is to backfill the hole with the soil removed and tamp; however, this provides very limited resistance to overturning and uplift forces. Attaching wooden blocks to the bottom end of the post or inserting dowels through the post and embedding them in concrete will greatly increase the withdrawal resistance. Stability against overturning can be increased by attaching a plank or casting a concrete collar at the groundline. A concrete beam or slab at the groundline will maximize resistance to overturning.

Girders may be attached to posts with nails or bolts and supported on bearing blocks. Occasionally, the post may be notched to provide a seat for the girder. Trusses may be supported on bearing blocks attached to posts, in notches in the posts, or on girders attached to the posts. The truss should be securely attached using sufficient nails, bolts, framing anchors, strapping. Figure 8.13 illustrates the details of girder and truss connections at a post.

Table 8-1. Spacing of pressure-treated Douglas fir or southern pine poles or posts

Size	Wind Load (psf)	(kPa)	9 ft	2.75 m	12 ft	3.67 m	15 ft	4.5 m	19 ft	5.8 m
6.7 in.	10	69	16	4.8	16	4.8	16	4.8	16	4.8
(170 mm)	12	83	16	4.8	16	4.8	16	4.8	14	4.2
	15	103	16	4.8	16	4.8	14	4.2	11	3.4
	20	138	16	4.8	14	4.2	10	3.0	8	2.4
6.0 in.	10	69	16	4.8	16	4.8	16	4.8	13	4.0
(150 mm)	12	83	16	4.8	16	4.8	13	4.0	11	3.4
	15	103	16	4.8	14	4.2	11	3.4	9	2.7
	20	138	16	4.8	10	3.0	8	2.4	–	–
5.4 in.	10	69	16	4.8	16	4.8	12	3.6	10	3.0
(137 mm)	12	83	16	4.8	13	4.0	10	3.0	8	2.4
	15	103	16	4.8	10	3.0	8	2.4	6	1.8
	20	138	12	3.6	8	2.4	–	–	–	–
6 in. × 8 in.	10	69	24	7.3	24	7.3	19	5.8	12	3.6
(150 × 200 mm)	12	83	–	–	–	–	16	4.9	10	3.0
	15	103	–	–	–	–	12.5	3.8	8	2.4
5.5 × 5.5 in.	10	103	23	7.0	13	4.0	8	2.4	5	1.5
(140 × 140 mm)	12	83	–	–	11	3.3	7	2.1	4	1.2
	15	103	15	4.6	8.5	2.6	5.5	1.7	3.4	1.0
3.5 × 5.5 in	10	69	14.5	4.4	8	2.4	5	1.5	3.3	1.0
(89 × 140 mm)	12	83	12	3.6	7	2.1	4.4	1.3	–	–
	15	103	9.7	3.0	5.4	1.6	3.5	1.0	–	–

Diaphragms

The need for knee braces may be eliminated by the use of the diaphragm effect which may be obtained by proper roof design and installation. The roofing and purlins must be carefully installed in accordance with the design to ensure proper stiffness of the diaphragm. The connections of the sheathing are very critical in diaphragm design. For instances, the metal roofing may be installed on the purlins with screws placed 12 in. (300 mm) apart in the flats (not the ridges) of the roofing. The 2 × 4 in. (38 × 89 mm) purlins may be 2 ft (600 mm) o.c. Actual designs are tested to determine panel stiffness and the measured values used to design the building.

Structural diaphragms are relatively thin, usually rectangular, structural elements capable of resisting shear parallel to their edges. A conventional frame roof, wall, or floor will normally function as a structural diaphragm with only slight design modification. Diaphragms are essentially deep beams with a shear-resistant web which is formed by the discontinuous sheathing. Beams, girts, studs, columns, joists, and purlins act as stiffeners.

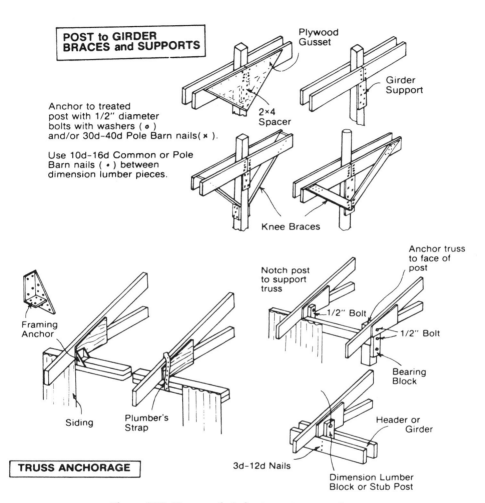

POST to GIRDER BRACES and SUPPORTS

Plywood Gusset

Girder Support

Anchor to treated post with 1/2" diameter bolts with washers (o) and/or 30d-40d Pole Barn nails(×).

2×4 Spacer

Use 10d-16d Common or Pole Barn nails (•) between dimension lumber pieces.

Knee Braces

Framing Anchor

Siding

Plumber's Strap

Notch post to support truss

1/2" Bolt

Anchor truss to face of post

1/2" Bolt

Bearing Block

Header or Girder

TRUSS ANCHORAGE

3d-12d Nails

Dimension Lumber Block or Stub Post

Figure 8.13. Truss and girder to post connections.

Diaphragms absorb lateral forces, such as wind, and transmit these forces to other resisting elements. Lateral loads on side walls produce horizontal loads against the roof framing system which acts as a large plate girder. Bending moment is resisted by continuous chords as flanges, while the sheathing resists the shear forces as the web. The horizontal loads from the side wall reactions are carried to the end walls, which act as cantilevers from the foundation.

Problems

8.1. Give examples in which the choice of each of the following frame types would be suitable:

(a) Balloon frame, (b) Pole frame, (c) Platform frame, (d) Rigid frame.

8.2. A post-frame building is to be constructed in central Iowa. The dimensions are 36×48 ft (11×14.6 m) with a 12 ft (3.7 m) eave height. The roof slope is 4:12 and the building will be enclosed and designed with knee braces. The soil conditions are soft. Determine a safe post spacing, post sizer, and post embedment.

9 Roof Framing

It is important to design roof framing to withstand the live loads expected in the particular climatic area and the dead load imposed by the framing, roof deck, and roofing material. Angle cuts tend to magnify measurement errors thus careful fitting is very important. Poorly fitting joints will result in reduced rigidity of the roof frame.

The shape of the roof will affect the structural design. Building planners must be familiar with different roof shapes in order to communicate their ideas. Various roof shapes are shown in figure 9.1. Various framing systems may be used to provide these shapes (fig. 9.2).

Common Roof Shapes

Flat Roofs (a)

These are simple to construct with clear spans of 16 to 18 ft (5.0 to 5.6 m) using roof joists. Greater spans are possible by using flat trusses. Being flat, these roofs require a membrane or a "built-up" asphalt roof covering which may be more expensive than some other types.

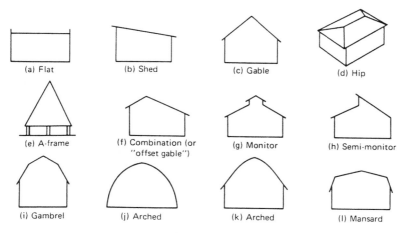

Figure 9.1. Roof shapes.

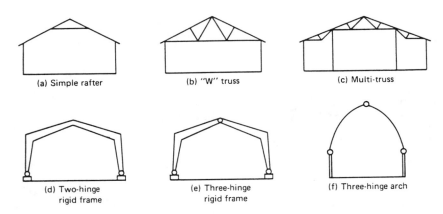

(a) Simple rafter   (b) "W" truss   (c) Multi-truss

(d) Two-hinge   (e) Three-hinge   (f) Three-hinge arch
    rigid frame   rigid frame

Figure 9.2. Roof frames.

Shed Roofs (b)

Shed roofs are inexpensive and, like a flat roof, can have clear spans of 16 to 18 ft (5.0 to 5.6 m) without resorting to truss construction. A less expensive roof covering may be used.

Gable Roofs (c)

These are medium in cost, easy to construct, and probably the most common style found on barns. Depending on the pitch, several different roof coverings are satisfactory. A medium-pitch gable roof is one of the most wind-resistant shapes available. Clear spans of up to about 26 ft (8 m) are feasible with plain rafters, while trusses may be used for greater widths.

Hip Roofs (d)

Hip roofs are most often chosen for their appearance. The framing and roofing are more complicated and expensive, and attic ventilation is more difficult than with a gable roof.

A-frame Roofs (e)

These are somewhat of an architectural novelty. Because of their shape, outside maintenance is largely restricted to roof covering while at the same time usable floor space is partially restricted by the sloping walls. Snow loads seldom present a problem.

Combination Roofs (f)

Sometimes called "offset gable," these roofs are often used on buildings that are open on one side. Depending on the requirements, the high side may be left open to provide maximum clearance or the low side may be left open for maximum weather protection.

Monitor or Semi-monitor Roofs (g-h)

Although more expensive to construct, these may be chosen if a considerable amount of natural light is required near the center of the building. Ventilation may be improved in buildings of 60 ft (20 m) or more.

Gambrel Roofs (i)

Barns with gambrel roofs came into use to provide greater storage space than was easily obtainable with gable roofs. They tend to be expensive, have uneven roof deterioration, and are subject to greater wind forces than most other shapes.

Arched Roofs (j-k)

Arched roofs may vary in shape from semicircular to high Gothic. The choice of shape and height depends largely on the space required. These roof shapes became popular with the advent of commercially available, glue-laminated rafters. Many of them have replaced gambrel-roof barns because of their lighter weight and lower cost to construct, while still offering large storage volume. Deterioration tends to be uneven on these roofs.

Mansard Roofs (l)

Mansard roofs are chosen primarily for their appearance. The low pitches commonly used in the center area may present some problems with leakage.

Common Rafters

The parts of a common rafter, extending from the plate to the ridge, are shown in figure 9.3. Note that when a rafter extends outside of the plate, the length of the rafter is measured along a workline parallel to the edge of the rafter and extending from the outer edge of the plate to the center of the ridge. All measurements are made in relation to this line and not the edges of the rafter.

The run of a rafter is the horizontal distance from the outside edge of the plate to a vertical (plumb) line dropped from the center of the ridge.

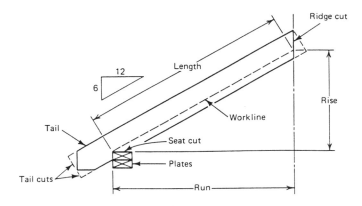

Figure 9.3. Parts of a common rafter.

The rise is the vertical distance from the top of the plate to the intersection of the ridge cut with the workline.

The pitch of the roof may be expressed either with an inverted right triangle showing the ratio of rise to run or it may be described with a fraction. The formula for the pitch fraction is:

$$\text{Pitch} = \frac{\text{rise}}{(2 \times \text{run})} \tag{9.1}$$

Note that with an even pitch gable roof, the span equals the run multiplied by two. However, on shed or combination roofs with unequal pitches, rafters for each pitch are designed separately and the equation should be used as shown.

For figure 9.3 the pitch fraction would be:

$$\text{Pitch} = \frac{6}{2 \times 12} = 1/4$$

Other relationships are as follows:

$$3:12 = 1/8 \qquad 8:12 = 1/3$$
$$4:12 = 1/6 \qquad 12:12 = 1/2$$

There are at least four ways to determine the length of a common rafter:

1. By taking the square root of the sum of the rise squared plus the run squared.
2. By using tables on rafter squares. The value under the inches per foot of run is the length in inches per foot of run.
3. By scaling with the aid of a steel square. Rafter squares have some scales divided into twelfths of an inch for easy conversion to feet and inches.
4. By stepping off the length with a steel square (fig. 9.4). Using the inches of rise on one outer scale and the 12 in. point on the other outer scale, one makes as many steps as there are feet of run.

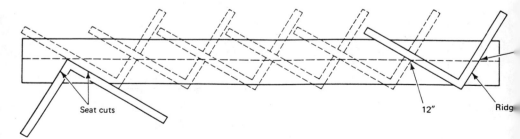

Figure 9.4. Stepping off the length of a rafter.

It is desirable to determine the length of a rafter to the nearest 1/8 in. (3 mm) to ensure a good fit. The first method, particularly with the aid of a pocket calculator, gives this precision. The fourth method provides a rough check of the accuracy of the first and also determines the angle of the ridge and seat cuts.

Briefly, the procedure for determining the length and the cuts for a common rafter with one-quarter pitch (6:12) is:

1. Find the rise and the run from the building print or with the pitch equation.
2. Decide on the depth of the seat cut and draw the workline. For low pitches, the seat cut often is deep enough so that the seat covers the plate. However, if there is to be a rafter tail, an extension beyond the plate, there must be sufficient material left to be of adequate strength.
3. Place the square on the workline near the ridge end of the rafter as shown in figure 9.4. In this case, that will be 6 in. on the tongue and 12 in. on the blade. Use the outside scales. Mark the ridge cut. Also mark the intersection of the workline with the 12 in. point on the blade of the square. Continue to place the square on the workline and mark the intersections for as many times as there are feet of run. Figure 9.4 shows 6 ft of run. The last mark should be the horizontal side of the seat cut. The millimeter values on a pitch triangle may be used in a similar manner.
4. Calculate the rafter length and measure from the ridge cut to the seat cut along the workline. Make any necessary corrections in length.
5. Complete the seat cut lines. Make both seat and ridge cuts. Cut out a second rafter and try the pair for fit.
6. If a ridge board is to be used, remove one-half the thickness of the board from each ridge cut.
7. Sometimes the remainder of a piece of dimension lumber from which a rafter can be cut will provide an adequate rafter tail. If not, then either a tail must be nailed to the rafter, or a longer piece of lumber selected for the rafter.

Figure 9.5 shows examples of hip, valley, and jack rafters. A good carpentry book may be consulted to obtain a method for designing these rafters.

Roof Loads

Chapter six covers in detail the types of loads to which roofs are subjected. The dead loads from the framing, roof deck, and roofing are easily estimated. Snow and wind loads are much more difficult to predict. Not only do they differ greatly from one area to another, but data may be based on a 25- or 50-year mean recurrence interval. In choosing a design load, it is necessary to comply with any code regulations and also desirable to obtain storm data for the local area. A final decision may be influenced by the hazard to life and property resulting from a roof failure.

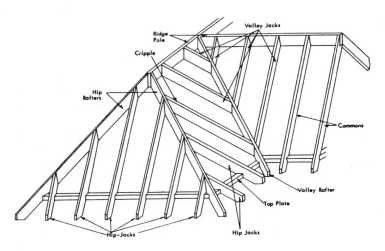

Figure 9.5. Types of rafters.

Trusses

A truss is a structure composed of members assembled to form one or more connected triangles, thus producing a rigid frame capable of supporting a heavy load over
a considerable span. Trusses are composed of chords and webs. Chords, top or bottom,
are the outer members where the loads are applied. Webs are the inner connecting, sta-
bilizing members and may be in either compression or tension. The points where the
members are joined are called panel points. Gussets are used to transfer forces across
joints. Plywood gussets which are only nailed may tend to allow excessive deflection
over a period of time. Plywood gussets which are both nailed and glued provide very
rigid joints that experience minimum deflection over time. Teethed metal plate gussets
tend to be intermediate in resisting long-term deflection. Light-frame trusses using
nominal 2 in. members and metal plates with punched teeth have become the most
common form of wood truss.

Commonly used timber trusses include parallel chord, pitched or triangular, bowstring, king post or scissors. The maximum economical span for a given type of truss
will vary with the materials, loading conditions, and fabrication methods.

Light trusses (made of nominal 2 in. lumber) are commonly used for spans up to
about 80 ft. The king post truss is simple and economical for relatively short spans. The
"W" type is suitable for spans of up to about 40 ft (12 m), while the Belgian truss might
be chosen for longer spans requiring a pitched roof. Pratt trusses have the advantage
for normal loading because the longer diagonal webs are in tension, whereas the shorter (vertical) webs are in compression. Parallel chord trusses may be economical in the
range of 20 to 50 ft (6 to 16 m) while pitched trusses may be economical from 20 ft to
80 ft (6 to 25 m). Bowstring trusses may be used for spans of up to 200 ft (62 m). The
scissors truss is recommended when a high ceiling clearance is required. Flat metal

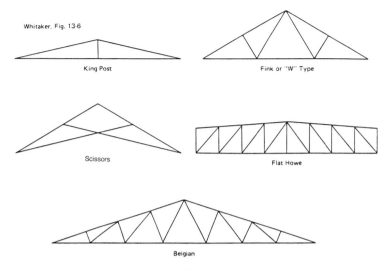

Figure 9.6. Types of trusses.

trusses are often used as joists or carrying beams. Several truss types are shown in figure 9.6. Figure 9.7 illustrates a complete truss design. The following are guidelines for truss depth to span ratios for timber trusses:

- Flat or parallel chord 1/8 to 1/10
- Pitched or triangular 1/6 or deeper
- Bowstring 1/6 to 1/8

Selecting a Truss

Trusses are intended to transfer loads (normally vertical) to the truss supports. Roof trusses must carry the weight of the roofing and structural members as well as snow. These loads are transferred to the vertical wall structural members, normally either studs or posts. The best selection of a truss is the one that will do the job safely and most economically. The optimum design of a truss will depend on the span (building width), roof slope, expected snow load, truss spacing, type of roofing, and any other loads that may be imposed.

Typical agricultural clear span buildings are 24 ft to 80 ft (8 to 24 m) using truss spacings of 4 to 12 ft (1.2 to 3.8 m). The most commonly used wood trusses for agricultural construction are pitch designs. Multiple trusses may be more economical for spans of more than 50 to 60 ft (15 to 18 m). Many short trusses are constructed of 2 × 4 in. (38 × 89 mm) lumber for all members. Truss members will have to increase in size to carry increasing loads as span and spacing increase. The slope of the truss has a compound effect. Steeper slopes reduce the design snow load and also reduce the bending stress in the top chord as the angle of the load changes. However, as the slope increases, the top chord length increases and this can increase the weight, and cost, of the truss.

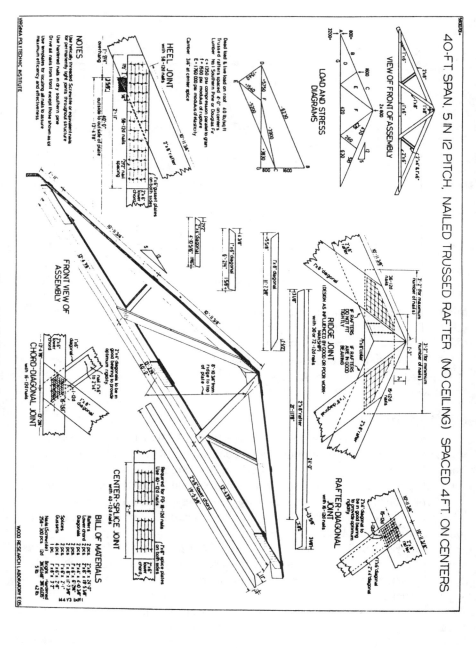

Figure 9.7. Nailed truss design.

A minimum roof slope of 3:12 is recommended for spans greater than 50 ft (15 m).

A 24 in. (0.6 m) spacing may allow a ceiling to be attached directly to the truss bottom chord. Additional framing will normally be required for ceiling support with wider truss spacings. Increasing spacing will also require that purlin size be increased and/or spacing be decreased.

For spans of up to 36 ft (11 m), a single "W" truss with only two compression members is often satisfactory. However, for spans of more than 36 ft (11 m), the use of additional members will reduce the required chord size. A king post (vertical member at the center) is desirable when a ceiling is to be installed. The pitch of a roof significantly affects the stresses in the truss members. The 5:12 ratio provides about the best balance and is recommended for long spans or heavy snow loads. A 4:12 ratio is suitable for most farm buildings in many areas, but 3:12 should be selected only for short to medium spans in low snow-load areas.

Wide truss spacings (e.g., 8 ft; 2.44 m) provide the greatest economy in labor and materials. However, a 4 ft (1.22 m) spacing allows the use of smaller size purlins and makes the installation of insulation easier when that is a requirement. Purlin spacing is largely determined by the maximum span of the roofing material that will be installed. Two feet (600 mm) is common. A 2 ft (600 mm) truss spacing is commonly chosen when a solid roof deck is being used.

Truss Stress Analysis

Chapter 10 provides information on stress analysis and the use of free-body diagrams. With these procedures applied to successive joints, the force in each truss member may be determined.

Example 9.1

A one-third pitch, "W" type truss shown in figure 9.8, will be used to illustrate the procedure. Trigonometric values used in the example:

$$\text{angle A (1/3 pitch)} = 33.69°$$

$$\text{tangent } 33.69° = 0.6667$$

$$\sin 33.69° = 0.5547$$

$$\cos 33.69° = 0.8321$$

$$\text{angle D} = 22.56°$$

If the direction of the member force is toward the joint, the member is in compression; if the member force acts away from the joint, the member is in tension. In this example the directions of the unknown forces are assumed; if the calculated force is negative, the assumed direction is incorrect—the force actually acts in the opposite direction.

T = tension, C = compression

At joint A:

$$\sum F_y = 0$$

200 lb − 50 lb − AB

$\sin(33.69°) = 0$

AB = 150 lb/0.5547

AB = 270.4 lb C

$$\sum F_x = 0$$

AC − 0.8321 AB = 0

AC = 0.8321 × 270.4 lb

AC = 225 lb T

$$\sum M_A = 0$$

$(100\ \text{lb} \times 10\ \text{ft} \times \cos(33.69°)) − (10\ \text{ft} \times BC) = 0$

BC = 100 lb × 8.321 ft/10 ft

BC = 83.2 lb C

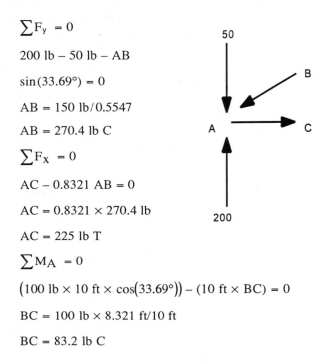

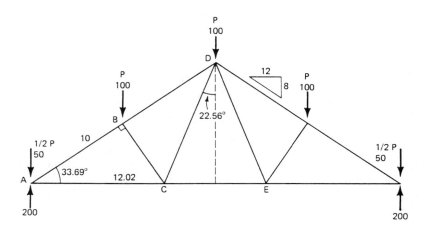

Figure 9.8. Example of truss analysis

At joint B:

$\Sigma F_X = 0$

$(0.8321\ BD) - (0.8321\ AB) - (0.5347\ BC) = 0$

$BD = \dfrac{((0.8321 \times 270.4\ lb) - (0.5547 \times 83.2\ lb))}{0.8321}$

$BD = 215\ lb\ C$

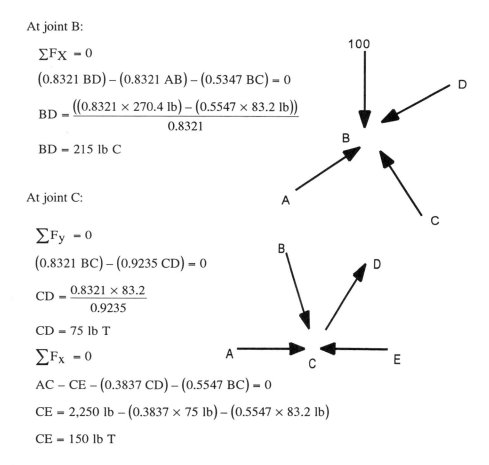

At joint C:

$\Sigma F_y = 0$

$(0.8321\ BC) - (0.9235\ CD) = 0$

$CD = \dfrac{0.8321 \times 83.2}{0.9235}$

$CD = 75\ lb\ T$

$\Sigma F_x = 0$

$AC - CE - (0.3837\ CD) - (0.5547\ BC) = 0$

$CE = 2,250\ lb - (0.3837 \times 75\ lb) - (0.5547 \times 83.2\ lb)$

$CE = 150\ lb\ T$

Since the truss is symmetrical, the forces for the remaining similar members correspond to those already determined.

Truss Design

By dividing the stress value for each member by P (100 in this case) a coefficient is obtained that may be used to find the forces for any value of P, as long as the loading is uniform and symmetrical. Table 9-1 provides the force coefficients for four pitches of the truss shown in figure 9.9. Similar tables for a variety of situations may be found in handbooks (Melaragno, 1981). This simple "W" truss has two members in each chord, 2 ft (600 mm) or less overhang at the eaves, and no ceiling load. The stresses in each of the members and joints may be calculated with the use of the tables. Once the stresses are known, an appropriate grade and size of lumber may be selected for a suitable truss spacing.

Since the truss design shown in figure 9.9 is symmetrical, the procedure involves

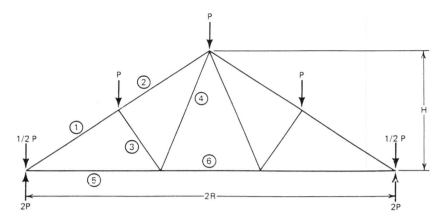

Figure 9.9. Truss member identification.

the loads and stresses for one side only. The load is the total uniform load to be supported by the trusses on both sides of the roof. For convenience, the load may be considered to be concentrated at the panel points (P). For figure 9.9, P = Load/4 and H = Pitch × 2R.

The force (G) in each truss member is determined by G = P × coefficient; the coefficient being chosen for the appropriate pitch in table 9-1. The length (L) of members is determined from the length coefficients in table 9-2.

Table 9-1. Member stress as a coefficient of P

| Member | Pitch* | | | |
	1/2	1/3	1/4	1/6
1	-2.12	-2.70	-3.35	-4.74
2	-1.14	-2.15	-2.91	-4.43
3	-0.71	-0.83	-0.89	-0.95
4	0.50	0.75	1.00	1.50
5	1.50	2.25	3.00	4.50
6	1.00	1.50	2.00	3.00

* A negative value indicates a stress in compression.

Table 9-2. Member length as a coefficient of H

| Member | Pitch | | | |
	1/2	1/3	1/4	1/6
1,2	0.707	0.901	1.118	1.581
3	0.707	0.60	0.559	0.52
4,5	1.00	1.08	1.25	1.667
6	0.00	0.82	1.50	2.67

Safe Design Strength

The analysis given in the section on truss stress analysis was very simplistic, since the truss was loaded only at the panel points. Many trusses are loaded at many intermediate points or continuously along the chords. In such cases, the chord must be designed for strength in both bending and compression. Members in compression only must be designed as columns. Lower chord members must be designed for safe strength in tension and also in bending, if there is a ceiling load. Wind uplift may result in stress reversal, thus members must be checked in both tension and compression.

It is easy to analyze stresses and select member sizes when only tension or compression forces are considered. Truss members except for short truss loaded at panel points will also be subjected to buckling and bending stresses. The effect of buckling stresses will depend on bracing of the member from roofing, ceilings or special structural members. When members are subjected to bending stresses as well as axial stresses, the interactions must be considered. The analysis of most trusses becomes quite complex and is best left to an engineer or stress analyst.

Truss Bracing

A system of bracing is required to provide resistance to lateral forces, to hold the trusses plumb, and to keep the compression elements from buckling. Bracing must resist transverse and longitudinal forces. The lateral bracing of the compression chord should be designed to withstand a horizontal force equal to at least 2% of the compressive force in the truss chord. Shear walls, diagonal bracing, buttresses, cantilevered columns or knee braces may be used to provide overall building stability and transmit the forces from the roof to the ground.

Cross bracing should be installed on the first 16 ft (4.8 m) of each end and at intermediate points not more than 32 ft (9.8 m) apart. Stiffeners should be installed between the bottom chords. Figure 9.10 illustrates how the bracing and stiffeners may be installed.

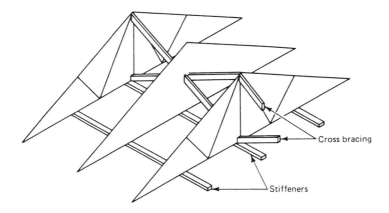

Figure 9.10. Bracing for trusses.

While trusses are well braced and rigid themselves, it is necessary to anchor and brace them to the supporting walls in order to obtain a rigid building. Commercial anchors, plumber's strap or wooden anchors should be used at each truss. Two or more will be needed for trusses installed on 8 ft (2.4 m) spacing over long spans. Knee braces may need to be installed between studs or posts and the truss every 8 to 12 ft (2.4 to 3.6 m) along a wall unless a diaphragm design or partitions make them unnecessary. Diaphragm construction is discussed in the chapter on building framing.

Truss Installation

Trusses should be handled carefully during erection. Large trusses are very fragile and easily damaged by mishandling during transport or erection. In particular, excessive lateral bending should be avoided. Truss members are easily damaged when bent laterally and joint gussets may be loosened. Strapped bundles of trusses can be handled with less potential damage. It is best to leave the trusses bundled until they are needed.

Short trusses, up to about 40 ft (12 m), normally can be erected by hand. Larger trusses should be lifted with a crane or forklift using a sling and/or a spreader bar. The truss should not be lifted from only the peak.

Trusses should be anchored to the supporting wall and cross braced as soon as they are placed. They should not be erected during a heavy wind. While a complete, well-designed roof system will withstand high winds, one or a few trusses can easily be blown over causing damage or personal injury.

Problems

9.1. A 20 ft (6.1 m) wide building has a gable roof with a 5:12 slope. Find the length of the rafter to the nearest 1/8 in. (5 mm). Determine the seat and ridge cut angles to the nearest tenth of a degree.

9.2. A gable roof building has a one-quarter pitch and is 24 ft (7.3 m) wide. The rafters are spaced 18 in. (450 mm) o.c. and are subject to the following vertical loads.

(a) Snow and wind 28 psf (137 kg/m^2).

(b) Roofing 200 lb/square (9.8 kg/m^2).

(c) Roof decking 2 psf (9.8 kg/m^2).

(d) Use 0.89 of the total to obtain a load normal to the rafter.

1. Find the length of the rafter to the nearest 1/8 in. (5 mm).

2. Assume the rafter and tail are to be cut from the next even-numbered length. Choose a grade and size that will be adequate.

9.3. Assuming the same 24 ft (7.3 m) wide one-quarter pitch gable roof building and the same load conditions, find a safe truss spacing using 2 × 6 in. (38 × 140 mm) lumber with the following specifications:

(a) Safe fiber stress in bending (f_b) = 1,500 psi (10 355 kPa).

(b) Safe fiber stress in compression (f_c) = 1,000 psi (6890 kPa).

(c) Modulus of Elasticity (E) = 1,500,000 psi (10.3 × 106 kPa).

(d) Using figure 9.9 find the forces involved in members one and five.

(e) Assume that P acts vertically and that the uniform normal load causing a bending force in member one is 0.89 of the vertical load.

10 Selection of Structural Members

The process of structural design involves the selection of components which will withstand the stresses induced by applied loads. Economical design requires that the least costly, normally the smallest, members that will safely provide the needed strength be utilized. Selecting the appropriate structural member requires that the effects of applied loads first be analyzed.

The intent of this chapter is to give the reader a rudimentary understanding of the concepts of stress analysis. A limited number of factors involved in the selection of structural members will be discussed. It should be realized that dimensions, spacing, materials, and methods of loading can be varied in order to achieve a safe and economical design. While simple analysis may be used to select small, lightly loaded members, efficient design requires careful and often complex analyses. The methods of analysis given in this chapter are not complete and are not intended to make the reader an engineer or stress analyst.

Building frame members may be classified based on the way in which the primary stresses act. The two general classifications are beams and columns. The stresses on a member, however, often require that it be considered as both a beam and a column.

A beam is a structural member which is subjected to loads that are primarily perpendicular to the long axis. Beams such as floor joists are ordinarily installed horizontally, but they may be inclined as in the case of a rafter, or installed as a wall stud in a vertical position where they are subjected to the lateral load of stored grain.

A column is a structural member which is subjected to loads that are primarily parallel to the long axis. Ordinarily, columns are installed vertically, such as a post under a beam. However, members subjected to similar compressive or tensile forces are also found at various angles in trusses and other structures.

Application of loads to structural members results in the development of fiber stress. Excessive fiber stress will result in failure (breaking) of the member. Beams and columns are subject to failure in any one or more of several ways, depending on the material and the type of loading. The stress that can be developed without danger of failure is called safe (or allowable) fiber stress and is measured in pounds per square inch (kPa). It is not always possible to predict exactly what stress level will result in failure, thus a member may occasionally fail at a stress level less than the safe value. Proper selection of members will result in a low probability of failure.

Loads and Reactions

Structural members are subjected to loads from snow, wind, stored products, installed equipment, and other building components. Forces that resist applied loads are called *reactions*. Structural members in which the sum of the reactions just balance the loads are in static equilibrium.

Structural systems in a building can be very complex and difficult to analyze; however, some simplifying assumptions are often useful. Beams are assumed to be planar members, that is, all forces act in a single plane. The forces need not be parallel or concurrent, i.e., passing through a common point.

Forces are *vectors* which means that they are defined by both a direction and a magnitude. Forces may act in any direction; however, it is convenient to resolve each force into vertical (y) and horizontal (x) components. The state of equilibrium then requires that the sum of the vertical components and the sum of the horizontal components each equals zero.

Forces acting on a member tend to cause rotation about any point other than the point through which they act. Such a rotation force is called a *moment*. The moment is due to a force acting at a perpendicular distance from the axis.

When a beam remains stationary and is in equilibrium, the sum of all the horizontal forces acting on the beam is equal to zero, the sum of all the vertical forces is equal to zero, and the sum of all the moments acting about a point is equal to zero. Any of the following combinations of equations expresses a state of equilibrium:

$$\sum F_x = 0 \qquad \sum F_x = 0 \qquad \sum F_y = 0 \qquad \sum M_a = 0$$

$$\sum F_y = 0 \quad \text{or} \quad \sum M_a = 0 \quad \text{or} \quad \sum M_a = 0 \quad \text{or} \quad \sum M_b = 0$$

$$\sum M_a = 0 \qquad \sum M_b = 0 \qquad \sum M_b = 0 \qquad \sum M_c = 0$$

For the purpose of making a stress analysis, upward forces, forces to the right, and clockwise moments will be considered positive; downward forces, forces to the left, and counterclockwise moments will be considered negative.

An example will illustrate the resolution of an angled force into the x and y components and the determination of the reactions (fig. 10.1). The 141 N forces is first resolved into x and y components by multiplying by the cosine and sine of the angle:

$$\cos 45° \times 141 = 100 \text{ N}$$

$$\sin 45° \times 141 = 100 \text{ N}$$

then,

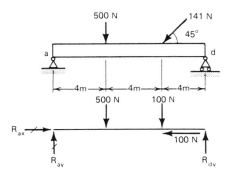

Figure 10.1. Force reactions.

$$\sum F_x = 0:\ R_{ax} = 100;\ R_{ax} = 100\,N$$

$$\sum M_d = 0:\ \left(R_{ay} \times 12\right) - \left(500 \times 8\right) - \left(100 \times 4\right) = 0$$

$$R_{ay} = \left(4{,}000 + 400\right) / 12 = 366.67\,N$$

$$\sum M_a = 0:\ \left(500 \times 4\right) + \left(100 \times 8\right) - \left(R_{dy} \times 12\right) = 0$$

$$R_{dy} = \left(2{,}000 + 800\right) / 12 = 233.3\,N$$

$$\sum F_y = 0:\ 366.7 - 500 - 100 + 233.3 = 0$$

Occasionally members may have some special configuration or connection which will require equations of condition. For example, in figure 10.2, assuming that the two members are connected by a frictionless hinge at b, the equation of condition would indicate that $\Sigma M_b = 0$. This is true regardless of whether the moment is determined from the left or the right.

$$\sum M_a = 0:\ \left(200 \times 4\right) + \left(300 \times 15\right) - \left(R_{cy} \times 20\right) = 0$$

$$R_{cy} = \left(800 + 4{,}500\right) / 20 = 265\,N$$

$$\sum M_c = 0:\ \left(R_{ay} \times 20\right) - \left(200 \times 16\right) - \left(300 \times 5\right) = 0$$

$$R_{ay} = \left(3{,}200 + 1{,}500\right) / 20 = 235\,N$$

$$\sum F_y = 0:\ 235 - 200 - 300 + 265 = 0$$

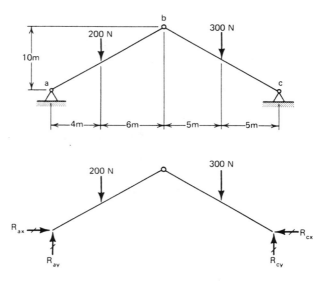

Figure 10.2. Equation of condition.

$$\sum M_b = 0: \ (235 \times 10) - (200 \times 6) - (R_{ax} \times 10) = 0$$

$$R_{ax} = (2{,}350 - 1{,}200) / 10 = 115\,N$$

$$\sum M_b = 0: \ (R_{cx} \times 10) + (300 \times 5) - (265 \times 10) = 0$$

$$R_{cx} - (-1{,}500 + 2{,}650) / 10 = 115\,N$$

In analyzing the stress in objects, it is often convenient to use free-body diagrams. A free-body diagram shows all of the forces acting on a body or member. If a body as a whole is in equilibrium, then it may be assumed that a cut at any desired point in the body will result in two members that are still in equilibrium. The solution for maximum bending moment using figure 10.3 will illustrate the use of free-body diagrams.

Maximum Bending Moment

The external forces acting on a beam that tend to bend or break that beam produce a bending moment. Although the magnitude of the moment varies throughout the length of the beam, it is the maximum bending moment (BM) that must be considered in designing a beam to safely resist the bending forces to which it is subjected. The steps in finding the maximum bending moment include:

• Determining the reactions at the supports.
• Drawing a shear diagram to locate the maximum bending moment.
• Calculating the maximum bending moment.

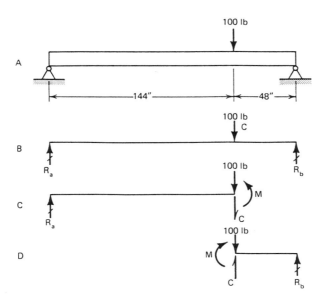

Figure 10.3. Free-body diagrams.

Having determined the reactions described above, the shear diagrams may be drawn. The diagram consists of a base line which represents both the length of the beam and the axis of zero shear. The vertical forces are represented by the displacement of the shear line from the zero axis. The shear force at any point is determined by the algebraic sum of all of the forces to the left of that point. Starting at the left end, the reactions and load forces are drawn in proper direction and magnitude. The point at which the shear line crossed the zero axis will indicate the point on the length of the beam at which the maximum moment occurs. The bending moment is then calculated for that location. Referring to figure 10.3B the reactions at either end of the beam may be found as follows:

$$\sum M_a = 0: (-100 \text{ lb} \times 144 \text{ in.}) + (R_b \times 192 \text{ in.}) = 0$$

$$[-45 \text{ kg} \times 3.66 \text{ m}] + [R_b \times 4.88 \text{ m}] = 0$$

$$R_b = 14,400/192$$

$$R_b = 75 \text{ lb } (or \text{ } 34 \text{ kg})$$

$$\sum M_b = 0: [-100 \text{ lb } (\text{-}48 \text{ in.})] - [R_a (-192 \text{ in.})] = 0$$

$$[-45 \text{ kg } (-1.22 \text{ m})] - [R_a (-4.88 \text{ m})] = 0$$

$$R_a = 4,800/192$$

$$R_a = 25 \text{ lb } (or \text{ } 11 \text{ kg})$$

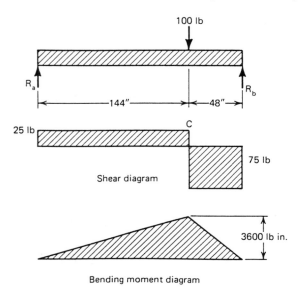

Figure 10.4. Shear and bending moment diagram.

Next, the shear diagram is constructed starting with the 25 lb (11 kg) reaction at the left end (fig. 10.4). Since that is a concentrated force and there are no other forces between it and the 100 lb (45 kg) load, the shear is represented by a horizontal line. At the point of the 100 lb (45 kg) load force, the shear line drops vertically to 75 lb (34 kg) below the axis. From there it is horizontal to the right end. The 75 lb (34 kg) reaction returns vertically to the zero axis. The fact that the shear line terminates at the zero axis is a check on the accuracy of the line. The shear line crosses the zero axis 144 in. (3.66 m) from the left end. This indicates the location of the maximum bending moment.

The bending moment around the point of zero shear (C) may be determined from either end of the beam. Usually the side with the fewest forces is chosen for simplicity. Using figure 10.3C:

$$\sum M_C \text{ (left)} = BM = 25 \text{ lb} \left(-144 \text{ in.}\right) = -3{,}600 \text{ lb-in.} \left(41.5 \text{ kg-m}\right)$$

As a check, the moment around point C from the right end may be calculated. Using figure 10.3D:

$$\sum M_C \text{ (right)} = BM = 75 \text{ lb} \times 48 \text{ in.} = 3{,}600 \text{ lb-in.}$$

The sum of all of the moments around point C is equal to zero.

$$\sum M_c = \left(25 \times 144\right) - \left(75 \times 48\right) = 0$$

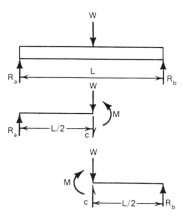

Figure 10.5. Free-body diagram.

The maximum bending moment for the beam is determined in pound-in. (kg-m). The beam cross-section dimensions are in inches and the strength characteristics of the beam material are in pounds per square inch. The corresponding SI units are newtons, meters, and pascals.

Bending moment equations may be derived from the equation used in analyzing the free-body diagrams. In figure 10.5, a simple beam with a load concentrated at the center is shown. The bending moment equations may be derived as follows:

$$M_c = R_b \times L/2$$

$$\text{however, } R_b = W/2$$

$$\text{therefore, } M_c = W/2 \times L/2$$

The bending moment is WL/4. Similar derivations, although often much more complex, may be made for beams with many combinations of support and loading.

When designing the beams for agricultural buildings, it is often necessary to make an assumption about the type of loading to which a beam will be subjected. In figure 10.6, the bending moment equations are given for seven commonly assumed situations.

Types of Fiber Stress

Beams and columns are subject to failure in one or more ways depending on the material from which they are made and the type of loading to which they are subjected. The unit force within a body which tends to resist deformation is called *stress*. It may be tensile, compressive, shearing or flexural. Structural members should be selected to result in an actual stress less than the design value. The allowable or safe fiber stress of a material in pounds per square inch (psi; kPa) is a measure of the strength characteristics of the material that resists failure in each of the following ways:

Beam and Loading	Diagrams	Maximum Shear (V) and Bending Moment (BM)	Reactions and Maximum Deflection
Cantilever Beam, Load Concentrated at the Unsupported End		$V_{max} = -W$	$R = W$
		$BM_{max} = WL$	$D = WL^3/3EI$
Cantilever Beam, Load Uniformly Distributed		$V_{max} = -W$	$R = W$
		$BM_{max} = WL/2$	$D = WL^3/8EI$
Simple Beam, Load Concentrated at the Center		$V_{max} = \pm W/2$	$R_1 = R_2 = W/2$
		$BM_{max} = WL/4$	$D = WL^3/48\,EI$

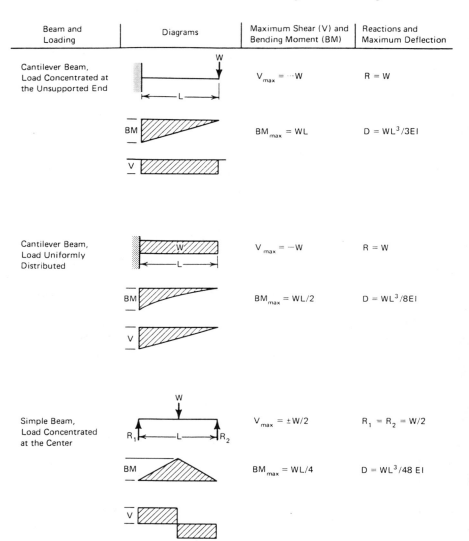

Figure 10.6. Beam equations.

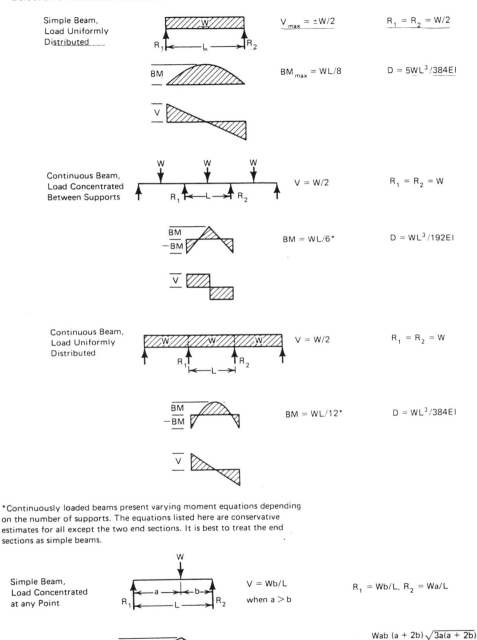

Simple Beam,
Load Uniformly
Distributed

$V_{max} = \pm W/2$

$R_1 = R_2 = W/2$

$BM_{max} = WL/8$

$D = 5WL^3/384EI$

Continuous Beam,
Load Concentrated
Between Supports

$V = W/2$

$R_1 = R_2 = W$

$BM = WL/6^*$

$D = WL^3/192EI$

Continuous Beam,
Load Uniformly
Distributed

$V = W/2$

$R_1 = R_2 = W$

$BM = WL/12^*$

$D = WL^3/384EI$

*Continuously loaded beams present varying moment equations depending
on the number of supports. The equations listed here are conservative
estimates for all except the two end sections. It is best to treat the end
sections as simple beams.

Simple Beam,
Load Concentrated
at any Point

$V = Wb/L$

when $a > b$

$R_1 = Wb/L, R_2 = Wa/L$

$BM = Wab/L$

$$D = \frac{Wab\,(a + 2b)\sqrt{3a(a + 2b)}}{27\,EIL}$$

Figure 10.6. *continued* .

1. Fiber stress in bending is the result of loading that tends to cause bending or breaking of a beam. In most cases, this is the critical stress factor on beams in farm buildings.
2. Fiber stress in horizontal shear is the result of loading that tends to cause parallel fibers to slip in relation to each other, much as slipping would occur between a number of thin wooden strips laid one on top of another, supported at the ends, and loaded at the center. Horizontal shear is most significant in short, very heavily loaded beams.
3. Fiber stress in tension occurs when forces tend to pull fibers apart. This is likely to be critical in the bottom chord of a truss.
4. Fiber stress in compression perpendicular-to-grain occurs at points of concentrated loading where the force tends to crush across the grain. This is most likely to be critical at points where beams or joists are supported.
5. Fiber stress in compression parallel-to-grain occurs at the ends of members subjected to column loading and tends to crush parallel with the grain. This is most likely to occur when heavily loaded short columns are bearing against a metal plate.
6. Modulus of Elasticity is a measure of the stiffness of a material found by the stress (psi; kPa) divided by strain (in./in.; mm/mm) within the elastic limit of a material. The unit of modulus of elasticity is psi (kPa).

The variation in values results from different qualities, species, and materials. Some representative values for safe fiber stress are shown in table 10-1.

Section Modulus

The ability of a beam to resist a bending moment depends not only on its safe fiber stress, but also on its section modulus (S) which is based on shape, dimensions, and position of installation. For a rectangular cross-section beam the equation is $S = 1/6$ (bd^2), where b is the breadth and d is the depth as installed (table 10-2). Other section moduli may be found in figure 10.7 or an engineering handbook.

Note that the section modulus of a rectangular beam, and thus its carrying capacity, is greatly affected by whether it is installed flat or on edge. For example, a 2 × 8 in. member installed on edge has $S = 1.5 \times 7.252/6 = 13.1$ in.^{3} [38 × 1842/6 = 214 000 mm^3], while it is only $7.25 \times 1.52 = 2.72$ in.^{3} [184 × 382/6 = 44 300 mm^3] when installed in a flat position.

Selection of Beam Size

Beam design involves the selection of a member (1) that is large enough to resist the maximum bending stress imposed, (2) that will not be crushed at the support (or at point of concentrated loads), (3) that will not fail in horizontal shear, and (4) that will not deflect excessively.

The allowable stress that is used in beam design is based on the lumber species and grade and must be adjusted for the following factors: (1) duration of load; (2) in-service moisture conditions; (3) preservative treatments, if used, and abnormal tempera-

Table 10-1. Safe bending loads for wood beams

The following values are for simple beams with a uniform load. You may convert to other types of beams and loadings as follows:

Cantilever, concentrated load	- table total lb × 1/8
Cantilever, distributed load	- table lb/ft × 1/4
Simple, concentrated load	- table total lb × 1/2
Simple, distributed load	- table lb/ft × 1
Continuous, concentrated load	- table total lb × 3/4
Continuous, distributed load	- table lb/ft × 1 1/2

			Safe Fiber Stress in Bending					

	Member Size		1,000 psi No. 1 Douglas Fir-Larch		1,200 psi No. 2 Southern Pine (2 × 8 in.)		1,500 psi No. 1 Southern Pine (2 × 8 in.)	
Span (ft)	Size	(bd ft)	(lb/ft)	Total (lb)	(lb/ft)	Total (lb)	(lb/ft)	Total (lb)
4	2 × 4	2.7	128	510	154	612	192	765
6	2 × 4	4	57	341	68	409	86	511
	2 × 6	6	140	840	168	1010	210	1260
8	2 × 4	5.3	32	255	38	306	48	382
	2 × 6	8	79	630	95	756	118	945
	2 × 8	10.7	136	1090	163	1310	204	1635
10	2 × 4	6.7	20	204	24	245	30	306
	2 × 6	10	51	505	61	606	77	756
	2 × 8	13.3	87	873	105	1050	130	1310
	2 × 10	16.7	143	1427	172	1710	214	2140
12	2 × 4	8	14	170	17	210	21	255
	2 × 6	12	35	420	42	504	52	630
	2 × 8	16	61	727	73	872	92	1090
	2 × 10	20	99	1190	119	1430	148	1785
	2 × 12	24	147	1760	177	2230	220	2640
14	2 × 6	14	26	360	31	432	39	540
	2 × 8	18.7	45	624	54	748	67	935
	2 × 10	23.3	73	1020	88	1222	110	1530
	2 × 12	28	107	1500	129	1800	168	2250
16	2 × 6	16	20	317	24	380	30	475
	2 × 8	21.3	34	546	41	655	51	820
	2 × 10	26.7	56	892	67	1070	84	1344
	2 × 12	32	83	1320	100	1585	125	1980
	2 × 14	37.3	114	1830	137	2195	171	2740
18	2 × 8	24	27	485	32	582	41	726
	2 × 10	30	44	793	53	950	66	1337
	2 × 12	36	65	1172	78	1405	98	1760
	2 × 14	43	90	1625	108	1950	135	2435

ture conditions; and (4) lateral stability considerations. Stress design values before adjustments are given in tables 10-3 and 10-4.

Table 10-2. Lumber dimension properties

Size	b* (in.)	d (in.)	A (in.²)	I (in.⁴)	S (in.³)	B (Equiv.)† (in.)	D (Equiv.) (in.)
2 × 4	1.5	3.50	5.250	5.359	3.063		
2 × 6	1.5	5.50	8.250	20.797	7.563		
2 × 8	1.5	7.25	10.875	47.635	13.141		
2 × 10	1.5	9.25	13.875	98.932	21.391		
2 × 12	1.5	11.25	16.875	177.979	31.641		
4 + 4‡	1.5	7.00	10.500	10.718	6.126	3.00	3.50
4 + 6	1.5	9.00	13.500	25.062	10.626	2.86	4.72
6 + 6	1.5	11.00	16.500	41.594	15.126	3.00	5.50

* b, d, I, and S are defined in figure 10.7 for a rectangular section. A = cross-sectional area.
† B (equiv.) and D (equiv.) were calculated to give the same A and S as the sum of the stacked members. The tabulated I was calculated from the equivalent B and D.
‡ Stacked 2 × 4s.

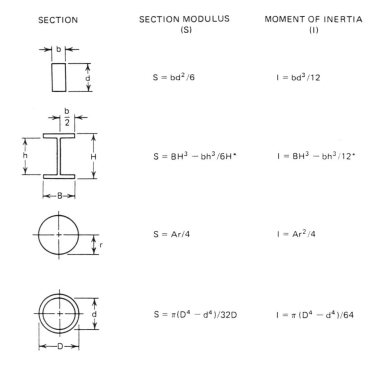

SECTION	SECTION MODULUS (S)	MOMENT OF INERTIA (I)
	$S = bd^2/6$	$I = bd^3/12$
	$S = BH^3 - bh^3/6H^*$	$I = BH^3 - bh^3/12^*$
	$S = Ar/4$	$I = Ar^2/4$
	$S = \pi(D^4 - d^4)/32D$	$I = \pi(D^4 - d^4)/64$

*Values for steel I beams will be found in a steel handbook. These equations provide an approximation.

Figure 10.7. Section modulus and moment of inertia for some common shapes.

Table 10-3. Base stress design values for visually graded dimension lumber* (psi)

Species & Grade	Bending	Tension Parallel to Grain	Shear Parallel to Grain	Compression Perpendicular to Grain	Compression Parallel to Grain	Modulus of Elasticity
Douglas Fir-Larch						
Select struct	1,450	1,000	95	625	1,700	1,900,000
No. 1	1,000	775	95	625	1,450	1,700,000
No. 2	875	675	95	625	1,300	1,600,000
No. 3	500	575	95	625	750	1,400,000
Stud	675	325	95	625	825	1,400,000
Construction	1,000	650	95	625	1,600	1,500,000
Standard	550	375	95	625	1,350	1,400,000
Utility	275	175	95	625	875	1,300,000
Hem-Fir						
Select struct	1,400	900	75	405	1,500	1,600,000
No. 1	950	600	75	405	1,300	1,500,000
No. 2	850	500	75	405	1,250	1,300,000
No. 3	500	300	75	405	725	1,200,000
Stud	675	400	75	405	800	1,200,000
Construction	975	575	75	405	1,500	1,300,000
Standard	550	325	75	405	1,300	1,200,000
Utility	250	150	75	405	850	1,100,000
Spruce-Pine-Fir						
Select struct	1,250	675	70	425	1,400	1,500,000
No. 1	875	425	70	425	1,100	1,400,000
No. 3	500	250	70	425	625	1,200,000
Stud	675	325	70	425	675	1,200,000
Construction	975	475	70	425	1,350	1,300,000
Standard	550	275	70	425	1,100	1,200,000
Utility	250	125	70	425	725	1,100,000
Western Woods						
Select struct	875	400	70	335	1,050	1,200,000
No. 1	650	300	70	335	925	1,100,000
No. 2	650	275	70	335	875	1,000,000
No. 3	375	175	70	335	500	900,000
Stud	500	225	70	335	550	900,000
Construction	725	325	70	335	1,050	1,000,000
Standard	400	175	70	335	900	900,000
Utility	200	75	70	335	600	800,000
White Oak						
Select struct	1,200	700	110	800	1,100	1,100,000
No. 1	875	500	110	800	900	1,000,000
No. 2	850	500	110	800	700	900,000
No. 3	475	275	110	800	400	800,000
Stud	650	375	110	800	450	800,000
Construction	950	550	110	800	925	900,000
Standard	525	325	110	800	725	800,000
Utility	250	150	110	800	425	800,000
Southern Pine, 2 in. × 6 in.						
Select Struct	2,550	1,400	90	565	2,000	1,800,000
No. 1	1,650	900	90	565	1,750	1,700,000
No. 2	1,250	725	90	565	1,600	1,600,000
No. 3	750	425	90	565	925	1,400,000
Stud	775	425	90	565	925	1,400,000

*Values are based on 4 in. nominal depth Construction, Standard, or Utility grade; 12 in. depth Select Structural, no. 1, no. 2, or no. 3; and 6 in. nominal stud grade lumber. The allowable bending stress values may be increased 15% for repetitive members (similar members in contact or spaced not more than 24 in. apart).

Safe Bending Load

A *moment* is a force tending to cause rotation. When a beam that is supported at one or more places is loaded so as to produce a tendency for bending, it is called a *bending moment*. Bending moments are measured in in.-lb (N-m). The bending moment on a beam depends on how it is loaded and supported. Some examples of the bending moments found in three types of beams subjected to either a load concentrated at the center or to a load uniformly distributed over the length of the beam are shown in figure 10.6.

The ability of a beam to resist a bending moment depends on its safe fiber stress (F_b) and its dimensions as installed. In its simplest form, the safe bending moment for a beam is found by $BM_s = F_b S$. The allowable stress value may need to be adjusted for (1) duration of load, (2) moisture conditions, (3) chemical treatments, (4) elevated temperature, and/or (5) lateral stability. A reduction of allowable stress will also be required for beams with depths greater than 12 in. (300 mm). The lateral stability factor relates to bracing the compression edge of the beam. If the compression edge is braced continuously or with closely spaced secondary structural members, no adjustment is necessary.

The actual bending moment will be related to the load (W) and the beam length (L) in accordance with the appropriate equation from figure 10.6. Knowing the safe bending moment (BM_s), the safe loading or safe length may be determined. If the actual bending moment has been determined, the required section modulus for the beam may be found for a given fiber stress. The value of the fiber stress depends on the lumber used. The member selected should have a section modulus equal to or greater than the value necessary to satisfy the following:

$$\frac{M}{F_b} \le S \qquad (10.1)$$

Example 10.1

Given a simple beam, 10 ft long, 2 × 6 in., with a safe fiber stress of 1,200 psi in bending, find the safe uniformly distributed load for this beam. BM for a simple beam and uniform load is:

$$BM = WL/8$$

thus, $WL/8 = F_b S$

$$S = bd^2/6 = 1.5 \text{ in.} \times (5.5 \text{ in.})^2/6 = 7.56 \text{ in.}^3$$

$$F_b S = 1,200 \text{ psi} \times 7.56 \text{ in.}^3 = 9,072 \text{ in.-lb} = WL/8$$

$$WL = 9,072 \times 8 = 72,576 \text{ in.-lb}$$

$$L = 10 \text{ ft} \times 12 \text{ in.} = 120 \text{ in.}$$

$$W = 72,576/L = 72,576 \text{ in.-lb}/120 \text{ in.}$$

$$W = 605 \text{ lb total load}$$

Note that it is essential to use actual and not nominal sizes when calculating section modulus. Had the nominal size been used in the above example, the section modulus would have been 12 and the safe load 96 lb/ft.

Although it is necessary to use equations to design beams involving unusual shapes or loadings, in many cases rectangular beams with symmetrical loading are involved. Table 10-1 may be used as a simplified means of designing a safe beam. The values given in the table are for simple beams with a uniformly distributed load. However, conversion to other types of beams and loadings can be accomplished by using the multipliers given with the table. It should also be noted that lumber and grading rules do change, thus a designer must insure that load table values reflect current allowable stress values.

Horizontal Shear

The horizontal shear stress on a beam may be determined with the formula:

$$f_v = \frac{3V}{(2bd)} \qquad (10.2)$$

where

f_v = horizontal shear (psi)

V = maximum vertical shear (for simple beam this is the reaction at a support) (lb)

b = the breadth (in.)

d = the depth of the beam (in.)

Excessive horizontal shear loads usually do not occur except in very short and very heavily loaded beams. Using the same information for the safe bending moment example, note that the horizontal shear is below the allowable stress found in table 10-4.

$$R = W/2 = 605/2 = 302.5 \text{ lb}$$

$$f_v = \frac{3 \times 302.5}{2 \times 1.5 \times 5.5} = 55 \text{ psi}$$

A shear factor may be defined as: $S_f = 2bd/3$ for use in determining the required member size. Note from the above equation that $S_f = V/f_v$. If F_v (the allowable horizontal shear for the species and grade of lumber to be used) is substituted for f_v, then satisfying the following will give the required member size:

$$\frac{V}{F_v} \leq S_f \qquad (10.3)$$

Safe Loads in Compression

The load in compression (both parallel and perpendicular) may be found by dividing the load at a joint by the area of contact at the joint. The value obtained is then

Table 10-4. Stress design values for visually graded timbers (5 × 5 in. and larger) (psi)

Species & Grade	Bending	Tension Parallel to Grain	Shear Parallel to Grain	Compression Perpendicular to Grain	Compression Parallel to Grain	Modulus of Elasticity
Beams and Stringers						
Select Structural						
Douglas fir-Larch	1,600	950	85	625	1,100	1,600,000
Douglas fir-South	1,550	900	85	520	1,000	1,200,000
Eastern hemlock	1,350	925	80	550	950	1,200,000
Eastern spruce	1,450	850	85	555	950	1,200,000
Eastern white pine	1,050	700	65	350	675	1,100,000
Hem-Fir	1,250	725	70	370	900	1,300,000
Mixed oak	1,350	800	80	800	825	1,000,000
Red pine	1,050	625	65	440	725	1,100,000
Redwood	1,400	950	95	650	1,200	1,300,000
Sitka spruce	1,200	675	70	435	825	1,300,000
Southern pine	1,500	1,000	120	375	950	1,500,000
Spruce-Pine-Fir	1,100	650	65	425	775	1,300,000
Western woods	1,050	625	65	335	675	1,100,000
No 2						
Douglas fir-Larch	875	425	85	625	600	1,300,000
Douglas fir-South	825	425	85	520	525	1,000,000
Eastern hemlock	750	375	80	550	550	900,000
Eastern spruce	575	275	65	390	375	1,000,000
Eastern white pine	575	275	65	390	375	1,000,000
Hem-Fir	675	350	70	405	500	1,100,000
Mixed oak	725	375	80	800	450	800,000
Red pine	575	300	65	440	475	900,000
Redwood	975	650	95	650	900	1,100,000
Sitka spruce	650	325	70	435	450	1,000,000
Southern pine	1,100	725	95	375	625	1,400,000
Spruce-Pine-Fir	600	300	65	425	425	1,000,000
Western woods	575	275	60	375	400	1,000,000
Post and Timbers						
Select Structural						
Douglas fir-Larch	1,500	1,000	85	625	1,150	1,600,000
Douglas fir-South	1,400	950	85	520	1,050	1,200,000
Hem-Fir	1,200	800	70	405	975	1,300,000
Mixed oak	1,250	850	80	800	875	1,000,000
Red pine	1,000	675	65	440	775	1,100,000
Spruce-Pine-Fir	1,050	700	65	425	800	1,300,000
Western woods	1,000	675	65	335	700	
No 2						
Douglas fir-Larch	750	475	85	625	700	1,300,000
Douglas fir-South	650	400	85	520	425	1,000,000
Eastern hemlock	600	400	80	550	400	9,000,000
Eastern spruce	450	300	65	350	325	900,000
Eastern white pine	450	300	65	350	325	900,000
Hem-Fir	575	375	70	405	575	1,100,000
Mixed oak	575	400	80	800	350	800,000
Red pine	475	325	65	440	475	900,000
Spruce-Pine-Fir	500	325	65	425	500	1,000,000
Western woods	350	225	65	335	225	900,000

compared to the safe load for the species or material. The required bearing area at a support may be found by solution of:

$$\frac{R}{F_{c\perp}} \leq A \qquad (10.4)$$

where
R   =   reaction load (lb)
$F_{c\perp}$ =   allowable stress perpendicular to the grain (psi)
A   =   l × b
l   =   length of bearing (in.)
b   =   breadth of beam (in.)

The total load on the simple beam in the above example was 605 lb. Since this was a uniformly distributed load, one half of the total would be supported at each end. If the allowable compression perpendicular to the grain, $F_{c\perp}$ = 385 psi, then the required bearing area, A = (605 lb/2) / 385 psi = 0.8 in.2, and a bearing length of l = A/b = 0.8 in. / 1.5 in. = 0.5 in., would be satisfactory for the 2 × 6 in.

Safe Loads in Tension

While safe loads in tension on wooden members are often limited by the connectors used, it is also desirable to determine the fiber stress in tension by dividing the load by the cross-sectional area. The stress may then be compared to the safe values.

Deflection in Members

While most agricultural buildings are designed to be safe from failure due to expected loading, there are cases, such as farm homes, where maximum deflection (elastic bending) of members becomes an additional factor. Excessive deflection can cause uneven floors, cracks in walls and ceiling panels, and a feeling of excessive vibration from active loads on a floor.

Two factors that are used in determining deflection are modulus of elasticity and moment of inertia. The modulus of elasticity (E) is a measure of the stiffness of the material (table 10-5). It is the ratio of the stress, psi (Pa), divided by the strain (deformation), in./in. (m/m), within the elastic limit of that material. The units of the modulus of elasticity are psi (MPa or GPa).

The moment of inertia (I) is a measure of the effect of the cross-sectional shape on a beam's resistance to a bending moment. The magnitude of the moment also varies with the cross-sectional area of the beam. The usual units are in.^{4} (m^4).

A number of methods for computing deflection may be found in structural analysis texts. In view of the relatively few cases of agricultural structures in which deflection must be considered, the study of deflection will be limited to inclusion of the formulas for the seven beams shown in figure 10.6.

When deflection criteria is used, the estimated maximum deflection is calculated using the design formula (fig. 10.6) and comparing this to some limiting value pre-

Table 10-5. Moduli of elasticity for wood

Species of Wood	Dry 10^6 psi (GPa)	Wet 10^6 psi (GPa)
Hardwoods		
Ash, white	1.44 (9.93)	1.74 (12.00)
Aspen, quaking	0.86 (5.93)	1.18 (8.14)
Beech, American	1.38 (9.52)	1.72 (11.86)
Birch, yellow	1.50 (10.34)	2.01 (13.86)
Cottonwood, black	1.08 (7.45)	1.27 (8.76)
Elm, American	1.11 (7.65)	1.34 (9.24)
Maple, sugar	1.55 (10.69)	1.83 (12.62)
Oak, red	1.35 (9.31)	1.82 (12.55)
Oak, white	1.25 (9.62)	1.78 (12.27)
Walnut, black	1.42 (9.79)	1.68 (11.58)
Softwoods		
Cedar, northern white	0.64 (4.41)	0.80 (5.52)
Cedar, red western	0.94 (6.48)	1.11 (7.65)
Douglas fir, coast	1.56 (10.76)	1.95 (13.45)
Douglas fir, south	1.16 (8.00)	1.49 (10.27)
Hemlock, eastern	1.07 (7.38)	1.20 (8.27)
Hemlock, western	1.31 (9.03)	1.64 (11.31)
Larch	0.96 (6.61)	1.87 (12.89)
Pine, eastern white	0.99 (6.83)	1.24 (8.56)
Pine, western white	1.19 (8.21)	1.46 (10.07)
Redwood	0.96 (6.62)	1.10 (7.59)
Spruce, Sitka	1.23 (8.48)	1.57 (9.83)

scribed by code, design standard or the owner's desires. The estimated deflection may be based on live loads only or live loads plus dead loads. Deflection limits are given in terms of some fraction of the beam length (L). The following are examples of typical deflection limits:

Use classification	Live load only	Live plus dead load
Industrial roof beams	L/180	L/120
Plaster ceiling	L/360	L/240
Floor beam (ordinary)	L/360	L/240
Floor joist (stiff)	L/480	L/360

Lateral Stability

Beams that are not braced along the top may may fail by buckling of the compression edge. The lateral stability to prevent this failure may be provided by floor or roof sheathing attached directly to the top of the beam. Closely spaced, secondary framing such as joist on a beam will also provide adequate stability. When lateral support of the compression edge does not exist or is inadequate, the allowable bending stress should be adjusted. A number of factors determine the amount of reduction in the allowable stress and will not be discussed further except to note that the closer the lateral bracing of the compression edge, the less the reduction.

Example 10.2

A 20 ft (6.2 m) bridge beam is supporting a concentrated load of 1,400 lb (635 kg) at the midpoint. What is the maximum bending moment?

$M = WL/4$

$\quad = 1,400 \text{ lb} \times 20 \text{ ft}/4$

$\quad = 7,000 \text{ lb-ft } (985 \text{ kg-m})$

Example 10.3

One end of an I-beam is welded to a vertical column. The I-beam (in a horizontal position) is supporting a hoist 8 ft (2.5 m) from the column. If the hoist load is 2,000 lb (900 kg), what is the maximum bending moment in the I-beam?

$M = WL$

$\quad = 2,000 \text{ lb} \times 8 \text{ ft}$

$\quad = 16,000 \text{ lb-ft } (2\ 259 \text{ kg-m})$

Example 10.4

Compare the cross-sectional area and the section modulus for a full size (R.C.) 2×8 in. (51×203 mm) and a 4×4 in. (102×102 mm).

$$A_{2\times8} = 2 \times 8 \text{ in.} = 16 \text{ in.}^2 \left(10\ 350 \text{ mm}^2\right)$$

$$A_{4\times4} = 4 \times 4 \text{ in.} = 16 \text{ in.}^2 \left(10\ 400 \text{ mm}^2\right)$$

$$S_{2\times8} = 2 \text{ in.} \left(8 \text{ in.}\right)^2/6 = 21.3 \text{ in.}^3 \left(350\ 000 \text{ mm}^3\right)$$

$$S_{4\times4} = 4 \text{ in.} \left(4 \text{ in.}\right)^2/6 = 10.7 \text{ in.}^3 \left(177\ 000 \text{ mm}^3\right)$$

Example 10.5

What is the allowable bending moment for a select structural Hem-Fir 2×10 in. (38×235 mm)?

$$M = F_b S$$

$$= 1,400 \text{ psi} \times 21.39 \text{ in.}^3$$

$$= 29,950 \text{ lb-in. } (345 \text{ kg-m})$$

Columns

Loads are applied to columns along their long axis and failure will occur because of crushing (compression parallel to the grain) as long as the column doesn't buckle. For columns of any practical length there is a tendency to buckle; long slender columns are more likely to buckle than short ones. Since the relation between column length and thickness affects the method of potential failure, this relationship in the form of a slenderness ratio is used in column design and analysis.

The formulas used for determining the safe loads on solid wood columns are based on pin-end (hinged) conditions. However, they may also be applied to square-end conditions. One of the factors affecting the design of columns is the slenderness ratio (l/d), where (l) is the unsupported length of the column. If the column has intermediate lateral support, such as is shown in figure 10.8, the l/d ratio is the greater of l_1/d_1 or l_2/d_2.

The factors determining the safe load on a column are the cross-section area and the adjusted safe fiber stress for the column. Given these two factors, the following formula may be used:

$$C = F_c'A \tag{10.5}$$

where

C = total safe axial load for the column (lb)
A = cross-section area (in.^{2})
F_c' = adjusted safe fiber stress (psi)

The safe fiber stress for the species in compression parallel with the grain (F_c) is adjusted for stability (slenderness), duration of loading, size of member, and conditions of use (moisture and/or temperature).

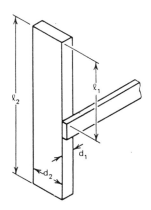

Figure 10.8. Slenderness ratio.

$$F_c' = (F_c^*)(C_p) \qquad (10.6)$$

$$F_c^* = (F_c)(C_D)(C_M)(C_t)(C_F) \qquad (10.7)$$

where

F_c = tabulated compression value parallel to the grain (psi)

C_p = column stability factor (fig. 10.9)

$$C_P = \frac{1 + (F_{cE}/F_c^*)}{2c} - \sqrt{\left[\frac{1 + (F_{cE}/F_c^*)}{2c}\right]^2 - \frac{F_{cE}/F_c^*}{c}} \qquad (10.8)$$

F_{cE} = critical buckling design value for compression members (psi)

$$F_{cE} = \frac{K_{cE} \ E'}{(l_e/d)^2} \qquad (10.9)$$

K_{cE} =   0.3 for visually graded lumber

K_{cE} =   0.418 for MSR lumber

c =   0.8 for sawn lumber

c =   0.85 for round poles

c =   0.9 for glued laminated lumber

l_e =   effective length (unsupported, in.)

d =   depth of member in buckling plane (in.)

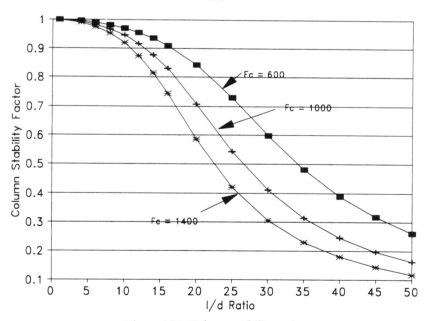

Figure 10.9. Column stability ratio.

F_c' =   design compression value parallel to the grain (psi)

C_D =   load duration factor

C_M =   wet service factor

C_t =   temperature factor

C_F =   size factor for sawn lumber

E' =   allowable modulus of elasticity (psi)

The allowable compressive stress values as modified by the column stability factor are given in figures 10.10 and 10.11. Note that for small (less than 5) l/d ratios the modified value is very nearly the same as the tabulated value. However, at l/d ratios of greater than about 30, the allowable stress is reduced to about 20%. Unbraced wooden columns should not be used with l/d ratios of greater than 50. Table 10-6 gives safe loads for a number of wood columns and table 10-7 has safe loads for some concrete columns.

For normal conditions, the adjustment factors are equal to one. Normal load duration is 10 years, and a 10% reduction should be applied for permanent loads while a 15% increase can be taken for snow loads. The other factors may vary for different species. In general, if the member is installed under high moisture conditions, the allowable load should be reduced by about 20%. No temperature adjustment is necessary unless there will be a sustained exposure to temperatures above 100°F (18°C). The allowable compression fiber stress should be reduced by 30% if temperatures will normally be up to 150°F (60°C). A size factor adjustment is unnecessary unless the member will exceed 12 in. (305 mm) in depth.

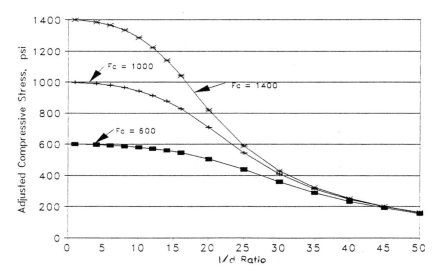

Figure 10.10. Allowable compressive stress vs. l/d ratio.

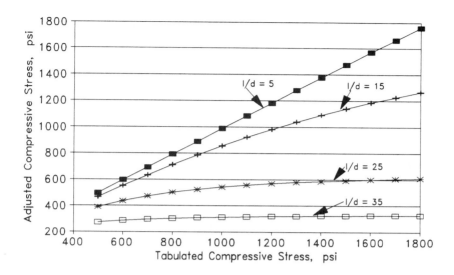

Figure 10.11. Allowable column stress as a function of tabulated values.

Table 10-6. Safe loads on solid wood columns (lb)

Column Length (ft)	Nominal Size (in.)	S4S			Rough Cut		
		End Area	Type A	Type B	End Area	Type A	Type B
4	2 × 4	5.25	2,305	1,633	5.89	3,033	2,150
	4 × 4	12.25	11,932	8,367	13.14	12,837	9,001
6	2 × 4	5.25	1,024	725	5.89	1,349	954
	4 × 4	12.25	10,645	7,473	13.14	11,644	8,176
8	4 × 4	12.25	7,327	5,178	13.14	8,431	5,966
	4 × 6	19.25	11,514	8,142	20.39	13,082	9,257
	6 × 6	30.25	28,193	19,772	31.64	29,678	20,806
10	4 × 4	12.25	4,692	3,320	13.14	5,401	3,824
	4 × 6	19.25	7,373	5,217	20.39	8,380	5,933
	6 × 6	30.25	25,234	17,756	31.64	26,862	18,857
	8 × 8	52.26	49,669	34,847	54.39	51,616	36,168
12	4 × 4	12.25	3,259	2,303	13.14	3,745	2,654
	4 × 6	19.25	5,121	3,619	20.39	5,811	4,119
	6 × 6	30.25	19,874	14,066	31.64	21,705	15,357
	8 × 8	52.26	46,574	32,692	54.39	48,625	34,122

Example 10.6
Given $E = 1,400,000$ psi and $F_c = 1,000$ psi, consider the following two columns:

(a) 3.5 ft × 4 in. × 4 in. (actual size)

$l/d = 3.5$ ft 12 in./ft/4 = 10.5

$F_{cE} = 0.3 \times 1.4\ e6/(10.5)^2 = 3,810$ psi

$$C_P = \frac{1 + \dfrac{3,810}{1,000}}{2\,(0.8)} - \sqrt{\left[\frac{1 + \dfrac{3,810}{1,000}}{2\,(0.8)}\right]^2 - \frac{\dfrac{3,810}{1,000}}{0.8}}$$

$C_P = 0.94$

Assume $C_D = C_M = C_t = C_F = 1.0$

$C = (0.94) \times (1,000\text{ psi}) (4 \times 4\text{ in.}) = 15,000$ lb safe load

(b) 6 ft × 2 in. × 4 in. (actual size)

$l/d = 6$ ft × 12 in./ft/4 = 36

$F_{cE} = 0.3 \times 1.4\ e6/(36)^2 = 324$ psi

$$C_P = \frac{1 + \dfrac{324}{1,000}}{2\,(0.8)} - \sqrt{\left[\frac{1 + \dfrac{324}{1,000}}{2\,(0.8)}\right]^2 - \frac{\dfrac{324}{1,000}}{0.8}}$$

$C_P = 0.30$

Assume $C_D = C_M = C_t = C_F = 1.0$

$C = (0.30)(1,000\text{ psi})(2\text{ in.} \times 4\text{ in.}) = 2,400$ lb safe load

Reinforced Concrete

Because ordinary concrete has very little tensile strength, it is necessary to use steel reinforcing imbedded in that portion of a beam, slab or column that will be subjected to a high tensile force.

Reinforcing Steel

Reinforcing steel consists of either deformed (rough surface) bars or welded wire mesh. Bar sizes and specifications are shown in table 10-8. Reinforcing steel should be clean and free of both rust and oil.

Concrete

Good quality concrete with the correct size aggregate is essential for constructing reinforced structures. Usually not more than 6 gal (21.3 L) of water per sack are used with enough aggregate to produce a medium slump concrete. Maximum aggregate size may be limited by the spacing of the reinforcing bars.

Before a reinforced concrete structure is designed, it is advisable to become

Table 10-7. (a) Safe concentric loads on concrete filled columns

Size			Load (kips)				
			Length (ft)				
Diameter (in.)	Weight (lb/ft)	Section Area (in.²)	6	8	10	12	14
3 1/2	15	9.62	45	40	33	26	—
4	20	12.57	58	53	47	39	30
4 1/2	24	15.90	72	67	61	54	45
5	29	19.65	87	82	76	69	61

Table 10-7. (b) Safe concentric loads on concrete filled columns (SI)

Size			Load (kN)				
			Length (m)				
Diameter (mm)	Weight (kg/m)	Section Area (mm²)	1.83	2.44	3.05	3.66	4.27
89	22.4	6 205	200	178	147	116	—
102	29.8	8 108	258	236	209	173	133
114	35.8	10 256	320	320	271	240	200
127	43.2	12 674	387	387	338	307	271

Table 10-8. Characteristics of round reinforcing bars

No.	Diameter in. (mm)	Area in.² (mm²)	Perimeter in. (mm)	Safe Bonding Stress (psi)‡		
				2,500	3,000	3,500†
2*	0.250 (6.35)	0.05 (32.)	0.786 (19.96)	160	160	160
3	0.375 (9.53)	0.11 (71.)	1.178 (29.92)	500	500	500
4	0.500 (12.70	0.20 (129.)	1.571 (39.90)	480	500	500
5	0.625 (15.88)	0.31 (200.)	1.963 (48.86)	384	421	454
6	0.750 (19.05)	0.44 (284.)	2.356 (59.84)	320	351	379
7	0.875 (22.23)	0.60 (387.)	2.749 (69.82)	274	301	325
8	1.000 (25.40)	0.79 (510.)	3.142 (79.80)	240	263	284

* No. 2 bars are not deformed, all others are deformed.

† psi compressive strength of concrete.

‡ May be converted to kPa by multiplying by 6.89.

acquainted with local code requirements so that all aspects of the design may be in compliance. Although some short-cuts and rules-of-thumb are used in the discussion that follows, the results of calculations should comply with standards established by the American Concrete Institute.

Reinforced concrete may be designed either for working stress or ultimate strength. The values and methods suggested here are for working stress. For example, the three, 28-day compressive strength values given in table 10-9 are about 40% below generally measured compressive strength values for the corresponding water-

Table 10-9. Allowable water-cement ratios and shear stresses
for concrete

Compressive strength	psi	2500	3000	3500
after 28 days	MPa	17.2	20.7	24.1
Non-air-entrained	gal/sack†	7.25	6.5	5.75
concrete	L/sack‡	26	23	20
Air-entrained concrete	gal/sack†	6.25	5.25	4.5
	L/sack‡	22	19	16
Maximum allowable	psi	55	60	65
shear stress*	kPa	379	413	448

* No web reinforcement. With properly combined stirrups and bent
bars, the values may be increased by a factor of 4.5. Consult a handbook for stirrup design.
† Customary sack has a mass of 94 lb.
‡ SI sack has a mass of 40 kg.

cement ratios. A tensile strength of 20,000 psi (138 MPa) is assumed for bars. This is
well below the yield strength of most reinforcing steels. It is best, however, to determine the working stress for the bars to be used for a particular job.

Concrete Beams

Beams have their main reinforcement in one direction in order to resist the bending moment. One-way slabs are similar to shallow beams, although they will carry
cross reinforcing to distribute the effects of temperature changes and nonuniform
loads. They will ordinarily be supported continuously along the sides that are perpendicular to the main reinforcing. Two-way slabs, either square or rectangular in
shape, have reinforcing designed to withstand bending moments in both directions.
They will ordinarily be supported directly by columns. Flat slabs or flat plates are
those that are supported directly by columns. They are also reinforced to withstand a
bending moment in each direction. Both two-way and flat slabs are highly indeter-
minate and require much more sophisticated analysis than one-way slabs or beams.
Only one-way slabs and rectangular beams that are cast integrally with a slab will be
discussed here.

Design Procedure for a One-way Slab or Beam

1. The following rules-of-thumb may be used to determine trial dimensions
for the member:
For floors, d = span/2
For beams, d = span
For floors and beams, D = d + d′
For floors, design based on b = 12 in.
For beams, b = d/w (approximate)
where

d   = depth from top surface to center of main reinforcing bar (in.)
span = length (ft)
b   = breadth of member (in.)
d'   = bottom of member to center of main bar
D   = total depth of member (in.)

Look ahead to procedure Step 4 where a value for d' may be determined from the required covering of the bars.

2. The methods used to determine loads for wood beams and the bending moments equations found in figure 10.8 may be used. Be sure to include the weight of the member. Concrete weighs 150 lb/ft^3.

3. The total cross-section area of reinforcing bars required may be found with:

$$A_S = \frac{BM}{0.86 \, f_s d} \qquad (10.10)$$

where

A_s = cross-section area of bars (in.^{2})
BM   = maximum bending moment
f_s = working tensile stress strength of steel (psi)
d   = depth of slab or beam, top surface to center (in.)

4. Having chosen a size from table 10-9, the required spacing for the bars may be determined. The minimum clearance between bars should be equal to the diameter of the bar, one and one-third the maximum aggregate diameter or 1 in. (25 mm), whichever is largest. The bars should be covered with concrete as follows:

	(To center of bars)
Concrete on ground	31/2 in. (89 mm)
Exposed to weather, > no. 5 bar	2 in. (51 mm)
Exposed to weather, no. 5 bar and up	21/2 in. (64 mm)
Not exposed to weather, slabs and walls	11/2 in. (38 mm)
Not exposed to weather, beams and walls	2 in. (51 mm)

5. Check for shear. Failure in this respect may cause a crack from near the top of the end diagonally toward the bottom of the beam.

$$V = \frac{W}{2}, \quad v = \frac{V}{bd} \qquad (10.11)$$

where

v   = shear in psi of cross-section area
V   = total shear (lb)
W   = total load on member (lb)

Note the maximum allowable shear from table 10-9. If the maximum allowable shear is exceeded, either the member may be made deeper or stirrups may be used to reinforce the web. Consult a reinforced concrete handbook for stirrup design. A girder which is not cast integrally with a slab will require web reinforcement.

6. Check for bonding between bar and concrete. Plain bars must be hooked at the ends.

$$u = \frac{V}{0.86\ E_o d} \qquad (10.12)$$

where

- u = bonding stress in psi of bar surface area
- E_o = sum of the perimeters of the bars (in.)

Note the maximum safe bonding stress in table 10-8. If bonding is inadequate, a larger number of smaller size bars will increase the safe bonding stress.

7. Check for minimum safe bearing area at supports.

$$B = \frac{V}{0.25 f_c} \qquad (10.13)$$

where

- B = safe bearing area (in.^{2})
- f_c = design compressive strength of concrete from table 10-9

8. Bars may be bent and placed as shown in figures 10.12 and 10.13.
9. Cross bars are needed for one-way slabs to distribute temperature and concentrated loads. Use bars of the same size as the main reinforcing and space them five times the member depth or 18 in. (457 mm) whichever is smaller.
10. When bars must be overlapped, the distance in inches should be 12, or three times the size number, whichever is larger. For example, no. 5 should overlap 15 in. Welded wire mesh is overlapped the larger of one mesh or 6 in. (150 mm).

Concrete Columns

Reinforced concrete columns are not often required in agricultural construction unless a high degree of fire resistance is needed. Piers of lengths up to four times the least diameter do not require reinforcing. Columns of lengths up to 11 times the least dimension can be reinforced with a bar in each corner embedded at least 1 in. (38 mm) from each surface. The minimum area for each bar may be found by:

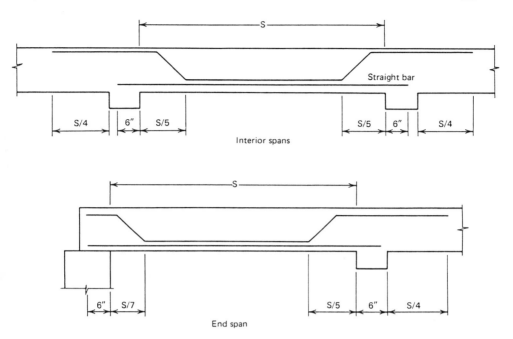

Figure 10.12. Shapes of reinforcing bars.

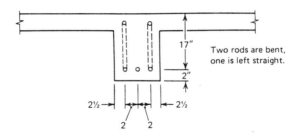

Figure 10.13. Beam cross-section showing location of reinforcing bars.

$$A_s = \frac{0.01a_c}{4} \qquad (10.14)$$

where a_c = cross-section area of column (in.)

The corner bars are held in place with no. 3 bars formed into squares and installed 12 in. (305 mm) on center (fig. 10.14).

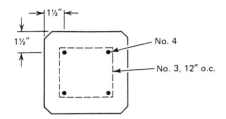

Figure 10.14. Reinforcing in a concrete column.

Example 10.7. Reinforced Concrete Design

Given a floor panel 18 × 24 ft (5.5 × 7.3 m) with a uniform 32 psf dead load
above the floor and a 50 psf live load. The floor will be carried on four,
18 ft beams, giving a 7 ft clear span to each slab. The beams will be carried on girders which in turn are supported by columns 24 ft o.c.

Design   (a) a 1 ft section of the slab
           (b) an 18 ft section of beam (17 ft clear span)
           (c) a column (8 ft unsupported length)

Solution

The panel may be assumed to be an interior section and al members are continuous. The girder may be assumed to weigh 225 plf.

(a)

1. d = span/2 = 7/2 =3.5 in.

   D = d - d' = 3.5 + 1.5 = 5 in.

   b = 12 in.

   weight of slab = (5 × 12 × 12/1728)150 = 0.42 ft^3 × 150 = 62.5 plf

2. w = 32 + 50 + 62.5 = 144.5 plf of slab

3. For an interior span continuous beam:

   W = w × L (ft) = 144.5 × 7 = 1,011.5 lb

   $$BM = \frac{WL}{12} = \frac{1,011.5 \times 84 \text{ (in.)}}{12} = 7,080.5 \text{ in.-lb}$$

4. $A_s = \dfrac{BM}{0.86\ f_s d} = \dfrac{7,080.5}{0.86 \times 20,00 \times 3.5} = 0.118$ in.^{2}

Bar spacing $= \dfrac{bar\ area}{A_s} \times 12 = \left(\dfrac{0.11}{0.118}\right) \times 12$

$$= 11.22 \text{ in. o.c.}$$

$$\left(\text{area of no. 3 bar} = 0.11 \text{ in.}^2\right)$$

5. Aggregate can easily be 1 in. maximum diameter.
6. Check shear stress.

$V = \dfrac{W}{2} = \dfrac{1011.5}{2} = 506$ lb

$v = \dfrac{V}{bd} = \dfrac{506}{12 \times 3.5} = 12.05$ psi

The stress is well below the maximum of 55 shown in table 10-8.
7. Check bonding.

12.11.25 = 1.07 bars/ft

$E_o = 1.07 \times 1.178 = 1.257$ in. for a no. 3 bar

$u = \dfrac{V}{0.86\ E_o d}$

$= \dfrac{506}{0.86 \times 1.257 \times 3.5}$

$= 133.7$ psi

The bonding stress is well under the 500 shown in table 10-8.
8. Bearing area required.

$B = \dfrac{V}{0.25 f_c} = \dfrac{506}{0.25 \times 2,500}$

$= 0.81$ in.^{2}

9. Bar positions are shown in figure 10.12.
10. Temperature and shrinkage bars: Spacing 5d or 18 in., $5 \times 3.5 = 17.5$, choose 18 in. o.c. Use same size (no. 3) bars as used for main reinforcing. Place bars just under main bars.

(b)

1. d = span = 17 in.

    D = d + d' = 17 + 2 = 19 in.

    $b = \dfrac{d}{2} = \dfrac{17}{2} = 8.5$ (use 9 in.)

2. $W = (178 + 1012) \times 17 = 20{,}230$ lb

3. $BM = \dfrac{WL}{12} = \dfrac{20{,}230 \times 17 \times 12}{12} = 343{,}910$ in.-lb

4. $A_s = \dfrac{BM}{0.86 f_s d} = \dfrac{343{,}910}{(0.86 \times 20{,}000 \times 17)} = 1.176$ in.^{2} of bar cross-section

    Choose three, no. 6 bars @ 0.44 in.^{2} = 1.32 in.^{2} total; space bars 2.5, 2, 2, 2.5 in.

5. Coarse aggregate may be 3/4-7/8 in. maximum diameter.

6. Check shear stress.

    $V = \dfrac{W}{2} = \dfrac{20{,}320}{2} = 10{,}115$ lb

    $v = \dfrac{V}{bd} = \dfrac{10{,}115}{9 \times 19} = 59.2$ psi

    This is over the safe stress for 3,000 psi concrete found in table 10-9 Stirrups should be used.

7. Check bonding.

    $E_o = 3 \times 2.356 = 7.068$ in.

    $u = \dfrac{V}{0.86\, E_o d} = \dfrac{10{,}115}{0.86 \times 7.068 \times 17} = 97.9$ psi

    This is well under the 351 psi found in table 10-8.

8. Bearing area required.

    $B = V/0.25 f_c$

    $B = \dfrac{10{,}115}{0.25} \times 2500 = 16.2$ in.^{2} minimum

9. Bar positions are shown in figure 10.12.

(c)

1. The total weight on a column is one-fourth the total weight from each of four 18×24 ft sections. Therefore the total weight from one section may be used.
   weight of 3 slabs and beams $= 3 \times 20{,}230 = 60{,}690$
   weight of 24 ft girder $= 24 \times 225 = 5{,}400$
   $$60{,}690 + 5{,}400 = 66{,}090 \text{ lb}$$

2. Column cross-section area determined by compressive strength
   $$= \frac{66{,}090}{3{,}000} = 22 \text{ in.}^2$$
   $$\sqrt{22} = 4.7 \text{ in.}^2$$

3. Column side determined by maximum slenderness ratio (l/d) of 11
   $96 / 11 = 8.73$ in. / side (use 9 in.)

4. $A_s = \dfrac{0.01 \, a_c}{4} = 0.01 \times \dfrac{81}{4} = \dfrac{0.2 \text{ in.}^2}{\text{bar}}$

5. Use a no. 4 bar (0.2 in.^{2}) in each corner, embedded 1 in. from each side. Use no. 3, 12-in. o.c., to form 6 in. squares to support no. 4 bars.

Problems

10.1.   What is the maximum bending moment in a 14 ft long floor joist? The floor load is 40 psf and the joists are spaced 2 ft o.c.

10.2.   What is the maximum bending moment in a fence post when a 2,000 lb pull is applied to a wire attached 5 ft above the ground? The post is set in concrete.

10.3.   Recalculate the above if the load is applied at one-half foot above the ground.

10.4.   Calculate the section modulus for a full size 4×4 in. post.

10.5.   If the section modulus is 12 in.^{3} and the safe fiber stress in bending is 1,200 psi, what would be the allowable bending moment?

10.6.   For each of the following determine the allowable bending moment:

   (a) No. 1 Douglas fir-Larch 2×4 in.

   (b) No. 3 Douglas fir-Larch 2×4 in.

   (c) No. 3 Douglas fir-Larch 2×8 in.

10.7. Use the computer program, WDESGN, to select the most economical section (member size) for each of the following applications. Assume a member length of 10 ft and use no. 1 Douglas fir. Note the program will give the results of an "interaction equation" in the following format:

Axial Stress Ratio   = _____

Bending Stress Ratio = _____

Sum   = _____

The sum must be less than 1.0, but the closer to 1.0 the more economical.

(a) Compressive (axial) load = 4,000 lb

bending moment applied = 12,000 in.-lb

(b) Tensile (axial) load = 4,000 lb

bending moment applied = 12,000 in.-lb

(c) Compressive (axial) load = 8,000 lb

bending moment applied = 8,000 in.-lb

(d) Tensile (axial) load = 8,000 lb

bending moment applied = 8,000 in.-lb

10.8. Design a concrete slab bridge to span 4 ft (1.2 m) over a drainage ditch. The bridge is 10 ft (3 m) wide and is subjected to maximum loads of 2,000 lb/ft of width (2982 kg·m) at the center of the 4 ft (1.2 m) span.

10.9. What size and grade of joist is required to support a uniform load of 55 lb/ft (82 kg·m) with a 10 ft (3 m) span?

10.10. If the same load was concentrated at the center of the beam, what size and grade would be required?

10.11. Find the total safe uniform load for a simple beam that is 2 × 6 in. (38 × 140 mm) and spans 13 ft (4 m). The piece is set on edge and has a safe fiber stress in bending of 1,300 psi (8957 kPa).

10.12. What size column would be required to support a 14,000 lb (6364 kg) load when the length is 6 ft (1.8 m)? What kind of bearing plate, if any, is needed?

10.13. Repeat problem 10.12 using a load of 5,000 lb (2273 kg) and a length of 12 ft (3.7 m).

11 Plans, Cost Estimating, and Economics

The subject of construction cost estimating will be discussed from the standpoint of the builder or his estimator. However, an understanding of the process of estimating by a buyer can be a helpful aid in choosing which of several contracts to accept. A knowledge of estimating can also help an owner determine the likely cost of a building to be constructed with farm labor. In order to estimate the cost of construction, an estimator must be well acquainted with all building terms and be able to read working plans and specifications.

Building Plans

Successful building construction requires an adequate plan. Drawings and specifications provide the means of communication between the various parties involved in a construction project. All of the information needed by the designer (engineer), and the builder (main contractor), subcontractors, and perhaps some components manufacturers should be available from the plans and specifications. The plans must have sufficient details and dimensions to convey their meaning accurately and without misinterpretation and be understood by all parties involved. While a very simple construction or repair job may be described by simple sketches, any sizeable project needs to have plans prepared by a professional draftsperson.

Although the information could be portrayed in different ways, use of standard drawing practices will make interpretation easier and reduce the chance for error. Building plans or drawings should be identified with a title block which includes the following information: firm name, title of the drawing, drafter, date, sheet number, and possibly scale.

The working drawings for a building may include the following: (1) plot plan or layout, (2) building floor plan, (3) foundation, (4) elevations, (5) construction details and sections, (6) environmental control systems, and (7) structural design.

Specifications ordinarily accompany the drawings to give additional details, list acceptable standards of work, and provide explanations on matters that are not easily shown on drawings. The specifications should include excavation, filling and grading, concrete work, carpentry and millwork, sheetmetal and roofing, painting, and plumbing, electrical, and heating systems.

Different types of drawings may be used, but most common for building plans are *orthographic projections*. The word orthographic is derived from Greek and means right-angle writing. In these drawings the line of sight to a point on an object is at right angles to the plane of the drawing. Typically, separate drawings are used to show different sides of an object.

An *oblique projection* is one form of three-dimensional depiction. The projectors (line of sight) do not form right angles to the plane of the drawing. Isometric (equal measure) drawings have equal angles between the axes, i.e., angle between length and vertical axes and the angle between the width and vertical axes are both 60°. A perspective drawing attempts to depict an object as nearly as possible as one sees it, i.e., the projectors intersect at the viewing point.

Drawings are made to a scale (ratio of the drawing to the actual). This may be expressed as the distance on the drawing that represents one foot for the actual object, i.e., 1/8 in. = 1 ft (10 mm = 1 m). While the scale value may be useful in determining actual dimensions, drawings may be distorted by photocopying resulting in errors. Adequate dimensions should be given on the drawing to allow determination of all significant points and locations without requiring measurement or calculations.

Schedules are used to provide information about repetitive items that would cause clutter if shown for each location used. Examples where schedules are useful include doors, windows, and trim items.

Drawing convention calls for five different line types. A solid, heavy line is used to show visible edges on the object. A medium solid line is used as an extension line to project from a point. Dimension lines are fine solid lines. The center of a circle or radius is shown by the intersection of center lines which are formed by alternating long and short dashes. Hidden lines indicate edges that are not visible from the point of view of the drawing. These are indicated by dashed lines.

Cost Estimating

Almost all building projects, whether new construction or remodeling, require some cost estimating. This may vary from a vague idea of the overall cost for the project to an attempt to predict very precisely all related costs. The approach to estimating will vary with the need. If only a general cost range is needed, such as for preliminary planning, a simplified approximation, unit basis method, should suffice. The unit of measure may be floor area (ft^2 or m^2), volume enclosed (ft^3 or m^3), animals housed (e.g., cow stalls), or product stored (ton, bu, etc.). A detailed estimate which includes all costs for labor, materials, and accessories will normally provide a more accurate estimate and would be desired for sound economical analysis. In order to obtain approval for financing or before agreeing to a contract, a complete estimate may be required. In addition to the costs mentioned above, the expenses for the following need to be included: land, legal fees, architectural and engineering services, bonding, financing, interest, taxes, and contractual services.

It is the estimator's responsibility to read a set of plans and specifications, estimate what materials and labor will be necessary, determine what parts of the job may be subcontracted and what they will cost, estimate an allowance where a definite cost figure is difficult, and determine a contract price including profit and overhead. It is also useful for the estimator to be conversant with code rules pertaining to foundation depths, ceiling heights, window size, and service entrance size, and thus to be able to point out any noncomplying specifications.

The essential parts of an estimate include: materials, labor, construction equipment usage, overhead, profit, and contingency. The estimated cost of items such as land, permits, clearing, excavation, water supply, sewage disposal, and landscaping may also be included as contract items or allowances.

Regardless of the size of the project, it is more important that the estimate be complete than precise. For example, it is not necessary to know exactly how every last stud will be used so that an exact number may be obtained, but it would be very costly indeed to forget to include the studs as a whole. An estimator should be conscious of the danger of errors which may occur by omission, incorrect estimate, rate changes, or events that interfere with work. Following is a list of items in which potential errors may be made: quantity of materials, amount of labor, changes in wage rates, material price changes, overhead costs, equipment breakdown, transportation problems, wastage, bad weather, and delays. And, of course, errors in transcribing, arithmetic, or decimal point location can affect an otherwise good estimate.

Many rules-of-thumb or conventions have been developed that are surprisingly accurate and considerably reduce the time and effort required to make an estimate. These rules take into account cutting waste, the difference between nominal and actual size, pattern matching, and breakage.

Cost vs. Allowances

An estimator will include all items in which the specified materials are relatively standard as a cost, and the builder will supply the labor as well as items on which a subcontractor will give a definite bid price. There is relatively little chance that these two types of cost items will change appreciably during construction.

On the other hand, there are many items on which the estimator simply does not have adequate information to calculate a definite cost. Therefore, an estimated allowance is included and the buyer either pays any extra actual costs or receives a discount if the estimated allowance proves to be too high.

Examples of allowances range all the way from the cost of an excavation where ledge may be encountered to light fixtures or floor coverings which come in a wide range of qualities and prices and are chosen by the customer well after construction has been started.

Estimate Sheets

A work sheet for each type of job should show all of the items, quantities, units, unit prices, and costs or allowances that are needed. Obviously, a work sheet for site clearing and excavation might look quite different from one for the electrical work. Once the work sheets have been completed, a summary sheet should be compiled that might have the format shown in figure 11.1. These sheets allow the estimator or builder to have immediate access to items when discussing them with a buyer.

Job _____ Location _____ Date _____

Work Sheet Title	Item	Subcontractor, Remarks	Cost	Allowance

Figure 11.1. Estimating summary.

Making the Estimate

It is desirable to develop the estimate in the sequence that work will be completed and the order in which materials will be needed on the job. It is helpful to keep a separate sheet on which to list all surface areas and wall lengths as they are calculated. Many of these values will be used several times and need be calculated only once. For example, the square feet of floor area may be used for estimating concrete for the basement slab, subflooring for the main deck, various materials for the finish floor, and even the labor cost for closing in the building.

The following examples of rules and procedures can aid in the process of cost estimating:

1. A medium size bulldozer can clear approximately 1,200 ft^2 (110 m^2) of land/h or excavate approximately 40 yd^3 (30 m^2)/h.

2. In estimating concrete, use full dimensions with no allowance for corners. Round up the results to compensate for form inaccuracies, etc. The delivered cost of a small quantity of concrete to make up for any shortage is very expensive.

3. Concrete blocks may be estimated on the basis of 1.2 blocks per ft^2 (0.09/m^2) of gross wall surface. This will allow for a limited amount of breakage.

4. Floor and ceiling joist numbers may be determined by dividing the length of the area to be covered by the joist spacing and then adding one. Estimates must take into account usable lengths and all openings that will need to be framed with headers or double joists.

5. The subflooring should be determined on the basis of the gross floor area for plywood, while with lumber, an additional amount must be included to account for the waste in cutting and the loss of width due to the tongue and groove.

6. In determining the number of studs required, allow one per foot (1/300 mm) of gross wall length. This will provide for cripple studs, jack studs, nonweight bearing headers, etc.

7. Choose the size for all weight bearing headers on the basis of the size required for the largest opening. This is done to simplify construction procedures.

8. Shoes and plates may be determined by gross wall lengths.

9. Sheathing quantity when using plywood, as with subflooring, is based on gross area. An extra amount must be allowed for tongue and groove lumber and diagonal installation.

10. Rafter numbers may be determined the same as joists with proper allowance for overhangs at the gable ends and the rafter tails at the eaves.

11. The estimated roof deck area should also take into account any overhang at the gable ends and eaves.

12. The quantity of nails to close in a building, including framing, floor deck, roof deck, and sheathing, may be assumed at 100 lb/1,000 ft² (50 kg/100 m²) of floor area.

13. Labor for the framing is often estimated on the basis of finished floor area.

14. Siding and roofing are usually sold by the square (100 ft²) and should be based on gross areas. One or two extra squares of roofing will allow for a starter course, as well as valleys and ridges.

15. The electrical system estimate is usually based on a cost per opening (switch, outlet or fixture) plus the cost of the service entrance. Fixtures should be listed as an allowance, with the customer's choice either raising or lowering the actual cost. Outside outlets must be protected with a ground fault interrupter at extra cost.

16. The plumbing estimate is often based on the number of major fixtures located in the kitchen, laundry, and bath. In addition, a cost for connecting equipment such as dishwashers and disposal units may be included.

17. A hot water heating system is likely to be based on floor area for radiation plus the cost of the boiler and burner. Zoned systems will add further to the cost. Hot air systems are likely to be based on a cost for each feed and return opening, plus the cost of the furnace and blower.

18. Insulation needs are estimated on the basis of gross wall, ceiling, and floor areas.

19. Inside wall and ceiling coverings such as gypsum board or paneling are based on gross areas.

20. In estimating finish floor coverings, an allowance for matching must be included as follows: sheet vinyl and carpeting, 10%; various tiles, 0 to 5% unless there is a special pattern consideration; hardwood flooring, 30% to take care of cutting waste and difference between nominal and actual sizes.

21. Labor for all interior trim work is often estimated on the basis of finished floor area.

22. Cost estimates for inside painting are usually based on medium sized rooms. Large rooms are counted as two. Two coats of paint per room with no more than two colors in the house is typical. An extra charge is assessed for more than two colors.

23. Outside painting is usually based on the area to be painted plus a charge for each window and each lineal foot of trim.

24. An estimated charge should be included for cleaning, both during and at the completion of construction. This is a cost that is frequently overlooked.

While there are many details omitted from the foregoing list, it does cover the major parts of a home and the pertinent parts may be selected for use in estimating the cost for other buildings.

The experienced estimator will not overlook the many little items that can add up to a substantial amount. Good specifications and a working list will help to prevent the omission of such items as joist hangers, bridging, screen for the soffit vents, door stops, etc.

The following is a list of items that are often given an allowance estimate:
- Site clearing and excavation
- Electrical fixtures and floor coverings
- Kitchen cabinets and appliances
- Bathroom vanities, cabinets, etc.
- Inside painting and wall papering
- Landscaping, but not seeding
- Septic tank and drainage field
- Well and water pump

Overhead and Profit

Whether a builder works out of a tool box in his pickup truck or has a headquarters building and a large staff, he has overhead—non productive costs, that must be considered. If he does not include these costs in his bid prices, he is only hastening the day when he will be out of business. Following is a list of typical overhead items:
- Secretarial services
- Advertising
- Office supplies
- Tools and depreciation
- Insurance and bonding
- Travel and entertainment
- Taxes and license fees
- Accounting and legal fees
- Utilities
- Education and subscriptions
- Office rent and equipment
- Interest and commissions

The overhead costs may be estimated as a percentage of the construction cost. Depending somewhat on the number of jobs completed during the year, it typically runs 6 to 10%. However, the most satisfactory method is to estimate the total overhead cost on the basis of previous years' records and then prorate that cost over to the number of jobs expected during the year. Profit is determined by a number of factors, not the least of which is the economic situation and building market at the time the estimate is made. Five to 10% of construction costs is probably a reasonable range. The amount of subcontracting used on a job can also influence the profit margin for the principal contractor.

The Buyer's Viewpoint

Let the buyer beware of the lowest and highest of several bids. The chances are that neither is a very good indication of actual cost. The buyer should go over the "allowance list" with each bidder and find out what items are so listed and how much has been estimated in each case. The chances are good that when differences in allowances are reconciled, the various bid prices may be much closer than they originally appeared.

"Bargain" jobs seldom turn out to be real bargains. Changes made during construction are likely to be expensive and allowances that have been given low estimates have a way of growing.

Finally, it pays to know your builder and have faith in him. Otherwise, it is best to give the bid to someone else.

Appraisals

Appraisals differ from construction cost estimating in that they are used after the project is completed. Building appraisals are used in: (a) assessing for property taxes, (b) selecting mortgage rates, (c) estimating maintenance and insurance costs, and (d) determining a value for income tax depreciation. Appraisals are based on opinion and cannot be reduced to an exact formula.

Three basic approaches:
1. Income capitalization. Estimate annual income from property and subtract total annual expenses to arrive at net income. e.g., a 5% income capitalization factor would mean the property value = 20 × net income.
2. Comparison. Estimate building value by comparison to other buildings of similar size, construction, usage, and condition. Location and surroundings influence the value.
3. Reproduction. Value = reproduction (or replacement) cost minus the observed depreciation and obsolescence.

Economic Feasibility

When constructing an agricultural building, the expense must be justified as a benefit to the enterprise. As mentioned previously, the use of a building results in an annual production or storage cost to the enterprise. In fact, it can be thought of as an item of production equipment. While there are no hard and fast rules concerning how much annual cost can be justified to house an enterprise, some effort should be made to estimate the cost and determine the feasibility of the related investment.

Approaches

Several approaches have been used to determine the economic feasibility of a farm building. One of these, the present practice theory, assumes that a building similar to others already existing in the area is justifiable. Another uses a percentage of gross income which is considered a reasonable amount to allow for annual building costs. A third, residual after cost theory, provides for building costs after all other costs have been deducted from gross income.

The first of these methods is likely to emphasize what the average farmer is doing or more likely has done in the past. It isn't necessarily correct for the present or the future. Also, an attractive building or system may actually have resulted in over-investment, thus making it a questionable example to follow. The second and third suggestions relate building cost allotments to gross income. They imply that high income-producing enterprises can and perhaps should be housed in more expensive facilities. Typical values used for the percentage of gross income method are: dairy, 11%; beef and poultry, 9%; and sheep, 8%. This method does not take into account the value of labor, the cost of which may justify a larger investment due to improved labor efficiency.

Two additional approaches for determining economic feasibility involve partial budgeting. The first of these shows the profit potential and the second estimates the minimum possible payback period for the building. However, before investigating these approaches, it is important to review some of the costs involved in owning a building.

Building Costs

Most costs of owning a building are considered to be fixed costs because they occur quite independently of the building's use. There are five categories of fixed costs: depreciation, interest, repairs, taxes, and insurance (sometimes referred to as the "DIRTI FIVE"). Of these costs, only repairs may be somewhat related to the degree of use. But even then, weather-related deterioration of such things as paint and roofing must be attended to even when a building stands idle. Consequently, repairs are ordinarily considered a fixed cost. An examination of each of these costs follows.

Depreciation

This is a noncash expense which provides a means of spreading the original cost of a building over the expected life of the building. There are at least two reasons for distributing the cost in this way: (1) the cost of an expensive building must be distributed over several years to justify the expense to the enterprise housed; (2) in completing a federal tax return, the cost of a building must be shown on a depreciation schedule. It cannot be taken as an ordinary business expense. In fact, even a new roof must be depreciated instead of being charged as an expense. While there are several ways of calculating depreciation, the one most commonly used for buildings is the straight line method; i.e., an equal amount is allowed for depreciation annually throughout the life of the building.

Interest

Interest may be either a cash or noncash expense. If the building is financed, the interest charge is a very real cash payout. However, even if the building is free of debt, an interest charge should be made against the owner's equity. If the owner did not have money tied up in the building, it could be earning interest in a bank.

Repairs

These hardly need to be explained. General deterioration due to weathering, plus wear and damage, will require continual repair to such things as paint, roofing, windows, doors, etc.

Taxes

Taxes are universally levied against real property although the amount varies considerably from place to place.

Insurance

Insurance is considered a necessity by most owners. But even if commercial coverage is not purchased, a charge should be included, because, in effect, the owner is self-insuring the property.

A variety of circumstances produces a rather sizeable range in these five fixed costs. The following examples are given as a percentage of the original cost or value of a farm building:

	2 1/2 (40 yr)	5 (20 yr)	10 (10 yr)
Depreciation	2 1/2 (40 yr)	5 (20 yr)	10 (10 yr)
Interest*	2 1/2	3	4
Repairs	1	2	2 1/2
Taxes	1 1/2	2	2 1/2
Insurance	1/2	1	1
Annual Cost	8%	13%	20%

* Rate divided by two as the average value of the building over its life is one half of the original value.

This wide range of annual costs (8 to 20%) results primarily from the length of the depreciation period chosen.

The Internal Revenue Service will probably not allow less than 20 years and prefers 30 years for depreciating a farm building. However, any period may be chosen for farm planning purposes. If during this period of rapidly changing economic conditions the depreciation can be completed in a reasonably short time, then much of the risk of a large investment is removed.

Partial Budgeting

Partial budgeting, in which variable factors are considered while omitting those factors that remain constant, can be useful in determining either the profit potential or the payback period which may result from the construction of a new housing system for an enterprise. Profit potential (the prospects of increasing profits by a change in the housing system) will be illustrated by using a partial budget and the economic base of an existing structure. From that base, any additional investment to improve the facilities must be proven reasonable by either increasing returns or decreasing costs. Increased returns with minimal increase in costs may result from increased production or improved product quality. Reduced costs with little change in income may result from improved labor efficiency, better feed conversion, or improved animal health.

The following assumptions illustrate this method: A dairyman has a 50-cow herd housed in a stanchion barn. He is interested in expansion and needs to decide whether he should abandon his present facilities, with a resulting small salvage value, and build a new free-stall and parlor system, or whether he should expand his present stanchion barn. Because of the flexibility of other enterprises on the farm he can make available whatever labor is required.

Although many degrees of basic condition and usefulness could exist, we will assume that the building is reasonably efficient and equipped with a pipeline milker and gutter cleaner. Only a minimal breakdown of barn, milking, and manure equipment costs is undertaken. It is assumed, however, that the daily labor requirements for each 10 cows is 1.6 man hours for a stanchion barn and 1.14 man hours for a free-stall system.

Following is a comparison of the cost of expansion to handle 100 milking cows (table 11-1). While the cost of the new free-stall system is greater, labor savings show it produces an increase in net profit of $1,535 over an expansion of the stanchion barn. While the stanchion barn may be used for other purposes if the free-stall barn is built, there is the possibility that high taxation will make it of questionable economic value.

Table 11-1. Cost comparison for dairy expansion

Costs incurred from enlarging existing barn:		
Annual cost of original barn, addition to barn, milk and manure equipment		$19,500*
Total annual cost of labor to care for the dairy herd (16 man hours × 365 days × $5.00/h)		$29,280
Cost incurred from constructing a new free-stall system:		
Annual cost of new free-stall barn, parlor, milk and equipment		$24,960†
Extra feed required resulting from lower temperature		1,400
		$26,360
Total annual cost of labor to care for the dairy herd (11.4 man hours × 365 days × $5.00/h)		$20,805
Annual cost (Housing)		
New free-stall barn	$26,360	
Enlarged stanchion barn	19,500	
Net change / Net added cost	+ $6,860	+ $ 6,860
Annual costs (Labor)		
Stanchion barn	$29,280	
Free-stall barn	20,805	
Net change / Net reduced cost	- $ 8,395	- $ 8,395
Total reduction in cost		$1,535

* Estimated as follows:

Existing barn	$750 × 50 cows	= $ 37,500
Addition	2250 × 50 cows	= 112,500
Milk and manure equipment		= —

$150,000 × 13% = $19,500

† Estimated as follows:

Cost of barn	$1,500 × 100 cows	= $150,000
Parlor and equipment		= 30,000
Manure equipment		= 12,000

$192,000 × 13% = $24,960

This is only an example and every farm presents its own unique situation that must be analyzed using the best information available at the time.

The payback period may also be illustrated by using partial budgeting. The payback period is an estimate of the number of years in which the margin over all other costs equals the original cost of the building. Having determined a reasonable estimate of this period of time, a decision may be made on the basis of the confidence in the future of the enterprise to be housed. The following partial budgets for a 100-cow dairy enterprise show the effects of three levels of building investment on the length of the payback period (table 11-2). All values are on a per-cow basis.

Table 11-2. Partial budgeting example

Investment:			
Building (only variable shown)	$1,600	$2,000	$2,400
Cow	1,400	1,400	1,400
Machinery	800	800	800
Land (2 acres/cow)	1,800	1,800	1,800
Total	$5,600	$6,000	$6,400
Interest and operating costs:			
Silage (16 tons)	$ 480	$ 480	$ 480
Grain (2.5 tons)	625	625	625
Miscellaneous	80	80	80
Fixed costs (cow, machinery, land)	400	400	400
Labor (60 h @ $3.25)	300	300	300
Interest (8% on 1/2 investment)	224	240	256
Total	$2,109	$2,125	$2,141
Gross income:			
Milk (16,500 lbs @ $13.40 cwt + 1 calf @ $150)		$2,361	
Margin for building expenses:			
Gross income	$2,361	$2,361	$2,361
Interest and operating expenses	2,109	2,125	2,141
Margin	$ 252	$ 236	$ 220
Annual building cost as a percent of original building cost:			
Repairs	2.5%		
Taxes 2.5%			
Insurance	1%		
	6%		
Original investment:	$1,600	$2,000	$2,400
Annual building cost (%)	0.06	0 .06	0.06
Annual building cost	$ 96	$ 120	$ 144
Margin for payback:			
Margin for building expense	$ 252	$ 236	$ 220
Repairs, taxes, insurance	96	120	144
Margin	$ 156	$ 116	$ 76
Years to pay for building:	$1,600/$156		
		$2,000/$116	
			$2,400/$76
Years to pay back:	10.3	17.2	31.6

It is logical to conclude that if all income and expenses shown can be reasonably expected to remain in the same ratio for some time to come, the $1,600 investment and the associated 10.3 year payback period seems a very good arrangement. The 17-year period resulting from the $2,000 investment might also seem reasonable. However, the 31.6-year period associated with the $2,400 investment involves a considerable risk in a rapidly changing agricultural economy.

In summary, it must be emphasized that the budgets illustrated are only examples. Every farm is an individual situation and all costs should be estimated carefully for the particular building being considered. The opportunity to keep farm building costs low is desirable but not at the expense of poor labor efficiency, low production, or reduced quality of products stored. The possibility for a rapid payback period greatly reduces the risk of a new investment. But remember, the conclusions that are drawn can be no better than the information used in budget calculations.

The previous examples of methods for determining the feasibility of investing in a new structure involve relatively simple calculations. A more sophisticated analysis may be made with the aid of linear programming which makes it possible to maximize profit potential while considering a wide range of variables. The Agricultural Extension Service or private consultants may have access to the computer services needed to solve a linear program.

Problems

11.1. Using figure 11.2, what is the pole spacing (a) along the back wall, (b) along the front wall, (c) along the endwall? What length of pole is required for the sidewalls?

11.2. Estimate the number and sizes of poles required. How many trusses are needed if the spacing is 4 ft o.c.?

11.3. Estimate the quantity required for sidewall nailing girts and pressure-treated skirting.

11.4. It is desirable to appraise the future prospects of any enterprise to be served by a new or expanded building. Agriculture is changing at such a rapid rate that a thorough study of the prospects for making the building pay off is essential. List some sources of information on the following subjects:

(a) Trends in farm production and prices.

(b) Management systems for an enterprise.

(c) Building plans for one or more management systems.

(d) Basic materials, prefabricated units, and manufactured buildings.

11.5. Assume that a father and son partnership is being formed. They want to increase the size of the business from a two- to a three-man operation. Choose a livestock enterprise and assume that it has been operating in buildings which have provided a minimum of controlled environment. Develop a partial budget to compare the relative merits of expanding along the present lines of operation compared to constructing a new housing system including a maximum of confinement and controlled environment. Assume that crop production is not a limiting factor and that full utilization of three workers is desired.

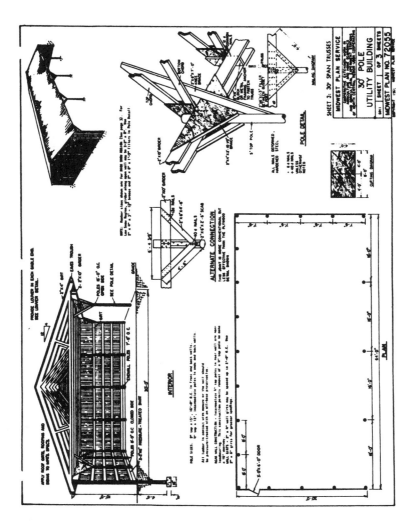

Figure 11.2. Utility building plan.

Part II

ENVIRONMENTAL CONTROL OF AGRICULTURAL BUILDINGS

Agricultural buildings provide security, containment, confinement, and environmental modification. The environment may be defined as the conditions that affect animals, plants or stored products. Environmental factors (physical, thermal, chemical, biological or social) influence animal health, behavior, breeding, production efficiency, product quality, human health, and deterioration of equipment and building materials. Wild animals and birds often modify their environment by seeking shelter, hibernating, migrating, etc. However, confined animals do not have such options. Buildings alter the natural climate (precipitation, wind, sun, temperature, humidity and gaseous concentration). The design and management of the building systems to provide the desired environment for domestic animals, plants, and products requires an understanding of physiological principles, animal and plant behavior, and environmental principles.

The quality of the environment in agricultural buildings has become increasingly recognized as an important influence on animal production, labor efficiency, and the value of products in storage. As agricultural systems have developed and become more complex and sophisticated, the economic significance of environmental control has increased. The control of temperature, moisture, light, dust, and odors within buildings is essential for high production, maintenance of quality of stored products, disease control, worker comfort, building and equipment longevity, and safety from explosion.

The goal of environmental control is not only to obtain the highest production and top quality from stored products, but to minimize stress for both animals and workers. Avoiding pollution from solid, liquid, and gaseous waste is being a good neighbor and may have social and legal aspects.

Collectively, the factors that make up an environment are complex. The importance of each factor varies with the specific requirements of each enterprise and with the climate of the area. For example, in a warm climate keeping a product storage cool may be of prime concern, while a similar storage in a cooler climate may need to be protected from freezing as a primary concern.

Control of the environment requires an envelope or isolation of the space or area to be controlled. Environmental control may require adding or removing heat, moisture, gases or light, and, in a few cases, noise. Site, climate, and operation make each environmental situation unique, so problems must be considered individually. In the past, improvements in feeding, breeding, and management have resulted in larger returns than improvements in environment factors; however, realization of the full benefit of changes will require fine tuning environmental control systems.

12 Fundamentals of Heat Transfer and Psychrometrics

THERMODYNAMIC PROPERTIES

The thermodynamic properties of a material depend primarily on the state of the material; that is, whether it is in a solid, liquid or gaseous state. A knowledge of the basic factors involved in thermodynamics, heat transfer, and temperature control is necessary before a system can be designed and equipment chosen to control the environment in an agricultural building. Following are definitions for a number of terms used in dealing with heat.

Heat is a form of energy. It is generally accepted that the molecules of a body are in constant motion and possess kinetic energy referred to as heat. Increased heat is indicated by more motion and energy. Heat is a measure of the total kinetic energy of all the molecules of a body.

Temperature is the degree or intensity of heat. It is a measure of the average kinetic energy of the molecules of a body. The difference in temperature between the two areas is the driving force for the heat transfer. Heat moves from one area to an area of lower temperature. The temperature of substances may be expressed in either relative or absolute units. On the Fahrenheit (F) scale, water freezes at 32° and boils at 212° at 14.696 psia. The freezing and boiling point on the Celsius scale are 0° and 100°. The following are the conversion relationships (table 12-1):

$$t_F = \frac{9}{5} t_C + 32 \qquad (12.1)$$

$$t_C = \frac{5}{9}(t_F - 32) \qquad (12.2)$$

Both the Rankine and Kelvin scales are used to indicate absolute temperatures. The temperature value in degrees Rankine is equal to the value in Fahrenheit plus 459.9; the temperature in Kelvin is equal to the value in Celsius plus 273.16.

Ambient temperature is the temperature of the medium surrounding a body, for example, the room air temperature.

The *pressure* of a substance is the force it exerts per unit area of its boundaries. Pressures may be designated as absolute, gauge or vacuum. If the *absolute pressure* is greater than the atmospheric or barometric pressure, then the *gauge pressure* is the

Table 12-1. Temperature scales compared

	Fahrenheit	Rankine	Celsius	Kelvin
Boiling point of water	212	671	100	373
Freezing point of water	32	491	0	273
Absolute zero	-459	0	-273	0

difference between the absolute and atmospheric pressures. If the absolute pressure is less than the atmospheric pressure the difference is equal to the *vacuum*. If water has a specific weight of 62.4 lb/ft^3 and the specific gravity of mercury (Hg) is 13.6, then the following conversions can be developed:

$$1 \text{ psi} = 144 \text{ psf} = 2.04 \text{ in. Hg} = 27.7 \text{ in.} H_2O$$

$$1 \text{ in.Hg} = 0.491 \text{ psi} = 13.6 \text{ in.} H_2O$$

$$1 \text{ in.} H_2O = 0.0361 \text{ psi} = 0.0735 \text{ in.Hg}$$

$$1 \text{ atm} = 14.696 \text{ psia} = 29.92 \text{ in.Hg}$$

Sensible heat is the heat which results in a temperature change only when a transfer takes place. It is sensible heat that is produced by a heating system, is lost through a building wall, or is removed by a refrigeration system.

Latent heat is that heat which causes a change in state, but no change in temperature. It is latent heat of fusion that is absorbed by ice as it melts at one temperature. It is latent heat of fusion that is removed as food is frozen for storage. In an evaporative cooler, which is usually a fibrous pad wet with water through which air is blown, it is latent heat of vaporization that is absorbed by the water as it changes to a vapor. Latent heat is given up to a dehumidifier as the vapor condenses back to a liquid. The amount of latent heat required for vaporization of water decreases with an increase in temperature. This is shown in table 12-2 which lists the latent heat of vaporization for water at several temperatures.

Thermal capacity is the amount of heat required to raise the temperature of a unit of mass of a material one degree.

British thermal unit or *Btu* is the unit of measure of quantity of heat in the IP system and is the heat required to raise the temperature of one pound of water 1°F.

Joule is the unit of measure of quantity of heat in the SI system. One calorie of heat will raise the temperature of 1 g of water 1°Celsius. This is equal to 4.186 joules (J). One kilojoule equals 0.948 Btu or 0.239 kilocalories.

Specific heat is the ratio of the thermal capacity of a material to that of water. Specific heat has no dimensions because it is a ratio. In customary units, the specific heat is equal numerically to the thermal capacity and may be treated as though it has the dimension Btu. However, in SI units the 4.187 J thermal capacity of water must be used with the specific heat ratio.

Specific heat is used in determining the quantity of heat involved in heating or cooling

Table 12-2. Latent heat of vaporization for water

°F	Btu/lb	°C	kJ/kg
0	1,220	-17.8	2 838
20	1,219	-6.7	2 835
32	1,075	0.0	2 500
40	1,071	4.4	2 491
80	1,048	26.7	2 243
87	1,044	30.6	2 428
120	1,025	48.9	2 384
160	1,002	71.1	2 331
200	978	93.3	2 275
212	970	100.0	2 256

a material. For example, specific heat would be used in determining the amount of refrigeration required to cool apples from harvest temperature down to storage temperature.

The *specific volume* of a substance is its volume per unit mass.

The *density* of a substance is its mass per unit volume; this is the reciprocal of specific volume. The specific volume and density of a vapor or gas are affected by both pressure and temperature.

The *specific gravity* of a liquid is the ratio of the weight of the liquid divided by the weight of an equal volume of water.

The *total heat content* of a body is greatly affected by its mass. A body with a large mass may have a considerably greater total heat than a body of lesser mass at a higher temperature. For example, the water under ice in a lake will have more than enough heat to supply a heat pump to heat a home for an entire winter. A match, on the other hand, will burn one's finger, but the heat lasts only a few seconds. In the first case, the water, even at near freezing temperature, has tremendous heat content, while the match has very little even though the temperature is much higher. The mass makes the difference.

The science of thermodynamics is based on two empirical principles. In simple terms, the *first law of thermodynamics* states that energy can neither be created nor destroyed. It is the law of conservation of energy. However, energy can be readily changed from one form to another. For example, heat and work are interconvertible.

The *second law of thermodynamics* states that it is impossible for a self-acting machine, unaided by any external source, to transfer heat from one body to another at a higher temperature. Heat will not flow spontaneously from one system into another at a higher temperature. External energy must be applied to move heat from a low temperature area to a higher temperature area. A refrigerating machine (heat pump) powered by some external source of energy is required to move the energy from a low temperature to a high temperature area.

The concept of the property of internal energy is based on the first law. Internal energy of a substance includes all types of energy stored within its molecules in both kinetic and potential form. The *enthalpy* of a substance is a composite energy term defined by the following equation:

$$h = u + \frac{Pv}{J} \qquad (12.3)$$

where
- h = enthalpy (Btu/lb)
- u = internal energy (Btu/lb)
- P = pressure (psf)
- v = specific volume (ft³/lb)
- J = 778 ft-lb/Btu

The concept of a property of *entropy* is a measure of the disorder in a closed thermo-dynamic system and is defined by the following equation:

$$ds = \frac{dQ}{T} \qquad (12.4)$$

where
- ds = differential change in entropy (Btu/lb-R)
- dQ = differential heat reversibly added (Btu/lb)
- T = absolute temperature (R)

For a finite amount of heat added, the change in entropy, $s_2 - s_1$, is found by integrating dQ/T.

Work and heat are related by the mechanical equivalent of heat. It requires 778 ft-lb of mechanical energy to raise the temperature of 1 lb H_2O 1°F, i.e:

- 1 Btu = 778 ft-lb
- 1 hp = 2,545 Btu/h
- 1 kW = 3,413 Btu/h

Refrigeration effect may be expressed in tons where 1 t = 12,000 Btu/h.

HEAT TRANSFER

All matter contains some internal energy. One component of internal energy is thermal, or heat. Heat will transfer from one body to another if there is a temperature difference between the bodies. Heat energy moves from one place to another in one or more of the following modes: conduction, convection or radiation. A person, or an animal, exposed to a cold window or wall will lose heat by radiation and convection. The convective loss will result from air currents caused by air density differences. Both of these transfer mechanisms will be affected by clothing or hair. If there is contact with a cold surface there will also be a loss by conduction.

Conduction

Heat movement by conduction involves the transfer of kinetic energy from molecule to molecule. Higher temperatures result in increased molecular activity and faster flow. Substances which transmit heat readily are termed *thermal conductors*; those that resist the flow of heat are *thermal insulators*. Conduction is the mode of heat transfer through opaque solids and across fluids in laminar, or streamline, flow. Although conduction also occurs in transparent solids and turbulent fluids, it is difficult to isolate that portion of the heat transfer attributable to conduction. An expression for heat flow by conduction is:

$$q = -k_c A\left(\frac{dt}{dx}\right) \qquad (12.5)$$

or

$$q = k_c A \frac{\Delta T}{t} = \left(\frac{A}{R}\right)\Delta T \qquad (12.6)$$

where

A	=	cross-sectional area normal to the direction of flow (ft^2; m^2)
dt/dx	=	temperature gradient (F/in.)
q	=	rate of heat transfer by conduction (Btu/h; W)
k_c	=	thermal conductivity of material [Btu/(h-ft^2-F/in.) [W/(m^2 K)/(m thickness)]
ΔT	=	temperature difference (°F; °K)
t	=	thickness (in.; m)
R	=	thermal resistance [(h-ft^2-F)/Btu; (m^{2}K)/W]

The range of thermal conductivity found in various materials is illustrated in table 12-3. Specific equations for thermal conductance through various shapes may be found in the *ASHRAE Handbook of Fundamentals*. Heat transfer through nonhomogeneous or composite materials will be discussed later in the chapter.

Example 12.1

As an example of heat flow by conduction, assume a concrete tank with a wall thickness of 10 in. (254 mm) and a surface area of 65 ft^2 (6.0 m^2). Water is inside and air is outside. The inside surface temperature is 50°F (10°C) and the outside concrete surface is 77°F (25°C). The total heat conduction through the tank wall in 10 h, if the k_c = 10 Btu-in./(h-ft^2-°F) (1.44 Wm/m^2-K), will be:

$$q = k_c A \Delta \frac{T}{t}$$

$$q = \frac{10 \text{ Btu-in.}}{\left(h\text{-}ft^{2}\text{°F}\right)} \times 65 \text{ ft}^2 \times \frac{(77-50) \text{ F}}{10 \text{ in.}}$$

$$q = 1{,}755 \text{ Btu/h} \ (510 \text{ W})$$

or in 10 h: Q = 17,550 Btu

Table 12-3. Thermal conductivities

Material	Conductivity (W/mK)	Conductivity Btu/(h-ft^2°F/in.)
Silver	423	2940
Copper	370	2564
Steel	47	326
Granite	2.82	19.6
Plate glass	0.81	5.6
Cotton, fiber	0.042	0.29
Polyisocyanurate	0.020	0.14
Air	0.0022	0.015
Freon 12	0.00068	0.0047

Convection

Convection involves heat transfer from a fluid to a solid or vice versa. This is a complex process. Assuming a surface that is warmer than the surrounding fluid, heat travels through a thin laminar layer by conduction; then by conduction and convection through a buffer zone, and finally mostly by convection in a turbulent zone. The most important factor in the heat exchange is usually conduction through the laminar layer. The following expression is used for heat transfer away from a surface by convection:

$$q = h_c A \left(t_s - t_f\right) \qquad (12.7)$$

where

q = heat transfer by convection (Btu/h; W)

h_c = surface coefficient [Btu/(h-ft^2°F); W/(m^2°K)]

A = surface area (ft^2; m^2)

t_f = fluid film temperature (°F ; °C)

t_s = surface temperature (°F; °C)

The value for h_c is influenced by the fluid involved, the shape and surface condition of the body, the rate of fluid movement, and the temperature difference as well as other minor factors. The method for finding the value of h_c for several conditions may be found in the *ASHRAE Handbook of Fundamentals*. The order of magnitude of h_c for several situations is given in table 12-4. For airflow in a duct at standard pressure, the convective coefficient can be calculated by:

$$h_c = c\frac{G^{0.8}}{D^{0.2}} \qquad (12.8)$$

where

G = mass flow rate = ρv (kg/m^2-s)

ρ = mass density (kg/m^3)

v = velocity (m/s)

Table 12-4. Range of heat transfer coefficients

	Btu/h-ft^2°F (W/m^{2}K)
Air, free convection	1-5 (6-30)
Air, forced convection	5-50 (30-300)
Water, forced convection	50-1000 (300-6000)
Water, boiling	500-10000 (3000-60 000)
Steam, condensing	1000-20 000 (6000-120 000)

D = hydraulic diameter of the duct (m)
c = coefficient based on thermal properties of the air
c = 3.09 for air at -18°C
c = 3.18 for air at 4°C
c = 3.26 for air at 49°C

Related to any convective transfer will be a transfer of heat by the mass movement of a fluid. Natural convection results from variations in density for different temperatures of the material, while forced convection is caused by moving the fluid with a fan or pump. If the fluid is moved from one location to another, such as air in a ventilating system, the rate of heat transfer is given by the expression:

$$q = m \, c_p \, \Delta T \qquad\qquad (12.9)$$

where

q =   rate of heat transfer (Btu/h; W)
m =   fluid mass flow rate (lb/h; kg/s)
c_p =   specific heat of the fluid (Btu/lb; J/kg)
ΔT =   temperature difference between the entering
            and exiting fluid (°F; °C)

Example 12.2
Air is flowing through a space at the rate of 20 lb/h. The air comes in at 10°F
    and leaves at 70°F. What is the heat transfer rate?
Solution
The specific heat of air is 0.24 Btu/lb-°F, therefore,

$$q = 20 \text{ lb/h} \times 0.24 \text{ Btu/lb-°F} \times (70\text{-}10)\text{°F} = 288 \text{ Btu/h}$$

Thermal Radiation
The transmission of energy by electromagnetic waves through space is called radiation. The emission of radiant energy occurs from the surfaces of bodies. Thermal emission from a body is also correlated to the wavelength of the radiation. This relationship is described by Planck's Law:

$$E_{bh} = \frac{\left(C_1\lambda^{-5}\right)}{\left(e^{\alpha} - 1\right)}$$ (12.10)

where

E_{bh} = monochromatic emissive power of a black body (J/m^4)
α = $C_2 / \lambda T$
C_1 = 4.99×10^{-24} (W-m^2) or 1.19×10^8 [Btu m/(h-ft^2)]
C_2 = 1.44×10^{-22} (m °K) or 25,900 [m °R]
λ = wavelength (m)
T = temperature (°K)
e = 2.718

All objects emit and absorb radiant energy in varying amounts depending on temperature and physical characteristics. The absorbed fraction causes the material to heat. A body that has a surface capable of absorbing all radiation that falls on it is referred to as a *black body*. While there is no perfect black body, a dull, black surface very closely approximates the condition. A black body is not only the perfect absorber of radiant heat, but it is also the best emitter of radiant energy. The energy emitted from a black body surface is proportional to the temperature raised to the fourth power.

$$E_b = \sigma T^4$$ (12.11)

where

T = absolute temperature (°R; °K)
σ = 0.1713×10^{-8} 10 Btu/(h-ft^2-°R4) [5.67×10^{-8} w/m^2(°K4)]

The proportionality constant, σ, is known as the Stephan-Boltzman Constant. The emissivity of a surface is the ratio of the actual energy emitted divided by the theoretical energy emitted from a black surface at the same temperature. $\varepsilon = E/E_b$ or radiation from a surface is given by:

$$E = \varepsilon \sigma T^4$$ (12.12)

The closeness to which radiation approaches black body conditions depends on the nature of the surface at a given temperature. The radiation from any surface is expressed by the equation:

$$q = AE\sigma T^4$$ (12.13)

where

q = rate of radiation (Btu/h; W)
A = surface area (ft^2; m^2)
E = the ratio of emissivity of a surface to that of a black body

When the radiation strikes an object within a greenhouse or other building, it changes to heat at a much lower temperature. Although radiation from those surfaces occurs, it is at wavelengths much longer than 4×10^{-6} m above which glass and most plastics are opaque to heat radiation. The energy is effectively trapped within the glass or plastic enclosure. An exception is polyethylene which still passes considerable energy at this wavelength.

It should be remembered, however, that heat may be carried to the glass or plastic by radiation and convection and then lost through the glass by conduction. As heat travels through these materials by conduction, small amounts of energy are radiated from their outer surface, although most is carried away by convection.

When radiation strikes a surface, it can be absorbed, reflected or transmitted through the surface. Often it will be a combination of the three. Water, for example, reflects some of the sun's energy, absorbs some, and transmits some through to another surface. On the other hand, a dull black surface will absorb most of the radiation from the sun, while a shiny, aluminum surface will reflect a high percentage of the radiation.

The sum of the absorptivity, transmissivity, and reflectivity will equal one. In an opaque object, the transmissivity will equal zero and the absorptivity and reflectivity will equal one. A so-called black body can theoretically absorb 100% of radiation. However, the best that is possible is usually 70 to 90% for a flat black surface. Surfaces with high absorptivity also have high emissivity, and, conversely, surfaces with high reflectivity have low emissivity.

For some materials the emissivity and the absorptivity are nearly equal, while in others there is a considerable difference. Black paint is an example where they are nearly equal—the emissivity is 0.9 to 0.98 and the absorptivity is 0.85 to 0.98. In contrast, aluminum varies considerably, the emissivity is 0.02 to 0.04 and the absorptivity is 0.1 to 0.4. Both of these coefficients are also influenced by temperature as well as surface characteristics.

The sun, with a surface temperature of approximately 100,000°F (55 500°C), emits about 90% of its radiation at wavelengths between 1×10^{-7} and 20×10^{-7} m. Clear glass transmits 90% or more of the radiation in that range of wavelengths and many plastics do nearly as well.

While the radiation from a single surface may be calculated with the above equation, ordinarily it is of greater interest to determine the net radiation exchange between two surfaces. The colder of two bodies will always absorb radiation until both bodies are the same temperature. The rate of exchange depends on the temperature difference and the nature of the surfaces. When the higher temperature surface is much smaller than the other, the following simplified equation may be used:

$$q = A_1 \, E_1 \, \sigma \left(T_1^4 - T_2^4 \right) \qquad (12.14)$$

where A_1, E_1, and T_1 apply to the higher temperature surface.

Example 12.3

For example, the surface of a small electric heater has 1/2 ft^2 of surface area that radiates toward the walls and ceiling of a room. The heater is 200°F and the walls are 65°F, while the emissivity ratio is 0.8. The net radiation is found as follows:

$$q = 0.5 \text{ ft}^2 \times 0.8 \times 0.1713 \times 10^{-8} \text{ Btu}/(\text{h-ft}^2\text{-}°R4)(6594 - 5244)°R4$$

$$q = 0.0685 \times 10^{-8} \left(1886 \times 10^{-8} - 754 \times 10^8\right)$$

$$q = 0.685 \times 10^{-8} \times 1132 \times 10^8$$

$$q = 77.54 \text{ Btu/h}$$

The value for E may vary with the temperature for some surfaces. However, on many surfaces the emissivity remains approximately constant. Such surfaces are called gray. Black paint is an example of a *gray surface*. The net radiation between surfaces will be also related to their geometry. A *shape factor* is used to relate the size and angles between objects, i.e., accounts for the amount of radiation leaving one object that strikes the other. These relationships are included in the following equation:

$$q_r = \sigma A_1 F_a F_e \left(T_1^4 - T_2^4\right) \tag{12.15}$$

where

A_1	=	area 1 surface
F_a	=	shape factor
F_e	=	factor to account for emission and absorption characteristic of both surfaces
T_1, T_2	=	absolute temperature °K

PSYCHROMETRICS

The atmosphere in and around our homes and agricultural buildings primarily contains air and water vapor. Under most conditions the moisture cannot be seen, although if the temperature drops quickly it forms a mist or fog in the air. The unseen moisture in the air also becomes visible when it condenses on cool surfaces. High moisture levels, particularly when combined with high temperatures, seriously affect the comfort of both men and animals and the production of livestock as well.

Controlling the moisture level in the atmosphere is one of the more important aspects of maintaining a desirable environment in farm buildings. Examples in which moisture levels are significant include: apple storages, in which a high humidity maintains the quality of the fruit; livestock buildings, in which it is desirable to keep humidity low enough to prevent condensation on walls; and heated buildings, such as the farm home, where moisture is often added in the winter to maintain comfortable conditions.

Planning environmental control systems for plants, animals or humans requires an understanding of the physical and thermodynamic properties of air-water vapor mixtures, that is *psychrometrics*. Normal air contains about 20% oxygen, 78% nitrogen, 0.03% carbon dioxide, and small amounts of other gases. Although air is not a "perfect" gas, it may be considered so for the purpose of solving environmental control problems.

Boyles Law, $PV = {}^{`}C_b$, states that the product of the pressure and volume is constant;

Charles Law, $V/T = C_c$, related the volume and temperature to a constant. Combining these two laws into the *Perfect Gas Law* gives: $PV/T = C$. If $C = m R$, then the Perfect Gas Law expresses the relationship between pressure and temperature as follows:

$$PV = mRT \qquad (12.16)$$

where

P	=	absolute pressure (lb/ft^2)
V	=	volume (ft^3)
m	=	mass (lb)
T	=	absolute temperature (R)
R	=	gas constant (ft-lb/lb-R)

The gas constants for air and water are: $R_a = 53.35$ ft-lb/lb-R, $[R_a = 287$ J/kgK] and $R_w = 85.78$ ft-lb/lb-R, [461.5 J/kgK]. Dalton's Law states that each component in a mixture of gases exerts its own partial pressure. For a mixture of air and water vapor:

$$P_t = P_a + P_w = M_a R_a\left(\frac{T}{V}\right) + M_w R_w\left(\frac{T}{V}\right) \qquad (12.17)$$

Assuming that each component is uniformly diffused throughout the mixture, and both components have the same volume and temperature, then the above equation can be reduced to:

$$\frac{P_w}{P_a} = \frac{(M_w R_w)}{(M_a R_w)} \qquad (12.18)$$

A number of terms used in dealing with air-moisture temperature relationships must be defined before a good understanding of the subject is possible. The water vapor mixed with air is called humidity and there are a number of ways of expressing its quantity.

Absolute or *specific humidity* (or *humidity ratio*), W, is the ratio of the mass of water vapor in the air to the mass of dry air. Humidity ratio is not affected by a temperature change unless it drops below the saturation temperature. Humidity ratio is useful in calculating the amount of moisture involved in a process, such as the amount removed by ventilating a stable or the amount added by an evaporative cooler used in a greenhouse. Humidity ratio is expressed as pound of water vapor per pound of dry air. Older references used grains of vapor per pound of dry air (7,000 grains = 1 lb.).

Relative humidity, RH (or ϕ), is the ratio of the actual vapor pressure to the vapor pressure of saturated air at the same temperature. A close approximation in ordinary terms is the ratio of vapor present in the air to the maximum amount of vapor that the air can hold at a given temperature. Relative humidity is expressed as a percentage.

Degree of saturation, μ, is the ratio of the actual density of water vapor in the air to the density of saturated water vapor at the same dry-bulb temperature.

Dry-bulb temperature, t_{db}, is the air temperature as determined with a common dry thermometer or other dry temperature sensor. It is a measure of the temperature of the sensible heat in the air.

Dewpoint temperature, t_{dp}, is the saturation temperature corresponding to the actual partial pressure of moisture in the air. It is the temperature at which condensation just starts to occur on a polished metal surface. The probability of condensation on or within a wall is determined by comparing the actual temperature at a surface with the dewpoint temperature at the same place.

Wet-bulb temperature, t_{wb}, is the steady state temperature obtained by the evaporation of moisture from the wick on a thermometer. The temperature is taken after the thermometer has been exposed to a rapidly moving air stream. The temperature is reduced because heat is removed by evaporation. The drier the air, the greater the rate of evaporation, and, thus, the lower the resultant temperature. Wet-bulb and the associated dry-bulb temperatures are read from a psychrometer, an instrument consisting of a pair of thermometers indicating both temperatures in the same location. Many air, moisture, and temperature conditions in a room can be determined by using the wet- and dry-bulb temperatures and a psychrometric chart.

Wet-bulb depression is the difference between dry-bulb and wet-bulb temperature readings and is often required for use with psychrometric tables. It is also a useful factor in planning grain drying.

Vapor pressure is the independent pressure exerted by the water vapor in the air. The vapor pressure is proportional to the humidity ratio. The natural tendency for pressures to equalize causes moisture to migrate through the wall of a building unless restricted by a vapor barrier.

Specific volume is the volume of dry air per mass of dry air at a given temperature. Specific volume is read from the psychrometric chart at zero relative humidity, that is along the base-line of the chart.

Humid volume is the volume of moist air per mass of dry air at a given temperature and relative humidity. It is this value, found on a psychrometric chart, which is most useful in solving ventilation problems. Humid volume is used in converting the rate of air movement from volume to mass or vice versa.

Enthalpy is the total heat content of an air moisture mixture. This is a relative value using an arbitrary temperature base. Differences in enthalpy are useful in determining the heat transfer involved in the change from one temperature-humidity condition to another.

Psychrometric chart includes the physical and thermal properties of moist air which have been defined (fig. 12.1, 12.2). The intersection of any two property lines establishes a point on the chart to which all other properties may be related (figs. 12.3, 12.4). The chart is most useful in tracing the changes that take place in the various properties during ventilation, cooling, heating, and humidifying processes (see fig. 12.5 through 12.8). The psychrometric charts are based on standard sea level atmospheric pressure. They are simple and have a rather coarse scale but are adequate for most agricultural building environmental problems. More accurate information can be obtained from tables of moist air properties (table 12-5).

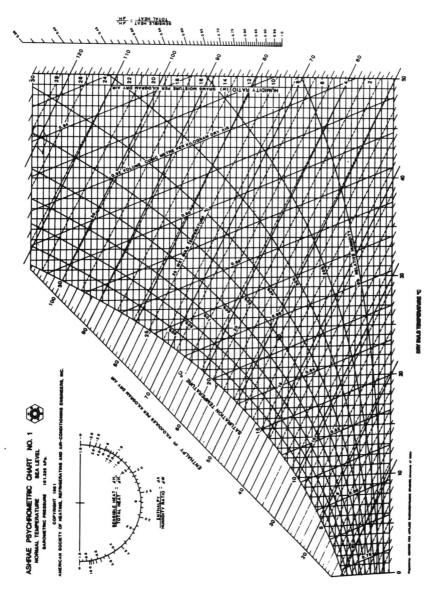

Figure 12.1. (a) Normal temperature psychrometric chart.

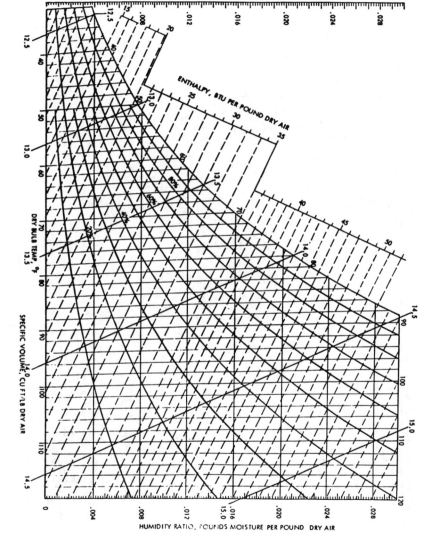

Figure 12.1. (b) Normal temperature psychrometric chart.

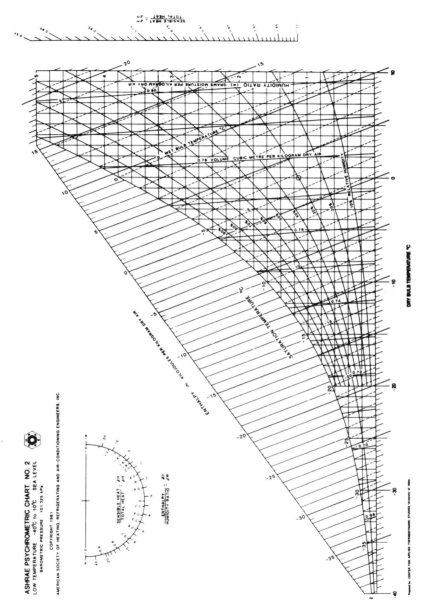

Figure 12.2. (a) Low temperature psychrometric chart.

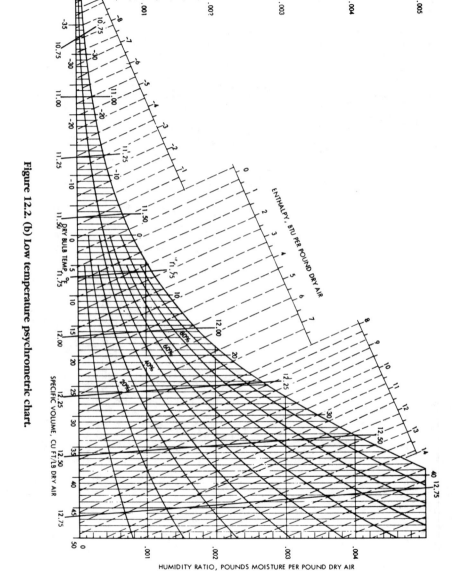

Figure 12.2. (b) Low temperature psychrometric chart.

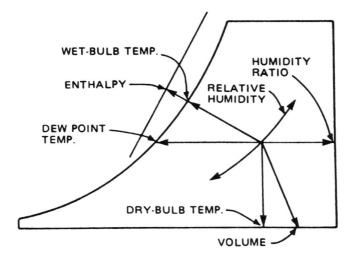

Figure 12.3. Properties of moist air on a psychrometric chart.

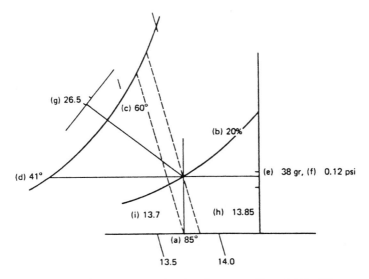

Figure 12.4. Properties of moist air at 73°F db and 20% RH.

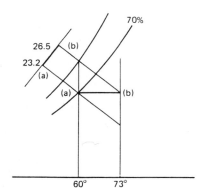

Figure 12.5. Sensible heating.

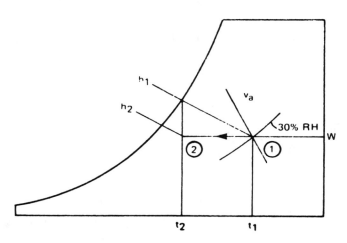

Figure 12.6. Sensible cooling.

Psychrometric Processes

A number of processes in agricultural engineering involve conditioning air-water mixtures. Livestock housing usually includes some degree of environmental modification. Crop drying is adiabatic (no loss or gain of energy) wetting of the drying air. Design of fogging, whether of water or pesticide, requires a knowledge of psychrometric processes. The processes that go on in ventilating, cooling, heating, or controlling the humidity in a building can be described most easily with the use of a psychrometric chart.

Sensible heating is adding heat to air without changing its humidity ratio. Applications of sensible heating include heated-air grain drying and winter heating of room air in buildings. This process follows along a horizontal line on the psychrometric chart, moving from left to right (fig. 12.5). The heating effect is equal to the product of the mass of air

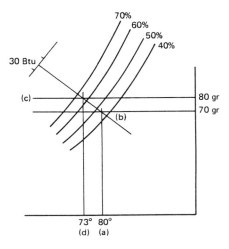

Figure 12.7. Evaporative cooling.

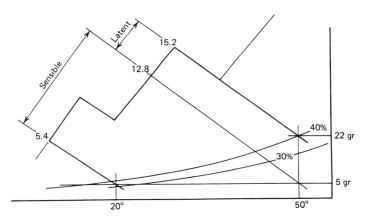

Figure 12.8. Heating and humidifying.

heated times the difference in the enthalpy of the air before and after heating.

Sensible cooling is cooling at constant humidity ratio. An example is air passing over a cooling coil with a surface temperature above the dewpoint temperature of the air. Sensible cooling follows a horizontal line from right to left (fig. 12.6). The final temperature cannot be below the initial dewpoint temperature, or water vapor condenses and the process removes latent heat.

Evaporative cooling is an adiabatic saturation process (no heat gained or lost) and follows upward along a constant enthalpy line (fig. 12.7). Air to be cooled is brought in contact with water at a temperature equal to the wet-bulb temperature of the air. The sensible heat of the air is used to evaporate the water, resulting in a decrease of the air's dry-

Table 12-5. Thermodynamic properties of moist air

Temp (°C)	Humidity Ratio (kg$_w$/kg$_a$) W$_s$	Volume (m³/kg) d.a.		Enthalpy (kJ/kg) d.a.		Vapor Press (kPa)
		v$_a$	v$_w$	h$_a$	h$_w$	p$_s$
-60	0.000007	0.603	0.0000	-60.35	0.02	0.0011
-55	0.000013	0.617	0.0000	-55.32	0.03	0.0021
-50	0.000024	0.631	0.0000	-50.29	0.06	0.0039
-45	0.000045	0.645	0.0000	-45.26	0.11	0.0072
-40	0.000079	0.660	0.0001	-40.23	0.19	0.0128
-35	0.000138	0.674	0.0001	-35.20	0.34	0.2235
-30	0.000235	0.688	0.0003	-30.17	0.57	0.0380
-25	0.000391	0.702	0.0004	-25.14	0.96	0.0633
-20	0.000673	0.717	0.0007	-20.11	1.57	0.1033
-15	0.001021	0.731	0.0012	-15.09	2.52	0.1653
-10	0.001606	0.745	0.0019	-10.06	3.99	0.2599
-5	0.002486	0.759	0.0030	-5.03	6.19	0.4018
0	0.003790	0.773	0.0047	0.00	9.47	0.6111
5	0.005424	0.788	0.0068	5.03	13.61	0.8725
10	0.007661	0.802	0.0098	10.06	19.29	1.2280
15	0.010692	0.816	0.0140	15.09	27.02	1.7055
20	0.014758	0.830	0.0196	20.12	37.43	2.3389
25	0.020170	0.844	0.0273	25.15	51.35	3.1693
30	0.027329	0.859	0.0376	30.18	69.82	4.2462
35	0.036756	0.873	0.0514	35.22	94.24	5.6280
40	0.049141	0.887	0.0698	40.25	126.43	7.3838
45	0.065411	0.901	0.0943	45.29	168.87	9.5935
50	0.086858	0.915	0.1272	50.33	225.02	12.3503
55	0.115321	0.930	0.1713	55.36	299.77	15.7601
60	0.15354	0.941	0.2315	60.41	400.46	19.9439

bulb temperature. Sensible heat is converted to latent heat in the added water vapor. Evaporative cooling is most effective in hot, dry climates, where the wet-bulb depression is large and the disadvantage of increased humidity is more than offset by a relatively large temperature drop.

Heating and humidifying of ventilation air occurs as the air moves through livestock buildings. Animals produce heat, vapor, and water; both sensible heat and water vapor are added to the ventilating air (fig. 12.8).

Cooling and dehumidifying lowers both the dry-bulb temperature and humidity ratio. The process path depends on the type of equipment used. In summer air conditioning, air passes over a cold finned-type evaporator coil of a refrigeration unit. The air is cooled below the dewpoint temperature and moisture condenses thus the humidity ratio is reduced. However, unless reheated or initially saturated, the final relative humidity of the moist air is always higher than at the start. Both sensible heat and latent heat are removed from the air in this process.

Adiabatic mixing of moist air is a common process to obtain air at a third condition. If mixing is adiabatic, it is governed by the following balances: air mass balance, heat balance, and water mass balance. The state point of the air-water mixture after adiabatic mixing of air at two different states falls on the straight line connecting the two initial state points on the psychrometric chart. The final state is the point dividing the line into two parts proportional to the weight of dry air being mixed.

Problems

12.1. A wet-bulb temperature of 50°F (10°C) and a dry-bulb temperature of 66°F (19°C) are read from a psychrometer. For these temperatures, read the following from a psychrometric chart: (a) relative humidity, (b) humidity ratio, (c) dewpoint temperature, (d) humid volume, (e) specific volume enthalpy.

12.2. If 20 lb of air is initially at 44°F, 63% RH and has 300 Btu of heat added, what would be the final temperature?

12.3. If the air temperature is 45°F, what would it be in Celsius, Kelvin, and Rankine?

12.4. What is the potential evaporative cooling capacity of 95°F, 40% RH air?

12.5. What will be the final temperature and relative humidity in a space that is 10 × 12 × 20 ft, if the initial conditions are 46°F, 60% RH, and 1,800 Btu is added? Assume no heat loss from the space.

12.6. At what rate must water evaporate to cool air from 96°F, 33% RH to 80°F?

12.7. How much moisture is gained when 1260 cfm of air goes from 38°F, 80% RH to 70°F, 76% RH?

12.8. What is the volume of 5 lb of dry air at 50°F and 14.7 psi?

12.9. One pound of dry air contains 100 gr of water vapor at 80°F. Determine the following: (a) volume, (b) relative humidity, (c) wet-bulb temperature, (d) dewpoint temperature, (e) enthalpy.

12.10. How would sensible heating be described in terms of the psychrometric chart?

12.11. What limits the potential cooling that can be derived by evaporating water?

12.12. If the thermal capacity of air is 0.24 Btu/lb-°F, how much heat energy must be supplied to heat 10 lb of air from 20°F to 50°F?

12.13. Use the psychrometric chart to determine the following:

Given: dewpoint temperature of 62°F and 50% RH

Find:

    (a) dry-bulb temperature   _____

    (b) wet-bulb temperature   _____

    (c) humidity ratio   _____

    (d) humid volume   _____

    (e) enthalpy   _____

12.14. At what rate is water absorbed by air going from 50°F, 50% RH, to 86°F, 30% RH?

12.15. If air is initially at 90°F, 40% RH, what dry-bulb temperature could be attained by evaporative cooling to saturation (i.e., 100% efficient)?

13 Animal Thermal Environment

Animals have a complex physiology which causes them to interact with their environment in various ways. Animal health, productivity, social behavior, and heat and moisture production are all influenced by environmental factors, and simultaneously these responses affect the environment. Adverse environments can affect breeding efficiency, human health, and cause deterioration of equipment and buildings. The objective of environmental control systems is to minimize stress in order to optimize productivity, health, and comfort.

Physical factors such as temperature, moisture, gaseous concentrations, light, sound, air velocity, and atmospheric pressure may affect animal production, health, and stress of animals. Animal performance can also be affected by the size of animal groups and the space available per animal. Microorganisms are also part of the environment and can have adverse effects on humans and animals.

Modification of the environment may range from something as simple as providing shade, to a sophisticated system that controls temperature, moisture level, and air movement within narrow limits. With many environmental factors that can be modified, it is useful to learn as much as possible about animal response to the environment in order to provide the best practical conditions. It is essential to know how animals respond to their environment, how to balance heat and moisture, understand psychrometrics, and how to control ventilation.

Besides the most important factors of temperature, moisture, air movement, and light, there are many other factors that may have minor or even substantial effects. They include:

- Radiation from or to surroundings
- Barometric pressure
- Water effects on skin
- Duration and quality of light
- Ultraviolet radiation
- Dust and other airborne particles
- Insects and parasites
- Carbon dioxide, ammonia, and other atmospheric gases
- Disease organisms
- Allergy-producing aerosols

To a lesser extent, such things as:
- Cosmic radiation
- Atmospheric electricity
- Terrestrial magnetism
- Gravity

As well as some of the physical aspects like:
- Space per animal
- Sound and color
- Wall and floor surfaces
- Feed and waste management practices

Homeothermy

Domestic animals are homeothermic which means they maintain a nearly constant core body temperature, i.e.:

$$\text{heat loss} = \text{heat gain} + \text{heat produced.}$$

The state of *homeothermy* refers to the constant core body temperature; however, under certain conditions the core body temperature will change. Normal body temperatures are given in table 13-1. If the body temperature falls below the norm, then a condition of *hypothermy* develops; if the body temperature increases above the norm then the state is called *hyperthermy*. The term *homeostasis* refers to the maintenance of a steady-state internal environment. *Homeokinesis* means a dynamic, yet consistent environment.

Table 13-1. Normal and critical temperature for animals

Normal Body Temperature, °F (°C)		
Species	Average	Range
Dairy	101.5 (38.6)	100.4-102.8 (38.0-39.3)
Beef	101.0 (38.3)	
Sheep	102.3 (39.1)	100.9-103.8 (38.3-39.9)
Swine	102.5 (39.2)	
Poultry	107.1 (41.7)	105.0-109.4 (40.6-43.0)
Horse	100.2 (37.9)	
Human	98.6 (37.0)	
Lower Critical Temperature		
Calf	50 (10)	
Lactating dairy	−22 (−24)	
Beef feeder	−40 (−40)	
Recommended Temp Ranges		
		Maximum
Calf	50-80 (10-26)	90 (32)
Lactating dairy	40-75 (4-24)	86 (30)
Beef	40-80 (4-26)	90 (32)
Sheep	40-75 (4-24)	90 (32)

Maintaining constant internal body temperature means balancing heat loss with heat production. Over a period of time, loss must exceed heat gain from surroundings, since heat is produced by metabolism, production, fermentation or heat increment of transformation and exercise. Body heat is lost by conduction, radiation, convection, and evaporation. In the comfort zone, evaporative losses are about 25% of the total. Above the comfort zone, evaporative losses increase and become the predominate mechanism. As ambient temperature increases, the temperature difference (body to ambient) is less, therefore, the sensible heat loss is reduced.

The animal's internal environment is controlled by many interactions, but a major role is played by the hypothalamus which is involved in sensation and regulation of body temperature, thirst, hunger, appetite, satiety, pain, and certain emotions. This is the animal's environmental control center. Different species and breeds have different tolerances to environmental conditions. The ability to dissipate heat relates to such factors as surface area, thickness of hair or wool, and whether the animal can perspire or must depend on panting for evaporative cooling.

The hypothalamus gland, the body's temperature regulator, attempts to maintain a constant body temperature by making physical or chemical changes in the body. For example, increased metabolic activity and greater conversion of feed-to-heat energy are used to counteract low ambient temperatures. In contrast, increased respiration and blood circulation in the skin counteract high ambient temperatures.

Heat production, heat loss, and deep-body temperature will vary with environmental temperature (see fig. 13.1). The effective temperature incorporates all components of the thermal environment, such as air temperature, air movement, radiation, and humidity.

There are five zones of environmental temperature shown in figure 13.1. The zone of thermal comfort, in the middle of the figure, is the range where there is minimal thermoregulatory effort, and very little change in rate of either sensible or evaporative heat with temperature change. Metabolic activity and, thus, heat production is constant and minimal across the zone of thermal neutrality, which includes the zone of thermal comfort. The lower end of this zone is bounded by the lower critical temperature (below which metabolism increases in order to maintain thermal equilibrium). The upper limit of the thermal neutral zone is the hyperthermic point (this is also the upper critical temperature). Above this temperature, heat production and core body temperature will increase. Below the lower critical temperature, the animal can maintain core body temperature by increasing metabolic rate, but efficiency decreases. At some point, the additional metabolic heat cannot be generated, homeothermy fails, and the core temperature and heat production decline. This pattern can lead to death from cold.

An animal is under stress when exposed to temperatures outside the zone of thermal comfort. When the environmental temperature begins to fall near the lower critical temperature, such physical adjustments as vasoconstriction and erection of hair or feathers are used to conserve metabolic heat. *Vasoconstriction* reduces blood flow to the skin reducing heat transfer by blood from the body core to the surface and the coefficient of thermal conductivity in that area. *Piloerection* increases the insulation value by holding more air in the coat cover.

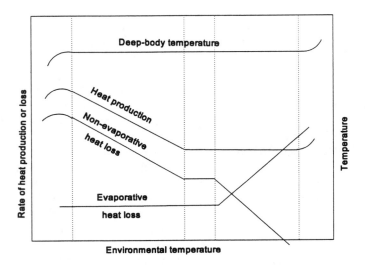

Figure 13.1. Relationship between heat production, heat loss, and deep-body temperature.

Physical regulation is the only means available to combat heat stress due to rising environmental temperature. The surface vascular vessels enlarge (*vasodilation*) increasing blood flow to the surface. This raises the skin surface temperature which increases the temperature difference between the skin surface and the environment and, thus, results in increased rate of heat transfer. Sweating, increased respiration or both begin in some species. The only common domestic animals which have the physiological ability to perspire to any great extent are humans and horses. Other animals depend on rapid respiration (panting) for most of their cooling under high temperature conditions and are much more likely to suffer seriously during periods of higher-than-average temperatures. Appetite also is depressed to reduce body heat production.

As temperature difference (body minus environmental temperature) decreases, less heat can be lost by conduction, convection, and radiation, thus sensible heat production decreases with increasing temperature. Latent heat production generally increases with increasing temperature. Evaporative heat loss becomes predominant at higher temperature. When evaporation reaches its maximum rate, the core temperature begins to increase. A rise in body temperature causes an increased rate of biochemical reactions (van't Hoff effect) which further increases heat production. If this continues, death will occur.

Environmental Temperature

Humidity has the effect of increasing the effective temperature in a livestock facility. At 95°F (35°C) and 100% RH, the effective temperature will be about 15 to 20°F (10°C) higher than if the humidity were near 0%. At low temperatures, wind makes the temperature seem even colder (table 13-2) and the heat production by animals will be increased in drafts. Hair acts to insulate animals and reduces the depression of the skin

Table 13-2. Effect of air movement on pig comfort

Temperature °F (C)	Minimum age of pigs that were comfortable (younger pigs were uncomfortable), days		
	Air Velocity (f/min; m/s)		
	< 30 (0.15)	30-50 (0.15-0.25)	50-60 (0.25-0.38)
70 (21)	All pigs comfortable		56
64 (18)	7	35	84
59 (15)	10	20	84
55 (13)	56	84	98
50 (10)	105	112	112
45 (7)	140	98	140
39 (4)	140	140	140
36 (2)	All pigs uncomfortable		

surface temperature when exposed to cold temperatures. Higher air velocity reduces the effectiveness of hair as an insulator and reduces the insulative boundary layer of air around the body. The effects of temperature and humidity may be expressed in the form of a temperature and humidity index (THI) such as the following:

$$THI = 1.0 \, t_{db} + 0.36 \, t_{dp} + 41.2 \quad (°C) \tag{13.1}$$

The effect of the radiant heat load is measured by mean radiant temperature (MRT). The MRT is not measured directly but may be estimated by using a black globe thermometer. The MRT is a function of (1) the solar radiation, (2) the geometry of the shelter, (3) the shelter materials, (4) air velocity, and (5) air temperature (Esmay and Dixon, 1986). Heat is exchanged with a black globe thermometer by radiation and convection. At steady state, $q_r = q_c$ which leads to the following expression for mean radiant temperature:

$$q_r = \varepsilon \sigma \left(T_m^4 - T_g^4 \right) \tag{13.2}$$

$$q_c = h_c \sqrt{v \left(t_g - t_a \right)} \tag{13.3}$$

thus:

$$T_m = \left[T_g^4 + \frac{h_c \sqrt{v} \left(t_g - t_a \right)}{\varepsilon \sigma} \right]^{1/4}$$

$$= \left[T_g^4 + \frac{13.46 \sqrt{v} \left(t_g - t_a \right)}{0.94 \times 5.67 \times 10^{-8}} \right]^{1/4} \tag{13.4}$$

$$= 100 \left[\left(\frac{T_g}{100} \right)^4 + 2.5 \sqrt{v} \left(t_g - t_a \right) \right]^{1/4}$$

where

e = emissivity of the globe surface (0.94)

s =   Stephan-Boltzman constant (5.67×10^{-8} W/m^{2}K^4)

h_c =   13.46 W/m^2 K (for a 15 cm diameter metal globe)

T_m =   mean radiant temperature

t_g =   black globe temperature

T_g = t_g + 273°K

v =   air velocity (m/s)

The above temperature is incomplete in giving a total measure of animal stress. It can be improved by including a measure of humidity. The black globe temperature and humidity index have been combined into a black globe humidity index (BGHI). This index, as given below, indicates the effects of radiant heat, humidity, and temperature on animals.

$$\text{BGHI} = 0.7\ t_{wb} + 0.2\ t_g + 0.1\ t_a \qquad (13.5)$$

where

t_{wb} =   wet-bulb temperature

t_a =   air dry-bulb temperature

Adaptation to Environment

It is nearly impossible for an animal to be continuously in balance or in harmony with its environment; however, slight variations in balance are not harmful. At some point the animal may react or make adjustments to the imbalances. *Strain* is a functional, structural or behavioral reaction to an environmental stimulus. Strain may be adaptive or non-adaptive. The effect on the animal is *stress*; a stressor provokes an adaptive response. Stress, which may be *chronic* (gradual and sustained) or *acute* (abrupt and often profound), can induce an adaptative response. The adaptation can be *acclimation*, compensatory alterations due to single stressor; *acclimatization*, resulting from reactions to many varying environmental factors;or *habituation*, resulting when certain stimuli repeated many times, i.e., an animal may become "used to" noise from an airport. Some stresses such as long-term climatic conditions may result in genetic adaptation.

Stress can have a significant impact on production. For instance, milk production may decline as a result of temperature increases. This response has been modeled as follows:

$$D = 1.365 + N \times f\left(T_{db},\ T_{wb}\right) \qquad (13.6)$$

$$f\left(T_{db},\ T_{wb}\right) = 1.94 - 0.0704\ T_{wb} + 0.00415\ T_{db}\ T_{wb} \qquad (13.7)$$

where

D   =   decline in milk (kg/day-cow)

N   =   normal level (kg/day-cow)

T_{db} =   dry-bulb temp (°C)

T_{wb} =   wet-bulb temp (°C)

or

$$D = 1.075 - 1.736N + 0.2474(N)(THI) \qquad (13.8)$$

$$THI = 0.72 \left(T_{db} + T_{wb}\right) + 40.6 \qquad (13.9)$$

The comfort, or lack of stress, of animals will be determined in part by the thermal environment. The interrelationship of temperature and air velocity on the comfort of various size pigs is illustrated in the table 13-2.

HEAT AND MOISTURE PRODUCTION

All living beings utilize substrate or food and process it for energy and/or new cell material. Only part of the feed that is consumed is converted to new cell material or product; much of the feed is converted to waste, heat, energy for use by the animal, or for maintenance functions (fig. 13.2). Under most conditions these processes are carried out under aerobic conditions in animals, i.e., oxygen is utilized. This means that healthy animals require oxygen to be supplied and carbon dioxide, a waste product of the digestion process, to be removed.

Temperature tolerance varies with species and animal size. The rate of internal heat production by animals varies with size, body weight, breed, health, growth stage, feed type and intake rate, production level, gestation, age, degree of activity, and environmental conditions (figs. 13.3 and 13.4). Approximately 25 to 40% of the feed energy intake may be converted to heat during digestion. As previously discussed, metabolic heat production varies with environmental temperature. A general equation for relating heat production to animal size was developed by Brody:

$$q_b = K \ W^{0.734} \qquad (13.10)$$

where

q_b = basal heat production (Btu/h)
K = coefficient
W = animal weight (lb)

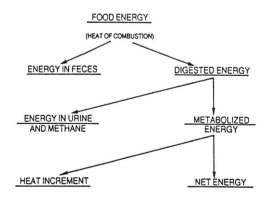

Figure 13.2. Feed energy partitioning.

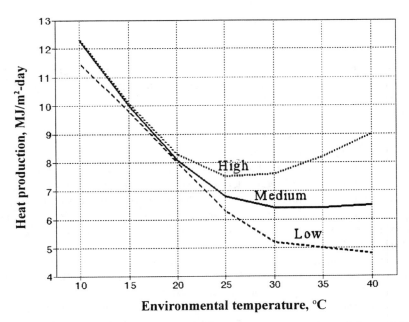

Figure 13.3. Heat production per unit surface area of a sheep at three different levels of feed energy.

The sensible heat fraction decreases from about 80% at 50°F to 0% at 95°F (fig. 13.5). At lower temperatures, most of the latent heat lost may be by respiratory vapor, but as the temperature increases this may shift to predominately surface vaporization.

Latent heat load in a livestock facility will vary depending on the building design. One study indicated that at 60°F, the latent heat load in a building with totally slotted floors was only about one-half of that found with 35% slotted floors (table 13-3). Total solid concrete floors had an even higher latent heat load. In all cases, the latent heat load increased with increasing temperature.

Heat production by livestock varies with environmental conditions (tables 13-4 and 13-5). As temperature decreases, heat loss increases; this effect is greater for smaller animals which have higher surface:mass ratios. Physical activity causes variation in the rate of heat production; the rates of heat and moisture production are greater during the day than at night when animals are less active. Latent heat production as measured in experiments usually includes some evaporation. Heat production by nursery pigs has been given as:

$$HP = -5.78 + 7.92\ Wt^{0.75} - 0.072T$$
$$+ 0.90\ VFI - 0.043T \times Wt$$

(13.11)

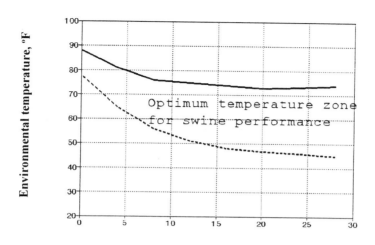

Figure 13.4. Apparent optimum temperature zone for swine.

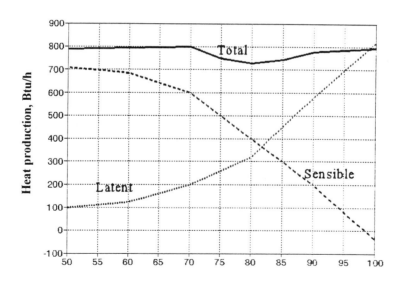

Figure 13.5. Effect of temperature on heat loss of three Ayshire bulls 6 to 12 months of age.

Table 13-3. Heat production from swine

Floor type	Solid		35% Slat	
Density (m^2/pig)	0.91	0.62	0.62	0.71
Temperature (average °C)	15.5	18.0	15.0	11.0
Water consumption: (L/day-pig)	7.7	10.0	10.0	5.5
Latent heat (kJ/h-pig)	224	257	163	136
Sensible (kJ/h-pig)	515	586	370	281
Floor latent (kJ/h-pig)	150	180	78	67
Floor latent:Total	0.20	0.21	0.15	0.16

Table 13-4. Heat production by 1000 lb (455 kg) cow

Temperature °F (C)	Latent lb/cow-h (kg/cow-h)	Sensible btu/cow-h (W/cow)	Total btu/cow-h (W/cow)
20 (-7)	0.67 (0.30)	3200 (940)	3900 (1140)
40 (4)	0.91 (0.41)	2650 (780)	3600 (1050)
60 (15)	1.28 (0.58)	1900 (560)	3240 (950)
80 (27)	1.82 (0.82)	1000 (290)	2900 (850)

where

HP	=	heat production (MJ/WK-pig)
Wt	=	weight (kg)
T	=	dry-bulb temp (c)
VFI	=	voluntary feed intake (kg/WK-pig) – a function of temperature, animal weight, and metabolizable energy

Heat Loss from Animals

The rate of heat production and, therefore, heat loss from animals, is affected by gross physical and internal (digestion) activity. Heat loss from pigs exhibits a 24-h cycle; it has been found to be maximum in late afternoon and minimum in early morning. The amplitude of the cycle was 20% of the mean value.

Heat loss may be expressed by:

$$Q = Ahk(t_1 - t_2)\theta \qquad (13.12)$$

where

A = surface area
h = coefficient of heat transfer
k = constant which varies with surface conditions
θ = time

The heat transfer rate is given by:

$$q = Ah(t_1 - t_2) \qquad (13.13)$$

Table 13-5. Sensible and latent heat produced from livestock, Btu/h-lb (W/kg)

	50°F (10°C)	68°F (20°C)
Dairy		
Sensible	1.1 (0.71)	2.3 (1.48)
Latent	1.4 (0.90)	1.7 (1.10)
Dairy in stanchions		
Sensible	2.4 (1.54)	1.7 (1.10)
Latent	1.0 (0.66)	1.4 (0.88)
Calf (50 kg)		
Sensible	3.7 (2.4)	2.5 (1.6)
Latent	1.9 (1.2)	3.1 (2.0)
Pigs (22 kg)		
Sensible	4.8 (3.1)	3.1 (2.0)
Latent	2.8 (1.8)	3.9 (2.5)
Laying hens		
Sensible	5.9-6.8 (3.8-4.4)	5.0-6.5 (3.2-4.2)
Latent	2.2-2.8 (1.4-1.8)	2.3-3.6 (1.5-2.3)

Applying the heat loss equation to animals requires determining the body surface area. The following equation may be used to estimate the body surface area:

$$A = kW^n \qquad (13.14)$$

where

A = surface area (m^2)
W = animal weight (kg)
k, n = coefficients as given below:
cattle: k = 0.12; n = 0.60
Holstein: k = 0.21; n = 0.48
Brown Swiss: k = 0.34; n = 0.39
Jersey: k = 0.26; n = 0.43
swine: k = 0.0974; n = 0.63

Part of the surface area will be subject to heat loss by radiation and convection, and part of the body will only lose heat by conduction (fig. 13.6). The fractions of the body surface which are subjected to the different modes of heat loss will vary depending on whether the animal is standing or lying and whether it is alone or huddled in a group. For general estimating, the following exposure may be assumed for the different transfer modes: 75% for radiation, 80% for convection, and 20% for conduction.

Heat loss from animals is controlled by laws of heat and mass transfer; chemical and physical regulation will be used to control the loss. Chemical regulation involves metabolism. Physical regulation involves blood circulation, hair/feather erection, and huddling. Sensible heat dissipation is mostly through the skin, while latent heat loss involves res-

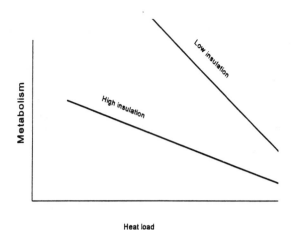

Figure 13.6. Heat loss rate per unit weight of
newborn pigs vs. air temperature.

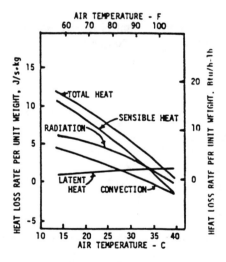

Figure 13.7. Relationship between heat load
and metabolism at two levels of insulation
and two levels of metabolic rate.

piration plus sweating. The percent of total heat that is dissipated by evaporation increases with temperature. The percentage lost by respiration varies with species as follows:

Cattle < Swine < Sheep (fleece) < Poultry (feathers)

Evaporative cooling rates for dairy cattle may be as high as 30 Btu/(h•ft^2) from the sur-

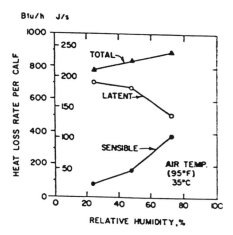

Figure 13.8. Effect of humidity on heat losses of Ayshire bull calves 6 to 10 months of age.

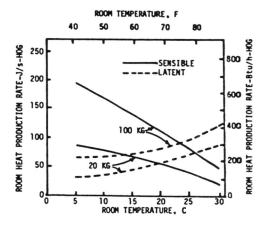

Figure 13.9. Room sensible and latent heat production rate in a hog house (solid floor).

face and the equivalent of 10 Btu/(h•ft^2) by respiratory evaporation. The rate of surface evaporation is a function of the wetted area, air velocity, and the difference in vapor pressure from the surface to the air (fig. 13.8). Water may arrive at evaporation site by:

- Passive diffusion through skin (transcutaneous diffusion). Depends on vapor pressure gradient and may go in either direction. The typical rate at 40°C is 10 g/m^2-h.

- Active deposit (sweating). Sweat glands are part of the hair-follicle unit, i.e., density essentially the same as hair density. Sweat rate in cattle may reach 200 g/m^2-h, while humans may evaporate 1000 g/m^2-h.
- External application (sprinkling or wallow). Swine may evaporate 800 g/m^2-h.

The hair-to-air heat transfer coefficient for dairy cattle has been given as about 2 $W/m^2°C$ in the range of −15°C to 30°C. The skin-to-hair coefficient was given as 3 $W/m^2°C$ at −15°C and 40 $W/m^2°C$ at 30°C. The heat conductance changes due to change in length and orientation of hair. The conductivity varies linearly with the ratio of hair coat depth to length (Esmay & Dixon), increasing from 15 W-$cm/m^2°C$ at 24% to 37 W-$cm/m^2°C$ at 72%. For a 4-cm hair length this would represent a overall heat transfer coefficient of 15.6 $W/m^2°C$ at the lower ratio and 12.8 $W/m^2°C$ at the higher ratio.

Problems

13.1. What is meant by homeothermy?

13.2. What is the meaning of lower critical temperature?

13.3. How might the feed ration be related to housing environment, i.e., could a change in the ration have any effect on the environment or the need to adjust the environmental control system?

13.4. In general, how does heat load (heat that must be removed) in livestock housing vary with animal size?

13.5. Part of the feed energy ingested by an animal is partitioned to "heat increment of transformation". What is significant about this, i.e., why is it important with regard to a ventilation system?

13.6. How does the hypothalamus gland relate to environmental control?

13.7. Does sensible and/or latent heat production by animals increase or decrease as environmental temperature increases?

13.8. Under what conditions might the body respond to the environment by increasing the rate of blood circulated to the skin surface?

13.9. What is the significance of vasodilation?

13.10. When and why might animals respond to environmental conditions by rapid respiration?

13.11. How are humidity and wind speed related to animal comfort?

14 Heat and Moisture Control in Buildings

Heat transfer theory is useful in determining heat loads in buildings requiring modi-fication of environment. The modification may require supplemental heat from a heating system or heat removal by either refrigeration or ventilation. A knowledge of how heat travels through building components can aid in wall, ceiling, and window design and allow insulation types and amounts to be chosen. It can also help in pre-dicting the probability of condensation on or within a wall.

Combined Heat Transfer

While there are occasions when it is necessary to study heat transfer by a single mode, in the field of agricultural buildings it is the total heat transfer which is usual-ly of interest. The transfer of heat from a warm space through a solid medium to a cooler air space (as in the case of heat loss through a barn wall in winter) involves all methods of heat transfer including conduction, convection, and radiation. The wall may be constructed of several materials, each with a different resistance to heat flow. In addition, the surface layers of air on either side of the wall and the air space with-in the wall will resist the flow of heat.

With a knowledge of the heat-transfer resistance coefficients (R), the thickness of the materials from which a wall or ceiling is made, and the area of the surface, it is not difficult to find the heat transfer for each degree of temperature difference between the two surfaces.

In determining the heat transfer through walls, ceilings, and floors, the following terms are commonly used:

U = overall coefficient of heat transfer through a wall [Btu/(h-ft^2°F); W/(m^{2}K)]

k = thermal conductivity of a material per inch of thickness [Btu-in./(h-ft^2°F); Wm/(m^{2}K)]

C = thermal conductivity of material for the thickness used [Btu/(h-ft^2°F); W/(m^{2}K)]

f = thermal conductivity of a surface air layer [Btu/(h-ft^2°F); [W/(m^{2}K)]

a = thermal conductivity of an air space [Btu/(h-ft^2°F); W/(m^{2}K)]

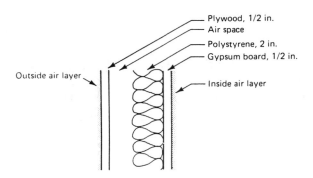

Figure 14.1. Heat transmission through a composite wall.

R   =   resistance to heat flow expressed as $1/k$, $1/C$ or $1/f$
R_t =   resistance to heat flow through a material or composite
        expressed as $1/k + 1/C + 1/f + R + ... = R_t$ (h-ft^2°F)/Btu [(m^{2}K)/W]
U   = $1/R$

To find the heat loss through a wall section, it is necessary to determine the conductivities for each film, layer of material, and air space. The reciprocal, or "R-value", of the material of each of these values is added to obtain an "R_t-value". The "U-value" is then $U = 1/R$. Note that the total resistance to heat flow is found by summation, but the total conductance is not, i.e., $R_t = R_1 + R_2 + R_3 + \dots$. However, U total does not $= C_1 + C_2 + \dots$. The total conductance, U, will always be less than the individual conductances through the layer with the least conductivity.

The heat transfer coefficients of different materials vary with density and moisture content of the material. The R-values, or insulation values, for some of the more commonly used building and insulating materials are given in table 14-1. The method for determining the conductivity (U) for a wall is illustrated in figure 14.1. The composite wall consists of the following layers: outside air layer, 1/2-in. plywood, an air space bounded by dull surfaces, 2 in. of polystyrene, 1/2-in. gypsum board, and an inside air layer. (The U-values for a number of wall and ceiling constructions are given in table 14-2.)

The heat transfer through a wall or ceiling may be determined with the following equation:

$$q = A\,U\,\Delta t \quad \text{or} \quad q = \left(\frac{A}{R_t}\right)\Delta t \qquad (14.1)$$

where

q   =   rate of heat transfer (Btu/h; W)
A   =   surface area (ft^2; m^2)
Δt =   temperature difference (°F; °K)

Table 14-1. Thermal conductivity properties of insulating materials

Material	Resistance as given, $1/C$	R-value per in., $1/k$	Conductance, C (Btu/h•ft²°F)	Conductivity, k (Btu/h•ft²°F/in.)
Air spaces (3/4 in.-4 in.):				
Non-reflective, horizontal $\Delta t = 20$	0.91		1.10	
Reflective, horizontal $\Delta t = 10$	2.27		0.44	
Non-reflective, vertical $\Delta t = 10$	1.25			
Reflective, vertical $\Delta t = 10$	3.40			
Reflective, vertical $\Delta t = 30$	2.70			
@ −40°F				0.12
@ 0°F				0.13
@ 80°F				0.15
@ 120°F				0.16
Air film (surfaces)				
Still air, inside, f_i	0.61		1.63	
Outside, 15 mph, f_o	0.17		6.00	
Gypsum board, 3/8 in.	0.32		3.10	
Gypsum plaster		0.32		3.12
1/2 in.	0.63		1.60	
3/4 in.	0.94		1.07	
Plywood, Douglas fir, 0.5 in.	0.62			
Particleboard, low density		1.85		
Particleboard, medium density		1.06		
Particleboard, high density		0.85		
Hardboard, 1 in.	0.18		5.60	
Insulating board, 1/2 in.	1.52		0.66	
25/32	2.37		0.42	
Asbestos-cement board, 1/8 in.	0.03		33.00	
Fir & pine lumber, 7/8 in.	0.98		1.02	
, 1 1/2 in.	2.00		0.50	
Bevel siding, 1/2 in.	0.81		1.23	
Concrete		0.08		12.00
Concrete blocks, 4 in.	0.71		1.40	
8 in.	1.11		0.90	
12 in.	1.28		0.78	
Cinder blocks, 8 in.	1.72		0.58	
Common brick		0.20		
Face brick		0.11		
Stone		0.08		12.50
Glass, single sheet	0.89		1.13	
Window glass, horizontal	0.81			
Window plus storm	2.00			
Insulating glass, one space	1.61			
Insulating glass, two spaces	2.13			

R_t = $1/U = \Sigma R_i$

R_i = resistance through a material

R_i = $x_i/k_i = 1/C$, h-ft²-°F/Btu (m²K/W)

x_i = material thickness (in.; m)

Table 14-1. (continued) Thermal conductivity properties of insulating materials

Material	Resistance as given, 1/C	R-value per in., 1/k	Conductance, C (Btu/h•ft²°F)	Conductivity, k (Btu/h•ft²°F/in.)
Glass, 2 sheets, 1/2 in. air space			0.55	
Glass, block 7 3/4 × 7 3/4 × 3 7/8			0.56	
Blocks, concrete, filled, 12 in.			0.39	
concrete, filled, 8 in.			0.34	
Asphalt shingles		0.44		
Wood shingles		0.87		
Lapped wood siding		0.81		
Glass or rockwool		3.70		0.27
Expanded mica		2.08		0.48
Shavings, 8.8 pcf		2.44		0.41
Sawdust, 6 pcf		2.00		0.29
Balsa wood, 7.3 pcf				0.33
Balsa wood, 20 pcf				0.58
White pine, 29 pcf				0.78
Oak, 38 pcf				1.02
Maple, 44 pcf				1.10
Batt or blanket:				
Glass or mineral wool		2.75-3.67		
Fiberglass, 0.5 pcf				0.33
Fiberglass, 1.0 pcf				0.26
Fiberglass, 1.5 pcf				0.23
Fiberglass, 3.5 pcf				0.21
Fill type:				
Cellulose		3.13-3.70		
Glass or mineral wool		2.20-3.00		
Vermiculite		2.13-2.27		
Rigid insulation:				
Expanded polystyrene				
Extruded, plain		5.00		
Molded beads, 1 pcf		3.85		
Molded beads, 2 pcf		4.35		
Expanded rubber		4.55		
Expanded polyurethane		5.56-6.25		
Glass fiber		4.00		
Wood or cane fiberboard		2.50		
Polyisocyanurate		7.20		
Formed-in-place insulation:				
Polyurethane		5.26-6.25		

Insulation

Buildings that are to be kept warm either by animal heat or supplemental heat will require that insulation be installed in the walls and ceilings, and around foundations and basement walls to achieve efficient use of the heat. Insulating materials have a high thermal resistance that conserves heat in cold weather and reduces heat gain in hot weather. The primary purposes of using insulation are to: (1) reduce heat transfer, i.e., conserve heat in an enclosure, reduce supplemental heat requirements or reduce heat gain; (2) improve comfort, i.e., reduce drafts, reduce radiation effects or provide more uniform temperatures; and (3) prevent condensation caused from low surface temperatures.

Table 14-2. R-values for building components

Material	R-value h·ft²°F/Btu	m²K/W
Windows (includes surface conditions):		
Single glazed, horizontal (winter)	0.81	0.14
Single glazed, vertical (winter)	0.91	0.16
with storm window	2.00	0.35
Insulating glass, 1/4 in. air space		
Double pane	1.69	0.67
Triple pane	2.56	0.45
Doors (exterior, includes surface conditions):		
Wood, solid core, 13/4 in.	3.00	0.53
Metal urethane core, 13/4 in., thermal break	5.88	0.88
Metal urethane core, 13/4 in., no thermal break	2.50	0.44
Concrete blocks:		
8 in. (203 mm) not filled	1.89	0.33
8 in. filled	2.56	0.45
12 in. filled	2.94	0.52
Concrete wall, 6 in. (152 mm)	1.26	0.22
Concrete wall, 6 in. with 1 in. (25 mm) polyurethane	7.54	1.33
Sheet metal wall	0.78	0.14
Plywood wall, 1/2 in. (12 mm) outside	1.40	0.25
Plastic sheet, 0.125 in. (3 mm) thick	0.94	0.17
Polyethylene film, 0.004 in. (1 mm)	0.80	0.14
Polyethylene double film with 3/4 in. (19 mm) space	1.25	0.22
Floor perimeter (per ft of exterior wall length):		
Concrete, no perimeter insulation	1.23*	0.22
Concrete, with 2 in. × 24 in. perimeter insulation	2.22*	0.39

* Per linear foot of perimeter (h-ft-°F/Btu)

Air is a good insulating material. Air films adjacent to surfaces or entrapped air will retard heat flow. The effectiveness of air films depends on the surface conditions and air velocity next to the surface. A dead air space up to 3/4 in. (19 mm) in thickness has a significant insulating value. Beyond a thickness of about 4 in. (100 mm), convection currents within the wall may actually increase the rate of heat transfer unless the currents are interrupted by use of insulation.

How Much Insulation?

Because of the great differences in insulating values of the materials available, the amount of insulation installed should be expressed as R_t and not as inches or millimeters. The R_t level chosen for a building will depend on several factors:

1. The climatic zone and the design temperature used. For example, the maximum heat loss from a 55°F (13°C) dairy stable in central Minnesota may be nearly twice as much as in Delaware. Consequently, nearly double the R-value may be justified in the Minnesota barn.
2. The use of the building and the inside design temperature. A livestock shelter which must be ventilated to remove moisture but which depends on the animals as the only source of heat, will require an R-value adequate to conserve the heat required for ventilation.
3. The cost of heating or cooling a building. When buildings are heated or refrigerated artificially, the fixed costs of insulation are charged off against savings in the cost of providing the heating or cooling for the building. High energy costs often justify installing the maximum amount of insulation that physically can be put into place. For example, wall cavities may be completely filled to the maximum level that will allow the necessary ventilation.

Choosing an Insulating Material

Having determined how much insulating effect is required for a particular application, it is necessary to choose an insulation that is suitable. Insulation is generally a lightweight, bulky material which entraps a lot of air or inert gas. Manufactured insulation is available in a variety of forms including reflective and fill types, batts, blankets, fiber and plastic panels, and foamed-in-place plastics. These insulating products are made from various materials including fiberglass, rockwool, mica, cellular glass, polystyrene, polyurethane, and urea formaldehyde. Some insulating materials are available in more than one form.

No one material or form can possibly be best suited for all applications. A thorough knowledge of the characteristics of each material will allow an appropriate choice for each installation. In addition to the type of insulation for the application and the particular characteristics of the various insulating materials, the last and perhaps most important factor to consider is the cost per unit of R. When selecting insulation, consideration should be given to the following factors:

- R-value. The higher the R-value the more effective the insulation.
- Ease of installation. This will depend on when the insulation is being installed, e.g., a rigid board is easy to handle and install during new construction, but impossible to install inside an existing wall without tearing the wall apart.
- What is to be insulated? The thickness of insulation may be limited in a wall but practically unlimited for a ceiling.
- Fire resistance. Materials that create toxic gases or contribute to flame spread should not be used unless they are covered or other provisions are made to prevent harm to occupants in case of fire.
- Protection required. Livestock, rodents or birds can cause severe damage to insulating materials. Some insulating materials will not withstand moisture or sunlight.

- Effects caused by the insulation. Fire retardant chemicals may be corrosive to metals such as electrical conduit or structural fasteners. Although the materials are normally lightweight, the amount of weight added can be significant if the structural strength is marginal.
- Cost. Cost of preparation, installation, protection, and material purchase must be compared to the benefit to be gained. For comparison, it may be desirable to express cost-in-place "per unit of R".

Forms of Insulation

Most blanket-, batt-, rigid-, and fill-type insulating materials reduce heat flow by conduction and convection. However, those that have one or more shiny surfaces may also resist radiant losses, if the shiny surface faces an air space. The type and location of the components to be insulated will influence the best choice of material to use. Some examples of the suitability of a type of insulation to an application are:

1. Insulation for an existing wall may be limited to a fill-type that can be poured or blown into the wall, a rigid type which is cemented on a surface or a foamed-in-place plastic material.

2. Blanket or batt material is often the least expensive to place within a new wall. It will be easy to install and will not settle. Batts are designed to fit 16 or 24 in. (400 or 600 mm) stud spacings.

3. Insulation placed between ceiling joists may be either batt or loose fill depending on which is least expensive.

4. The insulating value of materials with shiny surfaces increases in effectiveness as the temperature rises. For example, aluminum roofing is much more effective in insulating against summer sun than winter heat loss. To be effective, the shiny surfaces must not be in direct contact with any other material, but should abut an air space which cuts heat loss by conduction and convection.

5. Rigid insulation may have adequate structural strength to be installed under a concrete floor or a roof surface.

6. Some rigid insulating materials may be used as wall or ceiling surfaces. The savings in labor and cost of other surfacing material may make an otherwise expensive product the lowest cost when installed for the dual role.

7. Some materials are very porous and readily allow water vapor transmission while others may be completely impervious. The latter may not need a vapor retarder, while the former will need either an excellent vapor retarder or good ventilation across its cold surface. For example, expanded polystyrene panels need no additional vapor retarder. However, glass or mineral wool used in a wall would need a good vapor retarder. The need for a vapor retarder has been questioned when glass or mineral wool is installed in a ceiling with a well-ventilated attic above residential areas or similar spaces.

8.   Although a number of insulations are classified as "self extinguishing", "fire retardant" or "non-burning", serious flash fires can result in certain unusual circumstances. For example, the asphalt-attached paper found on some batt or blanket material may burn rapidly even though the insulation itself does not. Also, some foam insulations, when exposed to high temperatures and restricted ventilation, may fail to live up to their billing of being "non-burning". In the case of a large building, it is advisable to check with an insurance company before making a final decision about the choice of insulation.

Some of the more common insulating materials and their characteristics include:

1.   Fiberglass and rockwool are of medium insulating value, very permeable, and fireproof. They are available as loose fill, batts, and blankets, and fiberglass is available in low-density panels. The asphalt-attached vapor barrier found on some batts and blankets is flammable.

2.   Cotton, cellulose, and shredded bark are of medium insulating value, permeable, and available as fill or blankets. Cellulose is made from paper and pulp products. They are usually treated to improve fire resistance and may have integral vapor barriers.

3.   Shavings, sawdust, and straw are of rather low insulating value and have an affinity for moisture and vermin. It is usually poor economics to use them except for temporary purposes.

4.   Expanded mica is of rather low insulating value, but it is inert and sometimes the only fill insulation that can be poured into a wall, particularly masonry-block walls.

5.   Fiber insulating boards are of rather low insulating value but may be suitable for a wall or ceiling surface while at the same time offering some resistance to heat flow. In the thickness available for sheathing, they offer more insulation than plywood or lumber.

6.   Cellular glass has a rather low insulating value, but is impermeable and has sufficient structural strength for use under concrete floors that are to be heavily loaded.

7.   Expanded polystyrene is available in extruded form or as molded beads. The extruded form has better-than-average insulating value and is relatively impermeable to water vapor. The molded bead form has a lower insulating value and is more permeable. Extruded polystyrene may be cemented to masonry walls, installed under concrete floors, and used for ceiling and wall surfaces in protected areas. However, the material may have a low flame resistance, and if left exposed, care should be taken that code requirements are met.

8.   Expanded polyurethane is available as extruded panels or it may be foamed in place. It has excellent insulating value and it may be surfaced with

paper, polyethylene or aluminum. That which is not surfaced is prone to a decrease in insulating value. Its fire resistance is variable, and it is usually recommended that the insulation be covered.

9. Urea formaldehyde is usually foamed in place. It has good insulating value and is reasonably flame resistant. However, some early applications resulted in the release of irritating fumes for long periods after installation; it also may shrink over a period of time.

10. Polyisocyanurate is available in rigid sheets and may be used as a form core for prefabricated wall sections. It is more fire resistant than other plastic foam boards.

Insulation R-value

Insulating materials are rated in terms of R-value; however, a single number rating is not always sufficient to determine the total effect on heat flow. The R-value is intended to indicate the overall resistance to heat transfer through the material and this transfer can involve all modes of heat transfer. The standard temperature for determining the R-value rating is 75°F (24°C). Even when only conductive transfer is involved, remember that conductivity involves molecular activity which will change with temperature, therefore, conductivity is not actually a constant. Except for completely solid materials, expect radiant transfer to have a role other than as a simple function of temperature difference. Air or gases in insulating materials that are subjected to varying temperatures will have varying densities—this can lead to convective currents. Because of resistance to the convective flow of air, it should not be expected that the convective heat transfer would be a linear function of temperature difference. Also, if moisture gets into the insulation, then evaporation and condensation may have a role in the overall heat transfer.

The reduction in conductivity (increase of R-value) as temperature decreases (see figure 14.2) is a favorable phenomenon for cold climates, since this means that insulation is more effective at lower temperatures. It has been observed that at very cold temperatures (–20°F or lower), the measured R-value for loose-fill attic insulation actually decreases. This decrease, which may be as much as 59%, has been attributed to convection currents within the insulation. Covering the loose insulation with an air barrier or blanket is effective in preventing this convective loss.

The conductivity of materials also changes with density (fig. 14.3). The R-value of materials such as fiberglass and cotton-polyester increases as the density increases to a certain point and then begins to decrease. Increasing density from a very low level will reduce air movement within the material, but at some point the solid material becomes more of a factor than the air and the conductivity then begins to increase. Tests on loose fill cellulose showed a gradual decrease in R-value with increasing density without the initial increase. Presumably there is no reduction of air movement with increasing density so the only effect is the increasing percentage of solids.

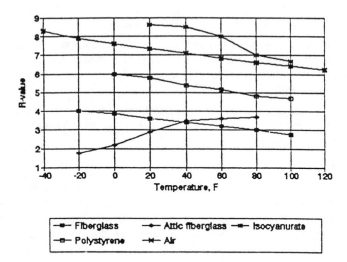

Figure 14.2. Effects of temperature on insulation R-value.

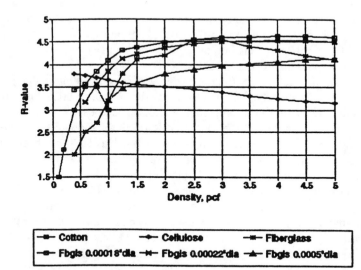

Figure 14.3. Effects of insulation density on insulation R-value.

Table 14-3. Surface heat transfer resistances (h·ft²°F/Btu)

Surface	Direction of Heat Flow	$\varepsilon = 0.90$	$\varepsilon = 0.05$
Horizontal (still air)	Up	0.61	1.32
Horizontal (still air)	Down	0.92	4.55
Vertical (still air)	Horizontal	0.68	1.70
Any position (15 mph wind)	Any	0.17	

Table 14-4. Air space thermal resistances (h·ft²°F/Btu)

Space/Direction of Heat Flow	Mean Temp. (°F)	Temp. Diff. (°F)	E = 0.82	E = 0.05
3/4 in. horizontal/up	50	10	0.87	2.21
3/4 in. horizontal/up	0	10	1.02	2.16
3.5 in. horizontal/up	0	20	1.03	2.18
3/4 in. horizontal/up	0	10	1.12	2.62
3/4 in. horizontal/down	50	10	1.02	3.59
3.5 in. horizontal/down	0	10	1.64	10.32
3/4 in. vertical/horizontal	50	10	1.01	3.46
3.5 in. vertical/horizontal	0	20	1.14	2.78

Surface and Air Space Resistances

Surface resistances combine the effects of conduction, radiation, and convection and are thought of as air films. In an air space, heat flows by convection and radiation. Heat transfer from surfaces or across a space is affected by the surface temperatures and emissivities, air velocity, orientation of the surfaces, width of the space, and temperature difference across the space or between the surface and air. The emissivity for bright aluminum foil is 0.05, but for most building materials the emissivity is about 0.90.

Convection is driven by differences in air density (function of temperature) and is an important factor. When the heat source is above the surface or space, stratification will reduce the formation of convective currents and, thus, increase the resistance to heat transfer. Surface resistances are given in table 14-3 and air space resistances are given in table 14-4.

Total Building Heat Transmission

The heating load or design heat loss for a building is the maximum total heat loss that might be expected from a building except under the most extreme conditions. In determining the heating load, inside and outside temperatures must be used that will represent the extreme conditions. Site specific minimum outside temperatures based

Table 14-5. Example of method for calculating total heat loss

Part	U	Area (ft²)	Outside Temp. (°F)	Temp Diff.	q (Btu/h)
Ceiling	0.05	1,000	5	55	$0.05 \times 1000 \times 55 = 2.750$
Wall	0.10	900	0	60	$0.10 \times 900 \times 60 = 5.400$
Windows	1.13	40	0	60	$1.13 \times 40 \times 60 = 2.712$
Door	1.00	100	0	60	$1.00 \times 100 \times 60 = 6.000$
Floor	0.50	1,000	50	10	$0.50 \times 1000 \times 10 = 5.000$

Total   21.862

on probability analysis of historic weather data are available. For most agricultural applications, 97% probability is suitable. To find the total heat loss from a building, it is necessary to find the U-value for each type of construction (wall, ceiling, window, door, and floor) and then multiply each by the area and the temperature difference. The heat loss for each part may then be added to obtain the total.

The method for obtaining the total heat loss (q) from a building is illustrated in table 14-5. It is assumed that the U-value for each part has been determined previously. The inside temperature is 60°F and the outside temperature is as listed. The floor and ceiling are isolated from outside temperatures.

A general worksheet for calculating heat loss from a building is given as table 14-6. This worksheet includes a "perimeter" which is used to estimate the heat loss through the foundation. Perimeter is a linear value while the other components are in area units.

To determine the heat transfer through a wall framed with wood with a high degree of accuracy, it is necessary to obtain the average coefficient of conductivity, U_{ave}, by combining the conductivity through the framing and the conductivity between the framing. A weighted average may then be taken by multiplying each U-value by the percentage of area and adding the two products.

For example, assume that a wall has 2 in. (38 mm) studs spaced 16 in. (406 mm) on center. It is found that the U-value is 0.5 Btu/(h•ft²°F) through the studs and 0.1 Btu/(h•ft²°F) between the studs. The average U will be $(0.5 \times 2 + 0.1 \times 14)/16 = 0.15$ Btu/(h•ft²°F).

Walls, floors or ceilings framed with metal sections of irregular cross-section present a special problem in determining heat transfer. A detailed method and example may be found in the *ASHRAE Guide*. In brief, the method involves adding the $U \times A$ (A = surface area ft²) for various sections through which the heat flows in parallel, and adding $1/(U \times A)$ for sections through which the heat flows in series.

Example 14.1

Find the heat loss from a 30×40 ft building maintained at 65°F. The outside temperature is −20°F. The building has two, 3×7 ft doors (R = 7.50) and 16 ft² of window area (R = 3.25). The 7 ft frame wall is set on top of a 2 ft concrete wall (R = 5.45) and the foundation is insulated. Ten inches of cellulose insulation is supported by 1 in. plywood for the ceiling. The walls have 1/2 in. plywood on the inside and 1/2 in. lap (wood) siding on the outside with 5 in. fiberglass insulation in between.

Solution (see table 14-6a)

Ceiling R-value:

inside air films (2)	1.22
1 in. plywood	1.24
10 in. cellulose	31.30
R_t =	33.76 (h•ft^2°F)/Btu

Wall R-value:

inside air film	0.68
1/2 in. plywood	0.62
51/2 in. fiberglass	16.50
lap siding	0.81
outside air film	0.17
R_t =	18.78 (h•ft^2°F)/Btu

Ceiling area = 30 ft × 40 ft = 1,200 ft^2

Door area = 2 × 3 ft × 7 ft = 42 ft^2

Stud wall area = 2 × (30 ft + 40 ft) × 7 ft – (42 ft^2 – 6 ft^2) – 16 ft^2 = 928 ft^2

Concrete wall area = 2 × (30 ft + 40 ft) × 1 ft - 6 ft^2 = 134 ft^2

$$\sum A/R = \frac{1200}{33.76} + \frac{42}{7.50} + \frac{16}{3.25} + \frac{928}{18.78} + \frac{134}{5.45} = 120 \text{ Btu/h°F}$$

$$q = A/R \, Dt = 120 \text{ Btu/h°F} \times (85°F - (-20°F)) = 10,200 \text{ Btu/h}$$

Heat Flow from Basements

When estimating heat loss from basements or underground tanks, the soil can be considered as insulation. The length of the heat flow path from an underground tank or basement will vary with depth. The total resistance to heat flow is equal to the sum of the air film, the wall resistance, and the soil resistance, $R_t = [1/f_i + R_w + L_s/K_s]$. The conductivity of the soil will vary with type, ranging from about 1.04 to 1.73 W m/M^{2}K. Assuming the soil conductivity is 1.38 W m/M^{2}K, R_w = 0.2 and 1/f = 0.12; the conductance for a 3 m deep × 1 m slice of a wall is calculated in table 14-7. For a 15 m wall with t = 40°C, the heat loss = 3.00 × 15 × 40 = 1,800 W.

Plotting a Temperature Gradient

The plotting of a temperature gradient on the cross-section diagram of a wall illustrates heat movement through the wall and emphasizes the effect of insulating materials (see fig. 14.4 and table 14-8). The gradient diagram also serves as a starting point in checking for condensation on wall surfaces and within walls, a topic that will be discussed later.

Table 14-6. Worksheet — heat loss calculations

Building Dimensions	(ft)	Surface Area	(ft^2)
Length (L)	_____	Ceiling area	_____
Width (W)	_____	Window area	_____
Frame wall height (H)	_____	Door area	_____
Concrete wall height (F)	_____	Frame wall area	_____
Perimeter	_____	less window & doors	
		Concrete wall area	_____

R_t Values		Design Temperatures	(°F)
Ceiling	_____	t_o (outside temperature)	_____
Windows	_____	t_i (inside temperature)	_____
Doors	_____	Δt	_____
Frame walls	_____		
Concrete walls	_____		
Perimeter	_____		

Building heat loss, q_b

Ceiling
$$q_c = \frac{\Delta t \times \text{ceiling area}}{\text{ceiling } R_t} \qquad q_c = \frac{(\quad) \times (\quad)}{(\quad)} \text{ Btu/h}$$

Windows
$$q_{wi} = \frac{\Delta t \times \text{window area}}{\text{window } R_t} \qquad q_{wi} = \frac{(\quad) \times (\quad)}{(\quad)} \text{ Btu/h}$$

Doors
$$q_d = \frac{\Delta t \times \text{door area}}{\text{door } R_t} \qquad q_d = \frac{(\quad) \times (\quad)}{(\quad)} \text{ Btu/h}$$

Frame walls
$$q_w = \frac{\Delta t \times \text{wall area}}{\text{wall } R_t} \qquad q_w = \frac{(\quad) \times (\quad)}{(\quad)} \text{ Btu/h}$$

Concrete walls
$$q_r = \frac{\Delta t \times \text{concrete wall area}}{\text{concrete wall } R_t} \qquad q_r = \frac{(\quad) \times (\quad)}{(\quad)} \text{ Btu/h}$$

Perimeter
$$q_p = \frac{\Delta t \times \text{perimeter}}{\text{perimeter } R_t} \qquad q_p = \frac{(\quad) \times (\quad)}{(\quad)} \text{ Btu/h}$$

$$q_b = q_c + q_{wi} + q_d + q_w + q_r + q_p = \text{_____ Btu/h}$$

Table 14-6. (a) Worksheet — heat loss calculations

Building Dimensions	(ft)	Surface Area	(ft²)
Length (L)	40	Ceiling area	1200
Width (W)	30	Window area	16
Frame wall height (H)	7	Door area	42
Concrete wall height (F)	2	Frame wall area	934
Perimeter	140	less window & doors	
		Concrete wall area	268

R_t Values		Design Temperatures	(°F)
Ceiling	33.76	t_o (outside temperature)	-20
Windows	3.25	t_i (inside temperature)	65
Doors	7.50	Δt	
Frame walls	18.78		
Concrete walls	5.45		
Perimeter	2.22		

Building heat loss, q_b

Ceiling

$$q_c = \frac{\Delta t \times \text{ceiling area}}{\text{ceiling } R_t} \qquad q_c = \frac{(\ 85\ ) \times (\ 1200\ )}{(\ 33.76\ )} \text{ Btu/h}$$

Windows

$$q_{wi} = \frac{\Delta t \times \text{window area}}{\text{window } R_t} \qquad q_{wi} = \frac{(\ 85\ ) \times (\ 16\ )}{(\ 3.25\ )} \text{ Btu/h}$$

Doors

$$q_d = \frac{\Delta t \times \text{door area}}{\text{door } R_t} \qquad q_d = \frac{(\ 85\ ) \times (\ 42\ )}{(\ 7.50\ )} \text{ Btu/h}$$

Frame walls

$$q_w = \frac{\Delta t \times \text{wall area}}{\text{wall } R_t} \qquad q_w = \frac{(\ 85\ ) \times (\ 934\ )}{(\ 18.78\ )} \text{ Btu/h}$$

Concrete walls

$$q_r = \frac{\Delta t \times \text{concrete wall area}}{\text{concrete wall } R_t} \qquad q_r = \frac{(\ 85\ ) \times (\ 268\ )}{(\ 5.45\ )} \text{ Btu/h}$$

Perimeter

$$q_p = \frac{\Delta t \times \text{perimeter}}{\text{perimeter } R_t} \qquad q_p = \frac{(\ 85\ ) \times (\ 140\ )}{(\ 2.22\ )} \text{ Btu/h}$$

$$q_b = q_c + q_{wi} + q_d + q_w + q_r + q_p = \underline{\hspace{3cm}} \text{ Btu/h}$$

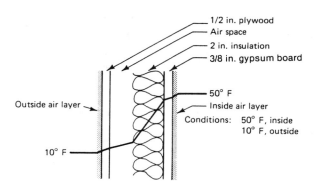

Figure 14.4. Temperature gradient across a wall.

The values t_1, t_2, ... t_n , found with the following formulas, may be plotted on a cross-section diagram of the wall to show the temperature gradient.

$R_t = \Sigma R_i$

$Z = \Delta t/R_t$

$t_1 = R_1 \times Z + t_0$

$t_2 = R_2 \times Z + t_1$

t_3 ... t_n similarly

where .

t_0 = the outside temperature

t_1 = surface temperature of first layer

t_2 ... t_n = succeeding temperatures

R_t = sum of R_1, R_2, ... R_n

Z = degrees per unit of R

R = resistance to heat flow of a layer of wall material

Estimating Temperature in Unheated Spaces

Heat which is lost from a heated space through an unheated space to the outside will cause a temperature change in the unheated space until equilibrium is reached.

$$Q = \frac{(t_i - t_o)}{R} = \frac{(t_i - t_x)}{R_x} \tag{14.3}$$

or

$$t_x = t_i - \left(\frac{R_x}{R}\right)(t_i - t_o) \tag{14.4}$$

After equilibrium, the heat flow into the space will be equal to the heat loss from the space. The following equation can be used to determine the temperature of the space:

Table 14-7. Heat flow through a basement wall

Depth (m)	R_t	U (W/m²°K)	$\Sigma U_i d_i$ (W/m°K)
0.2	0.32 + 0.2/1.38	2.15	0.75
0.5	0.32 + 0.36	1.47	1.34
1.0	0.32 + 0.724	0.96	1.82
1.5	0.32 + 1.09	0.91	2.18
2.0	0.32 + 1.45	0.57	2.61
3.0	0.32 + 2.17	0.40	3.00

Table 14-8. Temperature gradient calculation

Layer (left side)	R	°/ Unit R_t	Temp. Diff.	Plane Temp. (left side)
Outer air layer	0.17 × 3.18	=	0.54	10.00
Plywood, 1/2 in.	0.63 × 3.18	=	2.00	10.54
Air space, dull surface	0.91 × 3.18	=	2.89	12.54
Polystyrene (5 × 2 in.)	10.00 × 3.18	=	31.77	15.43
Gypsum board, 1/2 in.	0.27 × 3.18	=	0.86	47.20
Inner air layer	0.61 × 3.18	=	1.94	48.06
Room air temp.	—		—	50.00
Totals	12.59		40.00	

40°/12.59 = 3.18 °/Unit R

$$t_u = \frac{\left[t_i\left(A_1 U_1 + A_2 U_2 + \ldots\right) + \left(t_o K V_o + A_a V_a + A_b V_b + \ldots\right)\right]}{A_1 U_1 + A_2 U_2 + \ldots + K V_o + A_a V_a + A_b V_b + \ldots} \quad (14.5)$$

The following equation is written specifically for determining the temperature of an unheated attic:

$$t_a = \frac{\left[T_c A_c U_c + T_o\left(K V_c + A_r U_r + A_w U_w + A_g U_g\right)\right]}{A_c U_c + K V_c + A_r U_r + A_w U_w + A_g U_g} \quad (14.6)$$

where

K	=	1200
T_a, T_c, T_o	=	attic, ceiling, outside temperature
r, w, g	=	roof, vertical wall, glass
V_c	=	volume air flow rate (infiltration)

Example 14.2

Estimate T_a, if $T_c = 20°C$, $T_o = -10°C$, $A_c = 80m^2$, $A_r = 110 \ m^2$, $A_w = 10m^2$, $A_g = 1.0 \ m^2$, $U_r = 3W/m^2Km$ $U_c = 2W/m^2K$, $U_w = 1.6W/m^2K$, $U_g = 7.0W/m^2K$, $V_c = 2.5L/Sm^2 \ °C$

$$T_a = \frac{\{20(80)2 + (-10)[1,200(0.0025)80 + 110(3) + 10(1.6) +1(7.0)]\}}{(160 + 240 + 330 + 16 + 7)}$$

$$= \frac{(3,200 - 5,930)}{753} = -3.63°C$$

Energy Estimating

The annual energy demand for heating may be estimated by several different methods. A single-measure method using the concept of heating degree days (HDD) will be illustrated. A heating degree day occurs when the average daily temperature is one degree less than 65°F or, for a given period, the daily temperature differences are summed:

$$HDD = \sum |(65°F - T_{ave})|_i \qquad (14.7)$$

In the above, it is assumed that heat is required only when the outside temperature is less than the balance point temperature (65°F) which is the temperature when the steady-state heat losses equal internal gains:

$$T_b = \frac{T_i - Q_i}{UA} \qquad (14.8)$$

The energy for the period is calculated using:

$$E = \left[\frac{(H_L \times HHD \times 24)}{\Delta t}\right] K_c \qquad (14.9)$$

where

E	=	energy for period (Btu/h; kWh)
H_L	=	design heat loss (Btu; kW)
HDD	=	number of degree days (°F-day; °C-day) Note: normally based on 65°F (18.3°C) room temperature
Δt	=	design temperature difference
K_c	=	C_D/kV = correction factor (load efficiency, energy conservation, internal gains, solar, storage, etc.)
C_D	=	adjustment factor for difference between HDD base temperature and actual balance point temperature
k	=	efficiency factor
V	=	energy content per unit of fuel

The above is only for conductive heat loss, an additional factor for infiltration or ventilation may be included as follows:

$$E = \left(\frac{A}{R}\right) 24(HDD) + 0.4(ACH)V(HDD) \qquad (14.10)$$

where
ACH = air changes/h

V   = volume of space (ft^3)

0.4 (Btu-h/day-ft^2) = 0.24 Btu/lb°F × 24 h/day × (1/14) °F/ft^3

For SI, constant = 8.0 h^{2}W/K-m^3-day

The following examples illustrate these calculations.

Example 14.3

Estimate the annual energy demand for a home with a design heat load of 20 kW. The heating degree days for the area are 5,000 and the average temperature difference is estimated at 50°C. Use a K_c factor of 1.1.

$$E = \left[\frac{(20 \text{ kW} \times 5{,}000°C\text{-day} \times 24 \text{ h/day})}{50°C}\right]1.1 = 52\ 800 \text{ kWh}$$

Example 14.4

Assume a building 40 × 60 × 10 ft has an R_{ave} = 10 h•°F-ft^2/Btu and the infiltration rate = 2 ACH. Estimate the energy demand.

Solution

Total surface area = (40 × 60 ft) + 2(40 + 60 ft)10 ft = 4,400 ft^2

A/R = 440 Btu/h°F

$$E = 440 \text{ Btu/h-°F}(24 \text{ h/day})HDD + 0.4 \text{ Btu-h}/(ft^3\text{-day})$$

$$\times(2/h)(40 \times 60 \times 10 \text{ ft})HDD$$

$$= (10{,}560 \text{ Btu}/(°F\text{-day}) + 19{,}200 \text{ Btu}/(°F\text{-day})HDD$$

$$= 29{,}760 \text{ HDD Btu}$$

For 9,200°F-day location, this would be 2,738 million Btu/yr. Note that if the air exchange is reduced to 1 ACH, the estimated energy demand would be only (10,560 + 9,600) = 20,160 HDD.

Example 14.5

Determine the required frequency to fill a 500 gal fuel-oil tank. Assume a 75% burner efficiency.

Solution

HDD capacity = 500 gal × 132,000 Btu/gal × 0.75 = 49.5 × 10^6 Btu.

If the seasonal heating demand is 20,000 HDD, the tank filling frequency should be 49.5 × 10^6 Btu/20,000 Btu/°F-day = 2,475°F-day.

Example 14.6

Estimate the annual heating cost for a home in Fargo, North Dakota (HDD = 10,000). Assume the fuel-oil heating value is 132,000 Btu/gal, an annual heating system efficiency of 75%, and a heating load of 20,000 HDD.

$$\frac{[1.20 \text{ \$/gal} (20,000 \text{ Btu/°F-day})10,000°F\text{-day}]}{[132,000 \text{ Btu/gal}(0.75)]} = \$2,424/\text{yr}$$

Example 14.7

Find the effect of adding insulation by R-22 to an attic. The original attic insulation was R = 13 and the walls had R = 7.9. The ceiling area is 2,400 ft² and the total wall surface area is 2,000 ft². Original R_{ave} = 10 h°F-ft²/Btu.

$$\text{New } R_{ave} = \frac{4,400 \text{ ft}^2}{\left[\dfrac{2,400 \text{ ft}^2}{13 + 22} + \dfrac{2,000 \text{ ft}^2}{7.9}\right]} = 13.7 \text{ h°F-ft}^2/\text{Btu}$$

New A/R = 4,400 ft²/ 13.7 h°F-ft²/Btu = 320 Btu/°F-h

New ann. cost =

$$\frac{1.20 \text{ \$/gal}(10,000°F\text{-day}) \times (320 \text{ Btu/h°F} \times 24 \text{ h/day} + 9,600 \text{ HDD})}{132,000 \text{ Btu/gal}(0.75)}$$

$$= \$2,100$$

Savings = $2,424 - 2,100 = $324/yr

A better estimate of seasonal heating energy demand can be obtained by utilizing the frequency of occurrence of temperatures. The bin method of estimating seasonal heating load calculates the heat loss for temperature increments. This method is illustrated in the following example using 5°F increments.

Example 14.8

Estimate the seasonal heating load for a building in Bismarck, North Dakota. The indoor temperature is 70°F and the design outdoor temperature is −19°F. The ventilation rate is 400 CFM and the heat loss through the building (A/R) is 180 Btu/h°F. There is a constant sensible heat input of 9,200 Btu/h.

Solution

Heat loss by ventilation:

q_v = [400 ft³/min × 60 min/h × 0.24 Btu/(F-lb)/13.1 ft³/lb] × Δt

Heat loss through the building, q_b = 180 Btu/h-°F × Δt. The temperature difference ("t-diff" in table 14-9) is substituted for Δt for each bin, then q_{sr} is calculated by subtracting 9,200 Btu/h from the sum of $q_v + q_b$. I.E., for the first bin:

Table 14-9. Seasonal heating demand by the bin method

t-ave	t-dif	hours	q_v	q_b	q_{sr}*	E, total, Btu
52.3	17.7	637	7775	3180	1755	1118745
47	23	520	10120	4140	5060	2631200
42	28	518	12320	5040	8160	4226880
37	33	604	14520	5940	11260	6801040
32	38	653	16720	6840	14360	9377080
27	43	550	18920	7740	17460	9603000
22	48	474	21120	8640	20560	9745440
17	53	371	23320	9540	23660	8777860
12	58	338	25520	10440	26760	9044880
7	63	292	27720	11340	29860	8719120
2	68	278	29920	12240	32960	9162880
-3	73	208	32120	13140	36060	7500480
-8	78	131	34320	14040	39160	5129960
-13	83	77	36520	14940	42260	3254020
-18	88	80	38720	15840	45360	3628800
					Total =	98721385

* Based on q_s = 9,200 Btu/h.

$$q_v = 440 \text{ Btu/h-°F} \times 17.67 \text{ F} = 7,775 \text{ Btu/h}$$

$$q_b = 180 \text{ Btu/h-°F} \times 17.67 \text{ F} = 3,180 \text{ Btu/h}$$

The heat for the bin is:
E = (7,775 + 3,180 − 9,200) Btu/h × 637 h = 1,118,745 Btu. As shown in table 14-9, the total seasonal heat demand is 98.7 million Btu.

Specific and Latent Heat

Specific and latent heat (defined in chapter 12) values (table 14-10) are usually used in relation to problems dealing with the heating or refrigeration of agricultural products. It is necessary to use the specific heat values for a product in finding the heating or cooling load imposed by processing or storage. If either the processing or storage involves a change of state, the latent heat values must be considered. Specific heat may also be used in solving ventilation problems.

The following expressions would be used to find the total cooling load imposed on a refrigeration system in cooling a product from an above freezing temperature to a below freezing temperature:

$$q_1 = mc_i(t_1 - t_f), \quad q_2 = mL, \quad q_3 = mc_j(t_f - t_2)$$

$$q_t = q_1 + q_2 + q_3 \tag{14.11}$$

where

q_t = total heat removed (Btu; kJ)
m = weight of product (lb; kg)
c_i = specific heat above freezing

Table 14-10. Specific and latent heats

Material	Boiling Temp (°F)	Specific Heat — Liquid*	Specific Heat — Vapor*	Latent Heat of Vaporization (Btu/lb)
Water	212	1.0	0.49	970
Air	-317		0.24	
Refrig. 12	21.6	0.25	0.14	75

Material	Freezing Temp, °F	Specific Heat — Solid*	Specific Heat — Liquid*	Latent Heat of Fusion (Btu/lb)
Water	32	0.49	1.0	144
Milk	31	0.49	0.93	124
Fruit	28	0.45	0.86	122
Eggs	27	0.40	0.76	100
Potatoes	29	0.43	0.82	111
Beef	29	0.40	0.74	100
Poultry	27	0.37	0.79	106
Cheese	17	0.36	0.64	79
Peas	30	0.42	0.79	106

Material	Specific Heat*
Concrete	0.16
Pine	0.67
Steel	0.12
Glass	0.20
Corn	0.25

* Specific heats are in Btu/lb°F.

c_j = specific heat below freezing
L = latent heat of fusion
t_1, t_f, t_2 = initial, freezing, and final temperatures (°F; °C)

The specific heat ratio is based on water. One Btu is the heat required to raise the temperature of 1 lb of water 1°F (or 4.186 kJ is the heat required to raise the temperature of 1 kg of water 1°K).

Example 14.9

As an example of the total heat to be removed from a product in reducing the temperature from field level to storage level, it is assumed that 1,000 lb of peas with a field temperature of 65°F are to be frozen and reduced to a storage temperature of –15°F.

Solution

Using the values from table 14-10, the amount of heat to be removed is determined as follow:

q_1 = 1,000 lb × 0.79 Btu/°F-lb × (65 F – 30 F) = 27,650 Btu

q_2 = 1,000 lb × 106 Btu/lb= 106,000 Btu

$q_3 = 1,000 \text{ lb} \times 0.42 \text{ Btu/°F-lb} \times (30 \text{ F} - (-15 \text{ F})) = 18,900 \text{ Btu}$

$q_t = q_1 + q_2 + q_3 = 152,550 \text{ Btu}$

Moisture Control

Most agricultural buildings are likely to have relatively high moisture levels in the air. Therefore, it is necessary to design the buildings and environmental control systems in such a way to prevent moisture from condensing on or within the walls and ceiling.

Condensation on Surfaces

When the humidity in a room is high, and the temperature drop across the inside air layer is substantial, the wall surface temperature is likely to fall below the dewpoint temperature. Condensation will then occur on the wall surface (fig. 14.5). For example, if it is 55°F (12.7°C) with 80% RH in a building, condensation will occur on any surface of 50°F (10°C) or lower. Condensation on wall or ceiling surfaces can cause paint blistering, severe structural damage, and reduce the value of some insulation materials.

The remedies for this condition are: (1) reduce the humidity and therefore reduce the dewpoint temperature, (2) insulate the walls more heavily, and (3) circulate air within the room. The latter two methods tend to raise the wall temperature.

Condensation Within a Wall

If a dewpoint temperature is reached within a wall, condensation is likely to result

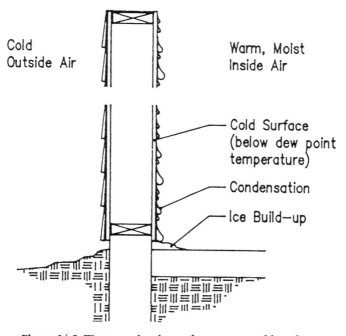

Figure 14.5. Warm, moist air condenses on a cold surface.

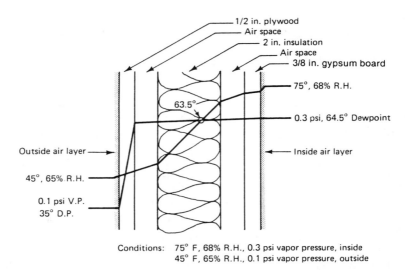

Conditions: 75° F, 68% R.H., 0.3 psi vapor pressure, inside
45° F, 65% R.H., 0.1 psi vapor pressure, outside

Figure 14.6. Condensation within a wall.

(fig. 14.6). However, it is difficult to predict where the condensation will take place. Experience has shown that condensation rarely occurs within a very permeable material (such as fiberglass or mineral wool) even though temperatures are reached that might be expected to be below the dewpoint temperature. Apparently, vapor moves away from the plane as rapidly as vapor approaches the plane, and saturation is never reached. However, where a sizeable change in permeability occurs, more moisture arrives at the plane than can leave, and condensation takes place if the surface is below the dewpoint temperature. A typical example is the inside surface of the sheathing of a wall insulated with mineral wool. If the vapor retarder is missing or defective, condensation is likely to occur on this surface during cold weather.

The remedies for condensation within a wall are: (1) use a better vapor retarder, (2) increase the permeability of the outer wall surface, (3) reduce the humidity on the warm side of the wall, and (4) design the wall or ceiling section so that there is no reduction in permeability beyond the insulation. The moisture can be readily removed by ventilation, for example, by having no floor above the ceiling level.

Moisture Transmission

Water vapor in the atmosphere exerts a pressure that is proportional to the amount of moisture present. This pressure, as stated in Dalton's Law, is independent from the air pressure. Inasmuch as warm air is capable of holding much more water vapor than cool air, a condition of considerably differing vapor pressures on opposite sides of a building wall is likely to exist. This pressure difference tends to equalize by the permeation of moisture from the high pressure to the low pressure side. Because warm air can hold more moisture than cool air, moisture almost always moves from a warm area to a cooler area.

If during the movement of vapor through a wall, the dewpoint temperature is reached, condensation will occur. The resulting free moisture can reduce the effectiveness of insulation and cause paint failure and even structural failure due to rotting. Thus, all warm livestock and high humidity product storage buildings should be designed with vapor retarders to prevent damaging condensation within the walls.

In order to understand air-moisture movement and to make the necessary calculations in a vapor transmission problem, it is necessary to understand the following terminology:

Perm is a unit of moisture transmission equal to 1 grain/(ft²-h-in. Hg) [g/(24 h-m²-mm Hg)].

A *grain* is a unit of mass frequently used for small quantities. 1 gr = 1/7,000 lb or 0.065 gm.

Perm-inch is the rate of moisture transmission through 1 in. of thickness of a material.

Permeability is the property of a material that allows the transfer of water vapor and is measured in perm-inches.

Permeance is the property of a material that allows the transfer of water vapor measured in perms for a thickness as used.

Vapor pressure units may be expressed in several different units. They relate as follows:

$$1 \text{ psi} = 2.036 \text{ in. Hg}$$

$$1 \text{ in. Hg} = 13.57 \text{ in. } H_2O = 0.4897 \text{ psi}$$

$$1 \text{ mm Hg} = 133.3 \text{ Pa} = 13.6 \text{ mm } H_2O = 0.039 \text{ in. Hg}$$

Permeability may be tested either by the dry cup or wet cup methods (table 14-11). The permeability of a thin material is measured by sealing a sample of the material to a standard test cup containing either water or a desiccant. In the dry cup method, a desiccant provides near 0% R.H. inside the cup, while in the wet cup method, water provides near 100% R.H. inside the cup. In either case, the cup is placed in a test location at 50% R.H. The cup is weighed periodically to determine the rate of gain or loss of water which passes through the material being tested. The wet cup method usually gives a higher permeability value.

Moisture transmission through walls may be determined in a manner similar to that for heat.

$$m = \frac{W}{T} = \mu' A \frac{\Delta P}{L}$$

$$= K A \Delta P = \frac{A}{D} \Delta P \qquad (14.12)$$

where
$$m = \text{rate of water vapor transmitted (gr/h)}$$
$$W = \text{total moisture, grains (g)}$$
$$T = \text{time (h, 24 h)}$$
$$\mu' = \text{mean permeability (gr-in./h-ft-in. Hg)}$$
$$A = \text{area (ft}^2\text{; m}^2\text{)}$$
$$\Delta P = \text{pressure difference (in. of Hg; mm Hg)}$$
$$L = \text{length of flow path (material thickness, in.)}$$
$$K = \mu'/L, \text{ permeance (grains/h-ft}^3\text{-in. Hg; g/[24 h-m}^2\text{-mm Hg)}$$
$$D = 1/K, \text{ water vapor resistance (h-ft}^2\text{-; in. Hg/gr)}$$

If the wall section is not homogeneous, the total M may be found as follows:
$$D_T = D_1 + D_2 + \ldots + D_n.$$

Vapor Retarders

A good vapor barrier, or retarder, with a very low moisture permeability, should be installed on the warm side of a wall to prevent the entrance of any appreciable amount of water vapor (fig. 14.7). The cold side of a wall or ceiling should be as permeable as possible. For dwellings it is recommended that a vapor retarder with a maximum rating of 1 perm (1.5 SI units) be installed, except under concrete and on cathedral ceilings where 0.5 perm (0.75 SI units) is desirable. Warm livestock and poultry

Table 14-11. Water permeability of materials

Material	Perms* K	Resistance D = 1/K	Method of Evaluation
Air, 1 in.	120	0.008	
Gypsum board, 3/8 in.	50	0.02	
Structural insulation board, 1 in.	50	0.02	
Interior plywood, 1/4 in.	1.9	0.53	
Exterior plywood, 1/2 in.	0.7	1.43	
Pine wood, 1 in.	0.4-5.4	0.2-2.5	
Concrete, 1 in.	3.2	0.31	
Brick masonry, 4 in.	0.80	1.25	
Concrete block, 8 in.	2.40	0.42	
Roll roofing	0.05	20	dry c
Aluminum paint	0.3-0.5	2-3.3	dry c
Latex paint	5.5	0.18	dry c
Enamel paint	1.5	0.67	
Mineral wool, 1 in.	116	0.01	wet c
Blanket insulation with asphalt paper	0.04	25	dry c
Extruded polystyrene	1.2	0.83	dry c
Polystyrene (bead)	5.8	0.17	dry c
Polyurethane, 1 in.	1.6	0.63	dry c
Polyethylene (4 mil)	0.08	12.5	dry c
Polyethylene (8 mil)	0.04	25	dry c
Aluminum foil (1 mil)	0.0		dry c

* To obtain g/(24 h-m²-mm Hg) multiply by 0.66.

buildings require a vapor retarder rating of no more than 0.5 perm (0.75 SI units). The following are desirable for storage room walls:

>30°F (–1°C)	0.2 perms or less (0.13 SI units)
0 to 29°F (–18 to –2°C)	0.1 perms or less (0.07 SI units)
–1 to –40°F (–20 to –60°C)	0.01 perms or less (0.007 SI units)

Care should always be taken to keep the vapor barrier as continuous as possible. Large sheets should be used, holes repaired, and joints well-lapped and sealed. The vapor barrier should always be installed on the predominately warm side of the wall. The justification for this recommendation can be verified by referring to the psychrometric chart.

Assume, for example, that it is 30°F and 100% RH outside and 70°F and 30% RH inside. Note that the vapor pressure is higher on the inside even though the relative humidity is much lower.

Only occasionally, and then for short periods of time, does one find a reverse situation, i.e., higher vapor pressure outside than inside. Moisture that penetrates a wall during such a period will soon be forced out again, usually in a matter of hours.

The attics of both agricultural buildings and homes benefit from year-round ventilation. In warm months, excess heat is removed; while during winter, moisture that may have penetrated through the ceiling and insulation is removed, reducing the possibility of condensation. It is recommended that 1 ft² of net louver area be installed for each 300 ft² (1 m²/300 m²) of ceiling area. The ceiling area is measured at the level of the eaves and the louver area is divided between the gable ends in a gable building or between the eaves and the ridge in a hip-roofed design. To compensate for screening and rain deflectors, the gross area of louvers should be 2.25 times the net requirement.

Ceiling vapor retarders are strongly recommended in areas where the winter design temperature is 0°F (–18°C) or lower and are desirable for design temperatures up to 20°F (–7°C). Between 20 and 30°F (–7 and –1°C) no vapor barrier is required

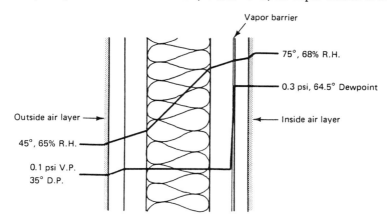

Figure 14.7. A vapor retarder prevents condensation within a wall.

if ventilation is adequate. When the design temperature is above 35°F (2°C) moisture may be moving in either direction due to alternate heating and cooling and a nonpermeable insulation is most suitable.

Predicting Condensation

In designing the insulation, vapor retarder, and ventilation for a building, it is important to determine that condensation is not likely to occur on the inner wall surface or within the wall structure itself.

A temperature gradient through the wall can be calculated based on inside and outside dewpoint temperatures. The dewpoint temperature gradient is then compared to the gradient based on dry bulb temperatures. If the dewpoint temperature gradient and the dry-bulb temperature gradients intersect, that point of intersection is the theoretical plane of condensation. This plane may occur within the insulation; however, condensation rarely occurs in a homogeneous permeable material. Instead it occurs at the next surface that is lower in permeability.

Figure 14.8 illustrates the dewpoint temperature gradient. With an outside dry-bulb

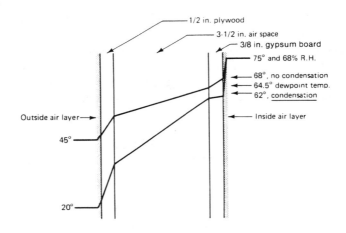

Layer (left side)	"R"	Degrees / unit of R		Temp at Plane	
		30° TD	55° TD	30°	55°
Outside air layer	0.17 × 11.6 =	2.0, × 21.2 =	3.6	45°	20°
Plywood	0.63	= 7.3,	= 13.4	47	23.6
Air space	0.91	= 10.6,	= 19.3	54.3	37
Gypsum board	0.27	= 3.1,	= 5.7	64.9	56.3
Inside air layer	0.61	= 7.0,	= 13.0	68	62
Total R	2.59	Room Temp.		75	75

30° / 2.59 = 11.6° / unit of R
55° / 2.59 = 21.2° / unit of R

Figure 14.8. Condensation on a wall surface.

temperature of 45°F (7.2°C), the inside wall surface temperature will be 68°F (20°C). Since that is above the dewpoint temperature of 64.5°F (18°C), condensation will not occur. However, if the outside temperature is 20°F (16.7°C), the surface temperature will be below the dewpoint temperature and condensation will occur.

The same general procedure used for the temperature gradient may be followed in determining dewpoint temperatures to be plotted on the same scale. Having plotted both gradients, a theoretical plane of condensation is predicted if the gradient lines cross. In figure 14.6, the temperature of such a plane is 63.5°F (16.9°C).

This theoretical plane of condensation occurs within the insulation. However, as has been mentioned previously, condensation rarely occurs in a homogeneous permeable material. Instead it occurs at the next surface that is lower in permeability, which in this case is the inner surface of the plywood.

Placement of a vapor retarder near the surface with the highest vapor pressure will cause a sharp drop in the vapor pressure, and the dewpoint temperature gradient. This will normally eliminate the danger of condensation within a wall.

Problems

14.1. Calculate the R-value of a 6 in. (150 mm) thick fiberglass [0.5 pcf (8 kg/m^3)] batt. What will the R-value be if this batt is compressed to 3 in. (75 mm); if compressed to 2 in. (50 mm)?

14.2. Determine the total R-value for a ceiling composed of tempered hardboard, with 4 in. (200 mm) air space, 3/4 in. (20 mm) oak boards, and 24 in. (610 mm) of straw. (Don't forget the air films.)

14.3. Determine the R-value for a wall which has 1/2 in. (12 mm) plywood on the inside, metal exterior siding, and 6 in. (150 mm) of fiberglass between.

14.4. Determine the total heat transmission (U) for a wall which has the following construction: 1/2 in. (12 mm) plywood, aluminum foil centered in a 31/2 in. air space, and 1/2 in. plywood. Include the inside and outside air layer effects.

14.5. A building is 30 ft (9 m) wide and 60 ft (18 m) long. The walls are 10 ft (3 m) high and include 200 ft^2 (19 m^2) of window and door area. The U-values are: ceiling, 0.02 (0.114); walls, 0.05 (0.284); windows and door, 0.9 (5.11). Find the rate of heat loss from the building when the temperature difference is 56°F (31°C). Ignore any heat transfer through the floor.

14.6. Construct a temperature gradient for the wall described in problem 3. Assume a temperature of 70°F (21°C) inside and 0°F (−18°C) outside.

14.7. Make a list of common insulating materials. Obtain price information and determine the cost per unit of R. Suggest an application for each material on the list.

14.8. Find the total heat required to thaw 660 lb (300 kg) of frozen eggs removed from storage at 0°F (−17.8°C).

14.9. A building wall is constructed with an inside surface of gypsum board, 31/2 in. (89 mm) fiberglass, and wood boards on the outside. When the outside conditions are 0°F (−18°C) and 80% RH and the inside conditions are 70°F (21°C) and 30% RH, would condensation be likely to occur within the wall? What is the effect of a polyethylene vapor barrier under the gypsum board?

14.10. Air enters a swine barn at 20°F (−6.7°C) and 50% RH. It is exhausted at 65°F (18.3°C) and 50% RH. How much heat and moisture are removed each hour when the air is moved at a rate of 500 ft³ /min (233 L/s)?

15 Ventilation Systems

Ventilation may mean removing dust from a flour mill to avoid explosion, removing a dangerous gas from a coal mine, supplying oxygen to a tunneling crew or removing odors from a poultry dressing plant. One of the important considerations in designing housing for livestock is the provision for a comfortable and healthy environment in which it is possible to attain maximum production. Likewise, buildings for storing agricultural products are designed to maintain maximum quality and to minimize losses.

Ventilation is a process for controlling several environmental factors by diluting the air in the space with outside air. Ventilation systems affect:

- Air temperature
- Moisture level
- Moisture condensation on surfaces
- Air temperature uniformity
- Air speed across animals
- Odor and gas concentrations
- Combustion fumes and disease organism level

Ventilation alone, which involves moving air through a building either by natural convection currents or with fans, will provide adequate conditions at reasonable cost for many agricultural enterprises. In some cases, however, supplemental heat may be required to maintain an optimum environment. Further environmental modification may be accomplished by employing equipment such as refrigeration, air filters, humidifiers, other atmospheric modifying equipment, and machinery for the continuous removal of manure. However, such methods are seldom economically feasible for commercial farms unless production or quality improves markedly.

As the ventilating system exchanges air, it brings in oxygen to sustain life and removes and dilutes harmful dust and gases, undesirable odors, and airborne organisms and moisture. A properly operating ventilating system:

1. Brings fresh air into the building through planned openings.
2. Thoroughly mixes outside and inside air, picks up heat, moisture, and air contaminants, and lowers temperature, humidity, and contamination levels.
3. Exhausts moist, contaminated air from the building.

The following examples briefly illustrate the range of systems, from the very simple to the complex, as they are used to control the environment in farm buildings.

1. In a free-stall dairy barn, temperature is of little consideration and a very simple system using natural convection removes sufficient moisture to prevent condensation under ordinary circumstances.
2. In a cage poultry house, wall and ceiling insulation conserves enough animal heat to maintain a warm temperature while ventilation removes excess moisture and odors.
3. In a farrowing house, low animal density and the need for a warm room temperature make the use of supplemental heat necessary. Ventilation controls moisture and odors.
4. Potatoes to be stored are harvested late enough in the season so that cool nighttime air moved through the bins is adequate to obtain storage level temperatures. No refrigeration is necessary.
5. Apples destined for storage are harvested earlier in the season during relatively warm weather. To provide the required storage temperature, mechanical refrigeration systems are essential. In addition, atmosphere modification is used to achieve maximum storage periods.

Ventilation systems may be natural, mechanical or a combination of the two. Mechanical systems move air through buildings with fans, while natural systems depend on wind and thermal buoyancy. Achieving proper air mixing and circulation inside a building requires careful design of air inlets and outlets. Mechanical ventilation systems may use either negative, positive or neutral pressure. Negative pressure systems discharge air from the structure with fans and the reduced inside pressure causes air to flow in through inlets. Positive pressure systems force air into the structure with fans; the increased inside pressure forces air out through outlets. Neutral pressure systems use fans to force air both into and out of a building. Heat exchangers and "push-pull" systems are typical examples.

Mechanical systems are less influenced by natural phenomena (wind and thermal effects), therefore they are easier to control. Thus when careful environmental control is required, such as for young or smaller animals, mechanical systems are often preferred for ventilation/environmental control.

MECHANICAL VENTILATION SYSTEMS

A large proportion of automatically controlled ventilating fans are installed in well-insulated buildings where the control of temperature and moisture are primary concerns. The proper selection and installation of ventilation equipment will provide the air volume required for uniform mixing, moisture control, and necessary temperature levels.

A ventilation system has the following components: (1) an envelope (building), (2) inlets, (3) fans or air movers, (4) control system, and (5) often a supplemental heat source. Important parts of the building envelope are the insulation and vapor barrier. Control systems may include thermostats, humidistats, timers, inlet controllers or integrated microprocessors.

Fans and Blowers

Fans used to move ventilation air through buildings are classified as axial flow fans or centrifugal blowers. With axial flow (propellers) type, the air is moved parallel with the fan shaft by two or more radially mounted blades. Centrifugal blowers discharge air at right angles to the "squirrel cage" shaft-and-blade assembly. The choice of a fan or blower depends on the static pressure conditions under which it must operate.

Propeller fans are useful for low pressure applications. The propellers may be mounted in a ring or orifice plate (possibly with a venturi). A small tip clearance is desirable to prevent backflow. Air is discharged from the propeller in a swirl pattern. Louvers in the exhaust air will interfere and reduce the efficiency of these fans. Properly sized louvers on the intake side do not effect fan performance, as intake air does not rotate. The fans may be direct or belt-driven; belt-driven may be slower and quieter. Tubeaxial and vaneaxial fans which have large hubs are modified designs and allow higher pressure. With the simple propeller type at high pressure air backflow will occur at the hub (fig. 15.1).

Centrifugal fans may have 10 to 16 blades with the blades inclined forward, backward or radially. The forward inclination gives greater flow rate, the backward inclination develops higher pressure, and the backward inclination is more efficient. The best fans can be 80% efficient in transferring energy to air; propeller fans are generally 40% efficient or less.

Static Pressure

When a fan either exhausts air from or blows air into a reasonably tight building, a difference in pressure between the inside and outside will develop. The pressure difference is small and is most easily measured with a manometer calibrated in inches (millimeters) of water. A simple manometer [fig. 15.2 (a)] may be constructed of plastic tub-

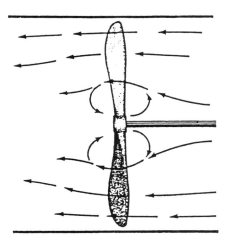

Figure 15.1. Recirculation that results when propeller or disc fan is operated against too great a static head.

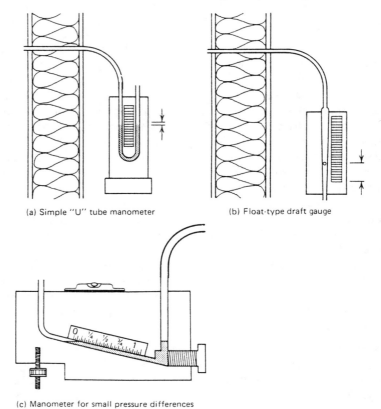

(a) Simple "U" tube manometer   (b) Float-type draft gauge

(c) Manometer for small pressure differences

Figure 15.2. Instruments for measuring static pressure.

ing. A more easily read commercial manometer is shown in figure 15.2 (c). A draft gauge, also shown, is readily portable and does not have to be mounted with as much precision as a manometer.

Fan Ratings

The ability of a fan to move air is inversely proportional to the static pressure against which it must discharge. A fan performance curve illustrating this is shown in figure 15.3.

The performance for fans in cubic feet per minute (m^3/s) is plotted versus static pressure, ranging from zero, or free air delivery, up to the maximum level against which the fan is expected to operate. Fans for farm ventilation are most often chosen on the basis of their capacity at 1/8 in. (3.2 mm) static pressure. The pressure drop across air inlets is usually less than one-half this amount. However, many fans are equipped with automatic louvers which are opened by air pressure and if they become dusty they can cause much of the 1/8 in. (3.2 mm) pressure drop.

The American Society of Heating, Ventilating and Air-conditioning Engineers

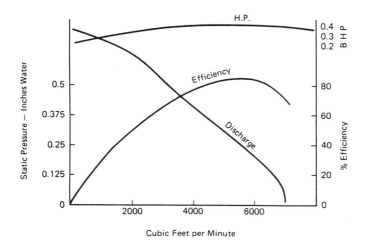

Figure 15.3. Fan performance curves.

(ASHRAE) and the Air Moving and Conditioning Association (AMCA) have established test procedures for fans. Fans that have been tested by an unbiased third party, such as AMCA or university testing laboratories, should be chosen for most ventilation systems as they are certified to deliver the stated volume of air at the specified static pressures. The test data can be applied to actual installations only if the complete fan system including all accessories was tested. Some manufacturers provide an air-volume per watt rating. This combines both fan and motor efficiencies and provides a useful indication of comparative operating costs. Some land grant universities have developed fan testing facilities and conduct tests of fan systems for agricultural applications.

Choosing a Fan

Propeller fans are the most commonly used type for ventilating agricultural buildings. They are the least expensive, exhibit high efficiency at low static pressure, and are easily installed and maintained. A two-blade propeller fan is suitable for static pressures under 1/4 in. (6 mm). Four-blade fans are suitable for pressures up to 3/8 in. (10 mm) and some six-blade designs operate at up to 1 in. (25 mm) or more. Multiblade fans tend to be less noisy.

Centrifugal blowers, although comparatively more expensive, will operate well against the pressures expected from long ducts. The blades on blowers may be forward-curved, radial or backward-curved. The latter type offers the best combination of efficiency and quiet operation for agricultural applications.

In selecting a fan model from performance tables in a catalogue, the volume for a wall-mounted fan may usually be taken at 1/8 in. (3.2 mm) static pressure. When used with a duct of less than 10 ft (3 m), capacity at 1/4 in. (6 mm) should be chosen. For longer ducts, fans rated at a higher pressure or perhaps a blower will be needed.

Many fans are belt-driven and therefore may be subject to changes in speed of operation. A knowledge of the effects brought about by changes in speed is desirable and may prevent some unfortunate results. Briefly stated, they are as follows:

• Fan capacity is proportional to speed.
• Static pressure is proportional to the square of the speed.
• Horsepower required is proportional to the cube of the speed.

Note that if the speed is doubled, as it might be by substituting a 3,450 rpm motor for a 1,725 rpm model, the power requirement increases eightfold.

Motors should be of the split-phase or capacitor-start type with built-in thermal overload protection and bearings with long lubrication periods. Fully enclosed frames are advisable for dust and moisture protection.

A shroud or housing that fits fairly closely to the fan, and in effect becomes a bell-shaped nozzle through which air flows, will improve efficiency substantially as compared to a plain circular opening (fig. 15.4). Fans with no ring are suitable only for free-air circulation within a room.

Shutters should be designed to operate very easily in order to keep static pressure losses low. Motor-operated shutters are expensive but offer the least resistance to air flow. Shutters need to be cleaned on a regular basis to prevent excessive pressure drop. A hood for weather protection is desirable. Welded wire guards should be installed over the fan to prevent accidental contact with the operating blades (fig. 15.5).

Fan Location

The location of fans will vary in different buildings, but generally midpoint on the lee side of a building up to 100 ft (30 m) long is satisfactory for exhaust fans. If the building is longer, the fans may be grouped at various points. Generally the maximum distance between an inlet, or any point on an inlet, and a fan should be 75 ft. Fans may be installed to exhaust directly from a high level on the wall or from a short distance above the floor. Although it appears that less heat would be removed at the lower level because of the lower temperature, in fact there is no particular advantage because the moisture level (humidity ratio) is also lower. As a result, the removal of an equal quantity of moisture requires a longer period of operation and approximately the same total amount of heat as compared to fans exhausting directly from a high level. In any case, high-level exhaust is desirable in warm weather. While mid-ceiling location is ideal, it usually requires an outlet duct.

If there is a particularly odorous area in a building, such as a manure pit, locating exhaust fans adjacent to that area should help to prevent the spread of odors.

Outlet ducts should be designed to provide $1 1/2$ ft^2 (0.15 m^2) of inside cross-sectional area per 1,000 cfm (472 L/s) of fan capacity. The duct should be insulated to an R of 3 (0.5) or more to prevent condensation.

Air Inlets

To a large extent, inlet location, shape, and size influence the distribution of air throughout a ventilated building. Although fans determine the rate of air exchange, they normally have little effect on distribution. A number of different types and designs of inlets are used such as slot inlet, box inlets, and porous ceiling inlets.

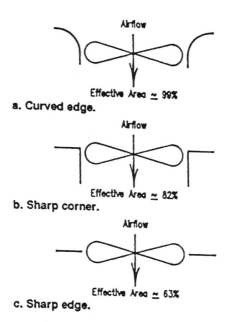

a. Curved edge.

b. Sharp corner.

c. Sharp edge.

Figure 15.4. Effect of fan housing on fan capacity.

Porous ceilings, although an old idea, have not been popular in the United States. With this system the air is brought from the attic through a material such as fiberglass insulation supported on perforated plywood or wire netting and woven nylon cloth. The porous ceiling filters dust and bacteria from the incoming air. Air velocity should be about 20 fpm which results in a pressure drop of about 0.01 in. Design criteria and operation performance for these systems are not well known.

A slot inlet around the perimeter of the ceiling [except within 10 ft (3 m) of an exhaust fan or the end walls] of a building provides uniform air distribution. These inlets may be continuous or intermittent. A slot wide enough for high air flow during the summer can be partially closed with an adjustable baffle during the winter months. In order to maintain a suitable and uniform velocity through the inlets, it may be necessary to close sections of the continuous inlets during cold weather. Air may be drawn from the attic during the winter to gain some warming and to provide wind protection. During summer it is best to bring the air directly from under the eaves to avoid heat gain in the attic.

An adjustable baffle installed along the slot can direct the air down along the wall surface or out along the ceiling (fig. 15.6). This not only uniformly distributes the air, but also provides a wiping action that helps to keep the wall or ceiling free of condensation. The choice depends on the specific conditions, but if the air is directed along the ceiling it will begin to fall as the velocity is dissipated and may result in drafts on animals. Also, the ceiling is frequently better insulated, thus condensation on the walls may be a greater concern.

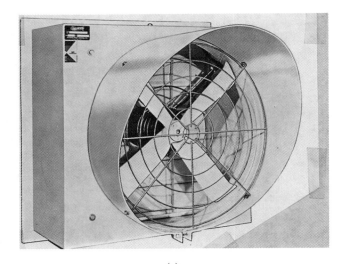

(a)

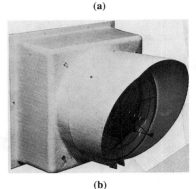

(b)

Figure 15.5. Ventilating fans.

For wider buildings, or those with high animal densities and significant obstructions, e.g., poultry cages with little clearance, additional inlets may be needed. These can be one or more baffled slots running the length of the ceiling and spaced so that each slot provides ventilation for an equal area. Another inlet system uses intermittently placed openings usually rectangular in shape.

The total opening of any type of inlet should cause an air velocity of between 700 and 1,000 fpm (3.5 and 5 m/s). This requires a static pressure across the opening of approximately 0.04 to 0.08 in. (1.0 to 2.0 mm) of water. Although one might calculate velocity by dividing the fan volume by the inlet area, the velocity in a tight building is likely to be somewhat higher due to the vena contracta of the air stream in the inlet opening. The vena contracta effect, occurring in any non-streamlined opening, is one of narrowing the air stream to 0.6 to 0.8 of the sectional area. The actual value is difficult to determine due to the variety of inlet shapes. The flow continuity equation expresses the relationship between air flow, velocity, and cross-section area of the flow opening.

$$Q = c \, A \, V \qquad\qquad (15.1)$$

where

Q   =   volume flow rate (cfm)
c   =   coefficient of vena contracta
A   =   cross-section area (ft^2)
V   =   actual velocity (fpm)

If the maximum velocity is 1,000 fpm and the coefficient of vena contracta is taken as 0.8, the above can be solved for required area as follows:

$$A = \frac{Q}{800} \left(ft^2 \right) \qquad\qquad (15.2)$$

The air velocity through an opening (orifice) can be estimated using the equation:

$$V = c \left(2gH \right)^{1/2} \qquad\qquad (15.3)$$

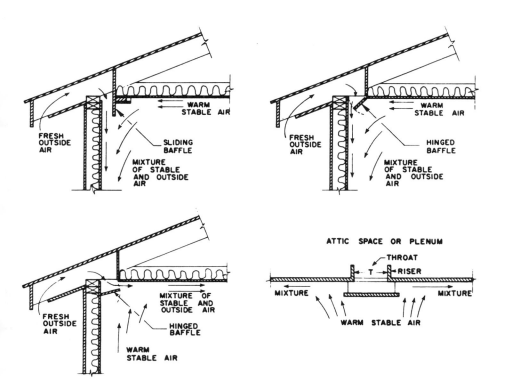

Figure 15.6. Examples of slotted inlet construction.

where

    g   = gravitational constant (32.2 ft/s^2)
    H = static pressure in ft (of column height)

For example, if a manometer is used to measure the static pressure difference between inside and outside as 0.05 in. of water column, the air velocity is calculated as follows:

$$H_{air} = 0.05\ \text{in.}_{water}\ \frac{62.4\ pcf_{water}}{0.077\ pcf_{air}} = 40.5\ \text{in.}_{air}$$

The effective air velocity can then be calculated as:

$$V = c\ \sqrt{2gH} = 0.8\ \frac{\sqrt{2 \times 32.2 \times 40.5}}{12}$$

$$= 14.7\ \text{fps or } 885\ \text{fpm}$$

A small draft gauge, similar to that shown in figure 15.2 with the tubing connected to the bottom, provides a simple means of checking velocity when the end of the hose fitting is held in the inlet opening.

The following equations may be used to estimate the airflow rate through inlets when the pressure is known:

For inlet type (a) in figure 15.5:

$$Q = 0.0012\,W^{0.98}\,P^{0.49} \tag{15.4}$$

For inlet type (b) in figure 15.5:

$$Q = 0.00071\ W^{0.98}P^{0.49} \tag{15.5}$$

For the continuous ceiling baffle inlet:

$$Q = 0.0013\ W^{0.98}P^{0.49}\left(\frac{D}{T}\right)^{0.08}\exp\left[-0.867\ W/T\right] \tag{15.6}$$

where

    Q = airflow rate (m^3/s per meter length of slot opening)
    W = slot width (mm)
    P = pressure drop across the inlet (Pa)
    D = baffle width (mm)
    T = width of ceiling opening (mm)

The inlet openings should be adjustable so that the desired range of inlet air velocity is maintained throughout the year. This often means a winter opening of less than one-fourth that was needed in the summer. Adjustable baffles may be operated by automatic controllers that sense the pressure drop across the inlets. Self-adjusting inlets which use a spring or counterbalance are also available. Manually controlled openings should be adjusted at least four times during the year to give at least 600 fpm (3 m/s) velocity with the minimum fan capacity expected for that season. As additional fan

Table 15-1. Ventilation inlet parameters (vena contracta = 0.8)

Static Pressure Water Column		Velocity		Area of Inlet	
(in.)	(mm)	(ft/min)	(m/s)	(in.^{2}/100 cfm)	(m^2/m^3/s)
0.020	0.5	570	2.9	31.58	0.437
0.040	1.0	806	4.1	22.34	0.309
0.060	1.5	986	5.0	18.24	0.252
0.080	2.0	1140	5.8	15.79	0.218
0.100	2.5	1274	6.5	14.14	0.195
0.125	3.2	1424	7.3	12.65	0.175

capacity is automatically cycled on and off with changing temperatures, the velocity will be in the desired range. However, care must be taken to ensure that the maximum desired velocity will not be exceeded with the maximum expected fan capacity during the period. If more precise control is desired, a pressure sensor and actuator can maintain a uniform static pressure and velocity regardless of the fan capacity that may be in operation at any particular time. Typical design parameters for inlets are shown in table 15-1. If a damp spot develops in a localized area of a building, increased inlet opening adjacent to the area may remedy the problem. Additional fan capacity in the area is not likely to help.

While supply air for a slot inlet may be brought in from the attic in the winter and from the outside through the soffit in the summer, this design entails extra construction cost and management. It is quite satisfactory to use outside air all year if the inlet supply opening is at the outer edge of the soffit. This location reduces the problem of drafts during the cold, windy weather. The opening should be covered with 3/4 in. (19 mm) hardware cloth to prevent the entry of birds. Screening should not be used as it will plug up with dust.

Inlets cannot be installed and forgotten; they must be managed. Since it is difficult to predict crack area in a building, there is no substitute for actual measurement of air velocity or pressure difference at the inlet openings. A direct-reading draft gauge may be used to adjust inlet openings to give 700 to 1,000 fpm (3.5 to 5 m/s) or a manometer may be used instead with corresponding readings of 0.04 to 0.08 in. (1 to 2 mm) of static pressure.

Fan Controls

The size of most livestock buildings requires several fans, thus allowing some flexibility in the type of controls that will provide the required conditions. The least complicated controller is an on-off thermostat with a set temperature. One or more fans may be operated continuously to provide minimum ventilation for cold temperature conditions. An optional thermostat may be set to serve as a safety device to prevent freeze-ups in severe weather. Additional fans may be controlled by thermostats set at near the minimum inside design temperature for the building, i.e., 50°F (10°C). The balance of the fans may then be controlled with thermostats set at the maximum desired temperature, perhaps 70°F (21°C). The result will be some continuous operation and some cycling operation during moderate weather, while the balance of the fans will operate only in warm weather. Where more than three or four fans are used, it may be desirable to stage the set-points, e.g., stage 1 fans set at 50°F (10°C), stage 2 fans at 55°F (13°C), stage 3 fans at 60°F (16°C), etc.

It should be noted that the continuous ventilation at a minimum level is a requirement in any system employing ceiling-level inlets. Stopping all fans will cause a natural reversal of air flow with attendant condensation problems in the attic, unless the inlets close automatically.

Temperature-sensitive, electronic controllers designed to be used with specific motors can provide continuously varying fan speeds. Although their original cost is somewhat higher and motor efficiency slightly lower, they should ensure more uniform environmental conditions. The range of modulation makes them suitable for up to one-half of the total fan capacity needed for summer heat removal. For small buildings with only one fan, a two-speed motor controlled by a thermostat with two set temperatures, may be used.

For most animal housing, thermostats are located about 6 ft (2 m) high near the center of the building. They will not operate satisfactorily if they are mounted too low. Either filled-type or bimetallic-type thermostats are adequately resistant to dust and moisture. From time to time, humidistats and program timers have been used for ventilation controllers, but thermostats have been the most dependable and satisfactory.

Integrated monitor/controllers have been developed that use a microprocessor to control the environment and monitor the health of the animals. Possible sensor inputs include dry-bulb temperature, dewpoint temperature, solar radiation, static pressure, animal weights, water usage, and feed bin weights. These systems can provide management information on water usage, feed consumption, weight gain, sudden temperature changes which may relate to animal health or equipment problems. They can sound alarms and/or dial the telephone to alert the manager of adverse conditions.

Exhaust, Positive or Neutral Pressure Systems

Up to this point, the discussion of ventilation has been based on the use of exhaust fans, that is, air is exhausted from a building creating a negative pressure that causes fresh air to enter through the inlets as well as cracks that are present. With a positive pressure system, fresh air is charged into a building through one or more distribution ducts, while stale air is forced out through outlet openings and cracks.

Although exhaust systems are more common, generally simpler, and provide better air distribution without ducts during cold weather, there are circumstances where the pressure system may be desirable. For example, if air in a building is very dusty or corrosive, a pressure system allows the fan to move fresh air, thereby avoiding the problems of dust accumulation and corrosion at the fan. A pressure system may also work better in a building where excessive crack area makes it difficult to design a satisfactory inlet system. Many old buildings fit into this category. A disadvantage of this is that forcing the humid air through the leaks may result in condensation inside the walls and ceiling. This can cause deterioration of building materials and reduce effectiveness of insulation.

A pressure system is often used for continuous recirculation of air within a building. Care must be taken to prevent cold drafts near the fans with positive pressure systems.

Neutral pressure systems use one fan to push air into a room while another fan is pulling stale air out. This system minimizes air leaks around doors, windows, etc. Heat recovery (exchanger) units frequently are designed to be neutral pressure.

Tunnel Ventilation

Tunnel ventilation may be an attractive summer or warm weather system. The primary emphasis of this system is to produce a cooling effect from wind velocity on the animals. The building design and equipment installed must allow free air flow for this system to be effective; solid pen partitions do not allow this. This is a sharp contrast to winter ventilation which must minimize drafts. Essentially long buildings can be thought of as similar to a tunnel in which the air enters one end and is exhausted from the other end. Other ventilation systems are designed to maximize air mixing and minimize transport of gases and organisms from one animal to another. These problems are not considered important with the tunnel system because of the large quantity of air being moved. If this system is used for winter ventilation with reduced air flow, large variation of temperature, relative humidity, and gas concentrations can be expected with building length.

The recommended air velocity in a tunnel-ventilated barn is 2.5 mph or 220 fpm (1.1 m/s). Designs for swine breeding may be as high as 350 fpm (1.8 m/s). The ventilation fan capacity (in cfm) is found by multiplying the room cross-sectional area by desired velocity (in fpm), e.g., 220. Inlet velocity should be about 400 fpm (2.0 m/s). The high volume air flow required for this system means a high energy demand.

Distribution Ducts

Polyethylene tubes punched with holes along their length provide inexpensive distribution ducts. Ordinarily they are sized to give an air velocity through the duct of 800 to 1,200 fpm (4 to 6 m/s). Usually two rows of holes are spaced uniformly at 24 to 30 in. (600 to 750 mm) intervals along the tube. Polyducts are not only used with pressure systems but may be used as inlets with exhaust systems as well. With either system, they would be sized in the same manner.

CLIMATIC DATA

The successful design of environmental control systems requires accurate climatic information such as the design temperatures shown in figures 15.7 and 15.8. As with snow loads discussed in an earlier chapter, a comparison of the national and regional maps will illustrate the desirability of obtaining data for local areas whenever it is available. Figure 15.9 provides average temperature data that may be used for estimating heating or ventilating costs.

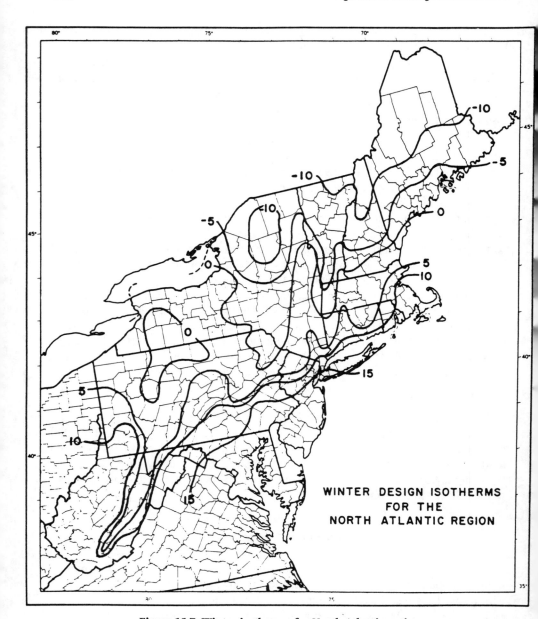

Figure 15.7. Winter isotherms for North Atlantic region.

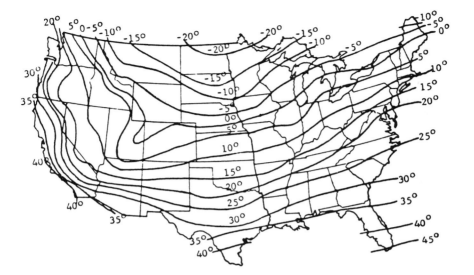

Figure 15.8. Winter design isotherms.

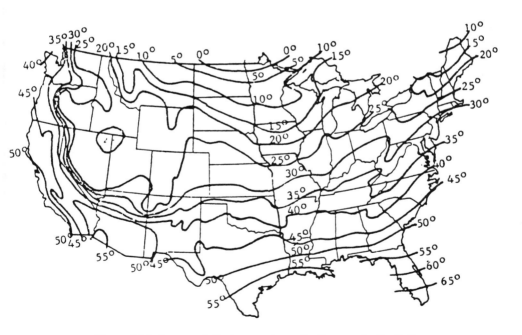

Figure 15.9. Average daily temperatures for January in the U. S.

Physiological Requirements

The physiological characteristics of livestock were discussed in chapter 13. Typical heat and moisture production values for animals are given in table 15-2. The following paragraphs discuss the specific needs of farm animals, human beings and some agricultural products.

Dairy cattle produce well in a temperature range of 40 to 70°F (4 to 24°C) and a relative humidity that does not causes condensation on building surfaces. In fact, production is not significantly affected by temperatures down to 10°F (−12°C), as long as the fluctuations are not too rapid or frequent. However, production will start to drop at 75°F (24°C) and may get as low as 50% at 90°F (32°C) or higher.

Calves appear to be more sensitive to drafts and poor ventilation than to temperature level. One of the most successful housing methods isolates each calf in a small, well-bedded shed that provides the only protection against weather extremes.

Table 15-2. Typical moisture and heat production by animals*

Livestock	Ambient Temp.		Moisture/h		Total heat/h	
	(°F)	(°C)	(lb/lb)†	(g/kg)	(Btu/lb)	(kJ/kg)
Dairy cow	20	7	0.00067	0.67	3.9	9.1
	50	10	0.00106	1.06	3.4	7.9
	80	27	0.0024	1.82	2.9	6.7
Dairy calves						
5 weeks	—		0.001	1.00	4.5	10.5
12 weeks	—		0.0023	2.29	6.5	15.1
6 months	—				4.0	9.3
Swine						
50 lb (23 kg)	60	16	0.0029	2.86	7.2	16.7
	70	21	0.0036	3.58	6.8	15.8
Swine						
100 lb (45 kg)	60	16	0.0019	1.86	4.7	10.9
	70	21	0.0021	2.15	4.3	10.0
Swine						
200 lb (90 kg)	50	10	0.00106	1.06	3.7	8.6
	60	16	0.00113	1.13	3.3	7.7
Layers	55	13	0.0029	2.86	9	20.9
	90	32	0.0049	4.86	6	14.0
Broilers						
2 weeks	85	29			24	55.8
7 weeks	75	24	0.0107	10.73	12	27.9
Sheep	50	10			5	11.6

* Total heat = sensible heat + latent heat.
† Moisture (lb) per animal (lb).

Beef cattle gain well at temperatures below 75°F (24°C). Low temperatures and exposure tend to decrease feed conversion efficiency slightly but may actually increase daily rate of gain. Some protection from snow and severe wind is desirable.

Swine make their best gains at about 68°F (20°C), although a range of 50 to 75°F (10 to 24°C) does not show a marked effect. Supplemental heat is usually needed to provide a temperature of 85 to 90°F (30 to 32°C) for newborn pigs. This can be gradually reduced to 70°F (21°C) during the first three weeks. The best gains will be made if this temperature is continued until market age. Brood sows and boars will do well at 60°F (16°C) but suffer badly at temperatures of 80°F (27°C) and above. Feeder pigs show reduced gains above 70°F (21°C) and actually lose weight at 100°F (38°C).

Sheep need protection from wind, rain, and snow, but tolerate a wide range of temperatures without significant effect. At temperatures below 45°F (7°C) at breeding times, ewes have shown improved reproductive efficiency. Heat lamps for newborn lambs are desirable for the first few days when lambing occurs in cold weather.

Horses should be protected from wind, rain, and snow, but tolerate a wide range of temperatures without discomfort. If they are to be kept in an enclosed, insulated building, supplemental heat will be required to maintain a 45 to 50°F (7 to 10°C) temperature because of low animal density.

Poultry environmental requirements vary greatly with age. Chicks, started at 95°F (35°C) may have the temperature gradually reduced to 75°F (24°C) over the first few weeks. Meat birds, both broilers and young turkeys, make most efficient gains at 70 to 75°F (21 to 24°C). Laying hens produce the greatest number and largest size eggs at 55 to 75°F (13 to 24°C). The best feed conversion efficiency is achieved between 70 and 75°F (21 to 24°C). Temperatures below 45°F (7°C) cause significantly increased feed consumption while temperatures over 75°F (24°C) result in a drop in egg production. A continued rise in temperature to 100°F (38°C) or more may well prove lethal. A relative humidity of 60 to 70% should help to control dust while still allowing adequate body cooling through respiration. High humidities at high temperatures create more lethal conditions because of a breakdown in this mode of cooling.

Inasmuch as working and living conditions are related to the success of an agricultural operation, it seems fitting to include physiological information for human beings along with that for the farm enterprises.

Most humans, when dressed in light clothing, seated and at rest, find 77°F (25°C) comfortable in winter and 78°F (26°C) in summer. At 72°F (22°C) most people feel slightly cool regardless of humidity, while at temperatures above 77°F (25°C) they feel warm, and an increase in humidity above 45% intensifies the feeling of warmth. At the most comfortable temperature, only humidities of more than 70% produce any change in comfort.

The metabolic heat produced by adult humans varies with weight and activity from as low as 250 Btu/h (264 kJ/h) while sleeping to around 750 Btu/h (791 kJ/h) at moderate work and up to 2,500 Btu/h (2638 kJ/h) at sustained heavy work. The need to shed this heat will make lower temperatures more comfortable.

Agricultural products require optimum storage temperature and humidity in order

Table 15-3. Environmental requirements for product storages

Product Area	Temperature		Humidity	Remarks
	°F	°C		
Milkroom	50-90	10-30	90% max	Prevent freezing and condensation
Eggs	55	13	60-80%	
Apples	38-34	-2 - +1	85-90%	Controlled atmosphere desirable
Potatoes	50-60	10-16	85-90%	First 7-10 days
	39-40	4	85-90%	Fresh and seed use
	45-55	7-12	85-90%	As required by processing use
Grain			< 14% m.c.	
Hay			< 20% m.c.	

to maintain top quality. Table 15-3 lists the requirements for several products. Like animals, they also give off heat energy which must be removed.

Potatoes produce 45 to 75 Btu/h-t (50 to 80 kJ/h-t) when held at a storage temperature of 50°F (10°C), and this is about 50% more when stored at 60°F (16°C). They produce enough moisture to maintain humidity and to require periodic ventilation. Apples produce 15 to 35 Btu/t (30 to 50 kJ/h-t) at 32°F (0°C). The amount is twice that at 40°F (4°C) and eight times as great at 60°F (16°C).

Greenhouse temperature requirements vary considerably with individual crops. Ventilation is largely related to the control of maximum temperature, although humidity control to prevent excessive condensation is also a factor. Added humidity or carbon dioxide may be required for some crops.

Exposure Factor

A comparison of the heat loss per animal unit for two or more buildings may be made with the aid of their exposure factors determined from the equation:

$$EF = \sum \left(\frac{A_i U_i}{N} \right) \qquad (15.7)$$

where

EF = exposure factor [Btu/(h °F); W/C]

A_i = surface area of various parts of the building (ft^2 ; m^2)

U_i = coefficient of heat transmission for the areas [Btu/(h ft^2 °F); W/m^2 °C]

N = number of animals housed

The American Society of Agricultural Engineers has published design graphs (fig. 15.10) in which the exposure factor and outside temperature are used to determine desirable ventilation rates. While figure 15.10 applies to dairy cattle, graphs for beef, swine, and poultry may be found in the *ASAE Standards*.

HEAT AND MOISTURE BALANCE

In order to maintain a desired temperature and a reasonable level of moisture within an enclosed livestock building during the winter months, it is necessary to maintain a heat and moisture balance. In many cases, this is possible with ventilation alone, if the building is well-insulated and is housing the number of animals for which it was designed.

Heat is supplied primarily by the animals. However, lights, equipment, and such sources as solar energy, supplemental artificial heat, and even a manure pack may also contribute to the total amount.

The heat produced by animals may be categorized as sensible and latent. The body heat given off by convection and radiation is sensible heat. The latent heat of vaporization is released during condensation of the moisture that has been respired by the animals in the vapor form. When using the total heat value given in table 15-2, all moisture removed in the ventilation air must be considered to be vaporized before being exhausted and the heat required to accomplish the vaporization must be included in the total heat required for ventilation.

At steady-state conditions, the sensible heat inputs will equal the sensible heat outputs. This can be expressed by the following equation:

$$q_s + q_m + q_{su} = q_e + q_b + q_v + q_{st} \qquad (15.8)$$

where

q_s =   sensible heat loss from animals (Btu/h; J/s)

q_m =   heat from mechanical equipment, lights, etc. (Btu/h; J/s)

q_{su} =   supplemental heat production (Btu/h; J/s)

q_e =   heat required to evaporate moisture (Btu/h; J/s)

q_b =   heat loss through building components (Btu/h; J/s)

q_v =   rate of sensible heat exchanged by ventilation (Btu/h; J/s)

q_{st} =   heat stored in building materials and equipment (Btu/h; J/s)

The heat from mechanical sources may be estimated using the following conversion factors:

3.4 Btu/h-W for incandescent lights
4.1 Btu/h-W for fluorescent lights
4,000 Btu/h-hp for motors
At steady state, $q_{st} = 0$

Moisture is contributed from four sources: incoming air, animal wastes, animal respiration, and feed and water. Moisture is removed by ventilation and in the waste material removed from the building. Except in rare cases, ventilation should remove all moisture entering the building to prevent condensation and uncomfortable humidity conditions for animals and workers.

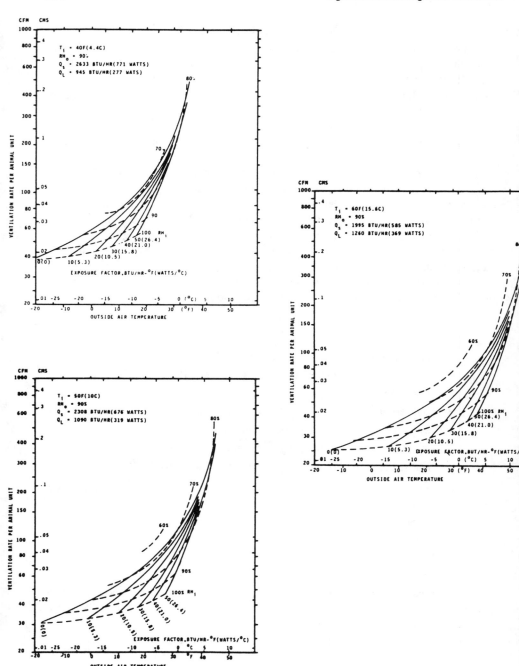

Figure 15.10. Design graphs for predicting ventilation performance for dairy cattle.

The moisture balance equation showing moisture in equals moisture out is:

$$Mw_i + W_a + W_e = Mw_o + W_m \qquad (15.9)$$

where

M = mass ventilation rate (lb/h; kg/s)

$$M = 60 \times Q/v \qquad (15.10)$$

Q = volumetric ventilation rate (cfm; m^3/s)

v = specific volume of air (ft^3/lb; m^3/kg)

w_i = humidity ratio of incoming air (lb vapor/lb air; kg/kg)

W_a = mN = moisture input from animals

m = rate of moisture production per animal (lb/h; kg/s)

N = number of animals

W_e = mass of water evaporated in space (lb/h; kg/s)

W_m = moisture removed in manure (lb/h; kg/s)

w_o = humidity ratio of out going air (lb vapor/lb air; kg/kg)

Example 15.1

An example heat and moisture balance will be completed to illustrate the use of the psychrometric chart and several other procedures previously discussed. The following situation is assumed:

Given: A central New York farm has sixty, 1,500 lb cows housed in a 36 × 140 ft stable with 200 ft^2 of window and door area. The barn temperature is maintained at 45°F.

R-values are:

window and doors, 2 h-°F-ft^2/Btu

ceiling, 15 h-°F-ft^2/Btu

wall, 12 h-°F-ft^2/Btu.

The relative humidity (RH) outside is 80% and inside is 60%.

Solution

It is assumed that the only significant heat input is from the animals and the only significant heat losses are through the building and by ventilation. Thus, the heat available for ventilation, $q_v = q_s - q_b$. From figure 15.8, the outside design temperature is 0°F; from table 15.2, the heat and moisture produced by dairy cows are interpolated to be 3.5 Btu/(h-lb) and 0.00106 lb/lb; from figure 12.2, 0°F and 80% RH gives 0.8 Btu/lb enthalpy and 0.00071 lb/lb absolute humidity; 45°F and 60% RH gives 15.0 Btu/lb enthalpy and 0.00371 lb/lb absolute humidity; from figure 12.1, the specific volume at 45°F and 60% RH is 13 ft^3/lb.

Heat input:

q_s = 60 cows × 1,500 lb/cow × 3.5 Btu/h-lb = 315,000 Btu/h

Heat loss from the building:

Ceiling:

36 ft × 140 ft/15 h-°F-ft²/Btu) × 45°F = 15,120 Btu/h

Walls:

$$\frac{\left(2 \times 8 \text{ ft} \left(36 + 140 \text{ ft}\right) - 200 \text{ ft}^2\right)}{12 \text{ h-°F-ft}^2/\text{Btu}} \times 45°F = 9,810 \text{ Btu/h}$$

Windows and doors:

$$\frac{200 \text{ ft}^2}{2 \text{ h-°F-ft}^2/\text{Btu}} \times 45°F = 4,500 \text{ Btu/h}$$

Total heat loss:

q_b = 15,120 + 9,810 + 4,500 = 29,420 Btu/h

Heat available for ventilation:

q_v = 315,000 − 29,430 = 285,570 Btu/h

Pounds of air moved:

$$M = \frac{285,570 \text{ Btu/h}}{\left(15 \text{ Btu/lb} - 0.8 \text{ Btu/lb}\right)} = 20,111 \text{ lb/h}$$

Moisture input:

W_a = 60 cows × 1,500 lb/cow × 0.00106 lb/lb = 95.4 lb/h

Moisture removed:

$M(w_o - w_i)$ = 20,111 lb/h × (0.00371 lb/lb − 0.00071 lb/lb)

$\qquad\qquad$ = 60.3 lb/h

Total fan capacity:

$$Q = \frac{13 \text{ ft}^3/\text{lb} \times 20,111 \text{ lb/h}}{60 \text{ min/h}} = 4,357 \text{ cfm}$$

Moisture removed by stable waste:

W_m = 95.4 lb/h − 60.3 lb/h = 35.1 lb/h

The 48.4 cfm fan capacity per 1,000 lb animal unit is close to the recommended capacity for continuous operation given in chapter 26 for dairy cows. This is logical since the conditions chosen for the example are near the coldest to be expected in the area. A similar analysis made at warmer temperature [e.g., 75°F (24°C)] might well show the need for an additional 200 cfm (5.6 m³/min) of fan capacity for each 1,000 lb (454 kg) animal unit. In between these two rates, fan capacity controlled by thermostats set at 55 to 60°F (13 to 16°C) would cycle on and off somewhat in relation to outside temperature.

On the psychrometric chart note that of the 14.2 Btu/lb required to change from inlet air to exhaust air condition, 10.3 Btu/lb warmed the air from 0° to 45°F and the remaining 3.9 Btu/lb vaporized and warmed the moisture. About two-thirds of the moisture produced by the animals was removed by ventilation, while the balance would be removed with the manure.

A similar analysis from a smaller number of animal units or a poorly insulated building might indicate the need for one or more of the following:
• a lower ventilation rate
• a lower inside design temperature
• the need for supplemental heat

It is convenient to use a psychrometric chart for the heat and moisture balance calculations. However, specific and latent heat values may be used with the following equations:

$$q_v = Mc_p\Delta t \tag{15.11}$$

$$q_e = mNh_{fg} \tag{15.12}$$

$$M_h = \frac{[q_s + q_m + q_{su} - q_e - q_b - q_{st}]}{c_p\Delta t} \tag{15.13}$$

$$M_m = \frac{mN}{[w_i - w_o]} \tag{15.14}$$

where

c_p	=	specific heat of air, [0.24 Btu/lb-°F; (J/kg-K)]
t	=	temperature difference between inside and outside °F (K)
h_{fg}	=	latent heat of water vaporization (Btu/lb; J/kg)
M_h	=	mass ventilation rate for heat control (lb/h; kg/s)
M_m	=	mass ventilation rate for moisture control (lb/h; kg/s)

Example 15.2
The following is an example of a heat and moisture balance problem.

Given: A 32 × 60 ft building with an 8 ft high ceiling, houses 240 finishing pigs in southeastern North Dakota. Assume the inside and outside RHs are 75%. The average R-value (walls, ceiling, and doors) is 16 h-ft^2-F/Btu. There are ten, 60 W lights in the building.

   (a) What should be the minimum ventilation rate?
   (b) How much supplemental heat is required to maintain a minimum temperature of 55°F?
   (c) What ventilation rate is required to limit inside temperature to 85°F when the outside temperature is 80°F?

Solution

(a) Expect that the requirement to control moisture will determine the minimum winter ventilation rate and assume that no moisture will be added by evaporation. Thus, the required ventilation mass flow rate is given by:

$$M = \frac{mN}{w_i - w_o}$$

From figure 15.7, the design outside temperature is found to be −18°F. The moisture and total heat production by 200 lb pigs at 55°F are found from table 15-2 to be 0.0011 lb/lb and 3.5 Btu/lb, respectively. The latent heat of the moisture can be converted to 1.14 Btu/lb by multiplying by (1,044 Btu/lb). The sensible heat production is found as the difference: 3.5 − 1.1 = 2.4 Btu/lb. From the psychrometric chart the specific volume and the humidity ratio of air at 55°F, 75% RH are 13.1 ft^3/lb and 0.007 lb/lb, respectively. The humidity ratio of air at −18°F, 75% RH is 0.000225 lb/lb. Using this information we calculate:

$$W_a = 240 \text{ pigs} \times 200 \text{ lb/pig} \left(\frac{7.65 \text{ gr/h•lb}}{7,000 \text{ gr/lb}} \right)$$

$$= 52.46 \text{ lb/h}$$

Or the volume flow rate = 7,743 × 13.1/60 = 1,690 cfm.

(b) The supplemental heat required is:

$$q_s + q_m + q_{su} = q_e + q_b + q_v$$

$$
\begin{aligned}
q_s &= 240\,(200)\,2.4 = 115.200 \text{ Btu/h}\\
q_m &= 10 \times 60 \times 3.4 = 2,040 \text{ Btu/h}\\
q_b &= \text{A/R } \Delta t = 32 \times 60 + 2(8)\,(30 + 60)/16\,(55 - 18)\\
&= 15,330 \text{ Btu/h}\\
q_v &= mc_p\Delta t = 7,743(0.24)\,(55 - 18)\\
&= 135,660 \text{ Btu/h}\\
q_{su} &= 15,330 + 135,660 - 115,200 - 2040\\
&= 33,750 \text{ Btu/h}
\end{aligned}
$$

(c) From figure 13.9, estimate q_s = 170 Btu/h-pig.

For Δt = 5°F, q_b = 1,050 Btu/h and at t_i = 80°F,

q_s = 240(170) = 40,800 Btu/h.

Now, $q_v = q_s + q_m - q_b = mc_p\Delta t$ or:

$$m = \frac{40,800 + 2040 - 1050}{0.24\ (5)}$$

$$= 34,825\ \text{lb/h}$$

Thus, the required volume air flow rate would be 8,125 cfm. Calculating the ventilation rate to maintain moisture control would show it to be 17,143 lb/h.

Ventilation Curves

It is instructive to calculate the required ventilation rate for both moisture and temperature control at various outside temperatures. Typical results are plotted on a graph of ventilation rate versus outside temperature (fig. 15.11). Note that the curves intersect. The point of intersection is the balance point—the heat from animals and other sources, excluding supplemental, is equal to the heat losses including ventilation at the rate required for moisture control. The outside temperature at which this occurs is called the "balance point" or "no-heat" temperature.

At lower ambient temperatures the ventilation needed to control moisture is greater than that needed to maintain temperature. At high ambient temperatures the reverse is true. If the temperature control ventilation rate is used at low ambient temperatures, excessively high humidity will result. If both temperature and humidity are to be maintained, then supplemental heat must be provided. Above the balance point temperature, ventilating at the temperature control rate will result in decreased humidity levels, but this is normally acceptable.

NATURAL VENTILATION SYSTEMS

Ventilation of buildings without the use of fans or mechanical devices is often called natural ventilation since the natural air buoyancy and wind are the driving forces. Building design and management are even more critical for these systems than the mechanical ventilation systems. Many naturally ventilated buildings are managed such that the winter temperature inside the building is only about 5°F (3°C) above ambient. In such cases, they are properly termed cold buildings and will be discussed in the next section. The design guidelines given in that section are appropriate for all naturally ventilated buildings. With careful design and management it is possible to use natural, or minimal supplemental heat, and still maintain a reasonably warm modified environment barn in all but the most adverse conditions. This is not true for all animals, i.e., baby pigs do not provide enough heat to keep a building warm and allow sufficient ventilation unless it is very mild.

Ventilating rates

Temp.	For heat	For moisture
50 F	4316 cfm	2250 cfm
40 F	2067 cfm	1339 cfm
30 F	1317 cfm	1032 cfm
20 F	942 cfm	874 cfm
10 F	717 cfm	802 cfm
0 F	567 cfm	758 cfm
-10 F	459 cfm	741 cfm

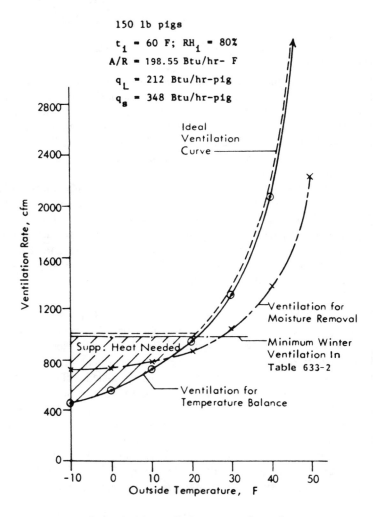

150 lb pigs

$t_1 = 60$ F; $RH_1 = 80\%$

A/R = 198.55 Btu/hr- F

$q_L = 212$ Btu/hr-pig

$q_s = 348$ Btu/hr-pig

Figure 15.11. Ventilation curves for swine.

The following is a simplified approach to estimating the wind effect on a general building:

$$Q_a = EAV \qquad (15.15)$$

where

Q_a = air flow (cfm; m^3/s)
A = area of opening (ft^2; m^2)
E = effectiveness
0.5 to 0.6 if wind is perpendicular
0.25 to 0.35 if wind is diagonal typically use 0.35
V = wind velocity (fpm; m/s) (fpm = 88 * mph)

Example 15.3

With a 9 m/s (20 mph) wind, a 76 mm (3 in.) eave inlet, and a 30 m (96 ft) long building:

$$Q = 0.35(2.4 \text{ m}^2)(9 \text{ m/s}) = 7.56 \text{ m}^3/\text{s} \ (16{,}000 \text{ cfm})$$

for 2.2 m/s (5 mph) wind,

$$Q = 1.9 \text{ m/s} \ (4{,}000 \text{ cfm})$$

for 18 m/s (40 mph) wind,

$$Q = 15 \text{ m/s} \ (32{,}000 \text{ cfm})$$

The temperature, or chimney, effect is given by the following equation:

$$Q = \theta A \left[2gH \left(\frac{T_i - T_o}{T_i} \right) \right]^{1/2} \qquad (15.16)$$

or

$$Q = v'A_o = A_o \times 481c \left[\frac{H(\beta_o - \beta_1)}{\beta_o} \right]^{1/2} \qquad (15.17)$$

where

θ = reduction factor (friction loss)
for rough uninsulated ducts, $q = 0.3 - 0.5$;
for smooth insulated duct, use 0.65
g = acceleration of gravity = 9.8 m/s^2
H = height difference between inlet and outlet (m)
T_i = absolute temperature inside (K)
T_o = absolute temperature outside (K)
A_o = cross-sectional flow area (m^2)
c = coefficient of friction at entrance

ß = air density (kg/m^3)

Example 15.3
If H = 2 m, T_i = 20°C, T_o = –20°C, and A = 4.8 m^2; then Q = 8.8 m^3/s
- For T_i = 10°C, T_o = 0°C:

$$Q = 0.65(4.8 \text{ m}^2)\left[2(9.8 \text{ m/s}^2)2 \text{ m}\left(\frac{283 \text{ K} - 273 \text{ K}}{283 \text{ K}}\right)\right]^{1/2}$$

$$= 3.12(1.385)\_$$

$$= 3.67 \text{ m}^3/s \ (7773 \text{ cfm})$$

- For T_i = 2°C, T_o = 0°C:

$$Q = 3.12\left(39\left(\frac{2}{275}\right)\right)^{1/2} = 1.66 \text{ m}^3/s$$

Ventilation of Uninsulated Cold Buildings

Cold buildings used to house livestock require attention to proper ventilation design if a desirable environment is to be maintained. Just as in a warm building, animal heat is a factor that helps remove moisture. However, orientation of the building and construction details that promote free air movement are more essential.

Location and orientation of the barn on high ground with one side (the back side of an open front building) facing the prevailing wind will help provide the air movement and pressure differences required for successful operation. Wind blowing perpendicular to the ridge of a building tends to cause a positive pressure on the windward side and a negative pressure on the leeward side, thus promoting air movement within the building. Trees and other structures will obstruct air flow if close to naturally ventilated buildings. A minimum of 50 ft between buildings is recommended. This separation distance should be increased for obstructions longer than 100 ft or higher than 10 ft. Use the following equation to determine minimum separation distance:

$$d_s = 0.4 \text{ H } \sqrt{L} \qquad\qquad (15.18)$$

where
   d_s = separation distance (ft)
   H   = total height of obstruction (ft)
   L   = total length of obstruction (ft)

A roof pitch of no less than 4:12 is desirable. Air movement appears to be sluggish under very low pitches while very steep slopes seem to carry inlet air off without adequate circulation within the animal zone. Also, the steeper pitches are more expensive and more difficult to work on during construction.

Sidewall height that provides adequate clearance for animals and equipment is usually satisfactory. Ten feet (3 m) over alleys or 12 ft (3.5 m) in bedded manure-pack areas are minimum desirable heights.

Eave and ridge openings are necessary throughout the year. In addition, provision must be made to open the sidewalls during mild weather. It is recommended that the eaves have a continuous opening equivalent to one inch for each 10 ft (15 mm/m of width) of barn width. This opening can usually be provided by leaving the space between the plate and the underside of the roof open. Unless blowing snow proves to be a problem, the space should be left open all year. If a hinged baffle seems necessary it should not close off more than one-half of the required opening.

To be compatible, the ridge should be 2 in. (50 mm) for each 10 ft (3 m) of building width. Ordinarily, no ridge cap is necessary. While a cap keeps out rain, it often causes an increased snow problem. If a cap is installed, it should never be wider than twice the width of the opening and it must be high enough to allow a vertical distance between the top of the roofing and the bottom of the cap equal to one half of the ridge opening. As an example, a 60 ft (18 m) barn should have 6 in. (150 mm) openings at the eaves, a 12 in. (300 mm) opening at the ridge, and the ridge cap should be no more than 24 in. (600 mm) wide with a minimum vertical clearance of 6 in. (150 mm). When a ridge cap is not used, the exposed rafters should be flashed down to the first purlins in order to prevent decay due to moisture accumulation between the rafter and purlins.

Sidewall openings may be provided by hinged panels or flexible curtains that will allow a continuous 2 ft (0.6 m) or more opening for the length of the building. If panels are mounted on a track to allow horizontal adjustment, they must be 4 ft (1.2 m) high to provide an equivalent area of opening.

Condensation will appear occasionally on the underside of the roof in the best of systems. However, this can be kept to a minimum by following the suggestions for roof slope and ventilation, as well as other controlling factors such as animal density, purlin design, roof material, insulation, and the location of other buildings.

Housing the number of animals for which the building was planned provides the maximum heat to support air circulation. A truss spacing that allows 2 × 4 in. (38 × 89 mm) purlins to be laid flat will provide the best air movement. Six- and eight-inch (140- and 184-mm) deep purlins should be avoided as they tend to create dead air pockets. A solid roof deck or insulation under the roofing will help to prevent condensation. However, either one adds to the construction cost and, in the case of insulation, moisture which can collect between it and the roofing may cause a serious corrosion problem with a metal roof.

Ventilation Cooling Systems

For some enterprises, ventilation systems are designed to provide cooling. For example, in enclosed livestock buildings, surplus fan capacity above that required for winter ventilation is used for summer cooling. Potato and nursery storages use cool, nighttime air to lower the temperature to storage level. Greenhouse systems require large fan capacity which is used primarily for cooling.

However, when the outside air temperature is excessive, air movement alone is not effective and water, evaporative or zone, cooling may be beneficial. Evaporative coolers reduce the temperature by vaporizing water which increases the relative humidity. Water dripping over shredded wood or cellulose pads creates a large wet area. Air drawn through the wet pads is cooled by the evaporation of the water. The range of pad area to air volume is approximately 0.5 to 0.7 ft^2 (0.05 to 0.07 m^2) per 100 cfm (47 L/s) of air flow, although the manufacturer's recommendations should be followed for specific installations. Efficient evaporative coolers are capable of reducing air temperatures to within 5°F (3°C) of the initial wet-bulb temperature of the air being drawn through the pads. The cooled air will have a relative humidity of 85 to 90%.

The value of an evaporative cooling system depends on its application and on the typical wet-bulb temperatures for the region. In the eastern half of the United States, wet-bulb temperatures at midday are commonly 12 to 17°F (7 to 9°C) below dry-bulb temperatures. Thus lowering the temperature 7 to 12°F (4 to 7°C) with an evaporative cooler is feasible. However, in the event of an unusually hot spell, air passing through the cooling pads may still be above 80°F (27°C) and be very high in humidity. This is a condition that might be fine in a greenhouse, but it is unacceptable for broilers and other animals that depend on respiration for body cooling at high temperatures.

In contrast, in the western half of the United States, excluding western Oregon and Washington, wet-bulb temperatures are commonly 25 to 30°F (14 to 17°C) below dry-bulb temperatures. Under these conditions, cooling the air 15 to 20°F (8 to 11°C) is possible without raising the relative humidity above 60 to 70%. The air is not only cooled appreciably, but humidity is still low enough to have little effect on animal comfort. Evaporative cooling is obviously much more practical in the drier regions of the country and should be considered on the basis of economic feasibility.

Water cooling systems wet the animal's skin and provide cooling by evaporation. Sprinklers which wet the animal are preferred to foggers which cool the air. A sprinkler directly cools the animal. Sprinklers may be used for swine and cattle. Drip cooling systems which emit small water droplets directly on the neck and shoulders are useful for swine. When used with farrowing sows the young pigs stay relatively dry.

Zone cooling which cools only the area around the head is also useful for swine, particularly farrowing sows and breeding stock. Air may be outside cool air, earth tube tempered air or mechanically conditioned air.

Problems

15.1.   A 50 × 600 ft (16 × 190 m) building with an 8 ft (2.5 m) high ceiling houses 100,000 laying hens in southeastern North Dakota. What should be the minimum ventilation rate? How much supplemental heat is required? Assume an average R-value (walls, ceiling, and doors) of 16 h-°F-ft^2/Btu (2.8 °K-m^2/W). It is desired to maintain a minimum temperature of 55°F (13°C) in the winter. There are 150, sixty-watt lights in the building. Assume the inside and outside relative humidities do not exceed 75%. If it is 80°F (27°C) outside, what ventilation rate is required to limit the inside temperature to 85°F (29°C)?

15.2.   If the total length of slot inlet in a building is 800 ft (250 m), how wide should the slot opening be for an air flow rate of 20,000 cfm (9.4 m^3/s)?

15.3.   Recommend (size) an inlet design for a 40 × 260 ft (12 × 80 m) building that has two banks of fans with a total air flow capacity of 132,000 cfm (62 m^3/s).

15.4.   Estimate the ventilation rate due to a 20 mph (32 km/h) wind blowing perpendicular to a 60 ft (20 m) long building with a continuous 6 in. (150 mm) eave opening.

16 Heating and Cooling

Ventilation in agricultural buildings removes excess moisture but may sometimes result in a negative heat balance. In such cases, supplemental heat will be required to maintain the desired temperature. It may not be possible to maintain the desired temperature by simple ventilation during hot weather. Ventilation air cooling can be accomplished by mechanical refrigeration, but this is seldom found economically justified. Earth tubes or evaporative coolers may be used to temper ventilation at a reasonable cost. Earth tubes may also be used to temper cold air in the winter.

Supplemental heat for agricultural buildings may be provided by various methods and sources. Radiant, floor, and unit heaters may be used. Heat may be produced by boilers or furnaces and then delivered to the location needed by a transfer medium such as air or water. Space heaters are used to warm room air and maintain room temperature. Radiant and floor heat provides localized animal comfort.

Warm Air

Warm air systems are very economical for large heating demands. Air is heated by a heat exchanger in the furnace and discharged to the space to be heated. Cool return air is withdrawn from the space and passed through the furnace. The burner is controlled by a thermostat in the space being heated. Warm air furnaces are available in a wide variety of sizes and use almost any fuel.

Recirculating warm air heating systems work well for farm shops, milking centers, and greenhouses, but not for livestock housing because of the dusty environment. Heaters which use outside air can discharge this to livestock facilities. The warmed air from the furnace will provide part of the required ventilation air.

Hot Water

Hot water systems are flexible, durable, and relatively trouble free. The boiler or heating unit provides a water supply of 140 to 215°F (60 to 100°C). One or more thermostatically controlled pump(s) circulate the hot water through the distribution pipes. Finned tube radiator pipes are used to improve heat transfer except in dusty areas where non-finned black iron pipe may be used to avoid clogging problems. Hot water systems can be zoned to areas with differing heating needs. Each zone will have a separate circulating pump and distribution loop.

Radiant Heat

Radiant heaters are good for zone heating of young animals. Radiant heat energy passes through air without warming it. When the energy strikes an animal or other surface, it is absorbed and warms the object. Objects not in direct line with the radiant heater will not be heated. This provides a variation in the environment and allows animals to move in or out of the heated zone to their level of comfort. Brooder chickens can be heated directly without warming the entire building. Milker in a milk parlor can be kept warm despite constant opening of doors. And workers in a shop can be provided heat without having to warm the entire building and its contents.

Natural gas, propane or electricity are suitable energy sources for infrared radiant heaters. A variety of radiant heaters are available ranging from the simple heat lamp to fan-driven pipe units designed to heat an entire building. A 250 W heat lamp is satisfactory for heating a farrowing creep area if it is supplementing floor heat. In cold climates a heat lamp alone will not be sufficient, three or four times that much heat may be required per litter of pigs. Heat lamps should be suspended in such a manner as to cause them to come unplugged before falling into bedding or the proximity of other readily combustible material.

Gas catalytic radiant heaters which have relatively low surface temperatures are flameless and do not require a flue when used in well-ventilated buildings. Catalytic heaters are usually not thermostatically controlled which makes them somewhat less efficient. The radiating surface must be kept clean to maintain heating efficiency.

When unvented gas heaters are used, the ventilation rate should be increased to provide 2.5 cfm/1,000 Btu/h (4 L/s-kW) to remove moisture produced by combustion.

Floor Heaters

Floor heat is useful for zone heating in farm shops, small animal housing, milking parlor pits or other heated work areas. In farrowing crates the floors in the creep areas can be heated, but the area under the sow should not be. In the heated area the input may be about 100 Btu/h/ft^2 (300 W/m^2). If the heated floor is wet, heat will be used in evaporating the water and the humidity of the air will be increased. Dunging areas and waterers should normally not be on heated floors.

Hot water pipes or electric resistance cables buried in sand may be used. Electric coils in fiberglass pads may be placed over an existing floor. Waterproof insulation should be installed under a heated floor, but the heating elements should not be placed directly on plastic insulation. A thermostat sensing bulb for controlling the floor heating system should be installed in plastic conduit or pipe in the concrete. Locate the bulb about 1 in. (25 mm) below the surface, but at least 4 in. (100 mm) from heat pipes or 2 in. (50 mm) from an electric heat cable.

Plastic heating pipe can supply about 35 Btu/h (10 W) for each foot if the inlet water temperature is 150°F (65°C).

Electric heating cable normally has a lower installation cost and eliminates freezing concerns. Electric cable can be installed to allow separate controls for each stall or pen. Typical rating for heating cable is 2 to 7 W/ft. Prefabricated pads are available with cables spaced in a plastic mesh to simplify installation.

Heat Storage in Sand Under Floors

Sand under concrete floors can store heat from animals, solar-heated air, hot water pipes or off-peak electricity. Sand depths of 6 to 8 in. (150 to 200 mm) and hot water pipe spacing of 10 to 12 in. (250 to 300 mm) will give about 10 W/ft^2 (110 W/m^2). When a solar collector is used to warm air, this can be used to heat sand by passing through ducts formed from concrete blocks. Recommended air velocity through the concrete blocks is 90 to 180 fpm (450 to 900 mm/s).

Unit Space Heaters

Unit space heaters are common and a relatively inexpensive method of providing supplemental heat. Room air which contains dust, moisture, and corrosive gases is heated directly. Unit heaters need frequent cleaning and lubrication. The units may be arranged to create a circular air flow within a room.

Alternative Heat Sources

A number of energy sources are available for providing heat. Electric, natural gas, LP gas, propane or fuel oil are the conventional sources. However, wood and coal are often used. Biomass, biological produced material, such as straw, stalks or other crop residues, can also be used as fuels. Biogas which is typically about 55 to 60% methane can be produced by anaerobic digestion of livestock manures. Methane is the major component of natural gas. Thus, biogas is similar to nature gas and with some slight modification or adjustment can be used as a replacement for natural gas. Solar energy is free, except for the cost of the collection system, and is environmental friendly. Solar collectors can be readily designed as part of the ventilation system to provide some heating of incoming air and reduce the amount of supplemental heat energy required. The major disadvantage of solar energy is the fact that sun is normally not shining during the coldest part of the day. Solar radiation and usage is discussed in the next chapter.

Preheating Ventilation Air

Preheating ventilation air can be used to prevent cold drafts on animals. Cold incoming air is mixed with heat in a separate room or hallway and then distributed to the animal area. It must be remembered that animals will add heat to the air thus the preheated air should enter the animal space below the desired temperature.

Air-to-Air Heat Exchangers

Air-to-air heat exchangers can be used to capture some of the heat from exhaust air and prewarm incoming air. About 70 to 90% of heat loss from animal confinement buildings during winter is lost through ventilation.

The amount of heat saved depends on the heat exchanger efficiency and the transfer area. The transfer rate depends on the temperature difference between incoming and outgoing air and the heat transfer coefficient. The heat transfer coefficient is the combination of a convective transfer coefficient on each side of the plate and the thermal conductivity of the plate. The convective coefficients will be affected by the surface conditions particularly the amount of dirt on the surface. Frost on the surface may decrease the efficiency, but condensation may increase efficiency.

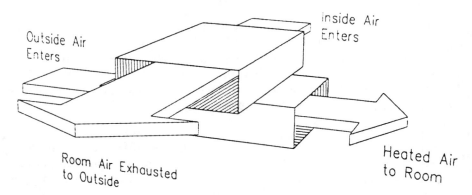

Figure 16.1. Crossflow heat exchanger.

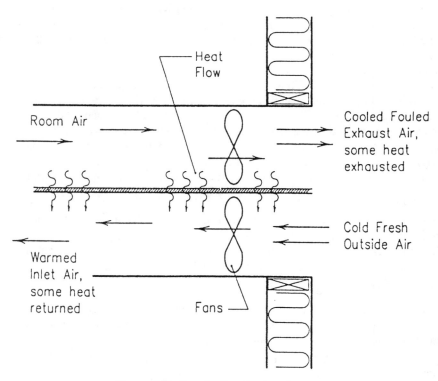

Figure 16.2. Counterflow heat exchanger.

Heat exchangers can be parallel flow, crossflow or counterflow (figs. 16.1 and 16.2). Counterflow is more common in livestock housing. The counterflow exchanger is more efficient because the heat transfer is more uniform throughout the exchanger. In the heat exchanger, the heat from one air stream passes through a highly conductive barrier to the other air stream. This barrier is typically steel and should be non-corrosive and yet be easily cleaned.

A variation in the air-to-air plate type heat exchanger is a rock bed heat exchanger (fig. 16.3). In this system warm, outgoing ventilation air is passed through a bed of rocks and transfers heat to the rocks, increasing their temperature. Periodically, the direction of the air flow is reversed. Thus the warmed rocks can then transfer heat to the incoming ventilation air. The rock beds are operated in pairs to allow one to be in the inlet and the other in the outlet. Smooth rocks of 3 to 6 in. (75 to 150 mm) diameter and a bed of 8 to 12 in. (200 to 300 mm) works well. During extreme cold weather, condensation will likely occur in the bed. Precautions must be taken to ensure that the bed does not freeze shut and prevent air flow.

Earth Tubes

Earth tubes take advantage of the fact that the average soil temperature 6 to 12 ft below grade is higher than air temperature in winter and lower in summer. Thus earth tube systems can heat ventilation air by extracting heat from the soil in the winter, and cool air in the summer transferring the heat to the soil. When hot, humid air is passed through earth tubes, condensation may occur; provisions should be made to handle this condensate.

Soil temperature at a 6 ft (1.8 m) depth will fluctuate about 22°F (12°C) from maximum to minimum during the year. This variation will be only about 12°F (7°C) at a depth of 12 ft (3.6 m). The peak soil temperatures will lag average air temperatures

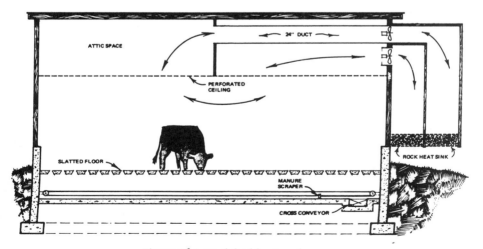

Figure 16.3. Rock bed heat exchanger.

by approximately three months at 12 ft (3.6 m) and 1 1/2 months at 6 ft (1.8 m). The minimum soil temperature at a 12 ft (3.6 m) depth in Iowa will be about 48°F (9°C) in late April and the maximum will be about 62°F (17°C) in October. The minimum at 6 ft (1.8 m) will be about 6 to 8°F (3 to 4°C) lower while the maximum will be about 6 to 8°F higher.

Soil type, soil moisture content, depth of tubes, and airflow rate will all affect the performance of earth tube systems. Generally the heavier and wetter the soil, the better the system performs. Dry sand does not store or transfer heat very well and should be avoided if possible.

For efficient heat transfer and minimal pressure loss in the earth tubes, air velocities should be about 600 ft/min (3 m/s). Typical installation uses plastic tubing with diameters of 4 to 24 in. (100 to 600 mm) and lengths of 100 to 400 ft (30 to 120 m). To be efficient longer lengths are required for the larger diameter pipe. The minimum length for 6 in. (150 mm) diameter pipe is about 100 ft (30 m); 12 in. (300 mm) diameter tubes should be at least 200 ft (60 m) long. These systems will provide exit air temperatures within 5 to 10°F (3 to 6°C) of the soil temperature. Higher velocities and longer pipe lengths will increase the total heat transfer, but doubling the length or airflow rate will not change the exit temperature more than about 4 to 6°F (2 to 3°C).

Installations will normally use several buried pipes arranged radially toward a vertical inlet pipe and sump or arranged laterally and use a manifold (fig. 16.4 and 16.5). The radial arrangement eliminates the need for a manifold but makes construction more difficult.

Cooling

Cooling may be used to reduce the effects of heat stress on animals. The loss of productivity resulting from reduced feed intake may be avoided, as well as the reduc-

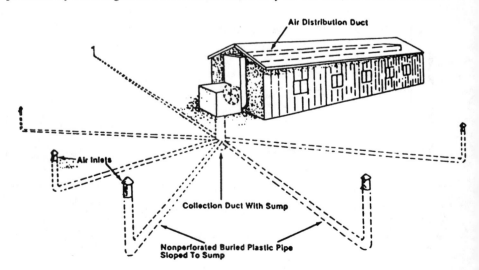

Figure 16.4. Radial earth tube heat exchanger.

tion in breeding efficiency which may be very serious during hot spells. Temperatures above 75 to 80°F (24 to 27°C) can cause losses in production for swine and dairy cattle. At high temperatures animals lose 60 to 70% of their heat by evaporative cooling, mostly from the lungs. High relative humidity makes this more difficult. Except for horses most livestock have very limited ability to sweat; however, high air velocity does have a cooling effect which can help to prevent heat stress.

Water Cooling

Sprinkling or dripping water on animals will result in cooling by evaporation. A water application rate of 0.1 gal/h-pig (6 mL/min-pig) is recommended for swine or 0.3 gal/h/ft^2 (0.2 L/min-m^2) for cattle. The water should be applied to the animal's surface as droplets and not misted as fog. For confined animals such as sows in a stall small droplets of water can be applied directly on the neck and shoulders. Dairy cattle should not be sprayed in resting areas because wet conditions can increase mastitis problems. Typically these systems would operate when air temperatures exceed 85°F (30°C). Intermittent application, i.e., 2 to 3 min every 15 to 20 min may be effective.

Evaporative Cooling

Evaporative cooling uses heat from the air to vaporize water and thus decreases the air temperature. This increases the relative humidity of the air and will be more effective if the initial relative humidity is low. Although relative humidity in the Midwest and East may be relatively high, it will generally be lowest during the hottest part of the day and some benefit can be gained by evaporative cooling. A lower maximum ventilation rate (a reduction of 40%) can be used when evaporative cooling is used.

Evaporative cooling systems draw air through wet pads or foggers into the area to be cooled. Fibrous pads mounted in openings in sidewalls have water applied at the top and excess is collected in a bottom sump for recirculating. Cellulose pads should provide an area of 4 ft^2 per 1,000 cfm (0.8 m^2/m^3-s); aspen chip pads need

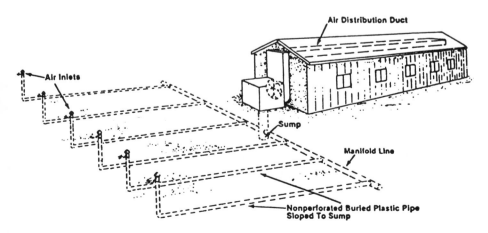

Figure 16.5. Lateral layout earth tube heat exchanger.

6.67 ft^2/1,000 cfm (1.3 m^2/m^2-s). The make-up water should be supplied at a rate of 1.0 gpm/100 ft^2 (7 mL/s- m^2). For a 6 ft high pad, the pump capacity should be 0.5 gpm/linear ft (0.1 L/s-m).

Example 16.1

Plan an evaporative cooling system for a 36 × 240 ft (11 × 73 m) barn housing 100 dairy cows. Use cellulose pads.

Solution

Total airflow: 100 cows × 335 cfm/1,000 lb × 1,400 lb/cow = 46,900 cfm

Reduce by 40%: 0.60 × 46,900 cfm = 28,140 cfm.

Required pad area: 28,140 cfm × 4.0 ft^2/1000 cfm = 112.6 ft^2

Required pad length, assume 4 ft high pads: 112.6 ft^2/4 ft = 28 ft.

Maximum make-up water required: 112.6 ft^2 × 1 gpm /100 ft^2 = 1.1 gpm

Pad pump capacity: 28 ft × 0.50 gpm/ft = 14 gpm.

Cellulose pads should last about five years. Pads should be hosed off about once every two months to remove dust and sediment. Algae buildup may be controlled by adding copper sulfate to the water or installing the pads in a light-tight enclosure. As water evaporates, salts and other impurities will build up; continuous bleeding of 5 to 10% of the water or monthly flushing can control this problem.

Zone cooling is used to make animals comfortable without cooling the entire room. This is particularly useful for sows with small pigs. The pigs are comfortable at a much higher temperature than the sow. Air for zone cooling can be unconditioned outside air, mechanically cooled air or earth tube tempered air. Evaporatively cooled air, which has high relative humidity, is not useful for snout cooling, since animals lose 60 to 70% of their heat by evaporation from the respiratory tract. Air from earth tubes is also expected to have high relative humidity during warm weather. Mechanically cooled air has the advantage of also being dehumidified.

A zone cooling system has a main duct and downspouts (or drop ducts) which direct the airflow onto the animal. The main duct should be insulated to an R-value of 6 to reduce condensation and heating of duct air.

Mechanical Refrigeration

Mechanical refrigeration is used to move heat from an area of low temperature to an area of higher temperature. Systems may cool air or products directly or they may cool water which in turn is used to cool the desired area or product. The direct expansion type is relatively simple and is used for most farm and home applications. The energy input to a refrigeration system maintains an internal pressure difference that allows continuous changes of state to take place. Heat absorbed or given off as the changes occur produces the refrigeration (fig. 16.6).

A mechanical refrigeration system works on the principle that if a vapor is compressed to a high pressure, it will condense and give up its heat of vaporization to its surroundings, and that when the pressure is reduced, the liquid again evaporates and absorbs heat from its surroundings. A refrigeration system consists of four main parts

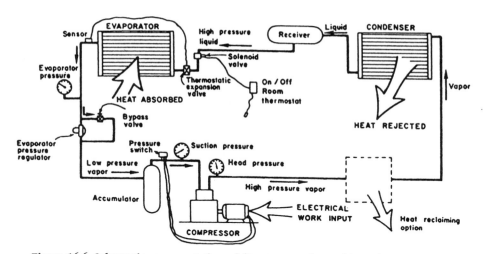

Figure 16.6. Schematic representation of direct expansion refrigeration system.

(fig. 16.6): (1) a pump or compressor, (2) a condenser (a heat exchanger that operates at high pressure and temperature and gives up heat to the surrounding air or water), (3) an evaporator (a heat exchanger that operates at low pressure and temperature and absorbs heat from the surrounding air or water), and (4) an expansion valve that is in fact a restriction in the line between the condenser and the evaporator.

Compression by the motor driven compressor causes the temperature of the refrigerant gas to increase. When the hot gas cools in the condenser, it loses heat and condenses to a liquid. The liquid then passes through an expansion valve or capillary tube into the low pressure area of the evaporator. Expansion cools the refrigerant and it can then pick up heat at a very low temperature as it evaporates to a gas. The compressor maintains the low pressure in the evaporator and the high pressure in the condenser. The adjustment of the expansion valve determines in large part the temperature at which the evaporator operates.

The evaporator is installed in the cold room and the condenser in a place where it can easily give up its heat, often outdoors. With the system charged with a refrigerant, the compressor operates by drawing a low pressure on the evaporator where the refrigerant boils, evaporates, and picks up heat from the room air. At the same time, the cold gas is compressed to a high pressure and temperature in the condenser, where the refrigerant condenses and gives up its heat. The expansion valve simply limits flow so that the pressure difference can be maintained on a continuous basis.

The evaporator and the condenser, which are discussed in more detail in chapter 18, are both heat exchangers and, in many cases, similar in construction. With a system of switching valves, the function of the two can be interchanged which allows the system to operate as a cooling system in warm weather and as a heating system in cool weather. In other words it is an air conditioner in the summer and a heat pump in the winter.

Two refrigerants that have commonly been used for apple storage refrigeration systems are: (1) Refrigerant 12 (R-12), dichlorodifluoromethane, which is odorless, nontoxic, nonflammable, and is piped with copper tubing, and (2) Refrigerant 717, ammonia, which is toxic, has a strong pungent odor, burns at certain concentrations in air, and is piped with iron pipe. Of the two, ammonia is cheaper, more efficient, and because of a higher heat of vaporization, much less of the refrigerant is needed in the system so that all components are smaller. In general, ammonia may be preferable for large systems because of economy, and R-12 for small systems because it is nontoxic and easier to handle.

Chlorofluorocarbons such as R-12 are being phased out because of their effects on the ozone layer and are being replaced by less toxic hydrofluorocarbons. Although its characteristics are less than perfect, HFC-134a is the apparent choice for replacing R-12.

The least complicated control system is a thermostat that turns the compressor motor on and off at a set room temperature. There are also, however, pressure systems that stop the compressor motor when the evaporator pressure drops to a set level. There is always a unique evaporator temperature related to the pressure of the refrigerant within the evaporator.

The capacity of a refrigeration system is often stated in "tons". A ton of refrigeration is equal to 288,000 Btu/day (3.5 kW), the amount of latent heat available when 1 ton of ice melts.

The efficiency of a refrigeration system is often given as the coefficient of performance (COP). It is the ratio of useful refrigeration or heating divided by the energy input to the system. The COP varies with the temperature range within which the system operates, it is much better with a small range, and may reach 4 in the heating phase and 3 in the cooling phase.

Problems

16.1.   Design an evaporative cooling system for a barn housing 40 gestating sows.

16.2.   If a sow and 8 pigs are confined to a 5 × 7 ft farrowing pen, how many feet of electric heating cable should be embedded in the floor? Sketch a layout of the pen and show the location of the cable.

16.3.   If the minimum ventilation air is to be brought in through earth tubes for 200 growing pigs, how many and what size of pipes would you suggest? If the outside temperature is −10°F and the air exits the tubes at 40°F, how much heat was gained?

17 Solar Energy

The use of solar energy dates back to well before the beginning of recorded history. Archimedes is reported to have burned the Roman fleet in 212 B.C. by setting up a barrage of mirrors along the harbor walls to direct the beams of sunlight to a common point on the fleet (Williams, 1974). Whether this actually happened or not is academic. Of more significance is the fact that from the very beginning of the practice of agriculture, farmers have made use of solar energy in the greatest collectors of all, their crops. The sun has also been used for centuries to dry meat, fish, and fruit. Even today examples of sun-dried products can be found throughout the world.

Investigation into the uses of solar energy between the 16th and 20th centuries was directed primarily at concentrating the sun's flux for high-temperature application. Experimental solar furnaces for melting metals and solar-powered steam engines captured the imagination of scientists. New interest in the utilization of solar energy was stimulated after World War II and solar heating became technologically feasible but remained economically prohibitive.

The real thrust into all phases of solar energy development came in the mid-1970s when fossil fuel shortages and the accompanying rise in price, together with the increasing public concern over the safety of nuclear reactors, made it apparent that an alternative energy source was essential. Along with a multitude of ideas for harnessing and using the sun's clean energy were many related to its use in agriculture.

The purpose here is to look at the nature of solar energy and briefly describe some applications in agriculture. This discussion will be limited—a comprehensive treatment would be voluminous. A plethora of information has been published on this subject during the past decades.

Solar Flux

Solar flux refers to the energy of the sun reaching the earth. Solar energy has high thermodynamic potential and is available in enormous quantities; however, it is dilute and not dependable. The abundance of solar energy striking the United States is indicated by the average flux of 1,555 Btu/ft^2-day (6470 MJ/m^2-yr). It is estimated that the sunlight falling on the earth could theoretically provide 100,000 times the total energy output of all existing power stations.

The fact that solar flux is dilute is illustrated by dividing the 1,555 Btu/ft²-day flux by 8,760 h in a year which results in 65 Btu/ft²-h (0.738 MJ/m²·h). At that rate, it would require 4,830 h to produce the energy equivalent of 1 gal of fuel oil from 1 ft² of surface area (37 h for 1.0 L/m²).

The dependability of solar energy is influenced to a great extent by geographic area. A portion of the northeastern United States receives less than 2,200 h of sunlight per year. In contrast, practically all of the Southwest receives in excess of 3,400 h of sunlight per year. Average solar energy over large areas is a misleading figure, however, due to seasonal and geographic variation. It is the day-to-day fluctuations in weather conditions, particularly periods of cloudiness, that make the sun's energy an undependable source of heat.

Solar Constant

The solar flux reaching a point normal (perpendicular) to the outer surface of the earth's atmosphere is given as 434.8 Btu/(ft²-h) [4.6 MJ/m²-h]. This is called the solar constant. Due to the effect of the earth's atmosphere, the energy that reaches the earth's surface is given as 318 Btu/(ft²-h) [3.6 MJ/m²-h]. In essence, the most energy available is approximately 300 Btu/(ft²-h) [3.4 MJ/m²-h], and that will occur only at a location where the sun's rays are perpendicular to the earth's surface.

The amount of solar radiation received on any surface will depend on the time of day, time of year, latitude, collector tilt angle, and the weather. The maximum amount of radiation that can be collected on a surface that is perpendicular to the sun's rays varies from about 2,000 to 3,000 Btu/day-ft² (150 to 230 kW/m²). The following factors will affect the amount of energy that is actually available for collection (table 17-1).

1. Latitude and season. Because the earth is tilted 23.5° on its axis in relation to the sun, there is a continuous change in the angle with which the sun's rays strike the earth. In the latitudes between 23.5°N and 23.5°S, there will be two days each year in which the solar flux is perpendicular. At latitudes farther north and farther south, the flux is never perpendicular.
2. Weather. The frequency of cloudy weather has a strong influence on the actual radiation reaching the earth's surface. The bands marked by 20° to 30°N and S are relatively dry and receive approximately 90% of the incident radiation. The great deserts of the world fall within these bands. Both nearer the equator and nearer the poles there is much more cloudiness and considerably lower average solar energy actually striking the earth.

Within general climatic zones, there are local variations of frequency and density of cloud cover due to topography, bodies of water, and prevailing winds. Consequently, it is only by measurements and records that the solar radiation for a particular location may be predicted.

Solar energy is mostly shortwave radiation that originates from thermonuclear reactions in the core of the sun. The atmosphere causes scattering of the sun's rays resulting in part of the radiant energy striking the surface at various angles. The scattered radi-

Table 17-1. Average daily solar radiation on a horizontal surface (MJ/m^2)

	Boston, Mass.	Ottawa, Ont.	Columbus, Ohio	Madison, Wis.	Lincoln, Nebr.	Winnipeg, Man.
Lat.	42°22'	45°20'	40°00'	43°08'	40°51'	49°54'
Jan	5.7	6.1	5.5	6.4	8.1	5.5
Feb	8.4	9.7	8.5	9.2	10.8	9.5
Mar	12.1	14.2	12.6	14.0	14.7	15.4
Apr	15.4	18.2	16.8	16.5	18.0	18.6
May	20.1	21.1	20.9	19.8	21.0	21.6
Jun	21.1	23.6	24.	23.0	23.1	22.2
Jul	21.1	23.2	23.1	23.2	22.8	24.1
Aug	17.8	19.9	17.8	19.7	21.6	20.0
Sep	14.4	15.0	13.5	16.4	17.5	13.5
Oct	10.2	9.4	10.4	11.3	13.8	8.7
Nov	7.2	5.2	5.4	6.3	8.8	5.0
Dec	5.0	4.6	4.9	5.6	7.3	3.9

	Davis, Calif.	Seattle, Wash.	Tucson, Ariz.	Fort Worth, Texas	Columbia, Mo.	Apalachicola, Fla.
Lat.	38°33'	47°36'	32°07'	32°50'	38°58'	29°45'
Jan	6.8	2.9	13.3	10.6	7.4	12.6
Feb	10.7	5.4	16.5	13.6	10.7	15.6
Mar	17.1	10.4		18.1	14.9	18.8
Apr	22.2	15.6	27.6	20.7	18.5	23.1
May	26.9	18.9		23.9	13.6	25.7
Jun	29.7	19.6	29.5	27.6	24.1	24.9
Jul	29.1	20.5	26.0	26.0	24.4	22.4
Aug	25.9	18.3	24.7	25.1	21.1	21.7
Sep	21.1	12.8	24.1	21.3	19.2	19.3
Oct	14.6	7.2	18.6	16.7	13.6	17.5
Nov	9.0	3.7	15.0	13.0	9.5	14.1
Dec	6.2	2.5	12.8	10.4	6.7	11.1

ation is termed diffuse. The total incident solar radiation striking a surface is given by:

$$I = I_{dn} K + I_d \qquad (17.1)$$

where

I	=	total incident solar energy
I_{dn}	=	direct normal insolation
I_d	=	diffuse solar radiation
K	=	cosine of angle of incidence

Collection

The type of device used to collect solar energy depends primarily on the application. Flat-plate collectors produce temperatures up to approximately 200°F (93°C) and are used mainly for heating water and buildings. Focusing collectors are used to obtain high temperatures by aiming parabolic reflectors at the sun and focusing the sun's reflected rays on a small surface where the energy is concentrated to produce a very high temperature. Another type of focusing collector is the parabolic cylinder which reflects the energy to a pipe parallel to its axis, producing temperatures higher than those obtained from a flat plate but lower than those from a parabolic concentrator. The focusing collectors require costly, sophisticated equipment to track the sun in order to obtain the maximum solar flux at all times. A third type of collector, the photovoltaic cell, converts sunlight directly into electricity.

While the flat-plate type is the simplest, it is the most important solar collector because of the broad range of potential applications. Basically most flat-plate collectors consist of either a wood or metal frame enclosing a black surface to absorb the heat which is then transferred to a circulating fluid, usually air or water, to carry the heat away (fig. 17.1). To prevent heat loss and improve efficiency, one or more transparent covers are usually placed over the collector surface and heavy insulation is installed behind the plate and around the edges.

A simple approach to using solar energy is to incorporate the collector into the ventilation system. An exterior wall can be painted black and then a duct formed using a translucent covering as shown in figure 17.2. As the incoming ventilation air is drawn through the duct it will be heated thus reducing the amount of supplemental heat required. By using a concrete block wall as shown in figure 17.3, thermal storage can be provided to allow the benefit of solar heating during the night.

Regardless of the type of collector used, the amount of energy collected at a given time and place is directly related to the surface area of the collector. Although energy may be concentrated and temperatures raised, the total energy cannot be greater than that which strikes the collector surface. On the other hand, the design of the collector influences how effective it is in turning solar radiation into useful energy.

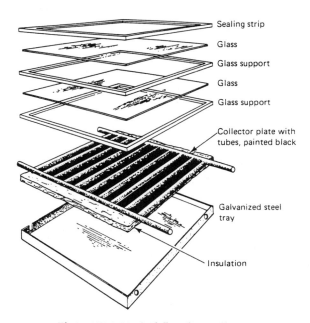

Sealing strip

Glass

Glass support

Glass

Glass support

Collector plate with
tubes, painted black

Galvanized steel
tray

Insulation

Figure 17.1. Typical flat-plate collector.

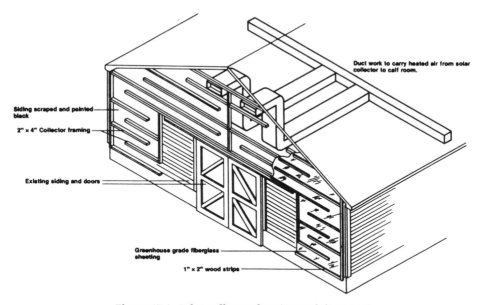

Figure 17.2. Solar collector framing and duct work.

Collector Efficiency

The two types of parabolic collectors mentioned may reach 50 to 75% efficiency. Although flat-plate collectors can do as well theoretically, few of them reach these levels in actual use. Operating efficiencies range from below 25% to more than 50% depending on design and method of operation.

The efficiency of a collector is expressed as the percentage of energy reaching the surface of the collector that is retained and carried off by the circulating fluid. The efficiency of a flat-plate collector is affected by its orientation, the covering, the absorbing surface, the temperature at which it operates, and the insulation of the case.

To receive the maximum radiation, a collector should be set at an angle perpendicular to the sun's rays. Of the total amount striking the collector, some will be reflected from the transparent cover surface, some will be reflected from the absorbing surface back through the cover, some will be lost by convection through the cover, and some by conduction through the back of the case. The balance is carried away by the heat transfer medium to the place of use or to a storage.

Collector designs have been developed that minimize these losses. Anti-reflective coatings allow greater transmission through the cover to the absorbing surface. Certain spectral coatings for collector plates have been developed that have very high absorptivity at wavelengths in the solar part of the spectrum but very low emissivity in the longer wavelength infrared portion of the spectrum. While these add to the cost of the collector, they are justified where relatively high operating temperatures are necessary.

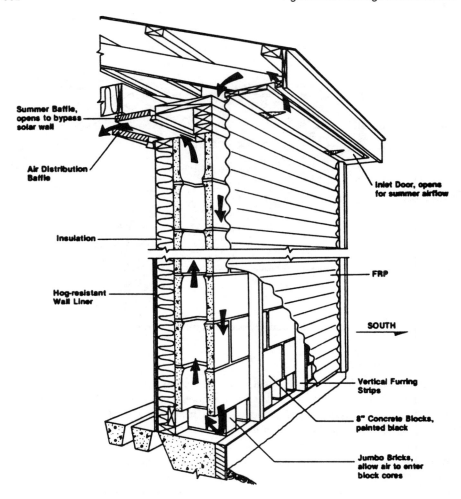

Figure 17.3. Iowa hollow-block-wall solar system.

Double or triple covers reduce convection losses and a high R-value reduces conduction losses through the insulated back.

To illustrate the effect of temperature on the efficiency of a flat-plate collector, let us assume that due to heavy cloud cover the collector is at ambient temperature; there will be no heat transfer either to or away from the collector. When the sun comes out, the collector temperature will rise and continue to rise until it reaches the balanced temperature situation of losing as much heat as it gains. The efficiency at this point will be zero. However, if water is circulated through the plate coils, the collector will be cooled and less heat will be lost; some will be carried away for use. If the temperature of the plate could be reduced to ambient level, only a small radiant loss would remain and the efficiency would be very high. The temperature of the heat transfer medium (water or air) is often determined by the requirements of the storage or the use to which the heat will be put. For example, operating a collector at 50°F (10°C) is ineffective if the purpose is to warm 50°F (10°C) well water. For this situation a higher operating temperature would be required and the loss in efficiency would be unavoidable.

The amount of solar energy that could be collected from a flat vertical wall collector can be estimated as follows. Assume the wall is 10×25 ft. The maximum radiation expected is 318 Btu/h-ft^2 and the daily average is 1,555 Btu/day-ft^2. If the system is assumed to be 40% efficient, this would give a peak rate of $318 \times 10 \times 25 \times 0.4 = 31,800$ Btu/h or $1,555 \times 10 \times 25 \times 0.4 = 155,500$ Btu/day. Note that the peak efficiency will probably be greater than the daily efficiency.

A combined solar collector-heat pump system makes use of much lower collector temperatures possible. Although higher efficiencies result, the high initial cost discourages the use of such a dual system.

Absorber Plates and Transfer Mediums

Either air or water may be used as a transfer medium. The choice is often based on the type of storage or the use to which the energy will be put. For example, if the solar collector is designed to supplement the existing water-heating system, water would be the appropriate medium. On the other hand, if warmed air is desired for a drying process, it would be logical to use air as the medium.

Absorber plates that are painted black absorb about 95% of the radiation. Several methods of removing heat are used. Collectors that use water as a medium may be designed so that a thin layer of water sweeps down the open surface picking up the heat as it moves. Or they may be designed so that the water flows through tubes bonded to a metal plate. Either metal or plastic can be used satisfactorily for an open collector surface. When water is carried in tubes, metal plates are desirable because of their high conductivity. Copper has the highest conductivity and the tubes are easily bonded to the plate. Aluminum also has a high conductivity, but it is difficult to bond the tubes. Steel is the least expensive but has the lowest conductivity.

Air-medium collectors range from black-surfaced ducts through which the air is moved to various finned-metal surfaces under a single or double transparent cover.

Glass, fiberglass reinforced plastic or plastic films may be used for covers. Glass transmits 90% of the energy and has a long life. Fiberglass-reinforced plastic transmits about 80% of the energy and if Tedlar-coated will last more than 10 years. (Tedlar is manufactured by the E. I. DuPont de Nemours Co.) Ultraviolet-inhibited polyethylene and copolymer plastics transmit in excess of 90% of the energy, but they also lose an appreciable amount through re-radiation. In addition they cannot be expected to last more than one or two years. Collector cases are usually made of wood, plastic or metal, but regardless of the material from which they are constructed, provisions must be made for expansion and contraction of glass covers. Plastic covers are not as critical in this respect.

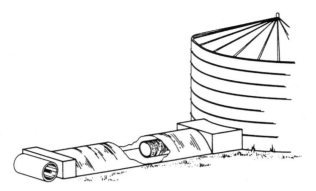

Figure 17.4. Solar-heated grain dryer using a duct collector.

Plastic-duct Collector

When using solar energy for a drying operation, a plastic duct can serve as a variation of a flat-plate collector. A single layer, black polyethylene duct, usually 3 ft (1 m)
or more in diameter, is kept expanded by the air which is blown through it. If a temperature rise of only 5 to 11°F (3 to 6°C) is adequate for the air being moved, the sin-
gle-layer duct provides a simple and inexpensive collector. However, if a greater temperature rise is required, the use of a clear plastic, air-inflated cover over the black duct
will give both a higher temperature rise to the air and improved efficiency (fig. 17.4).

Orientation of Flat-plate Collectors

To explain how the most desirable orientation for a collector is determined (table
17-2), it is first necessary to understand how the sun's position is indicated. The two
angles that indicate the position of the sun in respect to the earth are the azimuth and
the altitude. The azimuth is the horizontal angle of the sun in relation to the true north
meridian. In the morning it is measured in an easterly direction and in the afternoon

Table 17-2. Ratio of solar energy received on flat-plate
collector relative to horizontal surface

Latitude	Collector Angle	Summer	Equinox	Winter
45°	0°	1	1	1
30°	0°	1	1	1
45°	45°	1	1.34	2.37
30°	30°	0.84	1.14	1.59
45°	60°	0.76	1.39	2.46
30°	45°	0.66	1.17	1.63
45°	90°	0.34	0.97	2.49
30°	90°	0.15	0.64	1.45
45°	*	1.48	1.41	1.70
30°	*	1.35	1.43	1.54

* North-south oriented horizontal collector that tracks the sun from
east to west.

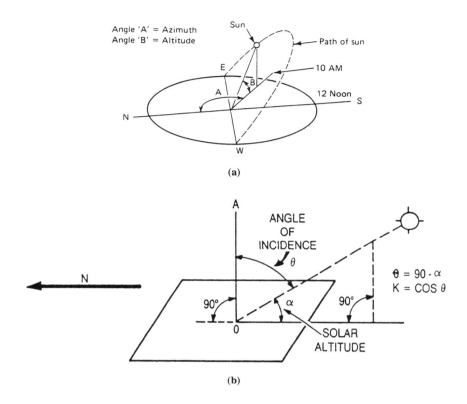

Figure 17.5. (a) Azimuth, (b) Altitude.

in a westerly direction. The altitude is the vertical angle the sun makes with the horizontal plane at the earth's surface.

Both the azimuth and the altitude of the sun are affected by the latitude of a location, the date, and the hour of the day (fig. 17.5). At greater latitudes, the azimuth angles have a much greater daily range, while the altitude angles will be lower throughout the year. Table 17-3 gives winter and summer azimuth and altitude angles for latitudes of 30 to 50°N.

The location of the sun's rays at any latitude and moment of time is described by the angle of incidence, q, which is related to sun altitude, a, (angle above horizon) and the solar azimuth, Z. The position of the sun is described by:

$$\sin \alpha = \cos L \, \cos \delta \, \cos H + \sin L \, \sin \delta \qquad (17.2)$$

where

L   =   latitude (angle above equator)

δ = seasonal declination

   = $23.45° \sin[360 \,(284 + n) \,/\, 365]$

n = day of the year

H = hour angle = $15° \,(T - 12)$

T = time (hours from midnight)

The azimuth angle of sun, z, is given by:

$$\sin z = \cos \delta \; \frac{\sin H}{\cos \alpha} \qquad\qquad (17.3)$$

At noon, the solar altitude is given by:

$$\alpha_{noon} = 90 - (L - \delta) \qquad\qquad (17.4)$$

The cosine of the incident angle, K, can be determined from:

$$K = \cos \alpha \; \cos(Z - U_c) \sin \beta + \sin \alpha \; \cos \beta \qquad\qquad (17.5)$$

α = sun altitude above horizon

Z = solar azimuth angle

U_c = roof orientation (ridge w.r. to south)

β = roof angle from horizon

Example 17.1

Determine the angle of incident on the south side of an east-west oriented building with a 4:12 slope at noon on 15 March at a latitude of 47°N.

$$\delta = 23.45 \times \sin \left[\frac{360(284 + 74)}{365} \right] = 23.33°$$

$$\alpha = 90 - 47 + 23.33 = 66.33$$

$$\theta = 90 - \beta - \alpha = 90 - 18.26 - 66.33 = 5.41°$$

If the direct normal radiation is 300 Btu/h-ft^2, the incident radiation on the roof slope would be $300 \times \cos (5.41) = 298.7$ Btu/h-ft^2.

Ideally a flat-plate collector should always be normal to the sun's radiation, that is, it should be perpendicular to the azimuth and the altitude angles. This can be accomplished by inclining and turning the plate to match the azimuth and altitude throughout the day. Since this would require expensive equipment, most collectors are installed to face within 5° of true south and are often inclined to be normal to the average position of the sun during the period of the year when the solar energy is most needed. For winter use only, the most efficient collector angle is equal to the latitude +15°. For summer use only, the latitude −10° is reasonable and for fall use, the latitude

−5° is a reasonable average. For example, if a collector is installed at 40° N and is to be used only for summertime water heating, the rule of thumb would indicate 30° (40 − 10) as the best average angle for the collector. Looking at table 17-3, one finds that at midmorning and midafternoon in the summer (10 A.M. and 2 P.M.) the altitude is 60°. Thus, installing the collector at 30° would place it perpendicular to the sun's rays at those times. To be perpendicular, the sum of the sun's angle and the collector angle must equal 90°. At noon, the collector would not be quite flat enough and at 8 A.M. and 4 P.M. it would be a little too flat. However, the 30° is a good compromise for a complete day in midsummer.

Quite aside from solar collectors, another use for altitude angles is in designing the appropriate roof overhangs to give shading protection from the summer sun. For example, if it is desired to completely shade 6 ft high, south-facing windows at noon in a house at 35° N lat, an overhang must be installed. The width of an overhang placed immediately above the windows can be determined as follows.

From table 17-3, the altitude at noon in midsummer is found to be 78.5°. The angle of the sun's rays with the window is then 11.5° (90 − 78.5) and the width of the overhang may be found with the expression:

$$\tan 11.5° = \frac{\text{overhang}}{\text{height}}$$

$$\text{overhang} = \tan 11.5° \times \text{height}$$

$$= 0.2 \times 6 \text{ ft} = 1.2 \text{ ft}$$

Table 17-3. Azimuth and altitude angles

Latitude	Winter			Summer		
	Noon	10:A & 2:P	8:A & 4:P	Noon	10:A & 2:P	8:A & 4P
30°N						
Azi	180	148.5	126	180	83.5	81.5
Alt	36.5	29	11.5	83.5	62.5	36.5
35°N						
Azi	180	149.5	126	180	105.5	85.5
Alt	31.5	25	8.5	78.5	61.5	37
40°N						
Azi	180	150.5	127	180	114	89
Alt	26.5	20.5	5.5	73.5	60	37.5
45°N						
Azi	180	151.5	127.5	180	121.5	93
Alt	21.5	16	2.5	68.5	57.5	37.5
50°N						
Azi	180	152	128.5	180	127.5	97
Alt	16.5	12	0	63.5	54.5	37

If the overhang were to be installed at a higher location, the distance from the bottom of the window to the overhang would have to be used.

Storage

During periods in which solar radiation exceeds heating requirements, energy from solar collectors may be stored in the form of sensible heat in water or in solids such as stone or concrete. At night, or during cloudy periods, the heat to warm the building or to heat water is removed from storage. A more efficient but expensive storage makes use of the heat of fusion of Glauber's salt or sodium sulphate decahydrate ($Na_2SO_4 \cdot 10H_2O$). It melts at 90°F (32°C) and has a heat of fusion of 251 kJ/kg (108 Btu/lb). The principal advantage is the high heat storage capacity per unit of volume. However, Glauber's salt is expensive and has a tendency to deteriorate, necessitating replacement. Ordinary water or stone storages can be designed to operate with about 50°F (28°C) temperature rise. To be used for storage, stones should be uniform in size, either 1, 2, or 3 in. (25, 50 or 75 mm) in diameter. Stone which has a specific heat of 0.2, and a specific gravity of 1.7, will require nearly three times as much volume as water for equal storage capacity.

Potential for Solar Energy

The increased use of solar energy is largely dependent on the cost of other sources of energy. Although standardized procedures and equipment are not yet common, the technology to use solar energy is available. As the price of fuel increases and as collectors become more efficient and less expensive, solar energy will become more attractive. Two factors that appear to increase the practicality of solar energy for agricultural use are (1) year-round application such as supplemental water heating, and (2) systems that are designed with low cost rather than high efficiency as the prime objectives as in the case of plastic-duct collectors for crop drying.

Energy from the sun is free, but solar energy delivery systems are not. But they can be economically feasible when they are used to provide supplemental heat to reduce the energy consumption of existing systems. An expenditure of an amount equal to 10 times the estimated average annual savings in fuel seems like a maximum feasible investment, since that would require something in excess of 20 years for payback unless fuel prices were to rise appreciably.

The use of solar energy in itself is not a solution to the problems of high fuel consumption. As with any heating system, the amount of insulation used has a significant impact on the total energy consumption. The fixed costs associated with solar energy systems are high enough to warrant extensive insulation in practically all applications. Adequate insulation is less expensive than a larger solar collector. Put another way, it is a waste of money to collect solar energy and then lose it because of inadequate insulation.

While a number of applications for the use of solar energy in agriculture have already proven their value, it is certain that many more will follow. A continued rise in the cost of fuel will surely hasten new developments, and with today's technology, the potential is enormous.

The farmer has for many years been harvesting some of the energy that flows freely from the sun. The following list of applications of solar energy to agriculture begins with some of those long-time practices and suggests new and more complex systems for today and the future.

1. Open-front livestock building facing south. This gives a drying effect on the bedding and alley floors.

2. Open-front building facing south with curtains or doors. Closing up at night maintains a somewhat higher inside temperature.

3. Windows facing south. Shutters or heavy curtains are essential to insure a net gain in heat.

4. Grain drying in the bin with warm air forced through a plastic film duct collector. A disadvantage of this low temperature system for large grain handling operations would be the slower drying and reduced capacity relative to conventional drying operations.

5. Drying hay in stack-wagon units with air heated in an air-inflated, triple-layer plastic duct that also serves as a roof over the stacks.

6. Grain or hay drying in a building roofed and sided with fiberglass-reinforced plastic to collect the necessary heat.

7. Attic collectors, with or without storages, for heating farrowing and nursery sections of hog houses, hog finishing barns, poultry houses, and calf barns.

8. Air heaters for dehydration of fruits and vegetables either by direct radiation or by the circulation of preheated air.

9. Solar collectors for heating water for milkroom and home use.

10. Solar collectors to warm water which is stored in the porous concrete floor of a greenhouse and then used for nighttime heating.

11. Solar collectors to supplement the farm home heating and cooling system.

Planning a solar energy system for drying grain may be illustrated with the following example.

Example 17.2
It has been estimated that to dry corn in storage would require air that is 5°C above ambient temperature to be moved at the rate of 1 L/s for each 9 kg of corn in the storage. Assume a storage, with a 9000 kg capacity, is located near Madison, Wisconsin, and will be operating effectively for about 10 h/day in early October. The collector will be a single-thickness polyethylene duct, 1 m in diameter, oriented north and south. As the sun's rays strike an area 1 m in diameter throughout the day, it may be assumed that the duct has the characteristics of a north-south horizontal collector tracking east to west.

1. From table 17-1 it is learned that in October, Madison receives a daily flux on a horizontal surface of 11.3 MJ/m^2.
2. From table 17-2 in the equinox season, a horizontal N-S oriented collector tracking east to west has a factor of 1.43.
3. As there is no cover on the collector it is assumed to be only 25% efficient even with the low temperature rise.
4. Heat/m^2 in 10 h = 11.3 MJ/m^2 × 1.43 × .25 = 4040 kJ/m^2 10 h.
5. Air moved in 10 h = 1 L/s × 9000/9 = 1000 L/s = 1 m^3/s = 3600 m^3/h or for 10 h this give 36 000 m^3.
6. Heat required in 10 h = 36 000 × 0.28 S.H. × 4.186 × 5°C = 210 974 kJ.
7. Duct area required = 219 974/4040 = 52.2 m^2.
8. Duct length = 52.2 m^2/ℓ m diameter = 52 m long.

Radiation Protection

During hot summer days, animals exposed to direct solar radiation can suffer heat stress. Shades or shields can reduce the radiant heat load even though they do not alter the air temperature. The radiant heat load depends on the mean radiant temperature (MRT) which was discussed in chapter 13. The mean radiant temperature, T_M, can be used to calculate the radiant heat load (RHL) as follows:

$$RHL = \sigma T_M^4 \qquad (17.6)$$

The RHL may also be calculated from the radiosity of the various parts of the surround. Radiosity is the total radiation which leaves a surface, i.e., sum of energy that is emitted, reflected, and (possibly) transmitted. Thus, radiosity is a function of absolute temperature and emissivity of the object. Each object can radiate in all directions and only part of this will be intercepted by the globe. A shape factor (sometimes called angle factor) is introduced to describe the portion of the total energy intercepted by the globe (table 17-4). Radiosity depends on building materials, surface conditions, and building geometry. The RHL of the total surround is given by:

$$RHL = \sigma \sum_{i=1}^{n} \varepsilon T_i^4 F_i \qquad (17.7)$$

where

σ = Stephan-Boltzman constant, 0.1717×10^{-8} Btu/(h-ft^2-R^4) $(5.67 \times 10^{-8}$ W/m^{2}K^4)

ε = emissivity of each surface

F_i = shape factor of each surface with respect to object

The net radiation between two surfaces is:

$$q_r = \sigma A_1 F_A F_E \left(T_1^4 - T_2^4 \right) \qquad (17.8)$$

Table 17-4. Radiation shape factors

Radiating Surfaces	Area, A	F_a	F_e
Infinite parallel planes	A_1 or A_2	1	$1/(1/\varepsilon_1 + 1/\varepsilon_2 - 1)$
Completely enclosed body, 1, small compared with enclosing body	A_1	1	ε_1
Completely enclosed body, 1, large compared with enclosing body	A_1	1	$1/(1/\varepsilon_1 + 1/\varepsilon_2 - 1)$
Flat surface, 1, and sun	A_1	$(r/R)^2 \cdot \cos \phi.$*	ε_1

* r = radius of sun, 432,050 mi; R = distance to sun (93×10^6 mi); ϕ = angle between sun ray and the normal to surface; $(r/R)^2 = 2.16 \times 10^{-5}$.

where

A_1	=	area of surface 1
F_A	=	shape factor which is 1 or less
		(from the sun to a flat surface, $F_A = 16e^{-5} \times \cos \theta$)
F_E	=	factor to account for emission and absorption characteristics of both surfaces
T_1, T_2	=	temperatures (°K)

Each of any two objects involved in a thermal radiation exchange has a shape factor for the other object. The shape factors for two objects are related as follows:

$$F_{1-2} A_1 = F_{2-1} A_2 \qquad (17.9)$$

where

F_{1-2}	=	the shape factor from object 1 to object 2
F_{2-1}	=	the shape factor from object 2 to object 1
A_1	=	surface area of object 1
A_2	=	surface area of object 2

Example 17.3

Determine the radiant heat loss from a 80 kg pig to a wall which has a surface temperature of 0°C. Assume the pig surface temperature is 38°C. The pig will have a surface area, A = 0.0974(80).63 = 1.5 m²; assume 1/3 exposure, i.e., A = 0.5 m². Assume E = 0.9, thus:

$$q_r = \sigma A_o F_a F_e \left(T_1^4 - T_2^4\right)$$

$$= 5.67 \times 10^{-8}(0.5)(1)(0.9)\left(311^4 - 273^4\right)$$

$$= 2.552 \times 10^{-8} \left(9.355 \times 10^9 - 5.55 \times 10^9\right)$$

$$= 97 \text{ W}$$

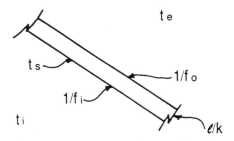

**Figure 17.6. Schematic diagram for inside
surface temperature calculations.**

Roof Inside Surface Temperature

The heat load on a roof in summer under a bright sun is difficult to assess. The effective temperature may be expressed as the sol-air temperature which would provide the same rate of heat transfer to the roof surface. Sol-air temperature may be described as (fig. 17.6):

Table 17-5. Solar absorptivity of surfaces and surface emissivities
at ordinary temperatures

	Shortwave Absorption	Longwave Emission
Aluminum, polished	0.26	0.04
Copper, polished	0.18	0.04
Copper, rolled, tarnished	0.64	0.64
Galvanized iron, new	0.65	0.13
Galvanized iron, oxidized	0.80	0.28
White enamel on steel plate	0.04	0.90
Green enamel on steel plate	0.76	0.90
White paint on aluminum	0.20	0.91
Black paint on aluminum	0.96	0.88
Gloss white paint	0.35	0.95
Red paint	0.87	0.96
Lampblack paint	0.98	0.96
Felt, roofing, bituminous	0.88	0.95
Asbestos cement board, white	0.59	0.90
Bricks, red	0.55	0.93
Grass, high and dry	0.68	0.90
Tree leaves, green	0.75	0.93
Alfalfa	0.97	0.95
Ground, dry plowed	0.78	0.90
Moist ground	0.90	0.95
Concrete	0.60	0.88
Asphalt pavement, dust-free	0.93	0.95
Snow, fresh, bright, sparkling	0.13	0.74

$$t_e = t_o + \left(\frac{\alpha I}{f_c}\right) \tag{17.10}$$

where

t_o = outside air temp
α = roof solar absorptivity (table 17-5)
I = combined incident radiation
f_c = convective film coefficient

The outside roof surface film convective heat transfer coefficient is often assumed to 22.7 W/m²°C. If a more accurate value is needed then the surface texture and wind velocity must be determined.

Example 17.4

If the air temperature is 35°C and the incident radiation is 800 W/m², the sol-air temperature under an oxidized galvanized roof can be estimated as:

$$t_e = 35 + \left(0.80 \times \frac{800}{22.7}\right) = 63°C$$

The rate of heat transfer to the surface from the outside air and by direct radiation would be determined by:

$$q = f_c(t_o - t_s) + I \tag{17.11}$$

or by using the sol-air temperature:

$$q = f_c(t_e - t_s) \tag{17.12}$$

The surface temperature, t_s, would be determined by the rate of heat transfer and thus in general is not known. Since the heat transfer to the surface will be equal to the heat transfer away from the surface, the temperature differences will be proportional to the thermal resistances.

$$\frac{t_e - t_i}{t_s - t_i} = \frac{1/f_o + 1/k + 1/f_i}{1/f_i} \tag{17.13}$$

Thus:

$$t_s = t_i + \frac{\left[\left(\frac{1}{f_i}\right)(t_e - t_i)\right]}{\left[\left(\frac{1}{f_o} + \frac{1}{f_i}\right) + \frac{1}{k}\right]} \tag{17.14}$$

Hot Weather Environment

When ambient temperature increases, the difference between $T_{body} - T_{amb}$ decreases which reduces the ability to transfer sensible heat. It is often more difficult to deal with high temperatures than low temperatures. Some of the alternatives are:

Table 17-6. Ranking of shade materials

Hay	1.20
Aluminum (white over black)	1.10
Louvers (wood)	1.07
Polyethylene, black 2-8 mil	1.04
Plywood	1.03
Aluminum, standard	1.00
Galvanized. steel, 1 yr. old	0.985
Aluminum, 10 yr. old	0.97
Snow fence, crisscross	0.82
Snow fence, single layer	0.60

1. Mechanical cooling—economical only in limited applications.
2. Evaporative cooling—need low relative humidity, tolerance to high relative humidity.
3. High air velocity—can increase convective losses, but air temperature must be $< T_{body}$.
4. Reduce surrounding surface temperature—prevent exposure to surfaces with temperatures elevated by solar radiation.

One effective, economical method of reducing heat stress is to provide protection from solar radiation by the use of shades. The following properties affect efficiencies of shade materials:

• Transmissivity and reflectivity of upper and lower surfaces
• Thermal diffusivity (including heat capacity, density, and thermal conductivity)
• Convective characteristics
• "Solidness" or percent open area

Various shade materials were evaluated by researchers at the University of California by comparing to new, bright aluminum. The effectiveness (resulting values are given in table 17-6) was calculated as:

$$E = \frac{RHL_{sun} - RHL_{sample}}{RHL_{sun} - RHL_{aluminum}} \qquad (17.15)$$

The radiant heat load based on the sol-air temperature of 63°C would be:

$$RHL = 5.67 \times 10^{-8} (273 + 63)^4 = 722.7 \text{ W/m}^2$$

If the galvanized steel were replaced with polished aluminum, the sol-air temperature would be:

$$t_e = 35 \times \left(0.26 \times \left(\frac{800}{22.7}\right)\right) = 44.2°C$$

$$RHL = 5.67 \times 10^{-8} \times (317.2)^4 = 574 \text{ W/m}^m$$

which is a 20% reduction in the heat load.

Problems

17.1. Find the total area of flat-plate collector surface required to collect an average of 285,000 Btu/day (300 MJ/day) in January. The collector, which averages 35% efficiency, is to be installed at an optimum angle for its location in Apalachicola, Florida. A storage is to be installed for a total of 570,000 Btu (600 MJ) with a 45°F (25°C) temperature differential. What mass will be required?

17.2. Determine the sol-air temperature under a black painted aluminum roof if the incident solar radiation is 270 Btu/ft²-h (860 W/m²) and the temperature is 82°F (28°C). What would be the decrease if the roof were painted white?

18 Product Storage

Agricultural products, most of which are living and biologically active, are stored to make them available over longer periods of time and to balance periods of plenty with periods of scarcity. Almost all products must be stored for at least short periods of time during the marketing process.

To be effective, the storage should be designed to maintain product qualities such as appearance, texture, moisture level, nutritive value, flavor, viability, and freedom from microbial activity. Quality degradation of bioproducts including forage, grains, fruits, vegetables, eggs, and milk may result from:

- Invasion by pests, insects or rodents
- Microbial or enzymatic activity
- Changes in physical structure or dehydration
- Sprouting
- Loss of viability

Most bioproducts are living organisms which respire, resulting in changes in composition or material characteristics such as the conversion of starch to sugar and sugar to oxygen, water, and heat. These conversion reactions may be retarded by high concentrations of carbon dioxide and/or low temperatures (table 18-1).

Ethylene gas produced by the respiration of apples hastens the ripening process; removal of the gas retards ripening; artificial addition can be used to enhance ripening. Fruits and vegetables lose moisture because of differences in vapor pressure at the product surface and the ambient atmosphere.

Table 18-1. Heat of respiration (W/t)

	0°C	15°C	30°C
Typical fruit	4-8	30-70	60-120
Typical vegetable	15-60	60-300	150-600
Broccoli	60-64	500-1000	1700-2600
Asparagus, corn, peas	80-165	280-415	830-1700
Apples	7-12	40-90	
Dry onions	8-9	30-33	80-86

(After *Canadian Farm Buildings Handbook*)

Table 18-2. Storage conditions for fruits and vegetables

Product	Storage Temperature			Heat of Respiration	
	°F	°C	% RH	Btu/ton-day	W/t
Apples	30-32	−1-0	90	700	9.4
Beets	32-40	0-4	95	1800	24.2
Cabbage	32	0	92	1400	
Carrots	32-35	0-2	95	900	18.8
Grapes	30-32	−1-0	85	900	12.1
Onions	32	0	75	1500	12.1
Peaches	31-32	−1-0	85		20.1
Pears	29-32	−2-0	90	700	9.4
Potatoes					
White	38-50	3-10	90	1500	20.1
Sweet	50-60	10-15	85	1000	13.4
Pumpkin	50-55	10-13	70		
Strawberries	31-32	−1-0	85	3500	47.0
Tomatoes					
Green	55-70	12-21	85	2500	33.6
Ripe	45-50	7-10	85		

Controlled atmosphere (CA) storages are used to provide a modified environment which allows year-round availability of some fresh-quality fruits and vegetables. For example, apples can be stored in a modified environment that contains 3 to 5% O_2 and up to 5% CO_2. When required, carbon dioxide may be added from combustion or manufactured gases, while any excess may be removed by water or caustic soda scrubber. (A cautionary note, workers must be warned **not** to enter CA storages without wearing breathing equipment.)

Typical optimum storage temperatures for storage of fresh fruits and vegetables are 30 to 32°F (−1 to 0°C). However, some crops require higher or lower temperatures such as 45 to 50°F (7 to 10°C) for eggplant, cucumber, and peppers (see table 18-2). The desired storage relative humidity is generally 90 to 95% or higher. Crops such as onions and pumpkins store best at lower moisture levels.

Forage crops and grains are typically dried to well under 20% moisture, and while they will tolerate fluctuating storage temperatures and humidities, an average relative humidity of 70% or under is desirable.

APPLE STORAGE

Well-designed and expertly managed storages allow high quality apples to be marketed during much of the year. Apples held in storage from a depressed market at the time of harvest to a strong market the following spring offer an opportunity for considerable economic benefit. To take advantage of this situation, however, requires only top quality fruit be stored and that careful attention be paid to the design, construction, and operation of the storage. Apple storages, particularly of the controlled atmosphere (CA) type, represent a large investment and it is only when a high quality product is marketed that the storage becomes profitable.

Pears as well as apples respond well to long-term storage and much of the material covered for apples relates equally to pears. Other fruits such as grapes, cherries, plums, apricots, peaches, and strawberries are held for short periods in refrigerated storages during the marketing period.

Storage Requirements

Apples, like all fruits, are alive at the time of harvest and continue to live and ripen after picking. During the ripening process, complex changes take place in which the sugar in the apple is depleted in the presence of oxygen, water and CO_2 are produced, and heat is generated. Respiration continues until the fruit is overripe and unpalatable. Lowering the temperature retards respiration, which increases two or threefold for every 20°F (11°C) of temperature rise. Four days at 68°F (20°C) "ages" an apple the equivalent of three to four weeks at a storage temperature of 32°F (0°C). Therefore, for maximum storage life rapid cooling of apples to storage temperature is very important.

Refrigeration capacity is designed so that the fruit moved into storage each day during the harvest season can theoretically be cooled to storage temperature. Actually the fruit does not reach the holding temperature in 24 h, but if the system is not capable of removing that much heat, it will fall behind the rate of harvest. As long as the storage refrigeration is adequate, hydrocooling of apples before storage offers no advantages.

A temperature of 30 to 32°F (−1 to 0°C) and a relative humidity of 85 to 88% is considered optimum for most apple varieties, but a few varieties such as 'McIntosh' and 'Greenings' tend to deteriorate at temperatures below 35°F (1.7°C). In addition to low temperature and high humidity, a reduction in the oxygen and an increase in the carbon dioxide in the atmosphere will slow down respiration and increase storage life. Controlled atmosphere (CA) storages, in which both oxygen and carbon dioxide levels are maintained at approximately 3%, are of particular advantage for varieties that are injured by low storage temperatures. These storages have become popular because of the long storage periods that are possible and the attractive marketing opportunities.

Air circulation is important to maintain uniform conditions throughout the storage room. Good controls and equipment are essential to reduce temperature and humidity fluctuations to a minimum as the system cycles on and off.

Storage Buildings

Site

A well-drained site that is convenient to the orchard and not too far from the home is desirable, and if retail sales are anticipated, it should be near the highway. Provision for parking, receiving, and shipping, as well as a storage for empty containers will be needed. In addition, room should be allowed for expansion.

Layout and Facilities

A service building will need to be constructed in connection with the storage. At a minimum it will serve as a location for refrigeration equipment and for receiving and loading out apples. Depending on the nature of the operation planned, it may be needed for much more. For example, storage for extra containers may be required, retail sales may be envisioned, and if the total apple production is large enough, a complete grading and packing operation may need to be housed. This will require more attention to insulation, heating, and special lighting. For example, deluxe, cool-white fluorescent lamps are ideal for grading apples, while deluxe warm-white lamps are better for a salesroom because of the additional red in the light. Once the extent of the operation has been resolved, a flow diagram should be drawn to show the path of all traffic as apples are received, stored, handled, and shipped.

Although a square storage would be ideal from the standpoint of the ratio of surface area to volume, the practical width is limited by the framing system. A clear span of 40 to 60 ft (12 to 19 m) is often found most economical. The total storage volume should be about $2^{1/2}$ ft^3/bu (2.9 m^3/t) to be stored. This allows for ceiling clearance and space between containers for ventilation.

Ceiling heights range from 10 to 22 ft (5.5 to 6.7 m) depending on container size and the number placed on a pallet. Although large-sized storage rooms are more economical, when planning CA storages, some growers sacrifice some of the economy and choose to construct several smaller rooms which will allow greater flexibility in handling the needs of different varieties and in marketing over a longer period of time. Also, as soon as a room is empty, the refrigeration may be turned off.

Building Construction

There is a wide choice of materials suitable for use in the construction of cold storage buildings. Each material has individual advantages and limitations. Masonry blocks or precast concrete panel structures are inherently resistant to moisture and fire damage. Pole buildings are inexpensive. Wood frame construction is medium in cost and easy to insulate. Clear spans of up to 50 ft (15 m) are practical with wood trusses. Steel frames with steel siding are usually the choice for wider buildings, although the installation of insulation may be more difficult.

Foundations should extend to below the frost level and be insulated to reduce heat transfer.

Level, concrete floors allow easy maneuvering of equipment and stacking of containers. The use of insulation in the floor is debatable. Eight to 10 in. (200 to 250 mm) of uniform gravel fill under the floor is desirable.

Insulation, Vapor Barriers, and Gas Seals

Once the site has been chosen and the building plan determined, the amount and type of insulation material must be selected to enclose the cold storage volume. Refrigerated and CA storages which are operated throughout the fall, winter, and spring in northern climates need a minimum of R-10 in the floor, R-20 in the walls, and R-30 in the ceiling. If the storage is to be operated during summer, the R-values should be increased to R-20, R-30, and R-40, respectively, as recommended by ASHRAE.

A number of insulating materials have been used in the construction of apple storages. Their performance has been largely related to the success with which moisture has been excluded. Ordinary refrigerated apple storages present a difficult problem in that at harvest time it is warmer on the outside of the building, requiring a vapor barrier on the outside. However, during January and February, the outside temperature is likely to average lower than the inside and moisture tends to move outward into the insulation. Controlled atmosphere storages further complicate the problem in that a gas-tight seal must be installed to allow the required levels of carbon dioxide and oxygen to be maintained. If a gas seal is installed on the inside of the wall, the vapor barrier on the outside must be exceptionally nonpermeable.

The most satisfactory method of excluding moisture from the insulation and producing an adequate gas seal is to use foamed-in-place urethane insulation. The closed cell insulation not only excludes moisture but also serves as a gas seal when applied as a continuous layer. Three things must be kept in mind when installing foamed-in-place polyurethane: (1) precautions against fire must be taken during installation, (2) a thermal barrier surface must be installed so that no polyurethane is left exposed, thus reducing the fire hazard, and (3) for CA storages, the insulation should result in a continuous layer.

Figure 18.1(a) illustrates methods of insulating and sealing different types of storage walls and ceilings. In figure 18.1(a), the foamed-in-place polyurethane provides continuous insulation and sealing over the entire wall and ceiling area. One-half inch (12 mm) of plaster offers physical protection and fire resistance. While cement plaster is harder, gypsum plaster offers slightly better thermal protection. The same insulation and sealing system may also be used on the inside of a plywood-surfaced wall.

Figure 18.1(b) shows the polyurethane sprayed on the outside of the plywood interior wall covering. This is done before the outside siding is installed. The plywood is installed on nailing strips on both the walls and ceiling. This leaves only small areas of contact that are not sealed with the polyurethane. This system could be used in either a pole building wall, as shown, or in standard stud construction. The nailing strips are required in either case. Perlite-gypsum board is used for the interior wall covering. All joints are filled with a nonhardening caulking material and sealed with a tape especially designed for CA storage applications.

Three to four inches (75 to 100 mm) of polyurethane will produce a total R-value of 20 to 26 (3.5 to 4.6) in any of these wall constructions. There are two reasons for choosing such a high R-value: (1) It reduces the refrigeration load and, more importantly, (2) the temperature drop across the materials outside the insulation is small enough so that condensation is not likely to occur on the outside of the polyurethane even though outside vapor easily penetrates to that plane.

For example, assume an R_t of 20 h-ft^2-°F)/Btu (3.5 m^{2}K/W) and an R for the concrete block of 1.45 (0.24). When the storage temperature is 32°F (22.2°C), the humidity could rise to 90% before condensation would occur at the junction of the blocks and the insulation.

$$\left(72° - 32°\right) \times \frac{1.45}{20} = 2.9°F \ (1.6°C) \text{ drop across block}$$

$$72° - \ 2.9°F \ = 69.1°F \ (20.6°C) \text{ temperature at junction}$$

(18.1)

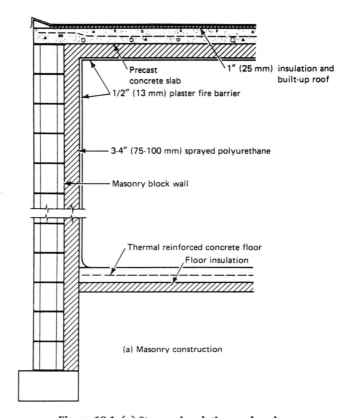

Precast concrete slab
1" (25 mm) insulation and built-up roof
1/2" (13 mm) plaster fire barrier

3-4" (75-100 mm) sprayed polyurethane

Masonry block wall

Thermal reinforced concrete floor
Floor insulation

(a) Masonry construction

Figure 18.1. (a) Storage insulation and seals.

The relative humidity of 72°F (22.2°C) dry-bulb and 69.1°F (20.6°C) dewpoint is 90%. This condition is likely to occur only on a hot summer evening.

Only closed-cell, nonpermeable types of insulation are suitable for installation on the outside of the gas seal. The final test of a CA storage is the adequacy of the gas-tight seal. This may be checked by blowing air into a storage at a pressure of at least 1 1/2 in. (38 mm) of water after which the pressure drop is checked with a manometer. A small room should not drop to zero in less than 1 h and a larger room in less than 1/2 h.

Refrigeration

Refrigeration is needed to maintain storage temperature while removing field heat at least as fast as apples are added to the storage. The term ton is used in referring to the refrigeration load. It derives from the heat absorbed in melting one ton of ice in 24 h and equals 288,000 Btu (84 kWh) per 24 h or 12,000 Btu/h (3.5 kW).

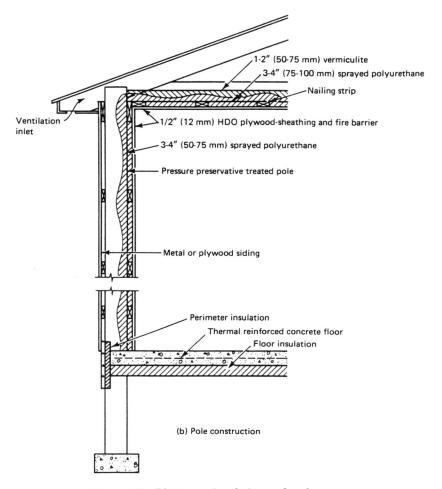

Figure 18.1. (b) Storage insulation and seals.

Refrigeration Load

The cooling load imposed on the system when the storage is being filled comes from four sources:

1. Heat transfer through the walls, ceiling, and floor.
2. Field heat (that which is stored in the apples as they are brought to the storage from the orchard.)
3. Heat of respiration given off by the apples.
4. The service load resulting from lights, equipment, workers, and air exchange through open doors.

Heat transfer through walls and ceilings has been previously discussed. Field heat stored in the apples may be calculated using outside air temperature, specific heat, and the average weight of apples added to the storage each day. This represents the largest portion of the refrigeration load.

Heat of respiration varies with temperature and product (table 18-1). Table 18-2 provides estimated values for a number of fruits and vegetables including apples.

The service load is usually taken as 10% of the sum of all other loads. Experience has shown that the following refrigeration capacities are adequate for apples in most cases:

No. days in filling period	Btu/h-bu	W/kg
10	12	0.16
15	9	0.12
20	8	0.10

Inasmuch as the field heat represents from one-half to two-thirds of the total load at the time of filling and is not repeated later, it is advisable to divide the refrigeration load between at least two compressors on a one-third to two-thirds basis. This will allow more efficient operation and provides a degree of safety factor in case of a breakdown. Mechanical refrigeration systems are discussed in chapter 16.

Evaporators

The unit cooler evaporator consisting of finned coils and a blower provides high capacity within minimal space. Ceiling-mounted unit coolers may be spaced in the storage to provide uniform cooling, or a larger cooler may supply the air for a duct system. Generally a tapered duct, sized to give a velocity of 800 to 1,000 fpm (4 to 6 m/s), is installed along the center of the ceiling with openings on either side discharging toward the walls where the air settles along the wall, moves through the stacks toward the center aisle, and back to the blower. Air can be thrown for a maximum of about 33 ft (10 m). When distances are greater, it is desirable to install additional ducts or more unit coolers.

Reversing ducts have been used in some installations to improve temperature uniformity. The first apples in the airstream are cooled more than the last, so reversing the flow periodically reduces the effect.

Regardless of the type of evaporator and the air distribution system, it is important to have sufficient evaporator surface and to move enough air so that there is very little change in temperature through the evaporator coils. This reduces to a minimum the moisture removed from the air. The change in air temperature through a cooler (evaporator) is called the "split" or "range". Experience has shown that 1,000 ft^3/min (470 L/s) will lose 200 Btu/min (3520 W) with about a 10°F (5.6°C) split. The relationship is straight line for splits of 5 to 20°F (2.7 to 11°C).

If the evaporator and air flow are designed for 10°F (5.6°C) split when the maximum refrigeration is required during storage loading, the split will drop to about 2.5°F (1.4°C) after field heat has been removed. Table 18-3 compares temperature split and maximum relative humidity of the air passing through the cooler. Note that

Table 18-3. Relative humidity vs temperature drop across
an evaporator (entering air temperature 32°F)

Temperature Drop		Maximum
°F	°C	Relative Humidity
1	0.5	96%
2	1.1	92%
3	1.7	88%
4	2.2	83%
6	3.3	76%
8	4.4	69%
10	5.6	62%

with a 10°F (5.6°C) split, the humidity is 62%. However, after the storage is loaded and the split can drop to about 2.5°F (1.4°C), the humidity is 90% and nearly ideal. The split can drop to 2.5°F (1.4°C) if the same amount of air is moving and the heat load has dropped by 75%.

Evaporators maintaining a 32°F (0°C) room temperature will operate at about 15°F (8.3°C) below air temperature. Since this is well below freezing, moisture condenses in the form of frost. Frost restricts both air flow and heat transfer and must be removed. Among the several automatic methods used are (1) warm water from the condenser which is fast and inexpensive but requires a drain, (2) electricity which is simple but costs more to operate, and (3) reverse refrigeration in which hot, compressed gas is fed back to the evaporator which is efficient but more costly to install.

With each of the methods of defrosting, it is important that the fan is shut off and stays off until the coils are not only defrosted but are back down to operating temperature. This avoids circulating warm air which would cause unnecessary fluctuations in both temperature and pressure.

Condensers

Condensers may be either water- or air-cooled. Air cooling is used mainly for smaller condensers and is inefficient in hot weather. While water cooling is more efficient, either large amounts of water must be pumped and "wasted" or else an evaporative tower will be needed to cool the condenser water. It is advantageous to arrange to use the condenser heat to help provide the packing room heating needs.

Controlled Atmosphere Storages

A properly designed and managed CA storage allows the apple producer to maintain the quality of the apples until late spring or early summer when market prices are favorable.

Basically, a CA storage is similar to any refrigerated storage except that it must be gas tight (fig. 18.1). With the tight construction, it is possible to maintain a 3 to 5% oxygen level and a 0 to 5% carbon dioxide level. In a gas-tight storage, this atmosphere will be produced by respiration of the apples over a period of approximately two weeks. If unrestricted, the oxygen level would continue to drop and the carbon dioxide level rise. However, the carbon dioxide level is monitored and reduced as needed. Adequate oxygen may enter through leaks or with slight ventilation if the level drops too low. The storage is opened only when the fruit is marketed and at that time it is emptied within a few days.

CA generators are available that can produce the desired room conditions in a matter of days instead of weeks as required by natural respiration. The room can also be successfully opened, partially emptied, and resealed, although this practice increases storage costs.

Excess carbon dioxide is produced in a CA storage, making it necessary to check the level daily. The excess may be removed with a caustic soda scrubber, a water scrubber, fresh hydrated high-calcium spray lime or a carbon dioxide absorber. The caustic soda is highly corrosive and the system is difficult to handle. The water scrubber may lack capacity during the pull-down period. However, the use of the lime in combination with a water scrubber is economical and satisfactory. Bagged lime at the rate of 3 to 5 lb/ton (1.5 to 2.5 kg/t) of fruit is placed in the storage room for this purpose. Carbon dioxide generators and absorbers, although the most expensive method of removing excess carbon dioxide, offer the most precise control over the atmosphere. These systems use catalytic oxygen burners and regenerating carbon dioxide absorbers. These may be controlled manually or with automatic gas sampling equipment.

Early CA storages were equipped with a gas expansion bag to limit pressure fluctuations. Today, with gas generators to maintain the correct atmosphere, a simple water trap allows pressure equalization.

Precautions

CA storages do not contain enough oxygen to support human life. Breathing equipment is necessary for anyone entering the storage for repairs and help should always be nearby. When the room is opened for unloading, sufficient time must be allowed for the oxygen level to rise to 18 to 20% before workers enter the room for more than brief periods.

POTATO STORAGE

The need to maintain high quality potatoes over an extended period of time to supply both the fresh and processing markets has resulted in increased emphasis on the design, construction, and operation of potato storages.

Potatoes continue to release moisture, heat, and carbon dioxide throughout the storage period. Proper environmental conditions slow these life processes and reduce shrinkage, retard sprouting, and discourage the development of rot organisms. Inasmuch as the profit margin on stored potatoes is often small, ventilation, which is less expensive than refrigeration, is depended on for cooling to storage temperatures and for humidification throughout the storage period.

Storage Buildings

Several types of buildings can serve adequately as potato storages, but they must incorporate certain important characteristics. The building should be easy to insulate and it should be resistant to the action of the very high humidity present throughout the storage period. In addition to the snow and wind loads typical of the region, there may be considerable force imposed on the walls by potatoes held in bulk storage. If the potatoes are held in bins, the bin walls must withstand the forces.

The combined requirements of considerable insulation and resistance to high, lateral loading make stud frame construction a good choice. Pole frames and masonry construction do not readily meet these requirements for above grade storages. Steel rigid-frame buildings are often used for large storages. If a storage is to be built partly below grade, the use of concrete or masonry construction is advantageous. The difference between soil and storage temperatures will be reduced, so less insulation is required below grade, and the lateral forces will be partially countered by the soil forces on the outside.

Storage structures must provide adequate space and support for the potatoes. Potato bulk densities range from 39 pcf (624 kg/m^3) to 44 pcf (700 kg/m^3), with smaller potatoes having the higher bulk density. If the potatoes are piled directly against the building walls, the walls must be designed to include the additional forces. The lateral force may be calculated using the equivalent fluid density (EFD) which has been found empirically to be 13.0 pcf (210 kg/m^3). Table 18-4 provides the expected bending moments for a few bin and filling configurations. The values are based on lateral forces from potatoes.

The use of the table in choosing a size and grade of a vertical member for a bin may be illustrated with an example.

Example 18.1

Assume a bin with 10 ft (3 m) sides, 8 ft (2.4 m) wide and filled to a depth of 8 ft (2.4 m). If studs are to be placed 16 in. (406 mm) on center, the required stud size is determined as follows:

From table 18-4 the bending moment is found to be 528 lb-ft (for wet potatoes) × 12 in./ft = 6,336 lb-in. based on a one foot spacing. For 16 in., the BM = (6,336 lb-ft × 16 in./stud)/12 in./ft = 8,427 lb-in.

$$BM = F \times S$$

Assuming a 1,200 psi allowable Fb:

$$S = \frac{8,427}{1,200} = 7.0 \text{ in.}^3$$

Assuming 2 in. nominal material (1 1/2 in. actual):

Table 18-4. (a) Force and bending moment on bin wall per foot of length

Wall Height (ft)	Pile Depth (ft)	Total Force (lb)	Sill Force (lb)	Plate Force (lb)	Location of Maximum Moment (ft)	Bending Moment (lb-ft)
			Shallow Bin			
Dry potatoes						
10	8	400	233	167	6.5	384
12	10	576	346	230	7.6	705
18	16	1,782	1,209	573	10.2	2,195
20	16	2,200	1,414	786	12.0	2,223
20	18	2,200	1,502	698	11.3	3,100
Wet potatoes						
10	8	550	321	229	6.5	528
12	10	792	475	317	7.6	969
18	16	1,944	1,319	625	10.2	2,394
20	16	2,400	1,543	857	12.0	2,426
20	18	2,400	1,638	762	11.3	3,382
			Deep Bin			
10	8	500	260	240	6.9	801
12	10	720	388	332	8.2	1,419
18	16	1,296	735	561	11.8	3,986
20	16	1,600	831	769	13.9	5,129
20	18	1,600	916	684	13.1	5,509

$$S = \frac{1}{6} bd^2$$

$$d^2 = \frac{6 \times 7.0 \text{ in.}^3}{1.5 \text{ in.}}$$

$d = 5.29$ in., therefore a 2×6 stud is adequate.

Bin or wall sills must be securely anchored in order to resist the lateral forces transferred to them from the stud. In addition, the stud must be well-anchored to the sill.

Storage foundations should extend below grade sufficiently to avoid any risk of frost damage. If the floor level in the storage is above the outside grade, it should be tied to the foundation wall with reinforcing to prevent outward collapse of the wall due to the high lateral force of the potatoes.

Storage floors should be of concrete, 6 in. (150 mm) thick, reinforced with 6×6 in., no. 6 gauge mesh and installed over well-compacted gravel.

A clear span roof design allows maximum flexibility in arrangement, including movable bins. Lateral loads imposed by the potatoes must be considered in planning the roof framing.

The required storage capacity will depend on the manner in which the potatoes are handled, the ceiling clearance allowed, and whether or not bin fronts are used. An

Table 18-4. (b) Force and bending moment on bin wall per meter of length

Wall Height (m)	Pile Depth (m)	Total Force (N)	Sill Force (N)	Plate Force (N)	Location of Maximum Moment (m)	Bending Moment (N-m)
			Shallow Bin			
Dry potatoes						
4	4	9 418	6 278	3 139	2.3	4 833
5	4	14 715	8 584	6 131	3.2	7 061
6	5	28 429	18 682	9 747	3.5	9 821
7	5	38 696	23 217	15 478	4.4	8 201
7	6	38 696	25 797	12 899	4.0	16 889
Wet potatoes						
4	4	12 792	8 528	4 264	2.3	6 565
5	4	19 988	11 660	8 328	3.2	9 591
6	5	33 727	22 163	11 563	3.5	11 651
7	5	45 906	27 544	18 362	4.4	9 729
7	6	45 906	30 604	15 302	4.0	20 036
			Deep Bin			
4	4	11 380	7 003	4 377	2.5	8 352
5	4	17 781	9 232	8 548	3.5	14 249
6	5	20 130	10 839	9 291	4.1	19 841
7	5	27 399	12 646	14 753	5.1	28 787
7	6	27 399	15 105	12 295	4.7	32 051

allowance of 2.5 ft³/bu (400 kg/m³ or 2.5 m³/t) of potatoes to be stored should be adequate in most cases.

Since the angle of repose for potatoes is only about 37.5°, considerable storage capacity is lost if bin fronts are not used. In addition, bins that are filled level ventilate more evenly. The forces on bin fronts are similar to the wall sections. Planks dropped into channel guides on the corner posts of bins are usually satisfactory for short spans, but reinforced fronts are required for larger spans. A means of removing the bottom 1 ft (0.33 m) of the front is necessary to allow a conveyor, flume or bulk scoop to start unloading the bin.

Environmental Control

The storing of potatoes can be divided into five management periods, each with a particular function and requiring carefully managed conditions:

1. Surface drying and heat removal
2. Suberization or wound healing
3. Cooling (gradually to storage temperature)
4. Long-term maintenance
5. Reconditioning (warming) for handling

Ventilation is used to remove field heat and surface moisture, but it is important to avoid excessive air velocity which will result in dehydration.

A certain amount of injury and bruising inevitably occurs during harvesting. Wound healing and curing is accomplished during the suberization period. These fresh wounds are subject to infection from disease and rot organisms. To prevent infection of the damaged tubers, the potatoes are initially held at 55 to 60°F (13 to 16°C) and 90 to 95% relative humidity for a period of 7 to 14 days. During this period the skin toughens and a corky tissue forms over the wounds, reducing the chance for infection. If any disease is present, a lower temperature is required.

Potatoes must be gradually cooled (about 5°F or 2°C/week for chipping potatoes and 10°F or 4°C/week for others) to a uniform storage temperature. Condensation must be avoided. Ventilation airflow rates of 0.2 to 0.67 cfm/bu (3.5 to 12 L/s-m^3) are recommended.

Potatoes have a natural dormancy period lasting from 6 to 12 weeks after harvest. In storing potatoes under controlled conditions, the objective is to extend the dormant state as long as possible and to keep shrinkage to a minimum. As soon as the curing is finished, the temperature is reduced to that recommended for long term storage. During this period excess heat and moisture are removed by intermittent ventilation at 0.5 cfm/bu (10 L/s-m^3).

Minimum long-term storage temperatures are limited by the final use of the potatoes. For seed stock, 38 to 40°F (3.3 to 4.4°C) will delay sprouting for up to eight months. For table stock, 40 to 45°F (6 to 7°C) will allow several months of storage without serious sprouting. Lower temperatures would increase the storage period but at the risk of converting starch to sugar and thereby reducing table quality. A higher temperature is used for processing stock to prevent discoloration and to keep the conversion of starch to sugar to a minimum. Potatoes to be used for french fries are stored at 45 to 50°F and chipping potato storage should be 50 to 55°F (10 to 13°C). A chemical sprout inhibitor may be used.

Cold, brittle potatoes are easily damaged in handling. For this reason it is recommended that the potatoes be warmed to 45 to 50°F (7 to 10°C) for a few days before removal to prevent bruising and cracking. The heat of respiration given off by the potatoes will produce sufficient heat, providing the air vents are closed to prevent cool air from entering the storage.

A relative humidity of 85 to 90% throughout the storage period limits shrinkage to 1/2 to 1.0% per month. Humidities below 85% result in excessive shrinkage, less weight to market, and reduced quality. Humidities over 90% are apt to result in condensation on wall and ceiling surfaces in spite of considerable insulation in both areas.

Insulation

Potatoes continue to produce heat throughout the storage period. A 24 h production of 1,465 Btu/ton (1700 kJ/t) may be used for design purposes. When the relative humidity is 91% in a storage at 45°F (7°C) the dewpoint temperature is only 1.25°F (0.7°C) below the dry-bulb temperature. If surface condensation is to be prevented, the R-value achieved with insulation must limit the temperature difference between the air and the wall and ceiling surfaces to less than 1.25°F (0.7°C). Table 18-5 shows several levels of

Table 18-5. Outside temperatures at which condensation is incipient
on storage surfaces (based on 45°F (7.2°C) and 91% RH)

Outside Temperature	
°F (°C)	R Value
20 (-6.7)	12.2 (2.1)
10 (-12.2)	17.1 (3.0)
0 (-17)	22.0 (3.9)
-10 (-23)	26.8 (4.7)
-20 (-41.8)	31.7 (5.6)
-30 (-57.7)	36.8 (6.4)

insulation R-values and the outside temperature at which condensation is incipient.

The R-values given in table 18-5 will not only prevent condensation under most circumstances, but they will also limit heat loss to the point that the heat produced by the potatoes will maintain storage temperature under design conditions and allow limited ventilation.

Vapor Retarder

Due to the very high humidity in the storage, the importance of a continuous vapor barrier between the insulation and the interior wall and ceiling surfaces cannot be overemphasized. Four to six mil polyethylene, with all joints lapped and sealed and all holes repaired, will make a good barrier. In addition, the outside walls if possible should be ventilated and the attic must be ventilated.

Heat

If a storage, insulated as recommended, is at least one-half filled, little or no supplemental heat should be required. However, if storage doors are opened frequently, if potatoes must be warmed for handling or if fresh air is needed for moisture control, then some additional heat may be needed. Usually 1.5 to 5.0 Btu/h-cwt (100 to 320 W/t) of supplemental heat is adequate.

Ventilation

The ventilation system in a storage performs three functions: (1) it brings in and distributes cool, fresh air to lower the temperature to storage levels; (2) it circulates air within the storage periodically to maintain uniform conditions; and (3) it introduces small quantities of fresh air periodically to correct the humidity or temperature. During the initial cooling period, a fan capacity of 16 to 20 cfm/ton (8.25 L/s-t) will insure rapid cool down. Fans should deliver the necessary capacity at operating static pressure. The static pressure may be from 1/2 to 11/2 in. (13 to 38 mm), approximately 3/4 in. (19 mm) is typical for wood ducts. Undersized ducts or dirty potatoes will result in higher pressures.

Air Distribution Control

As mentioned, the ventilation system must perform three functions. Each of these requires a somewhat different air distribution pattern. Of the numerous systems that have been used, probably the proportioning system that can be automatically controlled to circulate all fresh air, recirculate only storage air or circulate any of several proportions of fresh and storage air, provides the best storage environment.

The operation of a proportioning system is complex, but figure 18.2, showing the damper and fan locations, should help to illustrate how it functions. Soon after the potatoes are in the storage, rapid cool down to storage temperature is desirable. Since the storage temperature would be quite warm and the outside air temperature still moderate, the damper would probably shift to the horizontal position allowing 100% fresh air to be brought in. During the middle of the day the outside temperature may rise above the temperature in the storage. The differential thermostat senses the condition and, overriding the proportioning thermostat, moves the damper to the vertical position until the outside temperature drops. A timer would continue to call for intermittent recirculation. When the storage temperature is reached, the damper would shift to the vertical position and air would recirculate. Under these conditions a timer would operate the fan on an intermittent basis. With mild outside temperatures, the potatoes will produce an excess of heat and the storage temperature will rise. Under these conditions the proportioning thermostat will tip the damper just enough so that cool air will temper the recirculating air and bring the storage temperature down.

When the storage temperature drops below normal, heat and recirculation are required. When the humidity is too high, a small amount of fresh air can be admitted under control of a humidistat. This would probably drop the storage temperature enough to call for heat. Low humidities may be corrected automatically with humidifiers installed in the plenum and controlled by humidistats. However, as humidistats are rather undependable at high humidity levels, manual management may be substituted to adjust humidity. A safety thermostat in the plenum can shut the system down and sound an alarm in the event that other controls fail to function correctly.

Air Distribution

Air must be distributed through the potatoes with reasonable uniformity to maintain a quality product. Uneven air flow can cause pockets of high humidity, condensation, and resultant rotting, or areas of either high or low temperature that cause premature sprouting or conversion of starch to sugar.

Distribution of the air has been achieved successfully with several different systems. One of the more common methods is through ducts cast in the concrete floor. Another is through rectangular- or triangular-shaped ducts installed on the floor surface. In addition, corrugated metal ducts or ducts built into bin partitions have been used. Whatever the choice, there are characteristics that should be embodied in the system if uniform distribution is to result.

1. Delivery ducts under potatoes should be spaced 8 to 12 ft (2.5 to 3.7 m) apart.

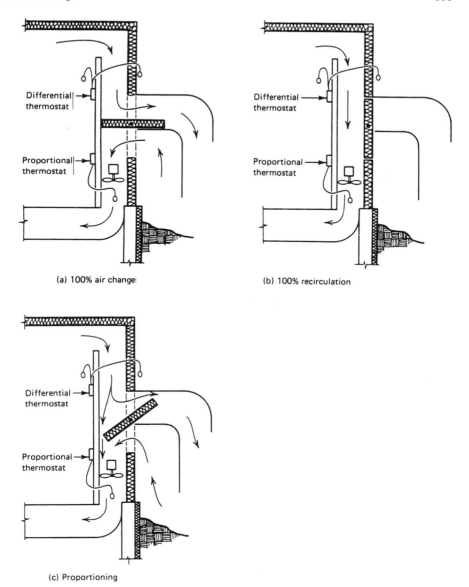

(a) 100% air change

(b) 100% recirculation

(c) Proportioning

Figure 18.2. An air proportioning cooling and ventilation system.

2. The maximum air velocity in either distribution or delivery ducts should be limited to no more than 1,500 fpm (7.5 m/s).
3. Distribution ducts should be reduced in cross-section after each branch opening in such a way that the velocity remains constant.

4. Delivery ducts may be tapered or stepped at 10 ft (3 m) intervals to maintain a uniform velocity, or the openings in the ducts may be restricted to provide enough static pressure for uniform distribution.

It has been demonstrated that if the total net area of the outlets in the delivery ducts is equal to the duct cross-section area, air will be distributed uniformly. However, if the potatoes rest on the openings as they would on the slotted cover of a cast-in-place floor duct, 75% of the opening area is covered. In this situation, a gross area of three times the duct cross-section area is required to provide the net area necessary to insure uniform air distribution without excessive static pressures.

Ducts cast in the floor that are a minimum of 20 in. (500 mm) wide will allow the use of a 16 in. (400 mm) conveyor in the duct for removing potatoes at the end of the season. To maintain a uniform air velocity, the cross-section area of the ducts may be reduced by decreasing the depth to a minimum of 14 in. (350 mm), this is also a limiting depth for a conveyor. Removable wood blocks may be used to further limit the cross-section area for air flow control. Curved metal corners installed in ducts at right angle turns reduce turbulence and improve the uniformity of distribution.

Once the desired storage conditions have been achieved by moving air through the potatoes, some managers prefer to have the air move along the storage walls (fig. 18.3).

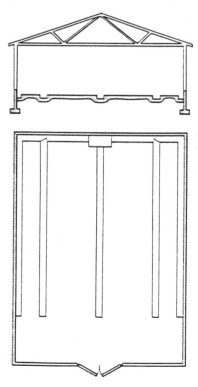

Figure 18.3. Potato storage air distribution ducts.

This is called shell ventilation and maintains uniform room conditions while reducing air movement through the potatoes, resulting in somewhat less shrinkage.

Humidification

In humid regions, nighttime relative humidities tend to be very high. Since it is primarily nighttime air that is used for cooling, satisfactory humidities are easily maintained during the initial stages of storage. In contrast, in some dry areas, nighttime humidities are so low that the fresh air tends to reduce storage humidity to an undesirably low level. Under these conditions, high capacity centrifugal humidifiers may be required. In marginal cases, duct bottoms may be kept covered with water or spray nozzles can be used to add moisture to the storage.

NURSERY STOCK STORAGE

Nursery plants have traditionally been lined out in fields or wooded areas where winter injury to evergreen foliage annually causes a considerable loss in salable plants. In the colder regions of the country, these plants are not available for the early spring market because of frozen ground.

These problems led to the growing of plants in containers which can be shipped as early as the market demands. But container growing introduced a new problem. Root damage to balled or containerized plants is much more common than to those left in the ground, especially among ornamentals including magnolias, dogwoods, and some hollys in which root damage occurs at 20°F (–7°C) or lower.

Both foliage and root damage can be avoided, however, by placing the container-grown plants in storages where a favorable environment is maintained. The growing demand for early spring sales of nursery stock has led to a considerable increase in the use of such winter storages.

Types of Storages

The two most common winter nursery storages are (1) temporary, plastic-covered structures erected over the area where the stock is growing, and (2) permanent buildings, often built partly below grade, insulated and ventilated so that ideal environmental conditions may be maintained.

Plastic-covered Storages

These are simple, inexpensive structures ranging from 3 ft (1 m) to 8 ft (2.5 m) high, 6 ft (1.8 m) to 17 ft (5.2 m) wide, and up to 500 ft (150 m) long, consisting of pipe hoop frames covered with polyethylene (PE). The frames are covered in late fall and uncovered in the spring.

These PE-covered structures have worked well for storing hardy plants. They have also been reasonably successful for less hardy species by using supplementary management practices such as irrigation of the containers, covering the plants with one or two layers of flexible foam insulation, and in some cases installing thermostatically controlled portable heaters. White plastic is used to cover the frames as it limits daytime temperature.

In the absence of heat, the hoop frames may collapse under excessive snow loads. Temporary support at the midpoint of the arches ordinarily is adequate to prevent damage.

Permanent Storages

Although investment in a permanent building is greater, and labor is required to move the plants into the storage, the opportunity to maintain ideal conditions and to assemble and ship plants easily and efficiently early in the spring has led to increased use of environmentally controlled storages.

While above-grade, insulated storages are generally satisfactory, the use of partially below-grade structures allows soil heat to assist in maintaining above freezing temperatures within the storage. Unlike potatoes, nursery stock produces negligible heat of respiration, so heavy insulation alone does not necessarily maintain the desired storage temperature. Uninsulated concrete floors and walls located well below grade should allow a minimum of 2 Btu/h-ft^2 (6.3 W/m^2) to pass into a 34°F (1°C) storage. On the average, this is enough so that with a well insulated ceiling and end wall, heat gain will exceed heat loss and occasional ventilation will be required to maintain storage temperature.

A winter nursery storage building includes the following recommended construction features:

1. A well-drained, sloping site to allow much of the building to be below grade.
2. Twelve-foot (3.5 m) side walls of reinforced concrete, placed 10 ft (3 m) below grade. The walls must be anchored to large footings with reinforcing to resist lateral soil forces.
3. A clear span of up to 50 ft (15 m) if wood trusses are desired.
4. Insulation to an R of 20 (3.5) in the exposed end and ceiling. The maintenance of high humidity means that vapor pressure will be higher inside the building than outside. Thus a vapor barrier should be installed between the ceiling and the insulation. To remove any moisture accumulation above the ceiling, large louvers should be installed in the gable ends of the building. An alternative means of avoiding moisture problems is to use a closed-cell insulation such as sprayed-on polyurethane or urea formaldehyde. Panels of polyurethane or polystyrene would also be suitable as long as a satisfactory covering is installed as a protection against fire. The upper part of the walls may be insulated with rigid insulation attached with an adhesive.
5. An insulated door large enough to accommodate trucks and fork lifts.
6. A ventilation system with an exhaust fan at one end of the storage with capacity to provide eight air changes per hour. Air is introduced through two or more motorized louvers at the opposite end of the storage and distributed through PE ducts suspended along the length of the ceiling. Ducts should be sized to carry air at 800 to 1,200 ft/min (4 to 6 m/s) and

each should have two rows of holes uniformly distributed along the length. The holes should be located to discharge down 30° from the horizontal and be spaced 24 to 30 in. (600 to 750 mm) apart. A total area for all of the holes equal to one and one-half to two times the cross-section area of the duct will provide sufficient velocity for good air distribution.

7. A ventilation system controlled by a pair of thermostats, one near the center of the storage that calls for ventilation whenever the storage temperature rises above 34°F (1°C) and one outside that prevents fan operation if the temperature is more than 34°F (1°C). An alternative and better control for the ventilation system is a single, differential thermostat that allows ventilation anytime it is required when the outside air is cooler than the inside.

8. Continuous air circulation provided by fans.

Handling the nursery stock within the storage will vary from place to place. However, pallets that can be stacked or placed on racks permit the use of a fork lift and allow for efficient use of the available storage space.

Although the plants do not need light during the storage season, adequate lighting is required for loading and unloading the storage. An adjacent building, maintained at a higher temperature, makes a convenient and more comfortable location to ball and burlap bare-root stock and complete other winter and early spring operations.

Problems

18.1. An apple storage is to be built to hold 20,000 bushels (436 t) equally divided into four rooms. Bulk boxes stacked 6 high will require 18 ft (5.5 m) ceilings. Recommend room dimensions for the storage. A bushel of apples weighs 48 lb (21.8 kg).

18.2. The storage will be filled at the rate of 1,000 bu (22 t) /day. The average outside temperature is 65°F (18°C) and the storage temperature is 32°F (0°C). The walls and ceiling are insulated to an R of 25 (4.4) while the floor, also insulated, may be ignored since the heat loss through a floor is insignificant. The building, which includes an equipment room, is designed so that each storage room has one wall in common with another. Therefore, there is no heat exchange through the common wall. Determine the total refrigeration capacity required. Include room loss, field heat, heat of respiration and service loss.

18.3. Explain why it is desirable to have an evaporator with sufficient surface so that it can operate just a few degrees colder than room temperature.

18.4. An air cooled potato storage is being designed to hold 10,000 bu (273 t). Recommend a ventilation rate and estimate the number of days it will take to cool the potatoes to 40°F (4.4°C) if during 12 h each day the outside temperature averages 38°F (3°C). Assume that the potatoes have a field temperature of 60°F (15.6°C) and that wall and ceiling heat trans-

fer balances out to zero during the period. Field heat and heat of respiration should be included in the calculations. For purposes of calculation, it may be assumed that the potatoes average 45°F (7°C) during the
cooling period and that the temperature of the air exhausted equals this
temperature. Assume 70% relative humidity for both inlet and exhaust
air.

18.5.   A storage is being designed in which potatoes will be piled 12 ft
(3.66 m) deep against the walls. The studs will be 14 ft (4.27 m) long
and spaced 8 in. (200 mm) on center. There will be no bin partitions.
Determine a satisfactory size stud, assuming a safe fiber stress in bending of 1,000 psi (6890 kPa).

19 Waste Management

Production of livestock results in the generation of a large quantity of manure. Management of the manure is often a major problem. The manure must be handled without causing environmental pollution. Manure management is of importance for all animal enterprises. A well-designed livestock production system will allow utilization of the manure, commonly as a source of nutrients for crop production. Collection, transport, and land application of manure are phases of the manure management system.

There are many ways to accomplish each phase of manure management. Manure may be collected by accumulation in lots or under slotted floors, scraped or flushed from alleys. Trucks, wagons, and pipelines are all used for manure transport. Land application may be by flail spreaders, injectors or sprinkle irrigation systems.

In addition to the phases discussed above, manure may be subjected to various types of treatment. Treatment systems may be used to reduce odors or pollutant strength. Or the objective of treatment may be to produce a more valuable product such as methane.

Complete descriptions and planning factors for manure handling and treatment systems for all animal species would be very voluminous. Only a few representative systems will be discussed.

Dairy Manure Handling

Handling and utilization of manure and disposal of wash water and milk room waste can be major problems that must be dealt with in the overall dairy housing plan. Before planning begins, local and state authorities should be consulted on related health and environmental regulations. Once the waste management system has been designed, the proposed plans should be approved by the appropriate authorities before starting construction.

Moving Manure Out of the Stable Barn

If bedding is used, the manure can be easily handled with a gutter cleaner and elevator to move it to either a storage or a manure spreader. If bedding is not used, an alternative is a large piston, manure transfer pump that forces the manure from a pit in the barn to a liquid manure storage. Another method, suitable when no bedding is used, is to let the manure drop through grates into a storage below. The manure can then flow on a continuous basis in a 3 ft (1 m) deep channel below the gutter grates to a sump at the end of the barn. The channel has three essential characteristics: (1) it must be level, (2) it must have a 6 in. dam (150 mm) at the outlet end, and (3) it should not be more than 60 ft (20 m) long. In longer barns, the channels are arranged in steps with manure flowing from the uppermost level into the next and so on to the sump or a cross channel.

Moving Manure Out of the Free Stall Barn

Alleys in a free stall barn may be scraped with a tractor-mounted blade or a skid loader with the manure pushed off a loading ramp into a spreader or storage. Alternatively, the manure may be pushed into a pit and then transferred to storage with a gutter cleaner and elevator or with a large piston pump which can move the manure up to 300 ft (90 m) from the barn. Mechanical scrapers discharging into manure elevators or piston pump pits are suitable for rectangular barns with uniform width alleys.

If little or no bedding is used, a slotted floor with manure storage under the building is possible. If a slotted floor system with storage outside the barn is preferred, the manure can be moved in a continuous flow channel, similar to the one described for stable barns, or with a scraper installed under the slats.

In mild climates, a hydraulic flushing system may be employed to clean free stall alleys and adjacent areas. The amount of water required for flushing alleys can increase the manure storage requirements by 10 to 100 times unless the liquid is recycled. The system is most practical in areas where large quantities of water are used for irrigation and the water can be "borrowed" for flushing and then returned to the irrigation system after removal of the coarse solids.

Experience has shown that a slope of 2 to 3% and a minimum water velocity of 2 to 3 ft/s (0.6 to 0.9 m/s) is necessary to remove and transport wet manure. Successful cleaning action requires a uniform flow over the entire surface area of the alley. Tipping buckets or trapdoor tanks provide the rapid discharge required for flushing. The frequency of flushing is related not only to the amount of manure to be removed but also to the weather. In hot, dry weather, flushing must be done more frequently to prevent the manure from drying and becoming difficult to remove.

Moving Waste from the Milking Center

The term milking center applies to the milk room in a stable system and to the parlor and milk room in a free-stall system. The waste from a milking center includes milk and milk solids, chemicals, dilute manure, and clean water. The volume of these wastes varies greatly depending on management practices and equipment.

The practice of designing milk room and parlor floors to slope 1/4 to 1/2 in./ft (20 to 40 mm/m) and locating drains in one corner or in a gutter helps direct the flow of wash water and simplifies floor construction. A high threshold is required between the parlor and the milk room and is desirable between the milk room and utility room and lavatory as well. All drains should be of an approved material and equipped with traps and vents to prevent the discharge of odors into the center. Piping the milk-room-floor waste through a corner of the milking pit provides the operator with a visual check of any malfunctioning equipment in the milk room. This would allow a shutdown before a major loss occurred.

If a liquid manure system is used, the milking center wastes may be included with the manure and serve as part of the diluting water. If a solid manure system is used, the milking center wastes must be disposed of separately, as discussed later in the chapter.

Manure Storage

Climate permitting, manure may be spread daily as it is produced. However, more of the fertilizer value of the manure may be conserved and the spreading operation integrated with crop production if a means of storage is provided. In addition, environmental considerations may restrict spreading on snow or frozen ground, thus making storage facilities mandatory. Both the length of the winter season in northern areas and the length of the growing season in all areas indicate the desirability of at least 180 days of storage capacity.

Storing Solid Manure

If a considerable amount of bedding is used, manure may be stacked on a paved area sloped to a point from which the leachate may be drained away for approved disposal. The paved surface will reduce nutrient losses and help eliminate both pollution and fly problems.

If little or no bedding is used, the manure will need to be confined by walls constructed of concrete or pressure-preservative-treated wood, or by earthen banks or dikes. An allowance of 2.5 ft^3/1,000 lb of animal weight (0.07 m^3/450 kg)/day of storage period is adequate.

One of the more successful means of draining precipitation from a solid or "as-produced" manure storage consists of picket dams (fig. 19.1). They are located at points along the storage wall where the manure level is expected to be the lowest. One of the low points will be along the edge of the ramp used to enter the storage for loading out. Another will be at the point farthest from the spot where the manure is loaded into the storage. Vertical 2 in. (50 mm) planks mounted on heavy horizontal stringers are positioned to give 3/4 in. (19 mm) vertical slots for the face of the dams. The recommended size and spacing for post and stringers is given in table 19-1.

The posts are set 4 to 5 ft (1.2 to 1.5 m) into the ground and the concrete floor placed around them. In addition, a U-shaped reinforcing bar should be placed in the concrete around the post and extended at least 15 in. (380 mm) into the concrete floor. Bending the ends of the bar will form a secure anchor in the floor. The bottom stringer is placed at least 10 in. (250 mm) above the floor to allow unrestricted drainage. It is essential that all wooden members be pressure-preservative-treated dimension or rough cut lumber.

Constructing the ramp 40 ft (12 m) wide allows room for the spreader to be backed to the edge of the manure for loading. The ramp, with a slope of no more than 1:10 (rise:run) and preferably less, becomes a large collecting surface for precipitation. Grooves formed in the ramp's surface at the time of casting should be angled to drain this water toward the dam.

The leachate that drains from the manure is a strong pollutant to be disposed of in a safe manner. It may be combined with milking center wastes to be held in a lagoon, or

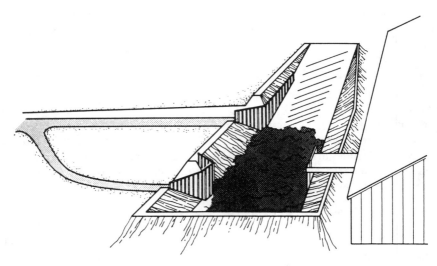

Figure 19.1. Picket dam drain for solid manure.

it may be spread on a grass filter bed. In estimating the necessary capacity for a lagoon or grass filter bed, provision should be made for a leachate volume equivalent to a 24 h storm over the storage area plus the volume of the milking center wastes. No milking center waste should be discharged into the picket dam storage and under no circumstances should the leachate from the storage be allowed to drain into a watercourse.

Storing Liquid Manure

Dairy manure without bedding is too high in moisture to handle easily as a solid and it is too thick to pump well. However, the addition of some water, including milk-

Table 19-1. Member sizes for picket dams

POSTS

Length Above Ground	Size	Spacing
ft (m)	in. (mm)	ft (m)
0-4 (0-1.2)	4 × 6 (89 × 140)	5 (1.5)
5 (1.5)	6 × 6 (140 × 140)	4 (1.2)
6 (1.8)	6 × 8 (140 × 184)	4 (1.2)
7 (2.1)	8 × 8 (184 × 184)	3 (1.0)

HORIZONTAL SUPPORTS (Stringers)

Below Maximum Manure Level	Size	Spacing
ft (m)	in. (mm)	ft (m)
0-4 (0-1.2)	4 × 4 (89 × 89)	3.0 (1.0)
4-6 (1.2-1.8)	4 × 4 (89 × 89)	2.5 (0.75)
6-8 (1.8-2.4)	4 × 4 (89 × 89)	2.0 (0.6)

ing center wastes and precipitation on open storages, will dilute the manure sufficiently to allow handling it as a liquid.

The least expensive liquid manure storage consists of an earthen basin with banks sloped 1:2 to 1:3 (rise:run) inside and about 1:3 to 1:4 on the outside. Provision for agitating and pumping the manure must be made during planning. The most common type of pump for emptying manure storages is pto driven. These pumps may have an inline or a right angle drive. The inline drive pumps are used with both the tractor and pump operating on a sloping ramp or storage bank. The right angle drive pump is operated in the vertical position from a platform and a vertical concrete wall or from a platform extending out into the storage (fig. 19.2). The vertical pumps may be able to handle liquid depths of up to 12 ft (3.6 m). Inline drive pumps are available to a length of 36 ft (11 m). Hydraulic or electrical submersible pumps with a hose are also available. Generally these pumps have a lower capacity or are very expensive. Handled with a mechanical boom, they allow pumping from storages that are not readily accessible with pto pumps. Although positive displacement pumps are used, the open or semi-open impeller centrifugal pumps with a chopper or cutter blade are most common for handling manure. With impeller diameters of 20 in. (500 mm) or more, these pumps may require 100 hp or greater and have capacities as high as 8,000 gpm (500 L/s).

Ramps for pumping should have slopes of 1:8 to 1:10 and be of roughened concrete. When vertical pumps are used, it is recommended that a 10×10 ft (3×3 m) concrete pad be provided in the storage bottom under the pump to prevent erosion.

Selecting the site for an earthen manure storage, whether close to the barn or 100 to 300 ft (30 to 60 m) away from the barn, should be given careful consideration. The soil must have a low permeability so that it will seal well; otherwise the storage must be lined with plastic or imported clay. Any fresh water pond, well or natural waterway must be far enough from the proposed storage to avoid the danger of pollution. Although odors from such a storage are likely to be serious only when the manure is being agitated and removed, proximity to neighbors and the farm home must be taken into account.

The location of the storage will also be influenced by the availability of space and the method of loading. If manure is handled with a tractor scraper or a mechanical alley scraper and barn cleaner extension, the storage must be located very close to the barn. However, the use of a large piston transfer pump allows the storage to be 150 to 300 ft (45 to 90 m) away from the barn.

In most regions, a six-month storage period is recommended and a one-year period should be considered. A capacity of 2.5 to 3 ft^3/1,000 lb (0.07 to 0.08 m^3/450 kg) of animal weight per day of storage is adequate, although some excess bank height should be allowed to prevent any possibility of overflow.

The soil type will influence the angle of bank slopes. Nevertheless, the inside should be as steep as possible while the outside of the banks should be seeded. If the banks are kept to less than 1:3 (rise:run) they can be mowed more easily. Providing the ground water level allows it, the basin may be 10 to 12 ft (3 to 3.5 m) deep or for the ramp design shown in figure 19.2, even deeper. Care should be taken that no sur-

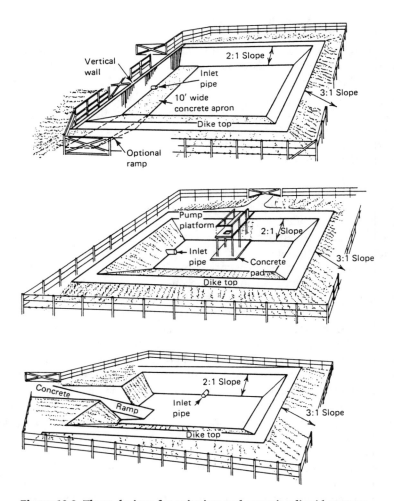

Figure 19.2. Three designs for agitation and pumping liquid manure.

face water drains into the basin. Agitation from one location up to distances of 50 ft (18 m) is satisfactory in most storages. However, if the basin is larger than that, additional agitation points should be provided.

Above-grade Storage

Above-grade storage should be considered in areas of high water table, shallow soils, or where insufficient area is available for an earthen basin. Generally, they are not such an attractive nuisance to children and are considered safer. They may be made of wood or concrete staves, poured concrete or corrosion protected steel. Each of these materials is satisfactory, but in each case care must be taken to provide a good foundation and adequate strength for the large forces developed. These tanks may extend into the ground a few feet if this does not interfere with emptying.

Filling can be accomplished with a large piston pump through the bottom or, alternatively, with a standard manure pump from a sump, or from a gutter cleaner into an elevator and over the side.

Agitation and removal of the manure from an above-ground tank may be done in either of two ways. The manure may be drained into a sump, pumped back into the tank, recirculating until the agitation is complete, and then pumped into the spreader for disposal. The second method is similar except that the pump is connected directly to the outlet of the storage tank.

Because above-grade storages have straight sides, they collect less precipitation. Consequently, the smaller volume of 2 to 2$1/2$ ft^3/1,000 lb (0.06 to 0.07 m^3/450 kg) of animal weight per day may be used to calculate the storage volume required.

Below-ground Storage

Storage below slotted floors requires good management to be successful. It is desirable for the continuously operating ventilation fans to exhaust air from the pit area. However, this will not ensure that all toxic gases will be removed during agitation and pumping. Therefore, it is recommended that animals be removed and the building left open during these periods.

The four principal gases released during agitation are carbon dioxide, methane, ammonia, and hydrogen sulphide. The first two are asphyxiants when they replace air, the ammonia is a powerful irritant, and hydrogen sulphide is lethal in concentrations that can be encountered in manure storages. The importance of caution and care in working with an underfloor system cannot be overemphasized.

Although the animal density may be increased and labor efficiency improved by the use of a slotted floor and a below-floor storage, the management of a liquid manure system using storages outside the building is generally less expensive and ventilation problems are less likely to develop.

Disposing of Milking Center Wastes

Milk solids, cleaners, and sanitizers do not degrade easily, so provision for the safe disposal of milking center wastes is essential. If a liquid manure system is used, the milking center wastes may be diverted into the manure storage where it will contribute to the necessary dilution. However, if the manure is handled as a solid, the milking center wastes must be disposed of separately. There are several methods from which to choose, but each requires careful management.

1. A grass filtration bed is simple and free of trouble, if it is designed correctly. There should be no low areas or concentrated point of discharge to cause pooling that will kill the vegetation. Furthermore, there should be no erosion or anaerobic conditions from overloading. But most importantly, there must be no drainage to a watercourse.

The recommended design criteria include the following:

(a) Five to ten square feet of area per gallon of daily discharge (0.12 to 0.25 m^2/L). Fifty to a hundred square feet (4.5 to 9 m^2) per cow should be adequate for most herds.

(b) The land must slope, but not more than 5%. Contoured furrows may be used for steeper areas.

(c) Reed canary grass or tall fescue is recommended for planting on the filter bed as they are resistant to wet conditions.

(d) The effluent should be distributed either through a manifold with holes spaced along its length, or over the edge of a shallow settling basin. The distribution edge of the settling basin should extend deep enough into the ground to avoid any displacement due to frost action.

(e) A settling tank with a capacity of 20 gal (75 L)/cow in the line between the milking center and the filter bed will prevent the accumulation of solids on the filter area.

(f) Animals should be fenced out of the area and the grass harvested periodically.

2. A lagoon is another proven method for disposing of milking center wastes. In an aerobic lagoon, microorganisms which depend on oxygen utilize nutrients from the waste and thus reduce the pollution strength. Lagoons intended to be aerobic must be designed to ensure transfer of sufficient oxygen into the liquid. The depth must be limited to reduce the potential of becoming anaerobic. Algae which use sunlight are one source of oxygen and the sunlight depth of penetration of light is limited. Although the quantity of wastewater is a variable factor, generally a 4 to 5 ft (1.2 to 1.5 m) deep lagoon with 100 ft^2 (9 m^2) of surface area per cow will be adequate for mild temperature zones. Increasing the surface area to 130 ft^2 (12 m^2) is desirable for colder regions. The effluent from the lagoon is distributed on cropland when soil conditions are suitable.

3. An automatic spray irrigation system that discharges onto a suitable grass-covered area can avoid some of the distribution problems that may occur with a grass filtration bed. On the other hand, more equipment and attention to operation is required. The system includes a pit which collects the waste material from the milking center, a float-switch-controlled pump, lines, and a number of sprinkler heads. The pit should be sized to hold three to four days of waste discharge. This limits sprinkling to approximately twice a week. The number and capacity of the sprinkler heads should limit the rate of application to 3/8 in. (9.5 mm)/h. It is imperative that the pump match the sprinkler capacity while maintaining a minimum of 40 psi (275 kPa) pressure at the sprinkler. The effect of gravity and friction head must also be considered in the selection of lines and pump.

Septic tank and drainage field systems have also been installed to handle milking center wastes on many farms. However, the waste is extremely slow to biodegrade, and the system usually proves to be little more than a holding tank that must be pumped frequently. Regardless of the system selected, care should be taken to avoid point discharge of untreated water.

Toilet waste must not be included with the manure or milking center waste. It should be disposed of through a separate septic tank and drainage field system or be piped into a city sewer.

Disposing of Waste from Open Lots

Unpaved lots are usually scraped and cleaned periodically and the manure spread on cropland. Paved yards need to be scraped more often and a storage may be required that is suitable for the consistency of the manure.

Runoff from either unpaved or paved yards must be handled in a way that prevents pollution. Settling basin design is discussed later in the section on beef manure management.

Swine Waste Management

A well-planned, complete waste management system is absolutely essential in a swine production enterprise. A complete waste disposal system is needed to maintain healthy livestock in sanitary conditions, to avoid polluting the air and water, and to comply with local, state, and federal environmental regulations.

The methods of waste disposal vary with the type of waste being handled. Hogs that are raised on pasture naturally distribute the manure throughout the area and thus reduce handling to a minimum. Wastes from bedded solid-floor houses are handled as solids and spread with a conventional spreader, while drainage from manure stacks, runoff from lots, and manure from unbedded floors and slotted floors are handled as liquids, and spread with liquid manure spreaders or through irrigation systems.

Completely slotted floors reduce labor requirements at the barn to a minimum. However, because hogs always tend to dung in the same place, partially slotted floors are probably a better choice since they require only a minimal increase in labor while saving significantly on the original investment. Locating the water fountain over the slotted area and the feeder near the resting area encourages the pigs to dung over the slotted portion of the floor while keeping the solid area clean.

Although the fully slotted floor is usually designed with pits that are capable of storing manure up to 180 days, many herdsmen prefer to store the manure outside the building because of odors and toxic gases. In that case, the smaller pits under partially slotted floors are completely adequate in size.

Manure Storage

Manure storage facilities are essential for most farms to meet environmental regulations and to hold the manure until a convenient or advantageous time to spread it on the land. Types of storage include:

Paved Areas

Paved areas are used to stack bedded manure. The floor should slope toward a picket dam that will drain off the seepage from snow and rain.

Pit Storages

These are located under slotted-floor buildings. The problem of odors and toxic gases at the time of agitation discourages many from using this method. Hydrogen sulphide and ammonia are strong irritants and can be lethal in sufficient concentrations. Carbon dioxide and methane are odorless but cause asphyxiation. Excellent ventilation and great care are imperative at the time of agitation and pumping.

Holding Ponds or Tanks

These are used to hold manure up to six months or longer. Some anaerobic decomposition may occur, but the primary purpose is simply storage. Holding ponds should be located so that there is no possibility of polluting streams or lakes. In areas of porous soil structure, sealing may be necessary.

Tanks may be either above ground, requiring the manure to be pumped from the barn, or below grade into which the manure flows by gravity. Both ponds and tanks present potential odor problems when they are agitated and pumped. A location well away from the farm home and from neighbors will minimize the likelihood of complaints.

Lagoons

Lagoons are designed to cause bacterial decomposition of the manure. Anaerobic lagoons are designed to provide an oxygen-free environment. Some microbes that thrive in this type of environment produce odorous gases, therefore improperly designed or managed anaerobic lagoons frequently cause odor problems. These lagoons may become simply holding ponds that need to be pumped periodically. Aerobic lagoons require a large surface area to enable a significant transfer of air into the liquid and for the sun to reach photosynthetic oxygen-producing microorganisms. With an effective decomposition of organic matter the lagoon water remains clear and without scum or odor. Both aerobic and anaerobic lagoons are satisfactory in mild climates.

Settling Basins

These are used as temporary detention ponds to allow settling of a high percentage of the solid material from yard runoff as it flows into a lagoon. The basin is cleaned periodically and dries out between storms. The design is discussed later.

Oxidation Ditches

Oxidation ditches are equipped with large agitators that stir air into the manure. Considerable decomposition results and odors are reduced to a minimum. However, costs are high, management difficult, and much nutrient value is lost.

Moving Manure from Swine Buildings

Gutters should be scraped and flushed daily. Deep gutters, 6 in. (150 mm) wide × 30 in. (760 mm) deep, are allowed to accumulate material, which has been scraped and flushed into them, for one to three days. They are essentially self-cleaning when

Table 19-2. Daily manure production from swine

Animal	Size lb (kg)	Volume of Manure ft^3 (L)
Pigs	40 (18)	0.04 (1.1)
	100 (45)	0.11 (3.1)
	150 (68)	0.17 (4.8)
	210 (95)	0.23 (6.4)
Sows and boars	300 (136)	0.17 (4.8)
	500 (227)	0.28 (7.8)
Sows and litter		0.54 (7.8)

allowed to drain. Pits under slotted floors are emptied either by pumping into above-ground tanks or by allowing them to drain periodically into a below-grade storage. Three to four inches (100 mm) of water added to the pit immediately after draining facilitates cleaning the next time.

With proper design, German farmers successfully allow the channels under slotted floors to drain continuously. The design includes level channels up to 60 ft (20 m) in length with a 6 in. (150 mm) raised edge at the end of the channel. The channel is filled with water initially and thereafter the manure flows with a low angle of repose. If the building is more than 60 ft (20 m) long, multiple channels may be used with a 12 in. (300 mm) step down at the end of each succeeding level section.

Table 19-2 shows the approximate manure production from animals at various stages of development.

Beef Manure Management

In managing the manure from a beef cattle enterprise one should strive for:
• The prevention of pollution of streams, lakes, and groundwater.
• The conservation of nutrients to provide maximum value to crops.
• High labor efficiency in handling the wastes.
• A feasible level of investment in storage facilities and handling equipment.

The methods used to obtain these objectives will be influenced by the type of housing system, the climate of the region, and the ultimate disposal of manure. Management methods for each of the three housing systems (open-lot, barn-and-lot, and total confinement) will be discussed.

Open-lot Systems and Barn-and-lot Systems

At the time of construction, diversion drainage should be installed to intercept surface water so it will not drain onto the feedlot and increase the amount of runoff. In addition, eave troughs and drains should be installed on barns to direct rainwater away from the lot and keep it out of the waste handling system.

The solid waste can be scraped from an unpaved yard periodically and spread on cropland. This is usually done when the moisture level of the manure is low. Paved yards will need much more frequent scraping, and storage facilities may be required. A paved storage with a picket dam as described earlier in this chapter and shown in figure 19.1 is designed for holding solid manure. Approximately $3/4$ ft^3 (20 L)/animal will be needed each day of the storage period.

All open yards will have liquid runoff from heavy rains or melting snow which contains high levels of pollutants and must be prevented from entering any natural waterway. Therefore, if runoff is not immediately dispersed over adjacent grassland in an acceptable manner, a holding pond is required to store the runoff until conditions are suitable for disposal on crop or pasture land. The effluent will usually be distributed through an irrigation system. The amount of runoff is estimated on the basis of rainfall records. Local rainfall data is the most satisfactory for design purposes. In addition to the runoff, the size of a holding pond will be influenced by the length of the holding period, the accumulation of solids, and the net effect of rainfall and evaporation.

In the eastern part of the United States and Canada, the rainfall and evaporation are roughly equal and have little effect on the storage capacity of a holding pond. In much of the western part of the United States and Canada, evaporation significantly exceeds rainfall. This increases the effective capacity of a holding pond used for periods of several months. Evaporation is of little significance, however, if the holding pond is emptied frequently.

During an intense storm of short duration, a large volume flow picks up solids and carries them along in the runoff. A settling basin, installed between the lot and the holding pond, greatly reduces the accumulation of these solids. With a detention period of 20 min or more, up to 85% of the solids can be removed from the runoff before it enters the pond. Detention period is defined as the time required for the flow volume to equal the design volume of the basin. In other words, a 20-min detention period is assumed if the drained basin is large enough to hold the expected runoff for the 20-min period. Additional capacity will be required to hold the settled solids. The amount of accumulated solids will be influenced by the area of the lot and the frequency with which the settling basin is cleaned.

A porous dam or a vertical, perforated pipe outlet may be used to restrict the flow to give the required detention time and to drain the basin at the end of the storm. Such dams can be constructed of planks with either horizontal or vertical spacing. A 1/2 in. (12 mm) expanded metal screen installed so that it tips away from the top of the dam approximately 30° will keep the dam from plugging. The reverse slope produces a self-cleaning action. In addition, periodically scraping the surface of the dam is necessary for proper operation.

Settling Basin Design

A settling basin is designed on the basis of the maximum expected runoff flow for a relatively short period of time. The 1 h rainfall expected 1 year in 10 is commonly used. It may be assumed that the first 1/2 in. of heavy rain will be retained on an unpaved lot, while 1/4 in. will be retained by a paved yard that is scraped frequently. The following steps are used in designing a settling basin (fig.19.3):

1. Determine the peak runoff rate per hour based on local rainfall records and lot area. Subtract the first 1/2 in. for an unpaved lot or 1/4 in. for a paved lot.

2. Find the necessary basin surface area by dividing the rate per hour in cubic feet by 4 ft.

3. Find the design depth of the liquid by multiplying the detention period in hours by 4 ft.

4. Determine the additional basin depth for solids accumulation with the formula:

$$D_b = \frac{(A_y \times D_y)}{(A_b \times TC)} \qquad (19.1)$$

where

D_b =   depth of solids in basin

A_y =   area of lot

D_y =   depth of solids lost from lot annually

A_b =   surface area of basin

TC =   times cleaned annually

The design depth is equal to the depth of the liquid plus the depth of the solids.

5. Find the total area of openings in a perforated pipe or porous dam that will match the maximum expected runoff flow rate. This is done by dividing the runoff rate by the appropriate flow value for the design depth. Table 19-3 gives the flow rate for a single 1 in. vertical opening or 12 in.^{2}/ft of length for perforated pipe. As the flow through an orifice is proportional to area, larger pipes or multiple dam openings may be used to obtain the required capacity.

6. Select an arbitrary width (W_1) for the bottom of the basin. Using a 1:3 slope (rise:run), determine the width (W_2) at the design depth (step 4). Use the formula: $W_2 = W_1 + (2 \times \text{depth} \times \text{slope ratio})$.

7. Find the length of the basin with the formula:

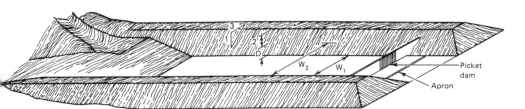

Figure 19.3. Settling basin with a picket dam.

Table 19-3. Flow values for perforated pipe or porous dam*

Depth		Flow	
(ft)	(m)	(ft³/h)	(m³/h)
0.5	0.15	348	9.7
1.0	0.31	990	27.7
1.5	0.46	1,818	50.9
2.0	0.61	2,808	78.6
2.5	0.76	3,900	109
3.0	0.92	5,148	144
3.5	1.07	6,480	181
4.0	1.22	7,943	222
4.5	1.37	9,450	265
5.0	1.53	11,040	309
5.5	1.68	12,780	358
6.0	1.83	14,550	407

* Based on a pipe with 12 in.^{2} (7,740 mm^2) of opening/ft (300 mm) of length or 1 in. (25 mm) of spacing between vertical pickets per foot of height. An orifice constant of 0.6 is assumed.

$$\text{Length} = \frac{2\,A_b}{W_1 + W_2} \qquad (19.2)$$

where

A_b = surface area of basin

W_1 = width at bottom

W_2 = width of liquid surface at maximum depth

8. Determine the dike and dam height with the following criteria:

   The dike height should be 2 ft (0.6 m) higher than the design depth. The porous dam or perforated pipe may be 1 ft (0.3 m) above the design depth.

9. Design the slope of the bottom of the basin to be no more than 0.5% and as uniform as possible to prevent ponding.

10. Ancillary features that are highly recommended include:

   (a) A ramp over the dike that will allow solids to be removed with a tractor loader.

   (b) An apron installed under the dam and extending downstream several feet.

   (c) A reverse-sloped, expanded metal screen in front of the dam.

   (d) A dike width sufficient to allow mowing and easy maintenance.

   (e) A pre-settling basin constructed in the lower corner of a paved yard using a protected perforated pipe or a dam. The solids accumulated are then removed in the course of regular cleaning.

Example 19.1

The design of a settling basin has the following information given:
Yard size, 200 × 400 ft, unpaved; 6 in. solids runoff annually; and the basin will be cleaned eight times a year. Design a basin for a 25-year, 1 h storm of 2.5 in. using a picket dam and a 30-min detention time.

1. $$\frac{(1.2.5 - 0.5)\text{ in.}/\text{h} \times 200\text{ ft} \times 400\text{ ft}}{12\text{ in.}/\text{ft}}$$

   $$= 13,333\text{ ft}^3/\text{h}$$

2. $\dfrac{13,333}{4} = 3,333\text{ ft}^2$ surface area

3. $4\text{ ft}/\text{h} \times 0.5\text{ h} = 2\text{ ft}$ liquid depth

4. $D_b = \dfrac{80,000\text{ ft}^2 \times 0.5\text{ ft}/\text{yr}}{3,333\text{ ft}^2 \times 8/\text{yr}} = 1.5\text{ ft}$ solids depth

   $2\text{ ft} + 1.5\text{ ft} = 3.5\text{ ft}$ design depth

5. $\dfrac{13,333\text{ ft}^3/\text{h}}{6480\text{ ft}^3/\text{h}/\text{opening}} = 2.06$ times the area of one picket

Therefore use two picket openings.

6. $W_1 = 12$ ft, chosen arbitrarily

   $W_2 = 12\text{ ft} + 2\text{ ft} \times 3.5\text{ ft} \times 3/\text{ft} = 33\text{ ft}$

7. The length $= 2 \times 3,333\text{ ft}^2/33\text{ ft} + 12\text{ ft} = 148\text{ ft}$ long
8. The dike height should be $3.5\text{ ft} + 2\text{ ft} = 5.5\text{ ft}$
9. The slope of the basin bottom $= 0.005\text{ ft/ft} \times 148\text{ ft} = 0.75\text{ ft} = 8\text{ in.}$
10. Include ancillary features listed.

The holding pond below the settling basin should have adequate capacity to hold the runoff from a 25-yr frequency, 24 h storm, and to hold effluent for the required storage period. In mild climates the storage is likely to be necessary to allow disposal at suitable times in relation to soil conditions and the cropping season.

In some areas feedlot runoff may be disposed of by infiltration on an adjacent grassland area. The distribution channel, after a settling basin, must be designed with a very slow slope in order to obtain uniform distribution.

Problems

19.1. Design a settling basin to be installed in the drainage channel to a holding pond receiving the runoff from a 2.5 acre (1.0 ha) unpaved feedlot holding 250 beef animals. Assume the maximum 1 h rain for a 10-yr recurrence period is 1 1/2 in.(38 mm). Also assume that 4 in. (100 mm) of solids will drain off the yard each year and that a settling basin will be cleaned 8 times a year. Design the basin for a 20-min detention time.

19.2. For problem 19.1, what size holding pond will be required to provide for a 6-month storage period? Assume a maximum of 24 in. (600 mm) of precipitation during the period and that evaporation equals precipitation on the pond surface.

19.3. Give specifications for an earthen storage basin for a 200-cow dairy herd. Provide for 180 day storage period.

PART III
Housing Systems

Part III deals with housing for specific enterprises. Unlike the enduring principles discussed in the first two parts, the design of housing for livestock and farm products tends to evolve continuously. What is common practice today is likely to be improved upon or changed radically tomorrow. New ideas are continually being tested for achieving maximum efficiency in handling materials and utilizing labor, for controlling the environment more precisely, and for obtaining maximum production or maintaining superior product quality. For this reason, the discussions in Part III will often be more general, limited in some cases to such basic requirements as space and environmental needs, yet provide a base from which new ideas may be developed.

A Systems Approach

It is a rare case in which several alternatives for the mechanization of an agricultural enterprise do not exist. Furthermore, these alternatives may occur at several steps along the production path. Figure III.1 illustrates a number of possibilities in the choice of equipment and handling forage from field to dairy cow. Similar diagrams can be drawn for grain, milk, manure, and even the herd itself.

In a systems approach, all of the possible methods of managing and handling the necessary items for an enterprise are considered both separately and in combination. Once the overall combined system has been decided upon, it is possible to choose a structure to house that system. The materials handling system will influence the size and type of building, type of frame, floor material, strength of members, and amount of insulation. The system chosen will affect such things as the type of silage and hay storage and the amount of land area required. The interaction between the system and the building also affects labor efficiency and investment. A systems approach to planning the buildings for an enterprise is essential if the most efficient, comfortable, and economical combination is to be obtained.

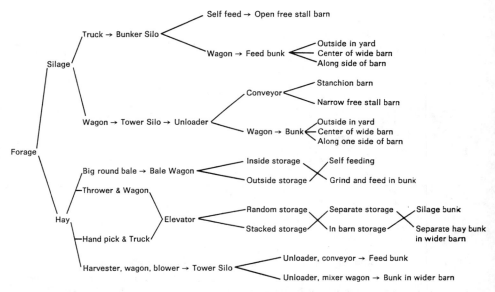

Figure III.1. Equipment and handling forage from field to dairy cows.

20 Farmstead Planning

Planning is the first and most important step in designing a farmstead. While it costs very little to change a plan on paper, the expense of altering a finished building can be prohibitive, and a poorly conceived arrangement of buildings can diminish profits far into the future. Construction of a new, or development of an existing, farmstead generally is a long-term project—good planning can hardly be overemphasized.

The modern farmstead layout should provide efficiency, security, and safety. Farmsteads need to meet many, often conflicting, demands. Easy, convenient access and maneuverability for off-road and over-the-road vehicles is needed, yet such access may reduce security and safety. Some farmsteads will have high demands for electrical power and/or water supply. The plan should provide for efficient distribution of these services. Significant expansion after these services are in place may reduce the original efficiency.

The overall goal of the enterprise should be evaluated carefully at the onset of farmstead planning. The planning process should clearly define the relationship of each structure, or farmstead feature, to the overall goal. A farmstead is primarily a workplace, but also may affect the relaxation, recreation, and play of workers, family members, friends, neighbors, guests or others.

Constructing a completely new farmstead on a new site allows the opportunity to develop an ideal farmstead. Most existing farmsteads have been modified in one manner or another over the years. Often these changes have limited future options and have led to inefficient operations. Such limitations might be avoided by evaluating the farmstead and comparing it to an ideal, before any modifications are made.

An ideal farmstead will be outlined and the factors to be considered discussed. Most of the factors also apply to expansion or replacement plans, although such a situation is often more difficult to control. By long-range planning with gradual change, the efficiency of an existing farmstead may be improved materially.

Every farmstead is unique. The various factors must be evaluated and reasonable compromises made. An example of such a compromise might be the distance between the home and a large, free-stall dairy barn. Convenience and efficiency might indicate very close proximity. Fire safety might indicate a minimum of 100 ft (30 m). Freedom from offensive odors might suggest several hundred feet. The compromise would be something in between—perhaps 200 ft (60 m). Conflicting factors are common and require subjective judgement. Careful planning with the very best information available will help to attain desirable compromises.

Selecting a Site

Certain factors which significantly influenced the selection of a farmstead site in the recent past have relatively less importance today. The location of the farmstead in relation to the fields, for instance, once was of prime consideration. Today large farms require considerable travel at best and most equipment is designed for efficient road speeds. While this aspect may be of secondary importance, some deliberation is needed particularly with regard to manure handling. Likewise, with modern snow removal equipment, distance from the road is of less concern. In some cases, farm practices such as the use of large irrigation systems, may influence the choice of a farmstead site. Nevertheless, there are several critical factors to consider in any farmstead development.

Drainage

This is the most important consideration in selecting a site for a farmstead. Adequate surface and subsurface drainage will ensure all-weather driveways and dry foundations and will prevent local flooding. Well-drained soil is essential for satisfactory operation of septic tank drainage fields and for the removal of feedlot runoff and other wastes. Fractured or limestone geologic formations may present as serious a problem as poorly drained soils, because pollution may be carried underground for long distances.

Manure Management

If the farmstead is to house a major livestock enterprise, one of the prime considerations is manure management. The ability to handle manure without serious problems is essential. If drainage and other factors are to be adequate for a livestock enterprise, all or most of the following questions should be answered affirmatively before a site can be considered satisfactory.

1. Can the site conform to all state and local environmental regulations? Additional regulations that may be issued in the future should also be anticipated.
2. Is the topography satisfactory for the required storage and drainage of manure and effluent produced at the farmstead?
3. Is there sufficient area to store and dispose of effluent from stables and yards without polluting a stream, river or lake?
4. Are prevailing wind directions, air drainage, and distances such that the farm home and neighboring homes will not be bothered by odors?
5. Can manure storage and treatment facilities be hidden from view by landscaping or topography?

Water

An adequate supply of good quality water is nearly as important as the possibility for good manure management. While water may reasonably be piped for some distance, it is advisable to ensure a satisfactory water source early in the site selection process.

Utilities and Services

These include telephone, electrical service, feed delivery, product pickup, snow removal, road maintenance, and the possibility for adequate access to drives and turn-around areas.

Soil

Soil, particularly around the house, should be well-drained and rich enough to provide landscaping, gardens, play areas, and a septic tank drainage field.

Orientation

Orientation on a gentle southerly slope may be desirable for air drainage and maximum sunshine. However, prevailing winds should also be taken into account and natural barriers used where possible. While much of the eastern half of the United States experiences westerly winds in the winter and the southern half of the country receives southerly winds in the summer, there is considerable local variation, and information should be obtained from the nearest weather station.

Expansion

Is there room for expansion? Any plans for farmstead development should anticipate growth in the enterprise and the layout should facilitate expansion of buildings and services. Increased production volume requires more than additional or larger buildings; expansion of all facilities from machinery inventories to utilities and drainage fields may become necessary. It is wise to look for twice as much area as that required initially and, in developing a layout, recognize the full impact of increasing production volume in the future.

Other considerations in selecting a site are the proximity of housing developments, other commercial or industrial enterprises, and airports.

Building Arrangement

The arrangement of facilities for maximum efficiency of operation should be the prime concern in farmstead planning. Proper arrangement increases efficiency by reducing walking distances to a minimum and providing adequate driveways and turnarounds. It can also minimize the negative and utilize the positive effects of climatic elements (sun, wind, rain, and snow) and will in turn be influenced by drainage, slope, and other topographic features. Finally, fire protection, safety, and security are all influenced by the farmstead layout.

When a site has been selected, a large-scale map should be drawn and all major details indicated. These should include contour lines, the direction of north, the direction of prevailing winds and the general slope, existing roads, and natural wind barriers and waterways. Using model cutouts drawn to the same scale as the map, buildings then can be arranged and rearranged until a satisfactory layout is designed.

Although not present on many farms, it is generally convenient to consider that a farmstead layout has four basic areas: (1) a house or operation center, (2) machinery storage/farm shop, (3) feed and grain storage and processing, and (4) the livestock areas. The operation center, which is likely to be the farm home with an office and perhaps a communications center, should be located first as a starting point and focal point. It should be situated at least 100 ft (30 m) from the road and located so that the flow of traffic to and from the farmstead may be observed from inside. It should also be oriented to make maximum use of sunlight and to take advantage of the best possible view.

The remaining buildings can be arranged in relation to the operating center. There are a number of factors to be considered, the priority of which will vary with the enterprise.

Slope

Buildings should be located on relatively high ground with surface drainage directed away from foundations. When constructing a building on an area that slopes, some cutting and filling will be required. Costs may be kept to a minimum if the structure is carefully positioned and planned at an elevation that allows the volume of cut soil to just equal the fill soil required.

Drainage

Assuming that drainage was found to be adequate in the original selection of the site, buildings should be arranged to take the greatest advantage of the natural conditions.

Prevailing Winds

Winds can blow from all directions, but the prevailing summer breezes and winter winds need to be considered in farmstead planning. As a general rule, winter winds sweep in from the north or northwest while summer breezes blow from the south, southwest, west, southeast or east. Local conditions may further alter wind patterns, and information on prevailing winds for a given locality should be obtained from the local weather station.

The arrangement of buildings shown in figure 20.1 should take advantage of the cooling effects of summer breezes and minimize the discomfort caused by cold winter winds. Open-front buildings faced away from the prevailing winter wind will usually benefit from the cooling summer currents.

Winds carry odors, dust, microorganisms, and noise, and prudent arrangement of buildings will use the wind to carry these away from the living center. Livestock yards and buildings should be located down wind from the farm home and farm neighbors. Buildings should be arranged to minimize the potential for the transport of airborne organisms being carried from larger animals to younger ones.

Several buildings lined up at right angles to the wind rather than parallel are less subject to the spread of fire. In areas with appreciable snowfall, care should be taken to arrange buildings and fences to reduce to a minimum the drifting of snow into yards, drives, and open-front buildings.

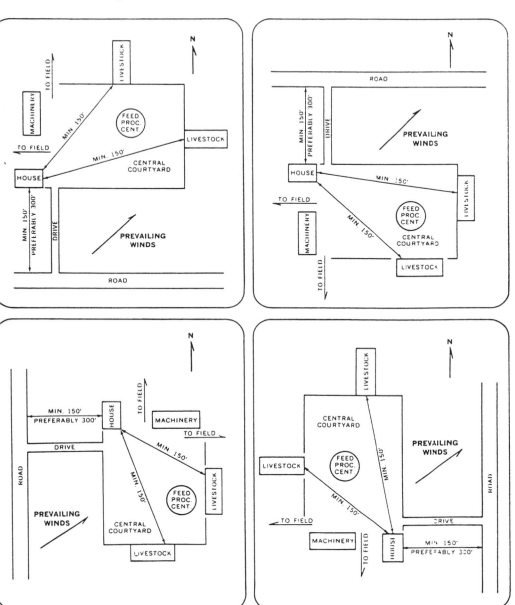

Figure 20.1. Farmstead and road relationships.

Solar

Proper design allows utilization of solar effects in the winter and minimizes solar heating in the summer. The general rule is to locate the long dimension east-west and

Table 20-1. Solar angle factors (SAF)

Date	Latitude (° North)			
	24	32	40	48
Winter*				
21 Dec.	1.5	2.0	3.0	5.4
21 Jan. and 21 Nov.	1.2	1.7	2.4	3.8
21 Feb. and 21 Oct.	0.4	1.0	1.4	1.9
21 Mar. and 21 Sep.	0.4	0.6	0.8	1.1
Summer*				
21 Apr. and 21 Aug.	0.2	0.4	0.5	0.7
21 May and 21 Jul.	0.1	0.2	0.4	0.5
21 Jun.	0.0	0.1	0.3	0.5

* SAF (Winter) = cos(9 A.M. azimuth)/tan(9 A.M. altitude).
  SAF (Summer) = 1/tan(noon altitude).

allowing maximum solar penetration on the south. Open-front buildings, stock yards, and solar-heated facilities should be arranged so that in winter they receive the full benefit of sunlight throughout the day. Tall buildings, such as tower silos, should be located so they do not cast a shadow on feedlots.

The late afternoon summer sun exposure is minimized by facing the smaller end wall toward the west. The direct radiation of the low angle winter sun on the longer south wall can enter through open walls, doors or windows along a long southern wall. A roof overhang will keep out the high angle summer sun.

The horizontal penetration of the sun can be calculated by multiplying the eave height by a solar factor. Solar factors are given in table 20-1. For example, a building at 45°N has an eave height of 12 ft (3.8 m). The winter (maximum) horizontal factor is 4.5, thus the solar penetration at noon is 12 ft × 4.5 = 54 ft (17 m) beyond the eave line. For this location, the summer vertical factor is 0.6, thus a 2 ft (0.6 m) overhang would provide 2 ft/0.6 = 3.3 ft (1.0 m) of vertical shading.

Distances

Labor efficiency is improved by reducing travel to a minimum. Buildings between which the most travel will occur should be located close together. If separate feed storage structures are used, locate them as close as possible to where the feed will be used. Arrange buildings in relation to drive and yard to allow easy maneuvering of large vehicles and equipment.

The distance between buildings usually is determined by a compromise involving efficiency, fire safety, odor control, disease control, and available space. Fifty to 100 ft (15 to 30 m) is usually considered a minimum safe distance between buildings or groups of buildings. This minimizes the risk of fire spread and permits access for fighting fire. It is advisable to check with an insurance company before starting construction.

Guidelines for distances between buildings can be useful. One method for designing a layout is to divide the map of the farmstead site into concentric zones 100 ft (30 m) wide with the farm home at the center. This facilitates using the recommend-

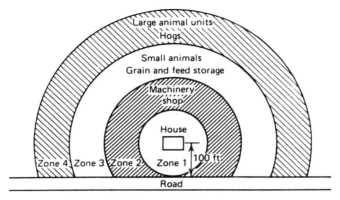

Figure 20.2. Farmstead planning zones.

ed distances to locate specific buildings (fig. 20.2). Zone 1 encompasses the family living area and should be protected from noise, odors, dust, and hazards to children. Machinery and supply storages and the farm shop may be located about 100 ft (30 m) from the house in zone 2 where they are easily accessible and, being relatively quiet and odor free, do not create a nuisance. Sheep and young animals that need supervision, but do not develop heavy odors and waste, can be located within 200 to 300 ft (60 to 90 m). In this same area, zone 3, dust-producing feed and grain storages are located a suitable distance from the house and at the same time close to livestock units they are to serve. Hog facilities and large animal units should be located 300 ft (90 m) or more from the center. This not only reduces the danger of odors reaching the home but also places the unit which is most likely to be expanded in an area where space will be available. These recommendations are for a large-scale, general enterprise; some adjustments would be made for specialized or smaller operations.

Drives, Turnarounds, and Parking Areas

Drives define the plan of circulation on the farm, directing traffic to service areas and parking. The layout of drives should allow space for vehicles to safely travel, maneuver, and park. It should also provide convenient parking for family and guests and, in cold regions, space for disposal of plowed snow.

Drives that will be carrying large equipment, and on which cars may meet, should be minimum of 16 ft (5 m) wide. In addition there should be several feet of clearance on either side to accommodate machinery overhang, drainage, and snow accumulation. The drive should be in view of the house or operations center and terminate in a turnaround with a minimum diameter of 110 ft (33 m). A small building, perhaps the fuel and lubricant storage, may be located in the center of the turnaround. Ordinarily, a U-shaped drive is not recommended. However, if the length is not great and the whole drive is visible from the house, it may be the most satisfactory design.

Branch drives may be as little as 8 ft (2.5 m) wide in straight areas, but should be wider on curves. A centerline radius of 25 ft (8 m) should be adequate for the curves.

Parking Areas

Parking areas should be provided near the home and, if in a different location, the farm office. If the house is designed with front and back doors about equidistant from the parking area, then one area should be enough. Otherwise two areas are desirable.

Yard Lighting

Automatically controlled yard lights are a desirable feature of the farmstead. They help prevent accidents by improving visibility, allowing a quick nighttime check of the farmstead from the house, in addition to discouraging theft and vandalism. Mercury vapor and metal halide lamps have greater efficiency and longer life than incandescent lamps. Fluorescent lamps are not generally satisfactory for outdoor use because they fail to start under cold or damp conditions.

Wind and Snow Control

Winter winds create a chill factor that causes a much greater stress on livestock than extreme cold alone. In addition, uncontrolled drifting snow can fill drives, yards, and even open-sided buildings. Also, extreme accumulations on roofs may cause structural failure.

In the north central states and Canadian plains provinces, tree windbreaks or shelter belt are commonly planted to reduce wind velocities and to control snow accumulations. From 6 to 12 rows are usually planted on the north and west sides of the farmstead. The shelter belts may be 125 to 150 ft (38 to 45 m) wide and offer wind protection for a distance equivalent to 10 times the tree height. Snow will accumulate for 50 to 100 ft (15 to 30 m) on the lee side of the shelter belt (figs. 20.3, 20.4).

In other areas, and also while the trees are still small, fences are an effective way of controlling wind and snow (fig. 20.5). Slat fences, either vertical or horizontal,

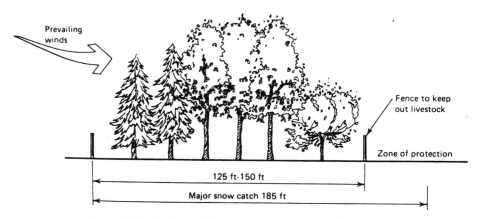

Figure 20.3. Shelter belt for protection from wind and snow.

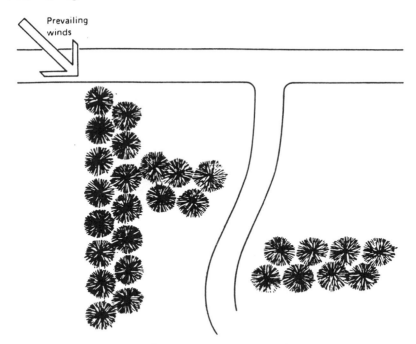

Figure 20.4. Drive opening in a windbreak.

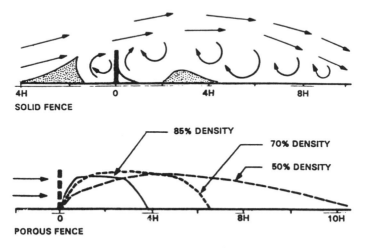

Figure 20.5. Snow drifting from solid and porous fences.

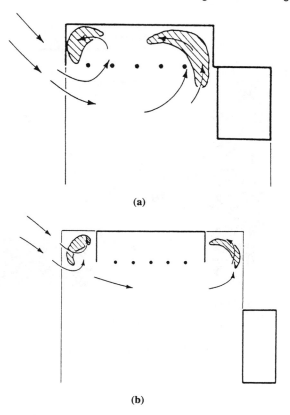

(a)

(b)

**Figure 20.6. Building and fence location rela-
tive to snow accumulation in open-sided
buildings.**

with a density of 75 to 85% will trap most of the snow in an area on the downwind
side equal in width to four to five times the fence height. A fence of this type also
offers good wind protection. Obviously these fences should be installed far enough
from buildings or yards to allow the snow to accumulate in an unused area. The yard
fence may be of solid construction, thus causing much of the remaining snow to accumulate on the windward side of the fence (outside the yard).

Fences should be attached to open-front buildings, somewhat back from the front
and the same distance from the building. This produces a swirl chamber that dumps
the snow outside rather than inside the building (fig. 20.6). Note also that buildings
too closely connected may cause air currents that dump snow inside open fronts.

Almost any open-front building with its back to the wind, regardless of roof shape,
is likely to have some snow accumulation just inside the open front. It has been found
that a 6 to 8 in. (150 to 200 mm) slot at the rear eaves will prevent much of this.

Finally, do not forget the aesthetics of the total farmstead layout. Is the arrangement attractive? Is the home oriented to take advantage of natural views or landscaped areas? Aesthetics certainly can influence pride of ownership and the quality of life even though farm income is not increased.

The following check list may help to avoid the omission of factors that should be considered in choosing a site and planning a farmstead:

Farmstead Planning Checklist

General	Home	Layout
Zoning law clearance	View	Spacing for fire safety
Title with no encumbrance	Near driveway	& freedom from odors
Environmental clearance	Good water supply	Silos and feed storage
Good drainage	Septic tank & drainage field	located to allow for barn
Good water supply	Garden	expansion
Space adequate for initial	Play area	Driveway width
and expansion needs	Garage	& location
Slope of land	Wind protection	Turnaround diameter
Cutting and filling required	Parking space	Farm pond possibilities
Prevailing wind		Wind and snow control
Soil quality		Full use of sunshine
Electricity		
Telephone		
School bus		
Road maintenance		
Central to crop land		

Problems

20.1. Prepare a map of an existing farmstead showing all details required to make an analysis of the layout. Using the checklist in the chapter, note the desirable features and those that could be improved.

20.2. With a separate map or overlay, show how housing facilities could be expanded and how other changes might be made in the farmstead layout to improve the efficiency and safety of the farmstead or to reduce the pollution potential.

20.3. Assuming that topography is not a limitation, lay out a new farmstead for a fruit farm that will sell at retail a part of the production at the storage. Assume that the farmstead will be located west of the highway and that the home and other supporting structures, as well as a storage and sales room, are to be constructed.

21 Shops and Non-product Storage

MACHINERY SHEDS

The reliability of farm machines contributes to the timely completion of production operations. A complex machine that has been stored under cover and given a complete off-season checkup is much more likely to be ready to go when soil and weather conditions are optimum.

Machinery sheds do not come free. They represent an annual cost that must be justified. Economists and engineers alike have surveyed and analyzed the value of housing farm machinery with varying results. Often the machines checked were simple, heavy pieces such as plows and harrows that suffer only from a bit of rust when left outdoors. The results of such a survey would be quite different with complex machines such as balers, combines, and tractors. One survey indicated that downtime for non-housed machinery was nearly twice (13.1% vs. 6.6%) as high as for housed machinery.

When precision machines are protected from the weather, several economic benefits accrue. The reduction in trade-in value attributed to storage of machinery is given in table 21-1. Not only are repair costs and depreciation likely to be lower, but that intangible advantage of timeliness also has a monetary value. It is estimated, for example, that first cutting hay decreases in value almost 3%/day after it reaches its peak quality. Late planting or harvesting reduces profits with most crops. It appears that when all factors are included, an investment in adequate machinery storage is justified.

The purpose of machinery storage is to offer protection from weather, theft, and vandalism, and to allow easy maintenance and adjustment of machines. To achieve these objectives, the design for a machinery storage should provide shelter from wind,

Table 21-1. Average percent difference in trade-in value
between housed and non-housed machinery

Tractors	3.3 %/yr
Harvesting machinery	4.7 %/yr
Planter & drills	4.4 %/yr
Tillage machinery	2.0 %/yr

rain, and snow, sufficient space to maneuver and park individual pieces of equipment without undue shifting of other machines, and a firm, dry floor, preferably concrete, that facilitates moving machinery and prevents moisture damage. Doors should be large enough to permit safe and easy transfer of machines into and out of the storage and they should have adequate locks. A good lighting system is necessary for maintenance and repair operations.

Site Selection

Ordinarily, the machinery storage and shop produce negligible pollution or nuisance and can be located relatively close to the farm home. As long as there is sufficient distance for fire safety, the proximity offers both convenience and additional protection from theft and vandalism. The site should offer good drainage and sufficient room for safe and easy maneuvering of large machines. Any service building should be located so that it adds to the attractive appearance of the farmstead. If possible, the machinery storage building should be oriented so that the front side faces away from the road and home to keep the equipment out of view. A blind of shrubbery will also improve the appearance.

Type and Shape of Building

There are three types of building layouts suitable for machinery storage. They vary in convenience, cost, and degree of protection (fig. 21.1).

Narrow, Open-side Shed

Machines are backed in from one side. The side may be left open or protected with a series of rolling doors along part or all of the length of the building. Construction is simple and the least expensive. Inasmuch as machines are seldom moved after they are parked by the tractor, a gravel floor is probably more practical in this type of storage than in others. The building needs to be just high enough to accommodate the highest machine. It is important to face this building to minimize snow drifting.

Wide, Open-side Shed

This design permits parking equipment in two rows. Machines are backed in as with the narrow shed to form one row. Additional space for a second row is reached through a wide door located in the back half of the end wall. Floor, doors, height, and orientation would be similar to the narrow version.

Wide, Enclosed Shed

This type might be classified as a drive-through shed. Although it is the most expensive, it offers the most protection. It should be 50 to 60 ft (15 to 20 m) wide to allow adequate room to maneuver a large machine. An extra door to allow entry without turning simplifies storing and will usually save space. Doors and the central alley should be up to 26 ft (8 m) wide and 14 to 16 ft (4.4 to 5 m) high. Probably the greatest advantage of this type of building is the opportunity for easy access for temporary storage. Loaded trucks and wagons can be put under cover quickly and easily. The building is also available for short-term storage of seed, fertilizer or newly harvested

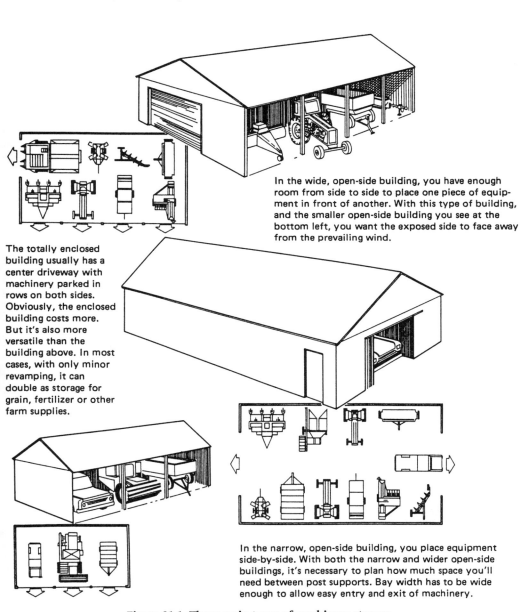

In the wide, open-side building, you have enough room from side to side to place one piece of equipment in front of another. With this type of building, and the smaller open-side building you see at the bottom left, you want the exposed side to face away from the prevailing wind.

The totally enclosed building usually has a center driveway with machinery parked in rows on both sides. Obviously, the enclosed building costs more. But it's also more versatile than the building above. In most cases, with only minor revamping, it can double as storage for grain, fertilizer or other farm supplies.

In the narrow, open-side building, you place equipment side-by-side. With both the narrow and wider open-side buildings, it's necessary to plan how much space you'll need between post supports. Bay width has to be wide enough to allow easy entry and exit of machinery.

Figure 21.1. Three main types of machinery storage.

grain, even at the expense of pushing machines very close together or moving some outside temporarily.

Materials of Construction

Ordinarily, temperature and air moisture conditions are not a problem in a machinery storage. This broadens the choice of building materials. Attractive appearance, durability, and low maintenance are the main prerequisites. With the drive-through layout, clear span construction is particularly important. Adequate overhead clearance for large machinery is an important feature (fig. 21.2). Doorways must be large enough for both the widest and the highest machines (fig. 21.3).

Lightweight construction such as pole and truss or rigid metal frame buildings are suitable. Almost any siding material may be used, but metal is attractive and offers some resistance to the spread of fire (fig. 21.2).

Regardless of the type of building, there are some important construction details that are common to all. Since there is no thermal protection over the ground either inside or outside the shed, to avoid frost damage, foundations or piers need to be deeper than for most other buildings on the farm. A deep uniform-size gravel base under a concrete floor will help prevent frost damage. While lightweight construction is suitable, care must be taken to provide adequate bracing and anchoring. A 5 to 6 in. (125 to 150 mm) concrete floor is highly desirable, but a well drained gravel floor is adequate and will save on investment.

Space Requirements

Every farm is unique in regard to space requirements, and thus each requires individual planning. A general guideline for total machinery storage space required may be

Figure 21.2. Metal machinery shed interior.

Figure 21.3. Metal machinery shed.

determined from figure 21.4. A more accurate estimate of space needed requires preparing a drawing using table 21-2. Using a scale of 1/4 in./ft (20 mm/m), rectangular cardboard cutouts may be made for all the machines present on the farm or anticipated in the near future. Then, using 1/4 in. (10 mm) graph paper as a background, the cutouts may be arranged to show how the machines might fit into a storage building.

It is important to keep in mind that some implements or components cannot be moved easily. For example, the extra harvesting heads on a forage harvester or combine are usually stored in the location where they are dropped off the machine. Plows, disks, and most mounted equipment are not easily moved and therefore space must be planned so that shifting is unnecessary. Finally, after all items are fitted into place, it is wise to add about 15% more space for equipment clearance and forgotten items. In addition, planning for future expansion is a good policy.

FARM SHOPS

A well-equipped maintenance shop is an essential service building for an efficiently operated agricultural enterprise. It increases the efficiency of the farm operation in several ways:

1. Fast and effective repairs are often possible in a short time, thereby avoiding expensive, prolonged breakdowns while waiting for a mechanic or parts.
2. Routine repairs and preventive maintenance of both equipment and buildings are possible during the off season or inclement weather. The year-round labor crew is kept busy, and expensive repairs by machinery dealers and contractors are reduced.
3. It is possible to build or modify some of the equipment to be used on the farm.

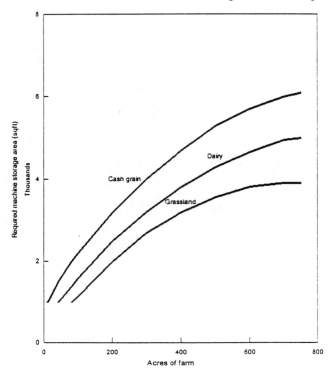

Figure 21.4. Machine storage area related to farm size.

A well-planned and equipped shop may encourage preventive maintenance of equipment resulting in extended useful life and reduced chances for costly failure. The shop may be the farm headquarters for management, employees, and visitors. In this case a heated office, washroom, and space for farm records, service manuals, and equipment catalogs will be needed. An adequately sized, well-equipped farm shop can pay for itself over a period of time. However, a factor limiting the effectiveness of a shop should not be overlooked. If no one on the farm has the skill or the inclination to use the shop, it becomes a useless expense, or in some circumstances it may actually contribute to additional expense due to poorly finished work or to increased accidents due to careless procedures. The size of the shop and the equipment it houses should certainly be related to the skill and interest of the farm crew.

Site Selection

The farm shop is usually located in the hub of the farmstead traffic pattern. The site should be adequately drained to prevent water from accumulating in or around the shop. A distance of 150 ft (45 m) between the shop and other major structures provides room to maneuver and park large machinery nearby, reduces fire hazard, and allows for expansion.

Table 21-2. Dimensions of machinery for storage planning

Machine	Length (ft)	Width (ft)	Length (m)	Width (m)
Tractors				
25-40 hp	12	6	3.6	1.8
40-70 hp	14	7	4.3	2.1
70-100 hp	15	8	4.6	2.4
over 100 hp	15	11	4.6	3.4
4-wheel drive:				
160 hp	21	8	6.4	2.4
> 200 hp	24	11	7.3	3.4
Plows				
2 bottom	6	4	1.8	1.2
4 bottom	12	6	3.6	1.8
6 bottom	16	9	4.9	2.7
Tandem disk				
7 ft	10	7	3.0	2.1
10 ft	11	10	3.4	3.0
14 ft	12	14	3.6	4.3
Grain drill				
12 × 6	7	8	2.1	2.4
23 × 6	9	16	2.7	4.9
Corn planter				
4 row	6	12	1.8	3.6
6 row	8	16	2.4	2.7
8 row	8	22	2.4	6.7
12 row	8	34	2.4	10.4
Sprayer	10	7	3.0	2.4
Mower conditioner	12	13	3.6	4.0
Mower trailer type	6	5	1.8	1.5
Rake	10	12	3.0	3.6
Self-propelled windrower				
7 ft bar	10	10	3.0	3.0
12 ft bar	11	17	3.4	5.2
16 ft bar	12	20	3.6	6.1
Baler				
Conventional	10	15	3.0	4.6
Large round	9	15	2.7	4.6
Large square	9	23	2.7	7.0
Forage harvest	9	9	2.7	2.7
Forage blower	10	5	3.0	1.5
Combine				
Pulled, 8 ft	22	12	6.7	3.7
Self propelled, 14 ft	24	16	7.3	4.9
Extr header, 4 row	8	12	2.4	3.7
Cotton picker	20	10	6.1	3.0
Wagon	20	9	6.1	2.7
Manure spreader	20	8	6.1	2.4
Manure loader	8	4	2.4	1.2
Pickup truck	20	8	6.1	2.4

Building Requirements

Lightweight, clear span construction is satisfactory unless a hoist is to be supported from the building frame. In that case, the frame must be designed for the expected loads. Rigid frames, post-frames and trusses or standard stud construction are all feasible. Metal siding is attractive, durable, and reasonable in cost. Wood, plywood, and punched hardboard interiors are convenient for developing wall storage areas. Some insulation is warranted to keep the building comfortable in winter and fire resistant materials such as gypsum board or metal should be considered for the ceiling.

Space Requirements

The size of the shop will be determined by the amount of shop equipment, particularly free-standing power tools, and the size of the largest farm machine that will be serviced in the shop. A large, self-propelled combine, cotton picker or very wide machine such as a six-row corn planter may be excluded from this rule since they may be worked on outside or in the machinery shed. Although templates may be used to arrange and plan a shop layout, it may still be difficult to decide on the necessary work space around the shop equipment. The space may be effectively planned by first deciding on the size of an open service area in which to park a machine to be repaired, and then arranging the shop equipment, storage facilities, and heating system around that area. In most cases, a minimum of 8 ft (2.5 m) should be allowed on one side and 5 ft (1.5 m) on the other. On farms with relatively small field equipment, a total of 24 ft (7.2 m) may be adequate, while on farms with large equipment, 35 to 40 ft (10 to 12 m) will be required. The minimum length will usually be 30 to 36 ft (9 to 11 m).

The layout will depend on personal preference and the type of work that is to be emphasized. The general areas in a shop are the service area, repair/overhaul area, bench area, welding area, and storage area (fig. 21.5). There are a number of features that are recommended for all shops:

1. A smooth concrete floor, 4 in. (100 mm) thick in most areas, but 6 in. (150 mm) thick in the service area where large machines will stand. A portion of the open floor area should be installed with great care to have it flat and level. This can be useful in constructing or setting up projects. On the other hand, sloping the service area of the floor to a drain provides a place to wash down machinery and prevents the water from draining into the work or storage area.

2. A large concrete ramp just outside the main entrance. This can be a very convenient place to work in mild weather. Natural lighting is better than artificial light.

3. An easily opened door that is wide enough to accommodate large equipment. Fourteen feet (4.4 m) × 12 ft (3.7 m) high is minimal. Overhead or rolling doors are preferable to hinged doors. The overhead type may be tighter and more convenient, but it may interfere with lights in the area where it opens. Large, mechanized bifold doors have become very popu-

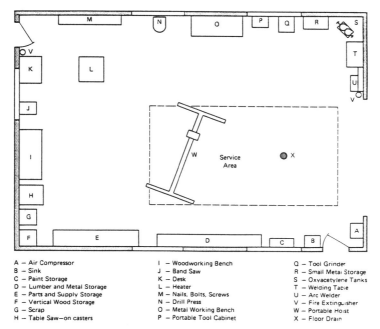

A — Air Compressor	I — Woodworking Bench	Q — Tool Grinder
B — Sink	J — Band Saw	R — Small Metal Storage
C — Paint Storage	K — Desk	S — Oxyacetylene Tanks
D — Lumber and Metal Storage	L — Heater	T — Welding Table
E — Parts and Supply Storage	M — Nails, Bolts, Screws	U — Arc Welder
F — Vertical Wood Storage	N — Drill Press	V — Fire Extinguisher
G — Scrap	O — Metal Working Bench	W — Portable Hoist
H — Table Saw—on casters	P — Portable Tool Cabinet	X — Floor Drain

Figure 21.5. A farm shop layout.

tighter and more convenient, but it may interfere with lights in the area where it opens. Large, mechanized bifold doors have become very popular and practical. A small door either in or adjacent to the large door is convenient. A second small door on the opposite side of the shop is an important safety factor in the event of a flash fire.

4. Safety equipment, such as that required by OSHA, should be provided even if not a legal requirement. Dry-powder fire extinguishers rated for B and C or A, B, and C fires should be located near the doorways and pails of dry sand should be placed strategically within the shop. All machines should be equipped with guards, and safety goggles should be located at each machine where required. A first aid kit should be readily available.

5. Adequate means for lifting machines. Both hoists and jacks are convenient and may be used together on some jobs. Machine stands and wood blocking are an absolute necessity for use with any lifting equipment. A rolling A-frame hoist is convenient and much less expensive than constructing the roof framing strong enough to support heavy loads.

6. A telephone or intercom system for convenience and safety.

7. A water supply and sink for convenience and safety.

8. A wall fan for general ventilation and a flex tube to remove the exhaust fumes from an operating engine through a wall port. A fan and duct system may be used to remove engine exhaust. The fan should be sized based on the engine size as follows:

$$CFM = \frac{CID \times RPM}{3,230} \qquad (21.1)$$

where

CID = engine displacement (in.^{3})

RPM = engine speed

9. A large-capacity heating system that is capable of raising the temperature to a comfortable level in a short time. The type of system is not important. However, ceiling-mounted heaters require no floor space and an automatic system that will keep the temperature above freezing is a protection for some supplies and the water system. Radiant heat allows heating only equipment and workers. The air temperature is maintained at a low level; therefore conductive heat loss is low. Floor heating provides comfort and can take advantage of off-peak electric rates.

10. Ample artificial lighting. Although recommendations for window area range up to 20% of the floor area, artificial light is still required since shop work is often done on cloudy days or in the evening. Limiting the window area to 5% of the floor area while emphasizing a high level of artificial light is most practical. General lighting should provide 20 ft candles at floor level. This requires a minimum of 1/2 W fluorescent or 2 W incandescent/ft^2 (20 W/m^2) in a typical shop. For example, 300 W lamps spaced 10 to 12 ft (3 to 3.5 m) in each direction will provide good lighting. For the type of general lighting required in a shop, light-colored wall and ceiling surfaces are more important than reflectors. Either fluorescent or incandescent lamps should be suspended above the front edge of the work bench and at each of the power tools. Portable lights on standards that can be used in hard-to-reach areas are also a requirement.

11. A minimum of a 200 A electrical service and numerous electrical outlets for both 120 and 240 V. The service entrance should have reserve capacity for future expansion. Convenience outlets should be located:
    • uniformly under the front edge of work benches
    • at every motor-driven tool
    • at 10 ft intervals around the rest of the shop perimeter
    Ground fault interrupters (GFIs) are recommended for all 20 A convenience outlets and are required for outside receptacles.

12. Location of the welder and compressed air supply near the main entrance. This is convenient for use both outside on the ramp as well as inside the

shop. A 1,000 cfm exhaust fan is recommended in the welding area. Ventilation and fire safety are improved by using the welder near the open door.

13.   Careful placement of shop equipment so that large or long pieces of material may be easily worked. Some power tools, a table saw, for example, may be mounted on casters for storage next to the wall but for use in the middle of the room.

14.   Well-organized storage space for materials, supplies, parts, and manuals.

PESTICIDE STORAGE

A properly designed pesticide storage area is important for the safety of the user and the environment. It is also required to meet federal and state regulations. Specific storage requirements for each pesticide are given on the Material Data Sheet (MSDA) and on the pesticide label.

Light and Temperature

Exposure to sunlight may cause breakdown reducing the effectiveness of the pesticide. Therefore, pesticide containers (especially glass and aerosols) should never be placed in front of windows.

High temperatures can cause liquid pesticides to expand causing increased pressure within the container. Under these conditions an explosion may occur or the pesticide may leak from the container. Freezing temperatures may cause some pesticides to separate or break down chemically and containers may crack.

Do not store pesticides at temperatures above 90°F (32°C). Follow label directions for further requirements.

Humidity

Excess moisture may cause caking or degradation of dry formulations making them useless. It also may cause metal containers to rust and develop leaks, and it may reduce the strength of paper bags causing them to rupture.

Contamination

Within the storage the different groups of pesticides (herbicide, insecticide, fungicide, rodenticide, etc.) should be kept separate to prevent cross-contamination. Special precautions must be taken when storing herbicides (weed killers), especially those containers that have been opened and reclosed. The phenoxy herbicides, like 2,4-D are among the most volatile and their fumes can temporarily contaminate soils, fertilizers, flats, pots, etc., thus injuring plants. Volatile fumes can build up in a closed area; therefore ventilation is necessary. Never store food, feed or fertilizer in the pesticide storage area as it may become contaminated.

Metal shelves are advisable when storing pesticides because they are much easier to decontaminate than wooden shelves. Leak proof plastic trays placed on shelves will contain spillage. Shelves, pallets, and drums should be placed along the walls of the shed, allowing the aisle to be kept clear.

Safety Requirements

Storage doors and windows should be kept locked at all times. Weatherproof signs, stating "Danger—Pesticides—Keep Out!" or a similar warning should be posted on each door of the facility and over all windows. In some cases, it may be advisable to post the warning signs in more than one language.

Fire Safety

Whenever large quantities of pesticides are stored, fire detection sensors and fire fighting equipment must be provided. A fire extinguisher Type ABC should be located near the door. In addition "No Smoking" signs are required. A floor plan showing the location and specific pesticides stored should be filed with the local fire department.

Storage of Personal Protective Equipment

Gloves, aprons, and respirators should be stored nearby but not inside the pesticide storage area. A source of clean water should also be provided in this area for clean-up.

FENCING

Well-built and well-maintained fences help to protect people from dangerous animals, crops from roaming animals, and animals from predators. Most states have laws relating to line fences dividing two properties as well as fences along highways and railroads. Good line fences help to make good neighbors by preventing disputes over crop damage. Fences may also be attractive additions to the farm home, but this discussion will be limited to fences related to the farm business.

Types of Fences

There may be no agricultural structure in the world with greater variety of design than the fence. Diversity of construction material as well as design seems limitless—from the prickly aloe hedge that surrounds the Zulu kraal in Africa and the beautiful woven sapling fences of eastern Europe, to the stone walled pastures of Britain and the endless wire fences on New Zealand sheep stations—from the white board fences in Kentucky horse country to the electric fences on American dairy farms. A comprehensive study of fencing materials and design used throughout the world would be a fascinating study for the global traveler.

North America has had its own array of traditional fences, but developments in fencing have kept pace with other developments in modern agriculture. The picturesque rail fence and stone walls that surrounded the farms of colonial America have all but disappeared from the scene except for some use in landscaping home grounds. The development of a wide variety of fencing materials and construction methods now makes fencing available to meet the specific needs of all classes of livestock and the special requirements dictated by topography.

Woven Wire Fencing

Figure 21.6 illustrates the five most common sizes of woven wire fencing: 1155, 1047, 939, 832, and 726. The last two digits indicate the height in inches while the

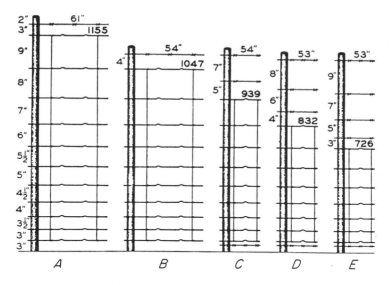

Figure 21.6. Standard types of woven wire fencing.

first one or two indicate the number of horizontal wires. For example, 1047 has 10 wires and is 47 in. (1.2 m) high. The stay or vertical wires are 12 in. (305 mm) on center for the 1155 and 1047 and 6 in. (152 mm) on center for the others.

Woven wire fences are used for sheep and hogs and are often recommended for cattle. If used for horses, a board is frequently used along the top to protect the fence and to give better visibility.

Barbed wire fencing

Over the years barbed wire has been made in so many different styles that today it has become a collector's item. However, most barbed wire is now made from two strands of no. 12 gauge wire twisted together with barbs made of no. 14 wire. Four-point barbs are spaced 5 in. (125 mm) on center and two-point barbs 4 in. (100 mm) on center.

Barbed wire is often used as bottom and top wires in combination with woven wire fencing. The barbed wires discourage the animals from trying to push under the fence or from riding the fence down. Multiple strands of barbed wire may also be used alone as a fence. This is probably most satisfactory as a cattle fence.

Stranded-cable fencing

Zinc or aluminum coated, 3/8 in. (9.5 mm), 1 × 7 strand steel cable is used for constructing cattle yard fences. It allows maximum air movement across the yard.

Panel Fencing

Panel fencing is similar to woven wire fencing, but the panels are made from heavier material, they are rigid and do not require stretching. The paneling comes in 16 ft

(4.9 m) lengths and is suitable for lot fencing for any type of livestock. Panels are installed on posts spaced 8 ft (2.44 m) or 51/3 ft (1.63 m) on center with staples up to 21/2 in. (64 mm) long depending on the post species.

Board Fences

Board fences are popular for horse paddocks and for working yards where animals are likely to be crowded into the fence. They usually prove to be too expensive for other areas.

Four-inch (100 mm) top posts, set 3 ft (1 m) deep in the ground, are spaced 6 ft (2 m) apart in crowded areas and 8 ft (2.4 m) apart in larger areas. Two by six inch or 2×8 in. (38×140 or 30×184 mm) boards are nailed to the posts on the paddock side so that the stock will not loosen them. Two 16d spikes at each board-to-post contact is adequate.

Electric Fencing

Electric fences are usually used for controlling cattle. They may also be used for controlling pasture rotation for horses and other stock but with less dependability. Sheep in particular need to be trained to respect the fence. Electric fences are most useful for temporary application such as managing pasture rotation, protecting hay stacks, and forming temporary lanes. They may also be used as the top wire on woven wire fence to keep animals from riding the fence down, or as a single wire, mounted on standoffs, to keep animals from crowding a fence.

Fence Posts

Most posts are made of wood or steel, although fiberglass posts are available and concrete posts are used on a limited basis. The choice of post depends on the type of fencing used, initial cost, durability, and ease of maintenance.

Steel posts. Steel posts are easy to handle, easily driven into most soils, fireproof, and durable. They also protect stock by grounding the fence against lightning. Lightweight, steel posts are easily bent, especially under crowded conditions. Ordinarily they cost more than pressure-preservative-treated (PPT) wood posts. However, most steel posts have at least a 25-year life expectancy.

Wood posts. Wood posts are available in lengths of 51/2 to 8 ft (1.7 to 2.8 m) and in diameters of 21/2 in. (64 mm) and more. Minimum top diameters are 21/2 in. (64 mm) for line posts and 5 in. (125 mm) for corner or gate posts. The larger the top diameter, the stronger the post, and the more durable the fence.

Except for a few selected species, wood posts that are untreated have such a short life that they are satisfactory only for temporary fences. Posts from black locust, Osage orange or red cedar may last as long as 15 years. The outer sapwood will deteriorate more rapidly than the heartwood. Other species should be treated to prevent decay and commercial pressure treatment is by far the most satisfactory. Preservative-treated posts are recommended in critical areas.

However, if posts are produced on the farm, home treatment can increase the life of decay prone species appreciably. Although there are a number of preservative materials and methods of introducing them to the posts, pentachlorophenol offers the best combination of effectiveness, reasonable cost, and ease of use. Complete directions for the process should be obtained before the trees are cut, and they must be followed carefully throughout. Briefly, the steps include cutting at the right season, completely removing the bark, drying, calculating the amount of preservative required for one batch, soaking the posts until that amount (but no more) has been absorbed, draining, and drying before using.

Fiberglass posts. Fiberglass-reinforced plastic posts have been designed for use with electric or barbed wire fencing. Lightweight fiberglass posts have the strength of steel. They bend under strain but return to their original position. They do not rust or rot, and they make insulators unnecessary when used with electric fencing.

Concrete posts. Concrete posts are durable and, due to their large diameter, make good gate or corner posts. They are also suitable for yard posts or they can be cast to be used with rails. They are usually cast 6 in. (150 mm) square and are reinforced with four, no. 3 bars (3/8 in. or 10 mm), one in each corner.

Woven Wire Fence Construction

1. Lay out the fence by first locating corners, ends, and gate openings.

2. Set corner and end posts and construct the necessary bracing as shown in figure 21.7. A single anchor and brace assembly is satisfactory for fences up to 160 ft (50 m), but double bracing is recommended for lengths of 160 to 660 ft (50 to 200 m). Intermediate braced-line posts are needed for lengths over 660 ft.

3. For contour fencing, install braced-line posts at 330 ft (100 m) intervals but only in straight sections. On rolling land it is recommended that braced-line posts be installed at the crest and foot of each hill.

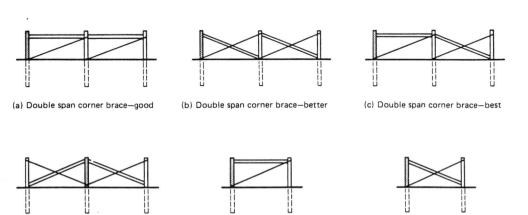

(a) Double span corner brace—good   (b) Double span corner brace—better   (c) Double span corner brace—best

(d) Line post brace   (e) Single span corner brace   (f) Single span corner brace

Figure 21.7. Bracing methods for fencing.

4. Wood anchor posts may be driven or set in dug holes depending on available equipment and soil characteristics. In either case, they should be set at least 3 ft (1 m) deep as they are subject to lifting as well as tipping forces. Steel anchor posts and braces are set in concrete in order to get enough bearing surface. The concrete should extend below the frostline.

5. Once the corner and end posts are in place, stretch a cord or a strand of barbed wire between them to establish a straight line as a guide for setting the line posts. A barbed wire is often used between the bottom of the woven wire fence and the ground. When this is the case, use the barbed wire for the guide line. If the fence is built on the contour, the line will need to be staked out first.

6. When the fenceline is established, locate and install the braced-line posts at 40-rod (200 m) intervals. Woven wire fencing is sold in 20-rod (100 m) rolls, so that on level land, two lengths will just reach the braced posts. Each 40-rod (200 m) section is stretched and installed separately and each fence end wrapped around the center post. A continuous fence, simply spliced together and stapled to the post, is not as strong and will pull loose if damaged.

7. Line posts have traditionally been spaced one rod (5 m) apart. However, there is no reason why cattle fences on flat land should not have a greater post spacing, while in heavy snow areas, a 13 ft (4 m) spacing will be more resistant to damage. Fences for hog lots will also require a closer post spacing to prevent the hogs from rooting under the fence. Post spacing for fences built on the contour may be determined by limiting the offset of any post located between two alternate posts to 8 in. (200 mm).

8. Woven wire fencing has tension crimping incorporated between the stay wires. This allows the fence to "give and take" with seasonal temperature changes. In tensioning a fence, use a hand puller—not a tractor—and pull until the crimp height is reduced by 1/4 to 1/2.

9. Figure 21.8 illustrates the proper procedure for driving staples. Use 1 in. (25 mm) staples for very hard woods, 11/2 to 13/4 (38 to 44 mm) for most others.

10. The use of a metal post every 100 to 150 ft (30 to 45 m) will reduce the danger of lightning to stock and people.

Barbed Wire Fence Construction

1. Corner, end, and line posts are located and spaced as with a woven wire fence.

2. Use a reel support so that the wire may be unrolled. Never pull the wire off a stationary roll. Barbed wire should be stretched with hand pullers and stapled.

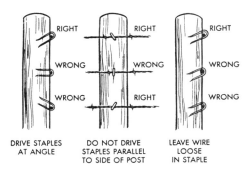

RIGHT   RIGHT   RIGHT

WRONG   WRONG   WRONG

WRONG   RIGHT   WRONG

DRIVE STAPLES   DO NOT DRIVE   LEAVE WIRE
AT ANGLE   STAPLES PARALLEL   LOOSE
TO SIDE OF POST   IN STAPLE

Figure 21.8. Use of fence staples.

3. For cow calf fences, four strands of barbed wire spaced 10 in. (250 mm) apart and 16 in. (400 mm) from the ground are adequate. For feeder cattle, the use of five strands started 12 in. (300 mm) from the ground is better. Barbed wire alone is not recommended for other stock.

Electric Fence Installation

1. Space lightweight posts as required to maintain clearance from the ground. Weeds, grass, and shrubbery must be cut to prevent grounding of the fence wire. Setting the posts far apart permits easier mowing under the fence.
2. Insulators prevent grounding of the fence and rendering it ineffective. Choose insulators to match the type of posts used (unnecessary with fiberglass posts). Gate wire should be charged through the hook so that the gate is not charged when it is open.
3. Only Underwriters' Laboratories (UL) approved controllers should be used. Solar powered or 120 V power chargers are recommended for dependability and reduced costs. The ground rod will need to be driven 6 to 8 ft (2 to 2.5 m) deep in dry soil conditions.
4. For cattle, two wires spaced 20 in. (500 mm) apart and 16 in. (400 mm) above the ground are recommended. For swine, one wire at 6 to 8 in. (150 to 200 mm) is effective. For sheep, two barbed wires spaced 10 in. (150 mm) apart and 8 in. (200 mm) above the ground are usually satisfactory, but sheep should be trained to respect the fence immediately after shearing.

Specifications

The American Society of Agricultural Engineers has established a recommendation, ASAE EP250.2, for fence construction (ASAE, 1995). The quality of materials is largely based on ASTM tests, while construction details are specified by ASAE.

These recommendations are useful in writing specifications for fences to be installed on contract.

Problems

21.1.   Make recommendations for a general type (closed or open) and size of machinery storage building for the following farm machines:

55 hp tractor	mower
120 hp tractor	forage harvester
6 bottom plow	forage blower
26 harrow	two wagons
12 row planter	manure spreader
sprayer	front-end loader

21.2   Discuss your reasons for the type of building recommended in problem 1. Also make recommendations for a type of frame and for materials to be used for the roof and sidewalls.

22 Hay, Grain, and Silage Storage

HAY

Most hay is handled in conventional rectangular bales of 25 to 75 lb (12 to 35 kg), large round bales of 800 to 2,000 lb (400 to 900 kg) or stacks of 1/2 ton or more. The use of elevators and conveyors allows the small bales to be stored in a variety of buildings, some of which may be many years old. When bales are stored in a random manner they can exert considerable lateral force against a barn wall, a fact that must be recognized when using an old barn or designing and building a new storage.

Although "big package" systems were designed for use in areas where light rainfall makes outside storage feasible, they have also become popular in high rainfall areas because of the improved labor efficiency. While some farmers tolerate the weather loss, which may exceed 20%, others find covered storages worthwhile. Balers are now available that apply a plastic wrap to the round bales, thus making outdoor storage much more feasible.

Ground-level drive-through structures not only allow handling equipment to place the packages directly into storage, but they offer protection at low cost. Pole or post-frame structures with open sides permit the equipment to be driven through the building for unloading and later for loading out.

An open building of this type is subject to strong lifting forces from wind. Special attention must be paid to fastening trusses to posts and to anchoring the poles securely in the ground. On well-drained sites, a slightly raised gravel floor may be satisfactory. If a concrete floor is necessary, it should slope to the sides to avoid any accumulation of water under the hay. A slope of 1:100 from the center should be adequate without affecting the stability of the hay piles.

Feeding out stacks of big bales should be under the controlled conditions of feed racks or fences. Without them, losses can be very high.

GRAIN

Grain may be grown on the farm and stored for use in livestock production, or it may be grown primarily for market and stored until it is sold. In either case, the construction of an adequate, efficient grain storage system requires a large investment and should not be undertaken without thorough planning.

One of the most important aspects of farm mechanization is materials handling. As the size of operation increases, the significance of materials handling also increases. The key to successful mechanization is the planning and organization of a materials "flow" pattern as it relates to machinery and equipment and to future expansion. Grain may be handled with a portable elevator and stored in one bin at the onset, but that one bin should be so located that additional bins can be constructed as needed where all of them can be served from a central elevating system.

Although there are several basic layout schemes for designing grain storage facilities and a number of types of handling equipment from which to choose, there are two principles of paramount importance that must be applied if the system is to operate efficiently and profitably:

1. It should always be possible to return the grain to the starting point for redistribution in a closed-loop system.
2. The system should be expandable without losing the closed-loop characteristic and with a minimum of additional equipment.

Centralization is a concept often recommended. A centralized layout meets the needs of both large and small operators and has the potential for expansion with a minimum of duplication of equipment. An arrangement enabling grain to be received, distributed, and returned to a central point keeps labor at a minimum. Equipment need not be moved and grain is easily transported to and from a single receiving and shipping point. However, a centralized layout requires a large initial investment. Although portable equipment may satisfactorily serve in several locations, as labor becomes increasingly costly, the centralized handling system becomes more economically feasible.

System Components

Grain is commonly moved through several component elements of a system linked together as a unit. It is essential that these elements be compatible, especially in capacity, or else surge bins must be added to take care of the uneven flow. In a continuous flow system, the lowest capacity unit controls the entire flow rate. It is best to locate this limiting unit at the beginning of the process. With evenly matched components, some surge allowance should be made for start-up or malfunction. A hopper located on the intake of each unit provides this insurance against plugging.

A typical flow pattern involves transportation from the harvester, off-loading, receiving, elevating, drying, storing, unloading, and either processing for feeding or transporting to a market. There are several alternative types of equipment from which to choose at almost every stage of the flow pattern. The problem is to select the most suitable system for a given operation and then choose the component parts that will fit and function together. A few of the alternatives will be discussed briefly.

Transporting

Transporting with either a truck or wagon is satisfactory. However, the means of unloading should be compatible with the receiver. Gravity or hydraulic dumping is efficient and fast, but the unloading rate must match the capabilities of the receiver.

Receiving

Receiving the grain in a drive-over pit that can hold most of a load permits the use of a slow-speed elevator without holding up the transport vehicle. Lower cost tip-up or swinging hoppers have little surge capacity and can receive grain only as fast as the elevator takes it away.

Elevating

The use of a portable inclined auger or chain-type elevator is undoubtedly the least expensive means of handling grain. A short and therefore inexpensive high capacity conveyor used at the initial stage elevates the grain into a working bin. From there the grain may be sent to a dryer, if necessary, or directly to the pit and from there on a slow-speed elevator to the storage bins.

A higher capacity, central-elevating system employs a vertical auger or bucket type elevator leg to lift the grain from the dump pit to a point where it can flow by gravity to a dryer or to one of up to four storage bins. The choice between an auger or a bucket elevator is based on capacity, cost, and efficiency. The auger will be less costly, but the bucket type will be more efficient and higher capacities are available if required.

Drying

Drying can be accomplished with several different systems at widely varying rates. This will be discussed separately.

Storing

Facilities for storing are selected primarily on the basis of the manner in which they will be used. Large, grade-level, flat-bottom bins, costing the least per bushel of capacity, are used for long-term storage of grain. A sweep auger in the bin bottom is required to unload the storage completely by mechanical means.

Where high moisture corn is harvested and not dried, it may be stored in a silo or treated chemically to prevent spoilage. In either case, it must be fed on the farm or sold locally for feeding purposes. High moisture corn may also be stored in a bunker silo if fed out by early spring. Considerable care should be taken in loading, packing, and sealing. Grinding the corn before storage is usually recommended. Conventional upright silos work well if at least 3 to 4 in. (75 to 100 mm) of corn are removed daily in warm weather. Sealed silos keep the losses of this rather high-value product to a minimum and can often be justified in spite of their high initial cost.

Small, overhead hopper-bottom bins which unload by gravity flow are used as working bins to compensate for rapid grain unloading and to feed grinders or dryers. They are used on a rotating basis whenever grain or feed is being handled.

Medium-sized, grade-level or elevated hopper-bottom bins are used extensively for short-term feed storage. They may be filled on a weekly or monthly cycle as required.

Unloading

Unloading bins is handled with horizontal conveyors that return the grain to the original receiving point. From there the vertical elevator moves it onto a truck, a working bin or another storage bin. An alternative means of unloading storage bins is with auger or chain elevators that transfer grain directly from the bin to a truck for transport to market. Feed storage bins unload directly into a feeding conveyor or feed wagon.

Processing

The processing of grain into feed on a livestock farm starts at the working bin. From there grain may be fed into a grinder, an automatic blender-grinder or a transport grinder-mixer. The same center building that serves a cash-grain operation can, with careful initial planning, serve the processing operation needed for a livestock enterprise.

Feeding

The flow in a grain-livestock operation is completed by feeding. A self-unloading wagon or one of the various types of conveyor feeders that distributes the ration uniformly along a feed bunk keeps labor at a minimum.

Planning the Layout

The site selected for a grain storage facility should be easily accessible with adequate room for expansion to at least double the initial size. A well-drained site is essential since some of the conveying equipment will be installed below grade. In addition, heavy vehicles and equipment will require firm roadbeds in order to maneuver in the area. Grain storages produce considerable dust and noise, factors that influence the proximity to the home.

To illustrate the principle of a centralized system with room for expansion, a hypothetical grain handling center will be developed step by step from one bin to as many as six. An area 100×200 ft (30×60 m) is bisected at the 50 and 90 ft (15 and 27 m) points (fig. 22.1) to form quadrants. The first bin is located in quadrant 1, seven feet (2.2 m) from the x-axis and 12 ft (3.6 m) from the y-axis. Initially a portable elevator is used with the single bin.

A second bin is constructed in quadrant 2, two feet (0.6 m) from the x-axis and 12 ft (3.6 m) from the y-axis. As additional capacity is required, bins are built in quadrants 3 and 4 in the mirror-image positions shown.

Eventually, the dump pit and elevator are constructed and housed within the center building. Space in the building adjacent to the elevator leg and beside the drive-through is available for processing equipment to be used on a livestock farm.

The storages in quadrant 1 and 4 are spaced 14 ft (4.4 m) apart to allow room for a high-speed dryer and work bin when they are required. Alternatively, they may be placed next to the drive going into the center building.

A non-centralized system is often a suitable option for the small grain operator or when initial investment must be kept to a minimum. Figure 22.2 shows three storage bins arranged to be filled from a single pit by swinging a slow-speed elevator. Grain may be off-loaded into a high-speed elevator and working bin combination. From the working bin, the grain may be directed to a dryer or directly to the low-speed elevator.

A number of grain handling system layouts and equipment components are shown in the Midwest Plan Service Handbook on Planning Grain and Feed Handling (MWPS-13, 1988).

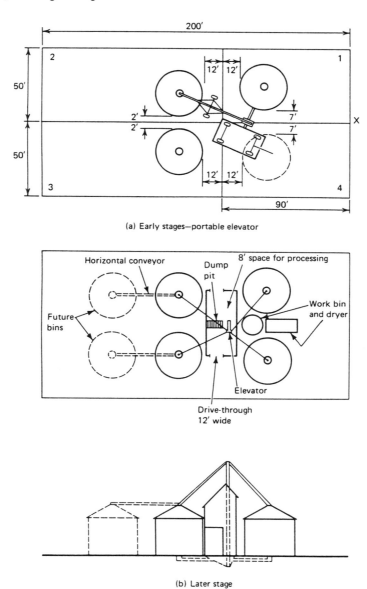

(a) Early stages—portable elevator

(b) Later stage

Figure 22.1. Grain center layout.

Drying Grain

Modern harvesting methods, late-maturing varieties, and adverse weather conditions have encouraged the use of artificial drying systems. High initial investment and

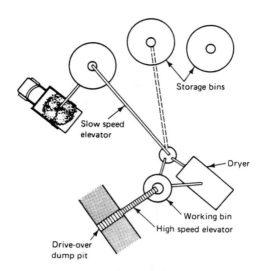

Storage bins

Slow speed
elevator

Dryer

Working bin
High speed elevator

Drive-over
dump pit

Figure 22.2. Non-centralized grain storage system.

increasing energy costs make the selection of equipment and the management of drying and storage systems critical factors in the production of grain.

All drying operations require air flow and most depend on some added heat as well.
The variation in systems is largely related to the amount of heat and the time required
to remove the moisture. Grain may be dried in the bin by one of four basic methods:

1. Layer drying. Damp corn is added to the storage in layers of 12 to 18 in.
   (300 to 450 mm) per day and dried by air warmed 5 to 20°F (3 to 11°C)
   above ambient temperature. This method is slow and requires careful
   attention to the rate of filling to avoid the growth of mold.

2. Batch drying. Two to three feet (0.6 to 1 m) of corn is placed on a perforated floor in the bin and air at 100 to 120°F (39 to 50°C) is moved
   through the grain at 10 to 20 cfm/bushel (130 to 260 L/s/m³). A drying
   rate of 1/2 to 3/4%/h allows a 24-h cycle. One and one-half to two hours
   of air circulation is required for cooling.

3. Dryeration. This is a term used to describe a process in which a batch of
   corn is dried to 16 to 18% moisture with high temperature air. The corn
   is then transferred to another bin where it stands for a few hours before it
   is cooled with a low-volume airflow. An additional 3 to 4% of moisture
   is removed in 8 to 10 h of cooling. The capacity of the dryer is increased
   by transferring the cooling operation to another bin. This also reduces
   cracking damage to the corn.

4. Continuous-flow drying. This takes place in a bin or portable dryer with
   heated air blown through a column of slowly moving grain. Damp grain
   is added at the top while dry grain is removed at the bottom. Typical air

temperatures are 180 to 220°F (80 to 105°C) and airflow rates as high as 75 to 100 cfm/bu (1000 to 1350 L/s-m^3). Cooling may be integral with drying or in a separate bin. A continuous-flow system typically operates about 16 h/day during harvest season but may be operated continuously with a sufficiently large, wet-grain bin.

The choice of a drying system depends on initial cost, energy cost, speed of harvesting, and the end use of the grain. As energy costs rise, the use of solar collectors and low-temperature (layer) drying become more attractive. Corn for seed or market may not be heated to as high a temperature as grain for livestock feed.

Summary

The number of alternative equipment systems to carry out each of the functions in a grain-flow process emphasizes the importance of long-range planning. Not only must the equipment be compatible in function but also in capacity. A slow conveyor in an otherwise fast system can slow down the whole system as well as cause mechanical breakdowns. Electric controls, wired in proper sequence, start equipment before any grain enters the system. Overload protection on all major motors in the system can be designed to shut down the whole system upon malfunction at any point.

In materials handling equipment, there are many parts moving at high speed. Shields are supplied by the manufacturer and should always be left in place. Hazards of any sort should be identified with easily seen warning signs. The adage, "Safety doesn't cost, it pays", is particularly true in the proximity of materials handling equipment.

SILAGE

To reap maximum profits, the beef and dairy farmer must provide a nutritionally balanced ration for his stock. The all-in-one ration, including a large percentage of silage, has led the way to achieving an efficient feeding program with a high degree of mechanization. Ensiling forage crops such as corn, alfalfa, and grass, as well as some grains like high moisture corn, has become popular for a number of reasons:

1. Harvesting high-moisture, immature crops in effect gives a longer growing season and the opportunity for increased yields.
2. Weather damage is reduced because crops require less drying in the field.
3. Forage crops stored as silage, rather than as dry forage, can be handled more easily with mechanical and automated equipment.
4. In many cases tests have shown that on a dry matter basis, feed efficiency is higher with silage than with dry forage; that is, for equal quantities of dry matter fed either as silage or as hay, the silage produces greater animal gains.

These advantages seem to outweigh the disadvantage of the extra investment in storage structures that is often necessary and the labor involved to handle the extra weight of the high moisture crops. On many farms, silage is either the only roughage fed, or it represents a high percentage of the total being used in the ration.

Silo Requirements

Top quality silage results from a combination of high quality forage, expertise in loading the silo, and a structure providing the necessary conditions. The following characteristics are essential for all silos regardless of type:

1. Sufficient wall strength to resist the lateral pressure of the silage.
2. Tight, smooth, nonabsorbent walls that completely exclude air from the silage.
3. A wall material that resists the effects of the acids in the silage.
4. A means of sealing the exposed surface of the silage.

Types of Silos

There are several types of silos and a variety of materials used in their construction. Cost, adaptability to mechanization, and storage losses vary considerably.

Upright or Tower Silos

These silos have a long life and are well-suited for mechanical unloading. They are filled with a blower and self-unloading truck or wagon. Packing is relatively easy and sealing the surface with a plastic cover is effective and not difficult.

Tower silos may be built of glass-coated steel, fiberglass-reinforced plastic, concrete or wood, with the cost decreasing in that order. The glass-coated steel and fiberglass silos are available as sealed structures with an expansion bag to allow for temperature-induced pressure variation. While the annual cost for these silos is considerably higher than for conventional silos, when properly managed, storage losses are minimal and with high value crops the extra cost is justified.

Both monolithic concrete and concrete stave silos provide excellent storage conditions, and given proper care will last for many years. Wood silos also provide good storage conditions, but they require more attention to maintaining proper hoop tension.

Horizontal Silos

These silos provide storage at considerably lower cost and are adaptable to self-feeding. However, they are not as easily automated and considerable care must be taken to properly pack and cover the silage to keep storage losses at an acceptable level. While it is not difficult to store corn silage with minimal losses, it takes great care to ensile grass successfully.

Horizontal silos are ordinarily built of concrete or pressure-preservative-treated lumber. If built above grade, adequate bracing is essential [fig. 22.3(a, b)]. If concrete is used below grade, good drainage behind the walls is particularly important to prevent frost damage [fig. 22.4(a, b)].

Stacks

Stacks may be used for short-term overflow storage, but losses are likely to be high.

Silage Bags

Large, heavy plastic bags holding 500 tons or more are available. The normal maximum size is 12 ft (3.6 m) diameter × 250 ft (76 m) long, but longer bags can be made

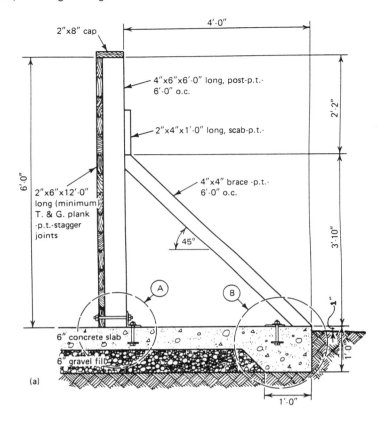

Figure 22.3. (a) Bunker silo details.

to order. Filled by a specially designed machine, these bags are convenient and provide a high quality product. Even though the annual cost is relatively high for replacing the bags each year, the savings in minimizing spoilage may prove economical.

Choosing a Silo

In considering what kind of silo to build and how to obtain the most efficient use, there are several factors to keep in mind:

1. Type of Silage to be Stored. Corn silage is relatively easy to ensile and can be stored successfully in any type of silo that is in good condition. Haylage, on the other hand, is lower in sugar and does not ferment as easily. Also, it is more difficult to pack, and therefore is best stored in a tower silo. It is easiest to store haylage in a sealed silo, but careful packing and sealing of the top surface with a weighted plastic cover will give good results in any tower silo.

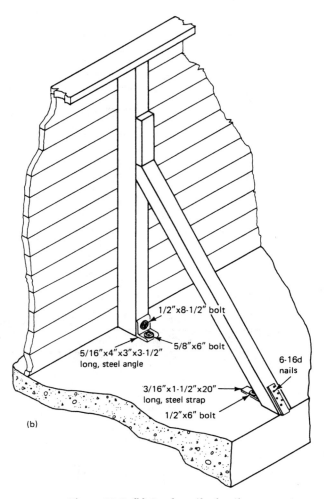

1/2"x8-1/2" bolt

5/8"x6" bolt

5/16"x4"x3"x3-1/2"
long, steel angle

6-16d
nails

3/16"x1-1/2"x20"
long, steel strap

1/2"x6" bolt

(b)

Figure 22.3. (b) Bunker silo details.

2. Value of Crop Stored. Crops grown for silage vary in nutritional and monetary value. Crops of high monetary value justify the greater investment in the more expensive types of storage which ordinarily have lower losses. Each percentage point saved is of greater dollar value with high value crops. For example, a sealed, gas-tight storage should be considered for storing high moisture shelled corn.

3. Possibility for Multiple Filling. Most operators use conventional unsealed silos for corn silage and fill once a year in the fall. However, a gas-tight unit to ensile haylage, nearly empty in late May, can be filled

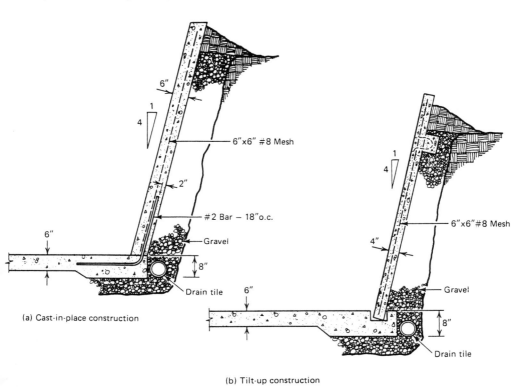

6" x 6" #8 Mesh

#2 Bar – 18"o.c.

Gravel

Drain tile

(a) Cast-in-place construction

6" x 6" #8 Mesh

Gravel

Drain tile

(b) Tilt-up construction

Figure 22.4. Concrete horizontal silo construction.

for summer barn feeding and refilled again in late summer for winter feeding. The sealed silo may be refilled with other materials in almost any combination and in any season. However, to realize the benefits of multiple fillings and to justify the high investment in this type of silo, the unit should be no larger than is necessary to carry storage from fall to spring filling. Filling the silo twice a year reduces the storage cost per ton to nearly half. On the other hand, if the silo has the capacity to carry a herd for the entire year, adding forage at two or three times is meaningless from an economic standpoint. An exception to this would be the extra capacity installed in anticipation of herd expansion.

4. Feeding System. Tower silos equipped with unloaders are well-suited for use in conjunction with a barn feeding conveyor, concentrate meter, and high moisture corn crusher. Horizontal silos fit well with a tractor front-end loader and mixer-wagon combination and offer considerable flexibility in the feeding program.

5. Available Capital. The funds available or the cost of borrowed capital
   will influence the choice of storage facilities. Many operators with limited funds have used either a temporary silo until sufficient funds were
   accumulated for a permanent silo or have built a less expensive, permanent horizontal silo.

6. Storage Losses. The moisture content, quality of the silage stored, and
   management practices all influence storage losses. However, for the same
   quality of silage stored, the losses are also affected by the type of silo. The
   range of typical losses to be expected are: sealed upright silo, 1 – 10%; concrete upright silo, 2 – 12%; horizontal, 10 – 25%; and stack, 15 – 35%. The
   annual cost of a silo will run 13 to 15% of the original cost. The difference in annual cost, the expected storage loss, and the value of the stored
   product can be used to determine the type of storage that offers the lowest cost per ton of feed removed.

Site Selection and Layout

Good drainage is essential for all types of silos. In the case of tower silos, a large
proportion of the silage load is transferred through the walls to the foundation. A firm,
well-drained soil is required to support the load. In the case of a below-grade, horizontal silo, good drainage behind the walls is necessary to prevent frost damage.
Adequate drainage must be provided to remove excess juices and rainfall from the site
and to divert surface water from draining into the silo. Firm ground is required for
heavy vehicular traffic handling the silage.

Silos must be located for convenient loading and unloading. During filling, wagons
and trucks should be able to maneuver with a minimum of turning and backing.
Unnecessary travel during the daily unloading can be eliminated by the careful placement of the silo in relation to the feeding area. This will depend on the type of animal
housing and the method of feed distribution. Arranging tower silos and feed storages in
a row so that one conveyor can "accumulate" a full ration is desirable. Greater flexibility in location is possible with horizontal silos since they are usually used with a mixer-
wagon and a little extra distance is not critical. Care should be taken that the silos are
not built in a place where the expansion of other facilities may be contemplated.

Tower Silos

The size and number of silos must be selected to match the requirements of the
herd. The diameter of the silo is determined by the amount of silage fed daily, while
the height and number of silos are determined by the amount fed annually. A suitable
diameter will allow the daily removal of at least 2 to 3 in. (50 to 75 mm) of silage
from the entire surface during the winter months and 3 to 4 in. (75 to 100 mm) in
warm weather. Spoilage is likely to occur if less is removed. If a decision must be
made between two silos that bracket the 2 to 4 in. (50 to 100 mm) removal rate, it is
better to choose the one with the smaller diameter and prevent any loss. However, the
height of a silo should be neither less than twice nor more than four times the diam-

Table 22-1. Capacity of tower silos

Depth of Silage ft (m)	Mass in a 10 ft (3 m) Diameter Silo ton (t)		Silo Diameter ft (m)	Multiplier*
20 (6.1)	27	(24.5)	12 (3.7)	1.44
24 (7.3)	35	(31.8)	14 (4.3)	1.96
28 (8.5)	44	(40.0)	16 (4.9)	2.56
32 (9.8)	53	(48.2)	18 (5.5)	3.24
36 (11.0)	63	(57.3)	20 (6.1)	4.00
40 (12.2)	74	(67.3)	22 (6.7)	4.84
44 (13.4)	85	(77.3)	24 (7.3)	5.76
48 (14.6)	95	(86.4)	26 (7.9)	6.76
52 (15.9)	108	(98.2)	28 (8.5)	7.84
56 (17.1)	120	(109.1)	30 (9.2)	9.00
60 (18.3)	132	(120.0)		

* Multiply mass for 10 ft (3 m) diameter by multiplier value to obtain mass for new diameter.

eter. The greater the depth of the silage, the greater the unit capacity and the higher the quality of the silage. Doubling the diameter increases the total capacity four times, doubling the height approximately triples the capacity. Doubling both the height and diameter increases the capacity 12 fold. The cost per ton drops rapidly as silos get taller and wider.

Silage weighs from 35 to 50 pcf (570 to 810 kg/m^3) depending on type and depth. Table 22-1 provides estimated capacities of tower silos of various sizes. The height and number of silos needed may be determined with the help of the table. If more than one kind of feed is stored as silage, multiple silos allow all feed to be used in the ration at the same time.

Tower silos require periodic maintenance to protect the inner surfaces from deterioration and to keep them airtight. Concrete and wood silos may be coated with raw linseed oil on a two-year schedule to protect and seal surfaces. Epoxy coatings work well on concrete if applied before any damage has occurred. Seals around doors and openings should be checked for tightness. Maintenance of wood silos includes periodic tightening of hoops and guy wires.

During the filling of tower silos and for two weeks after filling, there is danger from silo gas. Silo gas is nitrogen dioxide, a yellowish-brown gas with an odor similar to some laundry bleaches. It is lethal to both animals and humans. The gas will settle to the stable level because it is heavier than air. As a safety precaution, it is wise to keep the silo shut off from the barn for 10 to 14 days after filling and to make certain that the barn is well-ventilated. No one should enter a tower silo without first operating the blower for 15 to 20 min to purge any accumulation of silo gas. In addition, two or more persons should be present for safety.

Horizontal Silos

Horizontal silos may be built 6 to 10 ft (2 to 3 m) or more in height and wide enough to allow a minimum amount of silage to be removed from the open face each day. Two to three inches (50 to 75 mm) is satisfactory in cold weather, but up to twice that amount is desirable in the summer. Seven to eight feet (2 to 2.5 m) is the maximum suitable height for self feeding. The length is determined by the total silage needed for the year. Some farmers are reducing construction costs by building double silos with a common wall between them. Double silos also offer the flexibility of being able to feed out of one side while the other side is being filled. At the same time, there is less exposed area on the front surface, thus decreasing the possibility of spoilage. Horizontal silo capacity may be based on 35 pcf (570 kg/m^3).

Bunker silos should be built with tight, rigid walls and a solid floor. A simple design for a braced-wall bunker silo constructed of pressure-preservative-treated lumber is shown in figure 22.3. Lining the silo with plastic each year insures a smooth surface against which to pack silage.

Concrete horizontal silos installed below grade may be cast-in-place or tilt-up. Although they are frequently built as essentially non-reinforced structures, it is common practice to use 6 × 6 in. (150 × 150 mm) no. 8 gauge mesh to reduce temperature stress cracks and to provide sufficient strength to lift the tilt-up panels into place. Carefully placed and well-compacted gravel behind either the cast-in-place or tilt-up walls insures good drainage and adequate support to resist the lateral forces of the silage. Figure 22.4 shows a section of each type of construction.

Above-grade, horizontal, concrete silos must be designed as reinforced concrete structures. Sloping the sidewalls makes packing easier, but with smooth surfaces, vertical walls are satisfactory. The floor of the silo should be sloped for good drainage. A grade of 1:50 should be satisfactory to unload silos for feeding, but up to twice that much is desirable for self-feeding.

The most satisfactory material for covering horizontal silos is 4 to 6 mil polyethylene plastic, sealed with earth along the edges and with old tires placed as close as possible over the entire surface. In low to medium rainfall areas, molasses, hosed on the surface immediately after filling, has worked well. A 1 1/2 to 2 gal/ft^2 (60 to 80 L/m^2) rate gives the best results but is economically feasible only when molasses costs not over 80% as much as corn.

Horizontal silos are often packed by driving a tractor back and forth over the fresh forage. The tractor wheel tread should be adjusted to its maximum width and extreme caution used in operating the tractor, particularly in a bunker type silo.

Silo Construction

Tower silo construction requires considerable know-how and equipment. It is a job for professionals. The design of concrete stave silos is detailed in Design Standards for Concrete Stave Silos (National Silo Association, 1974) which covers such design factors as foundations, loads, soil bearing, hoops, materials, stave design and testing, and construction tolerances. Sealed silos are usually installed by the manufacturer or a representative. Horizontal silos are less complex than tower silos and may be constructed by general contractors or by farm labor.

Problems

22.1. Determine the capacity of a circular grain bin 18 ft (5.5 m) in diameter and 16 ft (4.9 m) high.

22.2. Determine the approximate quantity of grain that can be dried daily in two bins, each 18 ft (5.5 m) in diameter, using the batch method and high temperature air.

22.3. A herd of 150 cows is fed a daily average of 67 lb (30 kg) of corn silage per animal throughout the year. Make recommendations for the size and number of tower silos to provide adequate storage. Assume an average density of 44 pcf (714 kg/m^3). Allow a minimum of 6 ft (2 m) extra height for settling of the silage after filling.

22.4. Make recommendations for the dimensions of a post-frame building to store 500 tons (455 t) of baled hay.

23 Greenhouses

Greenhouses are structures that are covered with transparent material that utilize solar radiant energy to grow plants. Most greenhouses have heating and ventilating equipment to modify the environment and other systems such as irrigation, carbon dioxide, and lighting. Specialized materials handling equipment is also available to reduce the labor needs, the greatest cost in producing plants.

Crops that are grown in greenhouses include cut flowers, potted plants, bedding plants (annuals and perennials), vegetables, and nursery stock. Greenhouse-type structures without heat are also used to provide winter protection for nursery plants (over-wintering houses) and climate modification for field-grown vegetables (high tunnels).

Crop production in greenhouses is a rapidly expanding industry. In the United States in 1993, there were more than 4,500 acres under glass, 11,000 acres under plastic used for plant production, and 4,000 acres under plastic used for over-wintering.

Investment

The investment in a greenhouse is justified by the value of the crop grown and the length of the time it is used each year. For example, the investment in a greenhouse to be used year-round for producing cut flowers is amortized over a 10- to 20-year period. Housing costs become less important while labor and other production costs increase in importance. Under these conditions, a permanent structure, perhaps glass-covered, is easily justified.

In contrast, seasonal use for the production of bedding plants or wintering nursery stock cannot justify a large investment and temporary, plastic-covered houses are generally used.

Hobby greenhouses have become increasingly popular. Frequently they are attached to the home or another building which can house the heating system and provide storage. Minimal equipment for environmental control is usually adequate even though the environment throughout the house may not be uniform. In fact, the variety of plants grown may make just such a situation useful.

Types of Greenhouses

Commercial greenhouses may be classified in several different ways. One division is into free-standing and gutter-connected houses.

Free-standing Greenhouses

Free-standing greenhouses are suitable for small businesses or those that need several different growing temperatures. Some space is required between houses for maintenance operation and, in northern climates, for snow accumulation. There are a number of suitable frame designs from which to choose (fig. 23.1).

The Quonset House

This house is one of the simplest styles. For spans up to 10 to 12 ft (3 to 3.5 m), a semicircular frame may be constructed with thin-wall conduit (EMT). For greater spans, galvanized pipe, aluminum extrusions or arched trusses are employed. Either plastic film or flexible plastic sheets make a suitable covering. An inflated, double layer of polyethylene film, fastened at the base of the sides and at the ends with specially designed anchors, works well on the curved surface and can be put in place with minimal labor. The low arch shape with its nearly flat center area is prone to snow overloading and to problems with dripping from condensation. Also, because of the curved sides, it is primarily suited to growing or storing crops on the floor rather than on benches.

Gothic Arch Houses

These are framed with metal or laminated wood rafters and have a pleasing appearance. Their steeper sides allow benches to be used and they are not as subject to dripping or snow overloading. Covering is done in the same manner as on the quonset house.

Gable Greenhouses

With an even pitch, gable houses may be framed in a number of ways. Relatively narrow buildings with rigid side walls may use rafters without bracing, thus allowing maximum light to reach the crop. Houses up to 30 ft (9.1 m) wide may be framed with rafters braced with collar beams, while rigid frame construction will tolerate widths up to 40 ft (12 m). The widest houses, up to 60 ft (18 m), are spanned with trusses, usually fabricated of metal to keep shading to a minimum.

The gable shape will accept any type of covering and with a sufficiently steep pitch, (6:12 for glass, more for plastic), dripping from condensation is negligible. Either floor or bench crops are easily managed.

Gutter-connected Greenhouses

Sometimes referred to as ridge and furrow houses, gutter-connected greenhouses are a series of gable or low arch structures connected together at the gutter level. The individual bays vary from 12 to 25 ft (3.6 to 8 m) in width and usually have a minimum clearance of 8 ft (2.3 m) under the gutters.

The primary advantage of the gutter-connected house is the ability to cover a large ground area with a minimum of exposed wall area, thus reducing heat loss by as much as 25%. Also, less time is needed to travel to various points within the enclosed area rather than between several free-standing houses of equal total space. Perhaps the biggest shortcoming is the difficulty of removing snow with any means except heat.

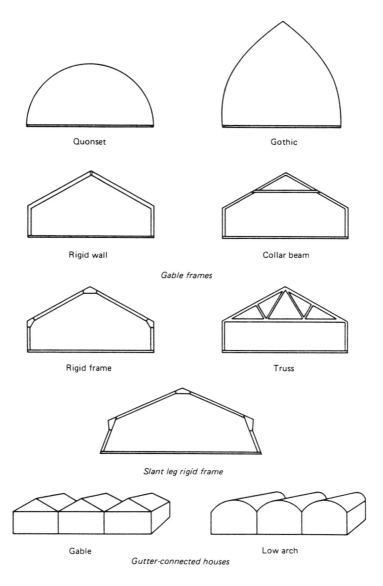

Figure 23.1. Types of greenhouse frames.

Consequently this type of greenhouse is most suitable in regions of limited snowfall. Gutter houses require many supports which may interfere somewhat with operations. However, with additional investment, flat trusses may be used to obtain up to 36 ft (11 m) of clear span in which to work.

The arched frames are suitable for either plastic film, flexible plastic or tempered glass covering, while the gable frames are built using tempered glass, poly carbonate or acrylic plastic sheets that extend from eave to ridge.

Structural Materials

Wood, galvanized steel, and aluminum are all commonly used for greenhouse frames. Because of the characteristically lightweight construction of greenhouses, only top grade lumber should be selected when using wood. The high moisture environment that exists in a greenhouse makes it essential that the most decay-resistant wood be used. Although a few species such as black locust, osage orange, red cedar, and redwood are naturally decay resistant, the use of preservative-treated lumber for all but temporary greenhouses is desirable. Only the water-borne type of preservatives, as described in chapter 2, should be used. If plywood is used for gussets in rigid frame construction, it must be exterior grade and preservative-treated. The edges of the plywood should be painted to prevent moisture from causing delamination. Glue used in the fabrication of trusses or frames should be of the waterproof, resorcinol type. Casein glues should never be used for greenhouse construction.

Steel is commonly used for commercially manufactured greenhouses. Because of the high moisture conditions, all steel should be protected from corrosion by paint or galvanizing. It is preferable to do the galvanizing after all cutting and welding of the frame members have been completed.

Aluminum extrusions are gaining favor for greenhouse construction because of the minimal amount of maintenance and the resistance to corrosion. Both steel and aluminum permit the use of slim structural members to reduce shading.

Covering Materials

For many years, glass was virtually the only covering used in greenhouses. Today, in addition to glass, we have a multitude of plastic materials with a wide range of cost and quality. In addition, they vary considerably with respect to ease of installation, light transmission, and durability.

Glass

Glass, the standard by which other materials are rated, transmits the most light (90%) and lasts the longest—but it is expensive. In the past, double-strength glass has been used. More recently, tempered glass was introduced permitting the use of larger panes. Several manufacturers offer large, 6 × 12 ft (1.8 × 3.6 m) flat panes that when installed bend to fit the curvature of a low arch greenhouse. This in turn allows framing members to be spaced farther apart, reducing both the cost and the shading effect of the frame. Glass requires special structural members and glazing techniques to ensure airtight and watertight construction. Increased light diffusion and reduction of shadows can be achieved with the use of stippled glass.

While glass retains its inherent light transmittance over many years, light reduction does occur as dirt, algae, and surface etching build up. Caulking and sealing glass panes presents a maintenance problem.

Polyethylene (PE)

Polyethylene film, with light transmitting characteristics similar to glass, is the least expensive covering available. PE is a less effective barrier to heat radiation than other coverings and houses tend to cool rapidly when the sunlight decreases in the afternoon. Condensation that may appear at about the same time, however, can reduce this radiant loss by up to 50%.

Regular polyethylene ordinarily lasts only one season because it is destroyed by ultraviolet radiation from the sun. Copolymer greenhouse-grade film has additives for UV resistance, strength, radiant heat retention and a wetting agent to keep moisture from forming droplets. Only greenhouse-grade films should be used, as there is a tendency for others to split along the folds. Metal or plastic anchors and wood furring strips are used to attach the plastic to the frame. In most applications, an air-inflated, double layer is applied for strength and insulation.

It has long been recognized that two layers of plastic film significantly reduce heat loss from a greenhouse. However, the necessity of using wooden spacers and furring strips to secure the plastic film and create an airspace between the layers not only increases the labor required but reduces the amount of light entering the greenhouse due to the thickness of the framing members. The inflated double-layer system has overcome these problems and at the same time allows the installation of two layers of plastic with even less labor than a single sheet. The single sheet must be fastened along most of the framing members. In contrast, in the inflated double-layer system, the two layers are draped over the rafters and then anchored only at the base of each side and at the ends of the building. Typical anchors are illustrated in figure 23.2. Once secured around the edges, a small blower-type fan, running continuously, maintains air pressure between the layers keeping them separated and rigid. The air space becomes an effective barrier to heat loss and the rigidity prevents the plastic from flapping in the wind and tearing. Snow also slides off the smooth, curved surface more easily. With this system there is less condensation on the underside of the plastic resulting in fewer dripping problems. The reduced condensation results in higher relative humidity and allows longer periods between watering.

Installation of an Inflated Double-layer Cover

1. On houses to be covered with inflated double-layer systems, the frame members may be safely spaced up to 4 ft (1.2 m) apart in snow areas and up to 8 ft (2.4 m) in southern climates.

Figure 23.2. Polyethylene anchors.

2. All corners should be smoothed and all rough edges taped to prevent the plastic from being punctured or chafed.

3. On a calm day, the double layer of PE may be draped over the greenhouse frame and secured at the edges along the base of each side and along the end frames (fig. 23.2).

4. A small squirrel cage blower that will deliver 100 to 150 ft³/min (47 to 70 L/s) at 0.5 in. (13 mm) of water pressure will be needed for each 5,000 ft² (465 m²) of area to be inflated. A simple "U" tube manometer made from a piece of plastic tubing will also be needed to measure the pressure (see fig. 15.2). The pressure is regulated with a sheet metal plate that can be adjusted to partially cover the fan inlet.

5. The blower should be mounted high enough on an end wall so that it draws in outside air without the possibility of being closed off with snow (fig. 23.3). The use of outside air prevents condensation from forming between the layers of plastic. A connection is made from the blower outlet to the inner layer of plastic with clothes-dryer vent tubing.

6. On houses with a ridge, it will be necessary to connect the two sides with a piece of vent tubing in order to equalize the pressures.

7. After the connections are completed, the pressure may be adjusted to 0.25 in. (6 mm) of water by changing the size of the blower opening.

Plastic Structured Sheets

Structured sheet glazing of polycarbonate or acrylic plastic has been available since the 1980s. The large sheet size and aluminum extrusion attachment system, make rapid glazing of a greenhouse possible. Structured sheets can also be adapted to reglazing older glass greenhouses by removing the glass and replacing the bars. As compared to glass, these materials are lighter in weight and require less structural framing.

Although available in several thicknesses, the 5/16 in. (8 mm) is the most commonly applied as a greenhouse covering. Sheet sizes of 4 ft (0.9 m) and 6 ft (1.8 m) widths, and lengths between 8 ft (2.4 m) and 16 ft (4.8 m) in 2 ft (0.6 m) increments are normally stocked by suppliers. Lengths to 39 ft (12 m) are available on special order.

In the installation of structured sheets, care should be taken to allow for expansion of the panels. The sheets are cut with a fine tooth saw. It is best if the channels in the glazing run vertical to allow any moisture to drain.

Polycarbonate is used more frequently than acrylic. It has the advantages of low flammability (meets Class A fire rating), high impact resistance to hail or vandalism, and the ability to fit over curved surfaces. The acrylic material has a slightly higher light transmittance, can be placed over a wider support spacing, and weathers better.

Both materials are coated with an ultra-violet inhibitor (UV) to reduce degradation and yellowing. They are also available with an anti-drip feature. Energy savings is about 40% as compared to glass.

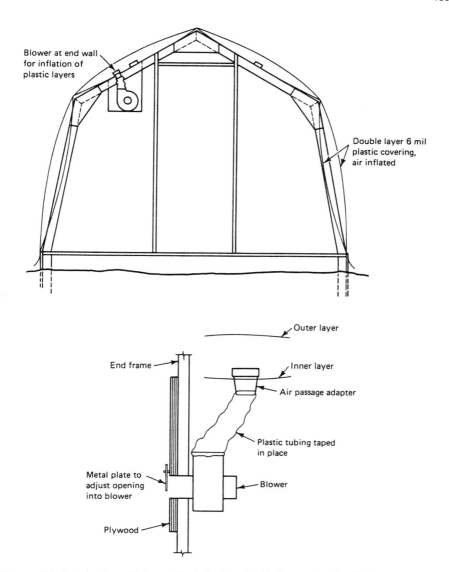

Figure 23.3. Installation of blower for inflating double layer of polyethylene covering.

Other Materials

Two, single-thickness, corrugated glazing panels are available. Fiberglass reinforced plastic (FRP) has a fiberglass mat encased in clear polyester. It has a 10- to 15-year life if recoated when the plastic starts to wear. The advantages are its low cost, high light transmission, and ease of fabrication. A disadvantage is its high flammability.

Corrugated polycarbonate sheets have generally replaced FRP as a glazing material. Its longer life, higher light transmittance, and better fire rating are the main advantages.

Both materials are available in several thicknesses and in panels 4 ft (1.2 m) wide and 8 ft (2.4 m) to 24 ft (7.2 m) long. The panels are installed with ring-shank nails or tek screws with rubber gaskets to the greenhouse bars and purlins. Formed wood or foam rubber strips are placed under the upper and lowers edges to provide a seal. The manufacturer's recommendations should be followed in regard to purlin and fastener spacing.

Greenhouse Site and Orientation

Greenhouses should be located away from buildings and trees that may cast shadows. The time of year, time of day, and latitude all influence the length of shadows cast. For example, at latitude 40°N (Philadelphia, Columbus, Denver), the angle of the sun's rays near noon in midwinter is only about 25° above the ground. Obviously, this means that very long shadows are cast and that greenhouses should be located well away from trees or buildings that may reduce the amount of sunlight. As a general rule, objects on the east, south or west sides of a greenhouse should be two and one-half to three times their height away from the house to avoid unwanted shadows. Windbreaks, as long as they meet this distance requirement, are desirable as they can make a significant difference in the heat loss from the house.

A greenhouse site should be level and well-drained. This may pose no problem for a small hobby house, but for a large commercial range, desirable sites may be difficult to find in rolling country. Except for houses used solely for holding-over nursery stock, water and electricity are essential services.

In latitudes south of 40°N, a north to south orientation of the building ridge is desirable for the best lighting. Houses north of 40°N benefit from an east to west orientation, particularly in midwinter. However, the gutters in gutter-connected greenhouses tend to cast long, lasting shadows that reduce production.

Structural Requirements

Regardless of the type of frame or the covering material, greenhouses should be strong enough to withstand expected wind and snow loads, and in some cases, loads imposed by equipment or crops. For example, tomatoes tied to the roof frame may impose a load of 4 lb/ft^2 (0.19 kPa).

U.S. Weather Bureau wind velocities are reported for a 30 ft (9 m) height. Most greenhouses are relatively low and would be subject to a wind pressure of about 75% of that caused by the 30 ft (9 m) velocity. The pressures caused by wind are discussed in chapter 6. Inasmuch as greenhouses are lightweight structures and the maximum wind pressures, particularly on the low, semicircular roof shapes, tend to impose lifting forces, it is imperative that the supporting frame be well-anchored.

Snow loads vary greatly from one region to another and local conditions must be considered in designing a house. However, in the case of heated greenhouses, the likelihood of a heavy snow load is reduced because the snow tends to melt and slide off.

Polyethylene-covered houses hasten the shedding process with the motion of plastic.

Design loads of 10 to 12 lb/ft^2 (0.48 to 0.58 kPa) have proven satisfactory even in the northeastern United States. The exception to this rule of experience is the gutter-connected house where there is no place for the snow to go except into the gutter to melt. A 20 lb/ft^2 (0.96 kPa) design load and a generous-sized heating system to hasten melting are both advisable.

Foundation requirements will vary with the type of house, but in general they are as important for anchoring a house as for supporting it. Piers or foundations of at least 18 in. (450 mm) in depth or below the frost level are necessary.

Greenhouse Heating

The successful operation of a greenhouse requires near optimum temperatures for plant growth. Although sunlight and ventilation contribute greatly to maintenance of the required temperature, it remains the function of the heating system to provide the necessary heat at night and during periods of cloudy weather. Since the cost of heating represents a substantial part of the total cost of production, an efficient system, together with conservation measures, is essential to keep heating requirements to a minimum (table 23-1).

Heat Loss

Heat is lost from a greenhouse in several ways. Of greatest significance is the loss of heat by conduction through the walls and roof. Temperature differences and fans used for air circulation provide the natural and forced convection currents that carry the warm air to the surfaces where the conduction takes place. On the outside, natural convection and wind carry the heat away.

Infiltration

The natural exchange of inside air, with outside air through cracks and openings (infiltration), is the second most important source of heat loss. The amount varies considerably, as shown in table 23-2.

Ventilation

Even in periods of relatively cold weather when artificial heat is necessary, some ventilation may be required for moisture control. Heat will be lost in the air that is exchanged. In the most severe weather, infiltration alone may provide adequate ventilation.

Table 23-1. Heating cost as a percentage of total cost
for various greenhouse crops

Cut flowers	15-20%
Potted plants	15-20%
Bedding plants	10-15%
Vegetables	35-45%
Nursery stock	5-10%

Radiation Losses

Radiation losses from glass and structured plastic houses are low. By comparison, polyethylene (PE) transmits as much as 80% of long wavelength (low temperature) radiation. This can be a significant source of heat loss when the greenhouse humidity is low and no condensation is occurring. However, as is frequently the case, if moisture does condense on the inner surface of the PE, the radiation loss is reduced to a level which is not much more than glass. The use of infrared retardant plastic can reduce this loss further.

Heat Loss Calculation

To find the total expected heat loss and determine the size of an adequate heating system, it is necessary to obtain the following information:

1. The surface area of the glass- or plastic-covered portions of the greenhouse.
2. The surface area of walls, ends or other parts made of different construction materials.
3. The "U" value for each type of construction from table 14-2 or by calculation.
4. The estimated infiltration rate from table 23-2.

The heat loss by conduction through the surfaces may be found with the following equation:

$$q_c = A \times U \times TD \qquad (23.1)$$

where

q_c = conduction heat loss (BTU/h; W)

A = surface area (ft^2; m^2)

U = heat loss factor [(BTU/(h-ft^2°F); (W/(m^2°K)]

TD = temperature differences (°F; °K)

The heat loss by infiltration may be found with the following equation:

$$q_i = C \times V \times SH \times TD \qquad (23.2)$$

Table 23-2. Typical infiltration losses

	Air exchanges/h
New houses	
Double polyethylene cover	0.5-1.0
Glass or fiberglass	0.75-1.5
Old houses	
Glass - good maintenance	1-2
Glass - in poor condition	2-4

where

q_i = infiltration heat loss (BTU/h; W)

C = air changes per hours

V = volume of house (cu ft^3; m^3)

SH = specific heat of air by volume of house (0.018 Btu/ft^3-°F; 0.33 Wh/m^2°K)

TD = temperature difference (°F; °K).

The total heat loss, q_t is the sum of q_c + q_i.

Although some winter ventilation will be required, under the minimum tempera-ture conditions used for design purposes, the infiltration should provide enough air exchange to maintain a satisfactory level of humidity.

Example 23.1

As an example of estimating the heat loss from a greenhouse, assume the following conditions:

• 0°F outside, 60° F inside, two layers PE on top, polycarbonate-struc-tured sheet ends and sides, house is located in a protected area, U-values are from table 14-2.

• Two layers of PE = 0.7 Btu/h-ft^2°F.

• Polycarbonate Structured Sheet = 0.6 Btu/h-ft^2°F.

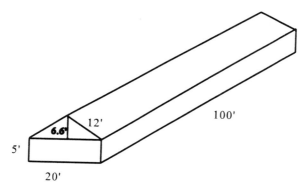

Conduction loss: $q_c = A \times U \times TD$

Roof: 2,400 ft^2 × 0.7 Btu/h- ft^2°F × 60°F = 100,800 Btu/h

Ends: 32 × 0.6 Btu/h-ft^2°F × 60°F = 11,952 Btu/h

Sides: 1,000 × 0.6 Btu/h-ft^2°F × 60°F = 36,000 Btu/h

q_c total = 148,752 Btu/h

Infiltration loss: $q_t = C \times V \times SH \times TD$

House volume $= 10,000 + 3,300 = 13,300 \text{ ft}^3$

$q_i = 1 \text{ ACH} \times 13,300 \text{ ft}^3 \times 0.018 \text{ Btu/ft}^3{}^\circ\text{F} \times 60^\circ\text{F} = 14,364 \text{ Btu/h}$

Total heat loss: $q_t = q_c + q_i$

$148,752 + 14,364 = 163,116 \text{ Btu/h}$

If the greenhouse is located in a windy area, it is good insurance to add 10% to the calculated heat loss before selecting a heating system. After deciding on the type of heating system, one that is large enough to supply the total estimated loss should be selected. Although considerable excess capacity will cost more initially and be somewhat less efficient to operate, up to 10% extra capacity will provide a desirable margin of safety for very severe weather conditions. In choosing the size of a heating system, heat output of the heating system should be used, not heat input.

Heating Systems

The most beneficial growing conditions result when temperatures remain nearly constant and are uniform throughout the greenhouse. Heat can be distributed in the house by natural convection from pipes or radiators along the sidewalls, or by forced hot air from free-standing furnaces or suspended unit heaters.

Hot Water Systems

Hot water, or in the case of older houses—steam, supplied to black iron or finned pipes along the walls of greenhouses has been the standard heating system for years. Due to the mass of heated metal and water, these systems tend to cycle slowly and maintain a uniform temperature. Steam boilers and some hot water boilers supply steam for soil sterilization which is a useful feature. However, they are expensive to install. The amount of pipe needed depends on the size of the pipe, the temperature of the water or steam and the number of runs of pipe together. In addition, with fin pipe the number of fins per foot and the size of the fins determine the heat output.

In gutter-connected houses, hot water radiation is frequently installed in a horizontal position at a level just below the bottom of the gutters. Although this location is not ideal for heat distribution, it does prevent the heating system from interfering with work operations. Modulating controllers that vary the temperature of the water in relation to outside conditions are able to maintain a more uniform greenhouse temperature.

A relatively new system using water is called root zone heat. Research has shown that root zone temperature is more critical than leaf temperature in achieving good plant growth. It can also reduce the time needed to root cuttings and germinate seed. Bottom heat can also reduce energy consumption as most of the heat needed by a greenhouse in the spring and fall can be provided by the root zone heating system.

Because the root zone is maintained at the ideal temperature, the air temperature for some crops can be lowered as much as 15°F (–9°C). This reduces heat loss from the greenhouse and thereby reduces energy consumption.

A typical system contains piping, a circulating pump, a water heater, and control system. To be effective the system must be designed to provide uniform temperatures over the floor or bench area.

The least expensive pipe is usually polyethylene, polybutylene or PVC. For floor installations, space the pipes 12 to 15 in. (300 to 380 mm) apart and 8 to 12 in. (200 to 300 mm) deep in the soil. In benches a 6 to 9 in. (150 to 230 mm) spacing covered by 3 or 4 in. (75 or 100 mm) of sand works well. The sand should be kept wet to transfer the heat and is usually covered with a sheet of plastic. An alternative arrangement consists of laying the pipe in the bottom of the bench and covering it with wire mesh and a layer of plastic. Some growers have attached the piping underneath the bench to get it out of the way and to allow the heat to spread.

Most commercially available systems use EPDM rubber tubing either as single tubes or as two or four tubes attached to a web. The 1/4 in. (6.4 mm) diameter tubing is connected to plastic or copper headers with plastic inserts or brass fittings.

The size of the heater needed depends on the amount of area to be heated and cropping system used. Research at Rutgers University by Roberts and Mears indicated a heat loss of approximately 20 Btu/ft^2-h (63 W/m^2-h) for beds or benches with plants growing in the soil or in pots and 15 Btu/ft^2-h for beds or benches covered with flats.

If the greenhouse is heated by a boiler, the bottom heating system can be tied into this. It requires a separate zone pump, thermostat control, and a mixing valve. The mixing valve allows the 180°F (82°C) boiler water to be combined with the cooler bench return water to give the desired 80 to 100°F (27 to 38°C) supply water for the bottom heat system.

For greenhouses that don't have a boiler, a hot water heater will do a good job. It can be oil, gas or electric.

Hot Air Systems

Hot air heaters may be free-standing oil or gas burners with built-in blowers or they may be smaller unit heaters suspended from the roof supports. The unit heaters can be fired with gas or oil or they may be supplied with heat from a hot water heat exchanger. All of the burners, regardless of type, must be vented to the outside of the greenhouse.

For houses up to 60 ft (18 m) long, the heating requirements may be divided between two units, one at each end oriented so that they discharge air along opposite sides of the house. This provides continuous air circulation and reasonably uniform temperature.

Unit Heaters and Polyethylene Duct System

The unit heater and a PE duct distribution system provide an economical method of heating and circulating the air to maintain uniform conditions throughout the greenhouse. In periods of mild weather, fresh air may be introduced through the system.

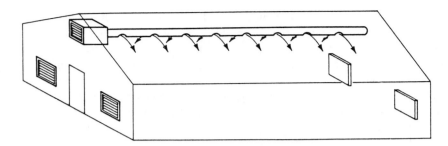

Figure 23.4. Polyethylene duct system.

For houses up to 30 ft (9 m) wide, a single duct down the center of the house (fig. 23.4) is connected to a fan and heater unit mounted on one end wall. Fresh air for heating and recirculation may be drawn in at the sides of the unit or through the louvers in the end wall. For houses more than 30 ft (9 m) wide, two or more parallel units will be needed.

While individual ducts may be up to 150 ft (45 m) long, the most uniform conditions will be maintained if units are located at both ends with ducts extending toward the center for any house more than 120 ft (36 m) long.

In the case of gutter-connected houses with a horizontal overhead heating system, fans and PE ducts are beneficial just to recirculate the warm air for more uniform conditions.

Polyethylene Duct Design

Although PE ducts are supplied ready for installation, the consumer should check them for the following characteristics.

1. A uniform hole spacing of approximately 2 ft (600 mm).
2. The total hole area should be equal to one and one-half to two times the duct cross-section area.
3. The holes should be about 30° below the horizontal on each side.
4. One duct is adequate for houses up to 30 ft (9 m) wide. Two or more are needed for wider houses.
5. While ducts are available up to 150 ft (45 m) long, it is better to start them from both ends and limit their length to 100 to 120 ft (30 to 36 m).
6. The system should be designed to recirculate the air, heat the recirculated air, or draw in fresh air as conditions require.

Temperature Control

Thermostats need to be of a type that will tolerate high humidity. They should be located at eye level near the center of the house and shielded from direct sunlight. Although they should not be in a stagnant air location, neither should they be in the airstream from a fan or distribution duct. Electronic temperature controllers with up to seven or eight set points are able to control a sequence of events over a range of temperatures. For example, the lowest point might control heat; the next step, air circulation; the next, minimum ventilation; the next two, additional ventilation, and finally, the last step, cooling.

In larger greenhouses, environmental control computers are used to integrate the many pieces of equipment to provide optimum control of the environment parameters. Sensors for temperature, humidity, carbon dioxide, light, nutrients, and irrigation may be installed. An interactive software program allows the grower to vary the settings with plant needs, stage of development, and weather conditions. An added benefit is a complete record of the conditions under which the crop was grown.

Heat Sources

It has been pointed out that heating systems may be fired with various fuels. The choice of fuel will depend on availability, cost, and convenience. Table 23-3 (a, b) provides a comparison of different heat sources.

Seasonal Heat Requirements

Heating degree-days is a useful index in determining fuel requirements. Although the index is designed for use as an aid in estimating annual heating costs for homes or for scheduling fuel oil deliveries, with proper adjustments it can be useful for estimating fuel requirements for greenhouse heating.

Heating degree-days are determined by subtracting the average of the maximum and minimum temperatures for a 24 h period from 65°F. Any negative value is taken as zero. For example, a minimum of 20°F and a maximum of 30°F for a day would result in 40 degree-days: $(65 - [20 + 30]/2 = 40)$. An oil company might find from its records that a customer uses one gallon of oil for every five degree-days. With that knowledge and a record of accumulated degree-days since the last oil delivery, the date of the next delivery can be pinpointed.

Table 23-3. (a) Heat output from fuels (IP)

Fuel	Unit	Btu/Unit	Typical Efficiency	Fuel Units/100,000 Btu Heat Output
#2 oil	gal	140,000	70%	1.02 gal
Coal	lb	12,500	65%	12.3 lb
Natural gas	ft^3	1,000	80%	125 ft^3
LP gas	gal	92,000	80%	1.36 gal
Electricity	kWh	3,413	100%	29.3 kWh

Table 23-3. (b) Heat ouput from fuels (SI units)

Fuel	Unit	kJ/Unit	Typical Efficiency	Fuel Units/100,000 Btu Heat Output
#2 oil	L	39 022	70%	3.66 L
Coal	kg	29 012	65%	5.30 kg
Natural gas	m^3	37 252	80%	3.36 m^3
LP gas	L	25 643	80%	4.87 L
Electricity	kWh	3 600	100%	27.78 kWh

Table 23-4. Trial values for heating estimate constant

Annual Hours of Sunlight	k	Annual Hours of Sunlight	k
2,200	17.75	3,000	13.00
2,400	16.25	3,200	12.25
2,600	15.00	3,400	11.50
2,800	14.00		

The total heating needs for a home for any period (probably a heating season) may be estimated by the following equation:

$$F = q_f \times HDD \times \frac{k}{f} \qquad (23.3)$$

where

F = units of fuel

q_f = total heat loss (Btu/h-°F)

HDD = degree-days for period (°F-day)

k = adjustment factor (includes conversion of 24 h/day) (table 23-4)

f = energy content of fuel (Btu/unit) (table 23-3)

The degree-days must be for the local area and for the period required. Local weather stations have the information. The value for k is influenced by the sources of heat other than the heating system. These include occupants, lights, equipment, and solar energy.

To use this equation effectively for a greenhouse, it becomes necessary to consider the average hours of sunshine per day in determining a value for k (fig. 23.5).

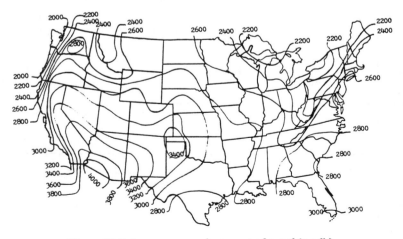

Figure 23.5. Average annual amount of sunshine (h).

In calculating degree-days for homes, a 65°F base temperature is used. For green-houses that operate at lower temperatures, a lower base temperature must be used to determine the heating degree-days. Local weather bureaus may have degree-days based on 55°F and 60°F as well as the standard 65°F. If not, a reasonable estimate may be made by direct proportion; that is, 55°/65° = 85% and the HDD for a 55°F base may be taken as 85% of the HDD for a 65° base.

Example 23.2

An example using the same greenhouse for which a heating system load was calculated is as follows:

$$q_f = \frac{q_t}{TD}$$

$$\left(\frac{\text{Total of 163,116 Btu/h}}{60°}\right) = 2,719 \text{ Btu/(h°F)}$$

Assume that the house is to be used for bedding plants for a period of 2,000 degree-days (based on 60°F) in a 2,600 h sunlight area and that oil with a net output of 98,000 Btu/gal will be used.

$$F = q_f \times DD \times \frac{k}{f}$$

$$\frac{2,719 \times 2,000 \times 15}{98,000} = 832 \text{ gal of fuel oil required for that period}$$

Ventilation

The exchange of air inside a greenhouse with air from outside is needed to lower the temperature, to reduce humidity, and to bring in fresh air to maintain the level of carbon dioxide. Ventilation is accomplished with either vents and doors or with fans.

Ridge and side vents are commonly used in glass houses. They depend on natural convection currents and wind to move the air through the house.

Exhaust fans and inlet louvers are commonly used for plastic-covered houses because it is difficult to combine vents with the large sheets of plastic that are used. This is particularly true with the air inflated, double-covered houses.

Vents or fans may be controlled either manually or with thermostats. As conditions can change rapidly, particularly during periods of partly cloudy weather, automatic controls are strongly recommended. Ventilation is most critical on bright, sunny days in mild weather when great quantities of solar heat must be removed. As shown in fig-ure 23.6, one air change per minute results in an inside temperature of about 10°F (5°C) above outside temperature. This rate is calculated by multiplying the floor area

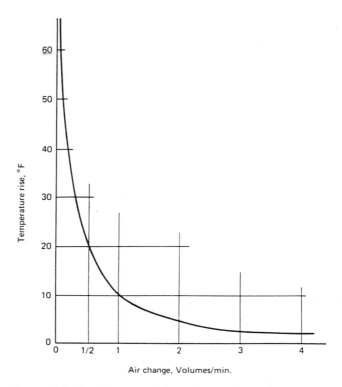

Figure 23.6. The influence of air exchange rate on temperature rise in greenhouses.

by 7 or 8 ft (2.1 or 2.4 m), the normal zone in which plants are grown. As this temperature difference is generally satisfactory, it is the ventilation rate that is commonly recommended. If lower temperatures are necessary, either shading or cooling or both may be used.

Fan capacity should be calculated at 1/8 in. (3 mm) static pressure. Winter ventilation, when it is required, should be at a rate of 10 to 20% of the summer maximum. In early spring or late fall, an intermediate rate is desirable to avoid chilling the plants from a sudden influx of cold air. These variations in rate of air movement may be obtained with multi-speed fans or by operating only one of several fans in cold weather.

In most greenhouses, air is brought in through inlet louvers at one end and exhausted by fans at the opposite end. The inlet louver area should equal 1.5 ft^2/1,000 cfm (0.14m^2/472 L/s) and they should be motor controlled for positive action. The louvers at the exhaust fans need not be motorized.

Where natural ventilation systems are being used, the area of the vents at the ridge should be equal to one sixth of the floor area and the side vents should total approximately the same. The ridge vents should open far enough to make a 60° angle with the roof.

Cooling Greenhouses

Under normal summer conditions the inside temperature will be higher than the outside even when shading material and a high level of ventilation are in use. If the resulting temperature is likely to reduce crop quality or result in serious plant damage, then cooling is desirable. Evaporative coolers are preferred over mechanical refrigeration because they are much less expensive. In addition they have the beneficial effect of raising the humidity which reduces plant wilting.

The most common evaporative cooling system consists of 2 in. (50 mm) thick pads of shredded wood fiber mounted in either a side or end wall. At least 1 ft^3 (0.093 m^2) of pad area is required for each 150 cfm (71 L/s) of fan capacity. Water is spread evenly over the pads from a manifold supplied with a float-controlled water level. As the air is drawn through the pads by the fans, moisture is picked up and then changed from the liquid state to the vapor state absorbing the latent heat of 970 Btu/lb (2260 kJ/kg). The air is then exhausted from the greenhouse.

Fog is another system that can be used to cool the greenhouse. Droplets less than 30 microns in diameter (about 1/10 the diameter of a human hair) are created using high pressure pumps and nozzles or spinning atomizers. The fog droplets created float around until the water is evaporated. Uniform cooling occurs when the fog is injected throughout the growing area.

For each gallon of water evaporated, over 9,000 Btu (9.5 MJ) of heat are absorbed. Ventilation air then carries this out of the greenhouse. Transpiration from plants and evaporation of moisture from soil surfaces also aids the process.

Heat Conservation in Greenhouses

Greenhouses are designed to produce a crop under controlled conditions often involving high energy consumption. Heating costs represent a substantial part of the total cost of production and even relatively small savings can be significant. But efforts to save energy, which will limit yield or interfere with a critical production schedule, may not be economical. So it is imperative to examine the ways in which fuel consumption can be reduced without undermining the profit potential.

The greatest loss of heat is through the roof and walls. Various insulating techniques have been developed to curb this loss and thereby save energy.

Inflated double-layer PE can save up to 40% as compared to a single layer of PE. Used over glass houses, savings up to 50% are reported. However, the level of lighting is reduced about 15% and this in turn may reduce crop yields.

Movable, horizontal curtains or thermal screens that can be drawn over the plant area at night have shown considerable promise. In the event of a winter storm, they can be opened to allow enough heat loss to prevent snow accumulation. Fixed curtains are not recommended because of reduced light and possibly dangerous snow accumulation.

Concrete and masonry foundations are very poor barriers to heat transfer. One inch of foam insulation installed on either the inside or outside of the wall can reduce heat loss through these materials by 75 to 80%.

In constructing a new house, the selection of a well-sheltered area can appreciably reduce heat loss from wind. In addition, tree windbreaks, located to the north and northwest and far enough away to avoid casting shadows on the house, provide permanent protection.

Maintenance plays an important role in heat conservation. Equipment that is kept in good condition will operate efficiently and houses that are kept tight will reduce heat loss. But these and other aspects of energy conservation in the greenhouse are a matter of management and not within the scope of this book.

Greenhouse Benches

The decision to use benches or to grow plants at ground level, either in flats or pots or in the floor soil, is largely determined by the crops to be produced, the shape of the house, and the management program. For example, tomatoes may be grown in the floor soil. Nursery stock containers might be arranged so as to completely fill the floor area. Cut flower crops are usually grown on open benches.

The use of benches however, has several advantages. They provide a comfortable working height, allow better air circulation and environmental control around the plants, and permit better disease and growth control.

Benches may be constructed of several different materials. Among the most satisfactory are wood that has been pressure-treated with water-borne preservatives, galvanized welded-wire fabric, and lath fence. Each has unique features and the choice depends on the manner in which the bench will be used. Support rails may be made of treated wood or galvanized pipe. Concrete blocks which can be easily leveled, make substantial supports.

Movable Benches

For production areas, movable benches increase growing space 10 to 25% and can reduce labor in greenhouses used for pot crops and nursery stock. Narrow folding conveyors are available to move the plants into and out of the growing area. An alternate design utilizes pallet trays 4 to 6 ft (1.2 to 1.8 m) wide by 6 to 16 ft (1.8 to 4.9 m) long that are handled on roller conveyors, tracks or by a lift truck (fig. 23.7). Trays are moved to a work area for transplanting, potting, and shipping.

The basic concept of the movable bench system is to convert all but one aisle to growing space. The bench tops are supported on pipe rollers and allowed to move sideways 18 to 24 in. (460 to 610 mm), the width needed for a work aisle. When there is a need to get to a particular bench, other benches in the house are pushed together, leaving an open aisle at the desired bench. Only one side of the bench can be worked on at a time. Because the benches move, connections for water, heat, and electrical systems that are attached to the bench are flexible. Benches as long as 200 ft (61 m) can be moved easily by turning one of the support rollers with a crank at the end of the bench.

There are many variations in bench design. Benches can be fabricated of wood or metal with either a solid or mesh bottom. Several manufacturers make an aluminum extrusion that adapts to an expanded metal bottom. A molded polyethylene grow tray is

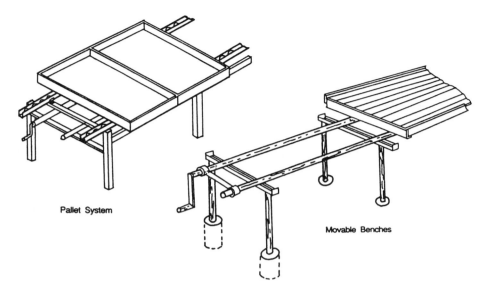

Pallet System

Movable Benches

Figure 23.7. Movable benches and pallets can improve space use and labor efficiency.

also available. The support unit can be made from pipe, tubing, or concrete blocks. The key to a smooth working unit is to have metal surfaces for the pipe rollers to move on.

Electrical and Water Systems

Electrical Service

In planning the electrical service for any building, one must determine what equipment, operating simultaneously, will cause the peak demand for electrical power. In a greenhouse, the period of maximum ventilation is almost certain to cause the peak electrical demand. A close estimate of the load during this period is made by combining the running currents of all motors, including doubling the current for the largest motor. If other electrical equipment is likely to be operating at the same time, that should also be included.

Special care must be taken to insure that distribution lines between houses are of sufficient size to prevent more than a two to three percent voltage drop.

Alarms

An alarm to warn of a malfunction in the environmental control system is essential for any greenhouse with a valuable crop that may be easily damaged by a major change in temperature.

The failure of the electrical supply or the ventilating or heating equipment can ruin a greenhouse crop in a very short time. When one air change per minute is necessary for summer cooling, a devastating temperature rise can occur in a matter of minutes in the event of a ventilation failure. The reverse can occur with a heating failure on a windy zero night in winter.

A combination power- and temperature-sensitive alarm will ensure the most rapid response. The alarm may be wired directly to a location where someone is always present, or in the case of greater distances, telephone lines can be leased for the purpose.

Watering

Hand watering, common in many operations, is facilitated by short hoses and several faucets rather than one long hose. Automatic bench-watering systems, in which nozzles are installed in lines along the edges of the benches, can be operated with a time clock. Potted plants may be watered more uniformly with a spaghetti tube system in which water is fed to each pot with a small-sized tube extended from a larger distribution line.

Problems

23.1.   Determine the heat loss from a gable roof greenhouse that is 18 ft (5.5 m) wide, 60 ft (18.3 m) long, 5 ft (1.5 m) to the eaves, and has a rise of 6.3 ft (1.9 m). All surfaces are covered with a double layer of polyethylene. The greenhouse is located in an area with a design temperature of 10°F (–12°C) and must be maintained at a minimum of 60°F (15.6°C).

23.2.   What fan capacity would be required for ventilation on a warm, sunny day?

23.3.   An evaporative cooler is installed to match the ventilation rate found in problem 23.2. How much pad surface area will be required?

23.4.   The air approaching the cooling pads is 95°F (35°C) and 60% RH. If the moisture evaporates to produce 90% relative humidity as the air passes through the wet pad, what is the resulting air temperature?

24 Swine Housing

Swine are the most efficient of the large animals in converting feed into meat products; however, they do not tolerate temperature extremes well and a controlled environment is needed for the most successful enterprise. Confinement housing contributes to labor efficiency, faster gains, and greater animal density. Specialization and growth in size of operations, typical of agriculture as a whole, has occurred, and along with increased size and concentration have come the problems of waste management and odor control.

Production Programs

Swine production may be divided into stages: farrowing, prenursery, nursing, growing, finishing, breeding, and gestation. Separate facilities will allow providing optimum environment for each stage. However, the cost may be greater and the stress of moving pigs may have a negative impact on production. Baby pigs may be kept in the farrowing facility and allowed to nurse up to six weeks. In some cases the sow and pigs will be moved at about three days into a sow-pig nursery. Typically, pigs are weaned and moved to a nursery (or weanling room) at about three weeks. The weanling pig is moved to the grower at about eight weeks (75 lb; 34 kg). During the finishing stage, pigs grow from about 150 to 250 lb (70 to 115 kg) and are marketed at 22 to 24 weeks. Some farms are organized to handle all of these stages in a farrow-to-finish operation. Other swine enterprises may be limited to feeder pig production or growing and finishing for market.

The choice of a production alternative is a management decision based on several factors including the availability of capital, skilled labor, feed supply, and markets. For example, top-quality labor and skilled management are required for the farrowing and starting operation. Feed costs are not critical. For a finishing operation, however, the most important requirements are an adequate source of feed grains, a reliable source of feeder pigs, and a ready market. To carry the whole operation from farrow to finish requires top management, considerable investment, and a good source of feed.

The production program and the management system together will determine the facilities required for a particular farm.

Management Systems

Management systems include: (1) pasture and portable houses, (2) concrete lot confinement, and (3) total confinement.

Pasture System

The pasture system is suitable only in mild climate areas—and even there the winter season may produce temperatures that will cause a slower rate of gain and reduce feed conversion efficiency. Labor demands are likely to be high and sufficient land for rotating the pasture on a three-year basis is required. The principal advantage is low investment in buildings.

Concrete Feedlot System

With open front buildings for shelter, this system reduces the land and labor required and allows greater automation of the feeding system. Although rate of gain and feed conversion efficiency will improve, they will not be as high as in the total confinement system. The considerably greater animal density introduces a manure management challenge.

Total Confinement System

This system provides the ideal conditions that allow for multiple farrowing practices and continuous operation throughout the year under a wide range of climatic conditions. Ventilation will keep moisture and odors under control while supplementary heat and cooling systems can maintain near optimum temperatures. The high density housing allows for maximum automation and labor efficiency. The principal disadvantage is high investment. However, with skilled management, increased production volume, and efficiency in feed and labor utilization, the annual cost per animal marketed is likely to be less than for an animal raised in either the pasture or open lot system.

Building Requirements

In the mild climate regions where a pasture management system is practiced, small houses with one or two farrowing pens are commonly used. Built on skids, the houses are easily drawn to a clean location as required. Sunshades, also on skids, may be necessary if natural shade is not available. Pasture housing requires enough land to permit a three-year rotation schedule; that is, a farrowing house can return to the original area every third year.

In partial or total confinement systems, separate buildings or sections within a building are often provided for each stage of hog production: (1) gestating gilts and sows, along with the necessary number of boars, (2) farrowing sows and the baby pigs through weaning, (3) weanling pigs, (4) growing pigs up to approximately 100 lb (45 kg), and (5) finishing hogs up to market weight. Smaller operations may combine farrowing and weanling, and growing and finishing. Size and intensity of operation largely determine how many separate sections are required.

Facility Scheduling

Swine housing design depends on the type of management, the number of stages to be used, and the intensity. A low intensity system which might be used in northern climates with very little housing would provide only one litter per year. A medium intensity operation might use several sow groups and farrow 6 to 12 times per year. Farrowing weekly would be considered a high intensity system.

Table 24-1. Swine scheduling table per 10 farrowing crates

	1	2	3	4	5	6*	7†	8‡
Farrowing frequency, no./yr	6	7	8	10	12	17	26	weekly
No. of sow groups	3	3	4	4	5	7	11	21
Total no. of sows	39	39	51	51	63	85	131	237
Sow in gestation	24	24	36	36	48	60	96	182
Sows in post-farrowing	15	15	15	15	15	15	15	15
No. of boars	2	3	3	5	5	3	4	4
Interval between farrowings	56	51	42	37	28	21	14	7
Pigs in nursery	80	80	80	80	80	160	240	320
Pigs in growing	-	80	80	160	160	160	240	640
Pigs in finishing	160	80	160	180	80	240	320	800
Pigs marketed/yr	520	575	695	830	1,040	1,390	2,085	4,170

* This column is based on 20 farrowing crates in 2 rooms.
† This column is based on 30 farrowing crates in 3 rooms.
‡ This column is based on 50 farrowing crates in 5 rooms.

Except for the very simple, low intensity operation, some planning is required to match he facility sizes for the various production stages. Table 24-1 can be used to determine the iize of facility for each stage.

Example 24.1
A producer has a 24-stall farrowing building and plans to farrow every five weeks.

Solution
The plan of farrowing every five weeks is about 10 times per year, therefore use column 4 in table 24-1. The multiplier factor of 24/10 = 2.4 should be used:

Total number of sows = 2.4 × 51 = 122
Boars needed = 2.4 × 5 = 12
Pigs in nursery = 2.4 × 80 = 192
Pigs in growing = 2.4 × 160 = 384
Pigs in finishing = 2.4 × 160 = 384
Pigs marketed per year = 2.4 × 830 = 1,992

Example 24.2
How many farrowing stalls are needed for 100 sows farrowing eight times per year and how many pigs will be marketed?

Solution
From column 3 the number of sows per stall is 5.1, therefore 100/5.1 = 19.6 or 20 farrowing stalls will be required. The number of pigs marketed per year will 19.6 × 69.5 = 1,362.7 or 1,363.

Breeding-gestating Buildings

Complete confinement buildings for gestating sows are increasing in popularity for sev- :ral reasons, including easier control over feeding and reduced incidence of parasites. A well-designed facility will allow easy heat detection and provide for animal handler safety.

Complete confinement of sows is not suitable on all farms. The large investment required for a total confinement building cannot be justified if capital is limited, ample marginal land is available, the farmer is operating on rented land or if there are limited rather than continuous farrowings during the year.

A partial confinement barn may provide pens for groups of 5 to 20 sows (fig. 24.1). With five to six animals in a pen, individual feeding stalls are necessary to limit each sow to her own allotment of feed. Restricted feeding space is provided for one third of the animals in the barn and they are moved in groups to the feeding pens.

Total confinement gestation buildings may be designed with pens and partially slotted floors or with individual stalls (fig. 24.2). Free stalls and a common area in pens for 5 or 6 animals allow sows room to exercise and a secure resting place. Free stalls are 5×2 ft (1.5 $\times 0.6$ m) while confinement stalls are 7×2 ft (2.1 $\times 0.6$ m). While tie stalls require somewhat more area, they simplify the restrictive feeding program and prevent fighting (table 24-2). Mechanical feeding can reduce the width of the barn by eliminating one or more feeding alleys.

The breeding and gestation barn shown in figure 24.3 houses 200 gilts and sows. Sows are penned in front of the boar/breeding pens and are easily brought together with the boar by opening the rear gate on the sow stall. Directly beyond the breeding area are pens for developing gilts that are to be incorporated into the breeding herd. Beyond the gilt area are stalls for gestating sows. The partially slatted floor and under floor plenum facilitates waste removal and provides for under-slat ventilation.

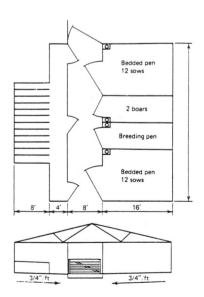

Figure 24.1. Open-front gestation house.

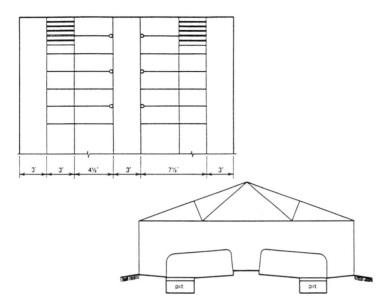

Figure 24.2. Gestation house with tie stalls.

Table 24-2. Space requirements for swine breeding stock

	Per Sow	Per Boar
TOTAL CONFINEMENT		
Concrete floor	30-35 ft² (2.8-3.3 m²)	35-40 ft² (3.3-3.7 m²)
Partial slotted floor	20 ft² (1.9 m²)	25 ft² (2.3 m²)
Full slotted floor	15 ft² (1.4 m²)	20 ft² (1.9 m²)
Tie stalls	2 ft × 6 ft (0.6 × 1.8 m)	
OPEN LOT		
Shelter resting area	25-30 ft² (2.3-2.8 m²)	30-35 ft² (2.8-3.3 m²)
Concrete lot	20 ft² (1.9 m²)	30 ft² (2.8 m²)
Dirt lot	100-200 ft² (9.3-19 m²)	150-250 ft² (14-23 m²)
PASTURE		
Animals per acre (ha)	10-12 sows (25-30 sows)	5-10 boars (12-15 boars)
Shelter	20-25 ft² (1.9-2.3 m²)	15-20 ft² (1.4-1.9 m²)
FEEDING AND WATER SPACE		
Self feeder (grain or complete feed)	2-3 sows/hole	2 linear ft (0.6 m)
Supplemental feeder	3-5 sows/hole	1 linear ft (0.3 m)
Water space	1 waterer/12 sows	1 waterer/3 boars

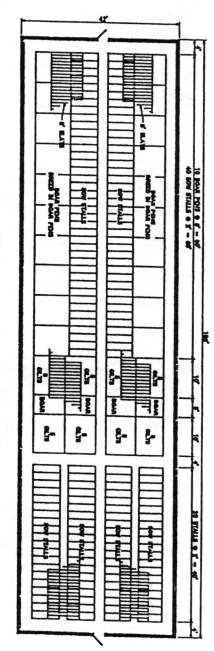

Figure 24.3. Four-row breeding and gestation building.

Farrowing Buildings

If gilts are farrowed only once a year, building investment must be kept to a minimum. Farrowing on pasture may be the answer. When sows are farrowed twice a year, a greater investment can be justified. With careful scheduling, buildings can be kept simple and provided with a minimum of environmental control equipment. When sows are grouped so that farrowing is continuous throughout the year, investment in a slotted floor system with supplemental heating and considerable automated equipment becomes economically feasible.

Farrowing usually takes place in either a stall (fig. 24.4), or an individual pen (fig. 24.5), with sloped floors to prevent any accumulation of liquid. Typical stall and pen sizes are given in table 24-3. The variation in details of design is almost unlimited. However, both stalls and pens will have guard rails to prevent the sow from lying on the young pigs and there will be a creep area at the side or in front of the sow, provided with extra heat from a warmed floor panel or from a radiant heater above the creep. Sometimes both sources are used for the first few days when a temperature of 90°F (32°C) is desirable. Since the temperature is decreased 2°F (1°C) daily until 70°F (21°C) is reached, both sources are not likely to be needed past the first few days.

A creep feeder and water cup should be provided to encourage the young pigs to feed and drink before they are weaned.

The choice between stalls (crates) or pens in a farrowing building is often determined by whether the building is used for farrowing only or for farrowing and growing. The stalls are advantageous for the single use system, while pens are more convenient in the multipurpose building where partitions can be easily removed to enlarge the pens for the growing operation.

Feeding in a stall rather than turning the sows out to a common feeding floor is more efficient and avoids the odor problems and cleaning associated with feeding floors. Although stalls may face in or out, the face-in arrangement permits easier feeding from a single alley, and the sows tend to be calmer when they can see another animal. Slotted

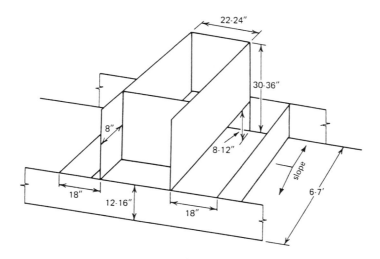

Figure 24.4. Dimensions for a farrowing stall.

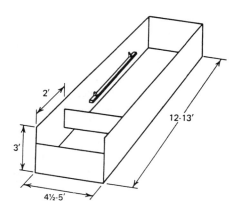

Figure 24.5. Dimensions for a farrowing pen.

Table 24-3. Space requirements for a farrowing house

	Stall	Conventional Pen	Long Narrow Pen
Gilt	22 in. × 6 ft (0.56 × 1.8 m)	6 × 8 ft (1.4 × 2.4 m)	5 × 14 ft (1.5 × 4.3 m)
Sow	24 in. × 7 ft (0.6 × 2.1 m)	8 × 8 ft (2.4 × 2.4 m)	5 × 14 ft (1.5 × 4.3 m)
Pigs	18 in. each side (0.46 m)	Creep in corner*	Creep in end of pen

* Both conventional pen and long narrow pen have a guard rail 8 in. (200 mm) high and 8 in. (200 mm) from pen side in addition to creep.

floors allow the manure to fall into pits where it accumulates for a period of time. A face-out arrangement is preferable when a solid floor is used, with the stalls sloping down to a center alley that is cleaned daily.

In pig production, disease and parasite control are critical during the first few weeks after birth. Therefore, sanitation becomes one of the most important factors in a farrowing operation. The thoroughness with which cleaning can be done is affected by the scheduling of the farrowing pens. If sows are brought into a single-room farrowing building in rotation, it means that individual stalls or pens must be cleaned and dried as each sow and litter are removed. One room farrowing barns obviously can never be completely sanitized. An alternative to this is to arrange the breeding schedule in such a way that the building is filled in about one week and used for three to six weeks. At the end of this period all animals are removed and one week is used for complete cleaning and drying. This eight-week cycle is continued throughout the year. However, the necessary interruption of the breeding schedule in order to have the sows farrow on an eight-week cycle decreases the reproduction rate of the herd.

The delay of rebreeding may be avoided by having multi-room buildings that are used on a cycle that allows one week for complete cleaning. The two-room house shown in figure 24.6 would work on an eight-week, continuous-breeding cycle but has little advantage over the single room system. However, in a house with four rooms (fig. 24.7), each isolated from the other and from outside contamination as well, groups of sows with their lit-

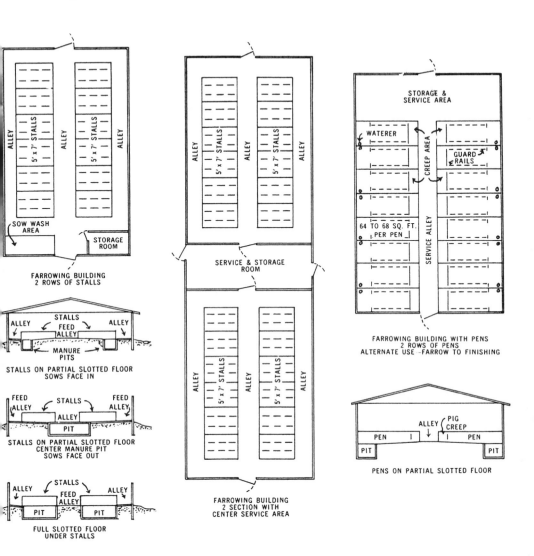

Figure 24.6. Farrowing buildings with stalls.

ters can be taken through the farrow-nursing stages on a rotation without interruption of the breeding schedule. Each room is emptied, cleaned, sterilized, and dried for one week at the end of each cycle. This system provides a superior sanitation program and allows greater uniformity in the age of the young pigs removed from the house. Multi-room farrowing houses are suited to large herds of 100 or more where management becomes most critical. Typical cycles are shown in figure 24.8.

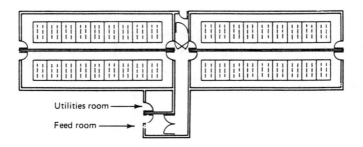

Figure 24.7. Four-room farrowing house.

N = Nursing	F = Filling	C = Cleaning	W = Weaning

Single Room:
5 week cycle
F N N N C, F N N N C, F N
8 week cycle (early weaning)
F N N N W W W C, F N N N
8 week cycle (late weaning)
F N N N N N C, F N N N
Breeding on a 5 or 8 week cycle is required.

Double Room:
1st room
8 week cycle (early weaning)
F F F F N N N C, F F F F N
2nd room
    F F F F N N N C, F F F F N
Continuous breeding cycle.

Four Rooms:
1st room
8 week cycle (early weaning)
F F N N N W W C, F F N N
2nd room
  F F N N N W W C, F F N N
3rd room
    F F N N N W W C, F F N N
4th room
      F F N N N W W C, F F N N
8 week cycle (late weaning)
1st room
F F N N N N C, F F N N
2nd room
  F F N N N N C, F F N N
3rd room
    F F N N N N C, F F N N
4th room
      F F N N N N C, F F N N
Continuous breeding cycle.

Figure 24.8. Typical cycles for one-, two-, and four-room farrowing houses.

Nurseries

Weaning pigs at three to four weeks of age is common with modern producers. Some producers find that weaning at 10 to 14 days reduces disease problems. The young pigs are very sensitive to stress and thus there is a need for a special nursery. The all-in-all-out concept in which pigs from only one farrowing group are confined in a room or building is recommended. The four basic needs of the nursery are:

1. A warm, dry, draft-free environment.
2. Minimum age spread within the group of pigs.
3. Complete and thorough sanitation of facilities and equipment between groups of pigs.
4. A waste disposal system that prevents a buildup of gases from the decomposition of manure.

Some farmers who practice early weaning (three weeks old) are using 3×3 1/2 ft floor $(0.9 \times 1$ m) weaner cages. The cages, which are stacked two high and hold about 12 pigs up to 30 lb (14 kg), have automatic feeding, watering, and manure removal systems similar to poultry layer cages. At 30 lb (14 kg) the pigs are divided into two cages of six each.

Single- or double-deck pens with flooring materials that are 50 to 60% open, such as woven wire or expanded metal, are well-suited for nursery pigs. Early weaned pigs will perform better in small groups of approximately litter size which makes a 4×4 ft $(1.2 \times 1.2$ m) pen a suitable size. Daily gain and feed efficiency decline and tail biting increases as the number of pigs per pen increases above about eight. Pens should be placed to allow good air movement and visual observation under and around the pen. A minimum clearance under the pen of 16 in. (400 mm) is recommended.

Growing Pens

Each stage in a pig's life requires specific housing, feeding, and environmental conditions. During the growing stage, from weaning to about 100 lb (45 kg) of weight, the maximum rate of gain and the highest feed conversion efficiency takes place in an environment where the temperature is between 60 and 68°F (16 and 20°C) and the humidity is moderate. Separate facilities for the growing stage can provide these optimum conditions.

Design recommendations include 20 to 25 pigs/pen with a water fountain and continuous feeding in each pen. A larger number per pen is likely to reduce the rate of gain. Full-slotted floors are desirable for growing pens as the young pigs are likely to be messy.

Finishing Pens

In mild climates an open-front building with a paved dry lot can be used for finishing each group of 20 to 25 pigs (fig. 24.9). About 6 ft^2 (0.6 m^2) per animal, both inside and on the paved yard, will be needed (table 24-4). For confinement housing, pens may be arranged so that those on one side of a central alley are one and one-half times as wide as those on the other. This allows groups of younger animals to be started in the smaller pens and then simply moved across the alley when they have outgrown the pen. The principal reason for this arrangement is to promote a calm and secure social relationship among the pigs. Whenever possible, swine groups should be kept together from weaning to market to avoid fighting and stress that will reduce gain. Partially slotted floors are an efficient way to handle the waste. An alternative is the use of deep, narrow gutters at the rear of a row of pens with a sloping floor. One water fountain and feeder per pen is adequate. Figure 24.10 shows two pen layouts and four floor arrangements for growing and finishing operations.

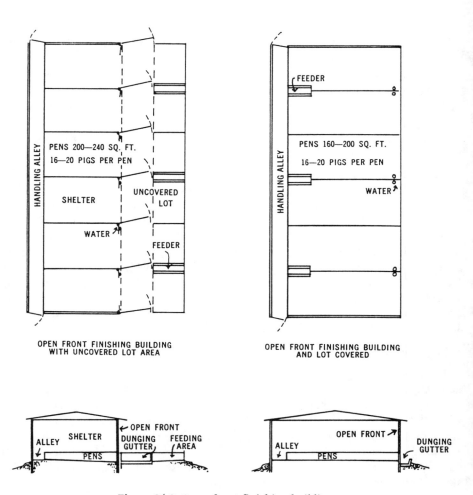

Figure 24.9. Open-front finishing buildings.

Location and Type of Construction

After a production program and a management system have been decided upon, all of the buildings that are planned initially or for future expansion should be located on a plan. As discussed in chapter 20, there are a number of factors that must be considered. A swine enterprise creates strong odors and large amounts of manure. Careful planning is necessary to minimize these problems. Therefore, it is worthwhile to review some of the questions that pertain especially to livestock operations.

1. Will all local and environmental regulations be met?
2. Is the location well drained?
3. Is there adequate space and suitable topography for manure storage?
4. Are adequate utilities, such as water, available?

Table 24-4. Space requirements for growing and finishing hogs

	Weaning to 75 lb (35 kg)	Grower, 75 - 150 lb (35-70 kg)	Finishing, 150 - 240 lb (70-110 kg)
TOTAL CONFINEMENT			
(10-20 head per pen)			
Slotted floor			
(full or partial)	4 ft² (0.4 m²)	6 ft² (0.6 m²)	8-10 ft² (0.7-0.9 m²)
Solid concrete floor	4 ft² (0.4 m²)	6.7 ft² (0.7 m²)	9-10 ft² (0.8-0.9 m²)
Additional building space			
(storage, isolation, etc.)	1 ft² (0.1 m²)	1 ft² (0.1 m²)	2 ft² (0.2 m²)
CONCRETE LOT			
(20-25 head per pen)			
Shelter floor area	6 ft² (0.6 m²)	7 ft² (0.7 m²)	8 ft² (0.8 m²)
Concrete floor	8 ft² (0.8 m²)	12 ft² (1.1 m²)	12-15 ft² (1.1-1.4 m²)
PASTURE			
Animals per acre (ha)	20-30 (50-75)	15-20 (35-50)	10-15 (25-35)
Shade	5-6 ft² (0.5 m²)	6-8 ft² (0.6-0.7 m²)	8-12 ft² (0.7-1.1 m²)
FEEDING AND WATER SPACE			
Self feeder			
(grain or complete feed)	6-8 head per hole	4-6 head per hole	3-5 head per hole
Supplemental feeder	8-10 head per hole	8-10 head per hole	6-8 head per hole
Waterer	20-25 head per cup	20-25 head per cup	10-15 head per cup

5. Will prevailing winds and proposed building separation minimize odor problems?
6. Will air-borne microorganisms be carried from older to younger animals?
7. Will buildings be arranged for easy movement of animals from one unit to another without risk of spreading disease?
8. Can feed, animals, and waste be moved efficiently?

Materials of Construction

Since most confinement buildings are single story and must be heavily insulated in both walls and ceiling, frame construction on concrete foundation is the most practical. Placing 2 in. (50 mm) of rigid polystyrene on the inside of the outer concrete form will allow the insulation to bond securely to the wall. The use of 2 × 6 in. (38 × 140 mm) studs will provide added strength and allow adequate space for the insulation. The ventilation inlets should be constructed at the time the walls and roof are being built.

Roof framing using clear-span, trussed construction eliminates any interference with pen location and facilitates any future modifications.

Either exterior-type plywood or sheet metal installed horizontally is suitable for the outer wall covering. After the insulation is in place, the studs should be covered with a vapor barrier before the inside wall surface is installed. Exterior plywood is a suitable material for both walls and ceiling, but the bottom 3 ft (1 m) of any wall exposed must be protected to prevent chewing.

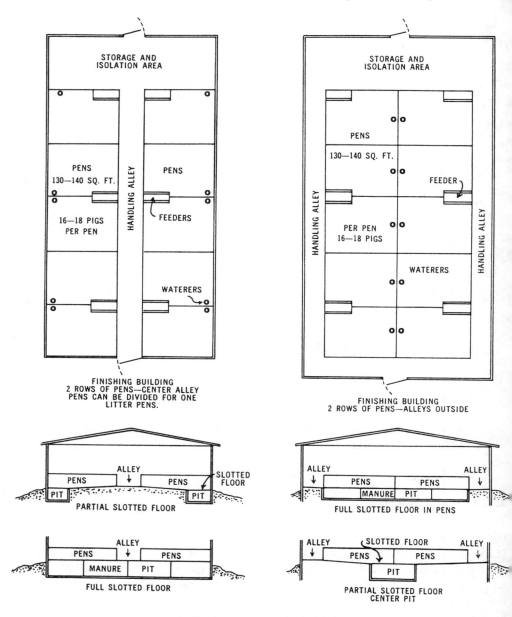

Figure 24.10. Growing and finishing buildings.

Concrete is the universal choice as the material with which to pave yards and build solid floors in swine houses. It is hard, durable, and easy to clean. As slotted floors have become popular, concrete has been the common choice for slat construction, again because of its durability and reasonable cost. However, a number of other materials including wood, steel, aluminum, and plastic have been used. Concrete is heavy to install but is relatively nonskid. The edges of the slats should be slightly rounded. Wood is inexpensive and light in weight but does not wear well and often warps and becomes slippery. The expected life is only two or three years.

Expanded metal has worked well for pigs under 50 lb (23 kg) but has not held up well for larger hogs. Early steel slats produced a satisfactory floor but had a short life due to corrosion. Aluminum is considerably more expensive than steel but is much more corrosion resistant. Some aluminum slats lock together for greater stability and strength. They have perforated openings punched in a staggered pattern in either of two widths, 3/8 in. (9.50 mm) for the farrowing house or 5/8 in. (16 mm) for the growing and finishing house. Aluminum slats tend to be very noisy.

Early slotted floors were designed with narrow slats. Experience appears to have shown that 8 in. (200 mm) slats with a 1 in. (24 mm) opening are best for all ages. The area under the sow should be covered with a piece of plywood or flat, expanded metal for two or three days at farrowing time to give the baby pigs a chance to become adjusted. It is generally recommended that a spacing of either 3/8 in. (9.5 mm) or 1 in. (25 mm), but not an intermediate value, be used for farrowing house floors. The baby pigs get their legs caught in the intermediate-sized spacing and the incidence of crushing by the sow increases. Casting the slats for the rear of the stall to a 11/4 in. (32 mm) spacing will improve the cleanliness of the farrowing stall.

Environmental Control

Swine are more sensitive to temperature than other domestic animals due in part to their lack of a protective coat of wool, hair or feathers. Because of this, growing pigs respond to the temperature of their house to a greater degree than other livestock. Newborn pigs need a temperature of 90°F (32°C) just to survive. The temperature is then gradually lowered until 70°F (21°C) is reached at about three weeks of age.

Research has shown that 70°F (21°C) is the optimum temperature for growth up to 150 lb (68 kg). From 150 lb (68 kg) to market weight, 70°F (21°C) remains the optimum level but temperatures down to 60°F (16°C) do not appreciably affect the rate of growth. At 90°F (32°C) and above, however, larger pigs suffer from excessive heat and actually lose weight. Breeding difficulties will occur at temperatures above 80°F (26°C).

Feed conversion is also dramatically affected by temperature level. The highest rate of feed conversion in pigs up to 150 lb (68 kg) occurs at 70°F (21°C) while the most efficient use of feed is obtained at 60°F (16°C) during the finishing stage.

Although prices of feed and fuel vary, and future prices are uncertain, in general it is safe to say that fuel is cheaper than feed and therefore it is economically feasible to provide some artificial heat during cold weather up to the age of 18 weeks and, under certain circumstances, right on through to market age.

Insulation

Given the importance of relatively high inside temperatures under all climatic conditions, high levels of insulation are essential. Table 24-5 suggests minimum R-values for mild, cold, and very cold zones. With these levels of insulation, a carefully installed 4-mil (0.1 mm) polyethylene vapor barrier is also important.

Table 24-5. Minimum R-values for swine buildings

Temperature °F (C)	Wall R-value ft²-h-°F/Btu (C-m²-K/W)	Ceiling R-value ft²-h-°F/Btu (C-m²-K/W)
10 (-12)	9 (1.6)	12 (2.1)
0 (-18)	13 (2.3)	18 (3.2)
-10 (-23)	17 (3.0)	24 (4.2)

Ventilation

Good ventilation in a swine barn controls temperature, humidity, odors, noxious gases, and the spread of disease. Supplemental heat is usually necessary during the winter. Although minimum ventilation will add to the heat load, it is essential for the removal of moisture and gases and for drawing in fresh air to dilute the airborne disease organisms. As outside temperatures moderate, fans are used to move more and more air through the building to maintain the inside temperature at the optimum level.

Fans may be located high on the wall on the protected side of the building. They may be grouped together in buildings up to 100 ft (30 m) long, but in longer buildings they should be divided into pairs and located at intervals along the wall. Locating thermostats for all fans at one point near the center of the building at eye level permits easy adjustment.

The distribution and circulation within the room is determined largely by the design and location of the fresh air inlets. They can be located either at the junction of the ceiling and walls or near the center of the ceiling. In either case, air which is a few degrees warmer may be brought in from the attic in the winter while for summer ventilation the side slots are supplied by air coming in through the soffits under the eaves. In the summer, the center inlet must be supplied by an insulated duct extending to gable-end louvers. Regardless of the vent location, baffles should direct the incoming air along the ceiling for winter ventilation. There the cool air mixes with the warm air uniformly and drafts are avoided. Summer ventilation is most effective when the inlet baffles are positioned so that the air is directed down toward the floor, thus providing the greatest cooling effect on the animals.

Air should pass through the inlets at high velocity to insure good distribution and maximum mixing. An inlet opening of not over 20 in.²/100 cfm of fan capacity (275 mm² /L s) will cause an air velocity of 700 to 1,000 fpm (3.6 to 5.0 m/s) and insure good ventilation. The velocity can be checked directly with a draft gauge or with the use of a manometer which will give the static pressure across the inlet opening (fig. 15.2). A static pressure of 0.03 to 0.06 in. (0.75 to 1.5 mm) indicates a satisfactory velocity.

Because of the very low ventilation rate needed in some swine buildings it is difficult to achieve good air distribution and mixing. In such cases additional measures should be taken. One or more circulation fans may be installed to enhance air mixing and prevent stratification. Removing exhaust air from near the floor or below slats is also recommended. If stratification occurs, this will remove the colder air and help pull the warmer air downward. When fans are located high on the wall, a duct may be installed to pull winter ventilation from near the floor. With pigs on slotted floors, it is nearly impossible to provide good air circulation through the pigs without pulling gases from below the slats. Thus it is recommended that at least some of the ventilation be exhausted from under the slats.

Table 24-6. (a) Ventilation rates and supplemental heat values for
swine housing (IP; wall R = 17, ceiling R = 24)

	Ventilation Rates ft³/min per Animal				Supplemental Heat Btu/h per Animal				
	Rate 1*	Rate 2*	Rate 3*	°F	-20°F	-10°F	0°F	10°F	20°F
Sow and litter	20	60	240	60	2,150	1,900	1,650	1,400	1,150
Prenursery pig	2	10	25	85	300	250	200	150	100
Growing-finishing pigs									
20-40 lb	3	12	36	70	300	250	200	150	100
40-100 lb	5	20	48	60	300	250	200	150	100
100-150 lb	7	25	75	60	500	400	300	200	100
150 lb up	10	35	100	60	500	400	300	200	100
Sows and boars									
200-250 lb	10	35	120	50	125	75	25	0	0
250-300 lb	12	40	180	50	125	75	25	0	0
300 lb up	15	45	250	50	125	75	25	0	0

* Rate 1 is for continuous operation and is put on a 35°F thermostat for freeze protection only. Rate 2 is in addition and would be controlled to come on at 5°F above heater shutdown. Rate 3 is in addition and would be controlled to come on at about 72°F for high room temperature control.
Note:
R = ft²-h-°F/Btu.
For wall R = 13 and ceiling R = 18 increase heat values 4%.
For wall R = 9 and ceiling R = 12 increase heat values 8%.

Table 24-6. (b) Ventilation rates and supplemental heat values for
swine housing (SI; wall R = 3, ceiling R = 4.2)

	Ventilation Rates L/s per Animal				Supplemental Heat w/animal				
	Rate 1*	Rate 2*	Rate 3*	°C	-29	-23	-18	-12	-7
Sow and litter	9.3	28	112	16	630	557	483	410	337
Growing-finishing pigs									
9-18 kg	1.4	5.6	17	21	88	73	59	44	29
18-45 kg	2.3	9.3	22	16	88	72	59	44	
45-68 kg	3.3	11.7	35	16	147	117	88	59	
68 kg up	4.7	16.3	47	16	147	117	88	59	29
Sows and boars									
91-114 kg	4.7	16.3	56	10	37	22	7	0	0
114-136 kg	5.6	19.0	84	10	37	22	7	0	0
136 kg up	7.0	21.0	117	10	37	22	7	0	0

* Rate 1 is for continuous operation and is put on a 2°C thermostat for freeze protection only. Rate 2 is in addition and would be controlled to come on at 3°C above heater shutdown. Rate 3 is in addition and would be controlled to come on at about 22°C for high room temperature control.
Note:
R = m² K/W.
For wall R = 2.3 and ceiling R = 3.2 increase heat values 4%.
For wall R = 1.6 and ceiling R = 2.1 increase heat values 8%.

Supplemental Heat

A heat balance is calculated by estimating the heat loss through the building walls and ceiling as well as the amount of heat removed by ventilation. From this total the heat produced by the animals is subtracted, leaving a balance to be supplied by a heating system. Table 24-6 provides approximate supplemental heat values and ventilation rates for swine buildings. Heating systems should be designed for safe, economical, and dependable operation.

Space Heating

For small buildings, gas or electric heaters, which can be suspended from the ceiling, help to circulate air as well as supply heat. For large buildings a central, hot water heating system, isolated in a fire-resistant room, will supply the necessary heat to maintain the room temperature. In addition, hot water can be used for heating floor slabs for creep and weaned pig areas.

The general heating can be supplied by black iron pipes mounted on the walls. Finned pipes or radiators should not be used because of dust. For the same reason, hot air systems are not satisfactory unless the normal filter area of the blower is doubled. Remember that with continuous fan operation there will be a small negative pressure in the building. This could adversely affect the combustion and flue draft of unit heaters or central heating systems that are not isolated. The best heating installations overcome this by providing fresh air from outside the building to support combustion.

Creep Heating

Newborn pigs require a very warm environment starting at 90°F (32°C) at birth with a gradual decline to 70°F (21°C) by the end of two or three weeks. At the same time, the sow is most comfortable at 70°F (21°C). Either floor or radiant heat in the creep area can supply the localized requirements of the young pigs without overheating the room for the sow.

Floor heat may be supplied to the creep areas by hot water pipes or electric heating cables set in the concrete. A hot water system is less expensive to operate and is particularly convenient to use if the boiler is also supplying heat for the room. Electrical heating permits individual control of the temperature at each creep in the building.

Fiberglass stall pads that cover slotted floors have electrically heated areas to provide for young pigs. Other slotted floor covers are designed to be used with quartz radiant heaters or heat lamps.

A relatively simple design for installing hot water pipes in a solid slab consists of preparing a smooth grade on which 2 in. (50 mm) thick pieces of polystyrene are placed in all locations where creep heat is desired. A pair of pipes, joined together at the far end of the house to form a loop, are laid across the polystyrene. Insulation is then placed around the pipes between the pieces of polystyrene insulation (fig. 24.11). A second pair of pipes is placed in the same manner leaving 12 in. (300 mm) between each of the four pipelines. Black iron, copper or high temperature CPVC pipe may be used. Concrete is then poured over the entire area, 4 in. (100 mm) thick between the insulation and 2 in. (50 mm) over the insulation. Water heated to 140°F (60°C) and circulated through the lines will produce an 85 to 90°F (29 to 32°C) floor surface temperature over the insulation when room temperature is 60°F (16°C). The required heater capacity to supply a floor pipe system of this type is calculated by assuming that about 10 Btu/(h-ft) (10 W/m) of pipe will be needed between

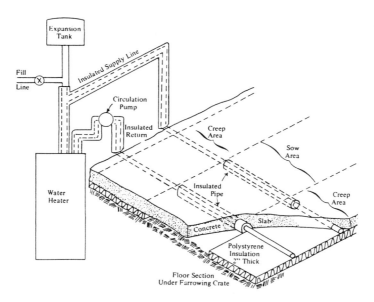

Figure 24.11. Hot-water heating of creep-area floor.

the warmed areas (where the pipe is insulated) and about 35 Btu/(h-ft) (34 W/m) of pipe will be needed for the heated areas. The heat for a small system may be supplied by an electric, gas or oil domestic water heater.

Example 24.1

To illustrate the method of calculating heating capacity, assume a 24 × 36 × 8 ft (7.3 × 11.0 × 2.4 m) farrowing house with ten, 5 ft (1.5 m) stalls in two rows. In each stall, a 3 ft (1 m) area is heated and a 2 ft (0.6 m) area is unheated. The outside temperature is 0°F (−18°C) and the inside temperature is 60°F (16°C). The average R is 20 h-ft²-F/Btu.

1. 10 stalls × 3 ft = 30 ft heated × 4 lines = 120 ft (37 m).
   10 stalls × 2 ft = 20 ft unheated × 4 lines = 80 ft (24 m).
2. 120 ft × 35 Btu/h-ft = 4,200 Btu/h.
   80 ft × 10 Btu/h-ft = 800 Btu/h.
3. The total heat per hour = 5,000 Btu.
4. This is well within the supply capabilities of a water heater. However, total heat for the house should be calculated to determine the type of heater required.
5. A 24 × 36 × 8 ft house has 1,824 ft² (170 m²) of surface area.
6. 1,824 ft²/20 h-ft²-F/Btu) × (60°F to 0°F) = 5,472 Btu/h wall and ceiling loss.
7. 20 cfm/stall × 10 stalls × 60 F × 0.018 Btu/(ft³-°F) × 60 min
   = 12,960 Btu/h ventilation loss.

8. Total loss = 18,432 Btu/h.
9. A 6,000 W electric heater or a 30,000 Btu gas heater would be adequate.
10. The 5,000 Btu for the creep floor heat does not add on to the total loss for the house; it is part of the radiation capacity of the system and at 44°F (6.7°C) outside temperature it would maintain a 60°F (16°C) air temperature in the room without further radiation.
11. The total heating system should have two circulating pumps controlled by two thermostats. One thermostat would sense slab temperature and control water flow to the slab, while the other would sense air temperature and control water flow to wall-mounted pipes.

When electric cable is used to warm creep floors, it is imbedded in a slab of concrete. Proper installation is crucial to avoid failure from burning out. Two inches (50 mm) of polystyrene insulation is covered with a sheet of 1/8 in. (3 mm) asbestos cement board to which the cable is carefully wired using the recommended spacing. A careful check to see that the wires do not come in contact with the insulation and that they are not crossed should be made before a 1 1/2 in. (38 mm) layer of concrete is poured. Either crossed wires or contact with the polystyrene will produce temperatures that melt the plastic insulation on the cable and cause it to burn out.

Cables are available with a number of different wattage ratings per unit length. Based on 30 to 40 W/ft^2 (320 to 430 W/m^2) the proper spacing can be calculated. The installation can be simplified by use of units in which the cable has been pre-spaced on a metal mat. A thermostat with the sensing bulb inserted in a conduit imbedded in the slab should be installed for each three to four stalls and a fuse and switch installed for each pen.

Heat lamps or quartz radiant heaters above the creep area should be equipped with guards and suspended by adjustable chains. As a safety precaution, it is wise to use ceiling mounted outlets and cords that are just long enough to serve the lowest level at which the heater will be used. If for some reason the heater falls, the cord will be pulled out.

Cooling

Feeder pigs subjected to high summer temperatures tend to gain more slowly or actually lose weight. Sows tend to be uncomfortable and lose their appetites at temperatures over 80°F (27°C). Conception rates drop when boars and early gestating sows are over 80°F (27°C). Reduced feed intake usually increases sow weight loss and decreases milk production. Sows that are kept cool tend to wean heavier pigs. To avoid these problems, a number of cooling methods are employed. For animals on pasture, shades and wallows are beneficial.

In the dry western half of the United States and Canada, evaporative coolers can reduce air temperatures by 10 to 20°F (6 to 11°C). However, they are not well-suited to eastern areas where temperature reductions greater than 6 to 9°F (3 to 5°C) are seldom practical.

The use of spray nozzles is one of the most practical methods to provide cooling for feeder pigs. One to two minutes per hour will wet the animal's skin and allow cooling by evaporation. The system consists of a thermostat set at 75 to 80°F (24 to 27°C) which operates a solenoid valve in the waterline supplying the nozzles. The nozzles should be of the hollow cone type producing a coarse spray pattern at the rate of about 0.05 gal/min

(0.2 L/min) per pig at line pressure. The coarse droplet size is important since the beneficial effect comes from wetting the pig and not evaporating water into the air. A time clock in series with the thermostat limits the spraying time.

Zone cooling has proved beneficial for sows confined in stalls. An insulated plywood duct extending the length of the room is located just above the front of the stalls. At each stall a small blower is installed in the duct with a short length of 2 1/2 in. (6 mm) flexible tubing that carries the air toward the stall. In the summer the tubing is bent down so that the sow can stand in the cool airstream. In areas where outside air is too warm and humid to supply the necessary cooling, air conditioners have been installed in the duct to provide about 1,200 Btu/h (350 W) of cooling for each sow. In the winter the tubing may be bent up to promote air circulation in the room and provide the minimum continuous ventilation. The small blowers should have a capacity of at least 50 cfm (1.5 m³/min) at 1/2 in. (13 mm) of static pressure. Depending on blower capacity and outside temperature, the use of every third or fourth fan can provide the necessary minimum continuous ventilation. Outlet openings in the building wall may need to be provided, but overhead inlets used in conjunction with larger exhaust fans should be closed tightly to prevent exhausting moist air into the attic.

Feed Management

Corn is the basic ingredient in most hog finishing rations and requires the greatest storage space (table 24-7). Dry corn is usually stored in steel bins. High moisture corn is commonly stored in glass-lined steel or concrete oxygen-limiting silos in the whole kernel form and then mixed on the farm with purchased concentrate using grinder-blender-proportioners. Concentrates and purchased feeds are usually stored in 5 to 20 ton hopper-bottom steel or fiberglass bins.

Self-feeders on pasture are filled from self-unloading feed wagons. Yard feeders near the fence line can be filled from the same type of wagon. However, auger feeders that run the length of the barn and fill each of the feeders have the advantage of requiring less labor and allowing the feeder to be located in the ideal location which is usually close to the rest area.

Feed is distributed by augers in totally confined growing and finishing operations. Where floor feeding is practiced, either feed carts or auger conveyors are used. The choice is often determined by the size of the enterprise and whether a time clock operation is desired.

Table 24-7. Estimated feed requirements for swine

	Customary (lb)	SI (kg)
Annual feed requirements for sows:		
Corn grain	1,820	825
Protein supplement	580	260
Feed requirements per pig		
40-210 lb (18-95 kg)		
Pig starter	12	5
Pig grower	70	32
Corn grain	490	225
Protein supplement	75	34

For feeding in gestation barns equipped with stalls, automatic feeders that travel on rails above the sow stalls meter out a predetermined amount of feed as indicated by the tab position at each stall. This ensures the correct individual ration of feed for each animal. Other automatic feeders accumulate a pre-set amount of feed and then drop it simultaneously into the feeders allowing all animals in a room to be fed within a few seconds. This prevents the emotional disturbances associated with sequential feeding along the row of stalls. Automatic feeders can eliminate the need for one or more feed alleys, resulting in a saving in building costs that would partially offset the cost of the feeder. On smaller farms where individual feeding is practiced, feed carts are used in both the farrowing and breeder-gestation barns.

Waste Management

A well-planned, complete waste management system is absolutely essential in a swine production enterprise. A complete waste disposal system is needed to maintain healthy livestock in sanitary conditions, to avoid polluting air and water, and to comply with local, state and federal environmental regulations. The methods of waste disposal vary with the type of waste being handled.

Hogs that are raised on pasture naturally distribute the manure throughout the area and thus reduce handling to a minimum. Wastes from bedded solid floor houses are handled as solids and spread with a conventional spreader, while drainage from manure stacks, runoff from lots, and manure from unbedded floors and slotted floors are handled as liquids, and spread with liquid manure spreaders or through irrigation systems.

Completely slotted floors reduce labor requirements at the barn to a minimum. However, because hogs always tend to dung in the same place, partially slotted floors are probably a better choice since they require only a minimal increase in labor while saving significantly on the original investment. Locating the water fountain over the slotted area and the feeders near the resting area encourages the pigs to dung over the slotted portion of the floor while keeping the solid area clean.

Although the full slotted floor may be designed with pits that are capable of storing manure up to 180 days, many herdsmen prefer to store the manure outside the building because of odors and toxic gases. Waste may be removed by flushing, with scrapers, or by using a pit recharge/gravity drain system. The frequent manure removal minimizes bacterial digestion and gas production in the pit and results in a better in-house environment. Flushing is normally done four or more times per day. With the recharge method the pit is drained weekly or more frequently and then recharged with new liquid to prevent manure from drying. If manure is allowed to dry it tends to adhere to the pit floor and is difficult to remove. Except in nurseries, liquids recycled from a lagoon may be used for the recharge. Scraper systems are effective in minimizing manure left in the house but can result in unpleasant maintenance when chains or cables break under slats.

Equipment

The equipment required for a swine enterprise will depend to a large extent on the production program and the management system being used. Feed-handling equipment and feeders will differ considerably from one farm to another. Farrowing stalls, for example, may be free standing or designed for anchoring to a wall at one end. They may be either commercial or home built. The same is true for many items used in swine production.

The wide range of equipment and the variety of designs from which to choose necessitate careful planning and complete integration of the entire system so that buildings and equipment are compatible throughout.

The Midwest Plan Service publications provide plans for many pieces of equipment needed for a swine operation. These plans include sorting chutes, loading chutes, breeding racks, pens and stalls, feeders, and fences.

Alarms

As with other complete confinement systems, the conditions in swine buildings can change rapidly in the event of either electrical or mechanical failure. Alarms that are both power and temperature sensitive are available and recommended for all completely enclosed buildings. An alarm may be wired directly to a location where it will always be noted, or it may be connected by a leased telephone line. Prompt warning of even one failure can result in a saving of livestock worth many times the cost of the alarm.

Problems

24.1. Using a four-room design, plan a building to provide farrowing facilities for the 80 sows on a farm. Within the same building or one attached to it, provide facilities for growing pigs from 8 weeks to 14 weeks of age.

24.2. Plan a separate building to provide space for finishing to market weight the pigs moved from the growing area in problem 24.1.

24.3. Make recommendations for the environmental control system for the farrowing house section of the building in problem 24.1. Indicate the level of insulation, supplemental heat, and ventilation. Assume a winter design temperature of $-10°F$ $(-18°C)$.

25 Beef and Sheep Housing

BEEF CATTLE

The facilities for a beef cattle enterprise should provide an optimum environment which will result in rapid growth, efficient feed conversion, good health, and reasonable comfort for the animals as well as security and safety for both animals and workers. The design should prevent pollution of air and water from manure, odors, dust, and insects. Capital costs, economic risks, and labor efficiency are also important factors. Beef enterprises may be classified according to the kind of animals:

- Cow-calf
- Breeding stock
- Fattening cattle
- Finishing

Beef cattle require only minimal shelter, and facilities are often simple and inexpensive. Protection from the weather—wind, snow, rain, sun, mud, and/or dust—is needed for good growth and efficient feed conversion. Experience has shown that beef animals convert a sufficient amount of food to heat to maintain body temperature. Consequently they do not suffer from the cold as long as they are dry. On the other hand, they do require protection from the hot summer sun. In some regions of the country, cow-calf herds are left on range or pasture land much of the year with little more than natural or artificial shade for shelter. A calving barn is useful for cold, windy, or wet weather.

The animals must have good access to feed and water and the systems should be reliable and have a low labor demand. Handling ease should be considered in planning for animal movement and treatment and during calving time in winter. Separate feedyards for mature cows, first calf heifers, bulls, and calves allow for feeding different rations and improved observation of the animals. Facilities for feeder cattle vary from mammoth feedlots where only space for feeding, drinking, and resting is provided, to total confinement buildings with mechanical feeding systems and slotted floors for manure control.

Beef production is ordinarily considered to be a low margin enterprise and even small savings in investment or improvements in labor or feed efficiency can spell the difference between profit and loss. Successful beef operations vary from a few animals on a general farm to thousands of animals in a feedlot. The small operator can be successful when he has a completely integrated system of feed production, feed use, manure management, and labor distribution—crops in the summer and cattle in the winter. The large feedlot is profitable because of the economy of scale even though all feed is purchased and manure becomes a nuisance instead of a resource.

Since it has been shown that the rate of gain by beef animals is influenced only minimally by weather conditions or the shelter provided, the type and amount of housing provided is often determined by climatic and management factors rather than the requirements of the animals. For example, in the Southwest, the mild, dry climate may indicate an open lot as the most practical. However, in the northern humid areas, high snowfall, wind, and difficulty in draining a yard without causing pollution may justify a complete confinement system.

Types of Housing

Although beef feeding systems vary greatly, they may be classified as (1) an open lot system, (2) a barn and lot system, and a total confinement system.
Each of these systems has characteristics making it suitable under certain conditions or circumstances.

Open Lot System

In areas where adequate space, good drainage, and moderate annual precipitation prevail, open yards with limited shelter for feeding and resting are sufficient, reasonable in cost, and may be designed for high labor efficiency. Figure 25.1 illustrates a typical open lot.

The actual layout of the yard will depend on the topography of the area available. However, provision should be made to intercept any surface drainage. A southern slope provides good sun exposure. Buildings and silos should be on the north side. Mechanically filled feed bunks or fenceline bunks on both sides of an alley should run in a north-south direction. Single fenceline bunks should be east and west with the animals on the south side.

Typically, feeding is done in fenceline bunks supplied from mixer wagons or trucks driven along the alleys between the yards. The width of the alleys is influenced not only by the equipment used but by the need to accommodate snow accumulation in the winter. Where snow accumulates, the alley width may need to be doubled or tripled.

A paved strip along the feed and watering areas keeps the animals out of the mud at least part of the time during periods when the ground is saturated. Sloping the concrete slab 1:12 away from the bunk helps to keep it clean. As the animals move around, the manure tends to work to the lower edge. A low step in front of the feedbunk effectively keeps manure out of the bunk because cattle will not back up onto a raised level.

Good yard drainage is essential. Ideally, yards should be located on a southern slope to allow the maximum drying from sunshine. A slope of 4 to 5% will allow runoff from rain or melting snow to drain from the yard to a settling basin and then into a holding pond or lagoon.

Earthen mounds in the lot will provide a dry resting area under most weather conditions. The mounds are constructed by pushing earth from the sides of the yard toward

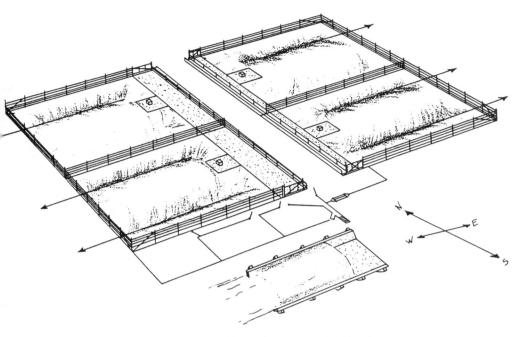

Figure 25.1. Open feedlot with fenceline feed bunks.

the center line, thus lowering the grade for controlled drainage along the edges and raising the grade in the center for an improved resting area. With this arrangement, about one third of the yard will ordinarily remain firm enough for resting even during heavy rains. The length of the mound may be determined from the estimated useful width and the resting area needed per animal.

The mound will need to be stabilized. This may done by working chopped straw, bedded manure, or agricultural lime into the surface. If lime is used, 10 lb/yd^2 (5 kg/m^2) should be disked into the top 4 in. (100 mm).

Depending on seasonal weather conditions and natural landscape features, a windbreak fence and/or a sunshade may be the only protection provided.

If space for yards is limited or drainage is questionable, a yard may be completely paved. The area required per animal will be only 10 to 20% of that needed for unpaved yards. However, facilities for handling runoff will be just as essential and it will be necessary to scrape manure from the yards more often.

Individual circumstances allowing, feed storage and processing structures should be located north of the yards to avoid continuous shadows on the lot and allow the full benefit of the sun to be available for thawing and drying.

Barn and Lot System

In cold humid climates, barns that provide shelter from wind, rain, and snow, and a bedded resting area may increase animal comfort enough so that improvement in feeding efficiency will at least partially offset the investment in the building. Barns for this purpose are usually built with one side open to the east or south to afford protection from the prevailing wind.

As shown in figure 25.2, a paved area extending a short distance in front of and into the building will help improve conditions during rain or snow and spring thaw. To ensure good drainage, the floor of the barn should be slightly raised and sloped toward the open side.

The yards may be partially or completed paved depending on drainage and space available. As in open lots, complete paving allows a reduction in the area required. In unpaved yards, earthen mounds similar to those described under the open-lot system will encourage the animals to rest outside, thus reducing the bedding needed and the amount of manure to be removed from the barn.

The considerably smaller yard required when resting space is provided within the barn make mechanical bunk feeders practical. Mechanical feeding systems of over 200 ft (60 m) have been used. The length limits the number of cattle lots that can be developed around one mechanical feeder system and the storage facilities related to it. Approximately 350 head is the maximum number of cattle that can be fed at one time with a feeder system. Groups of cattle can be rotated through a feedlot to allow feeding over 1,000 head with a single feeding system. The feed bunks may be either centered in a yard or built into a fence between two yards. Yards for small herds are usually laid out in a rectangular arrangement. For larger enterprises, however, fan-shaped layouts with the feed center at the apex allow multiple mechanical feeders to be serviced from one storage facility. This type of layout (fig. 25.3) will accommodate 500 head of cattle.

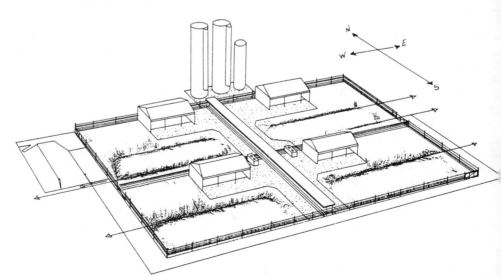

Figure 25.2. A barn and lot system.

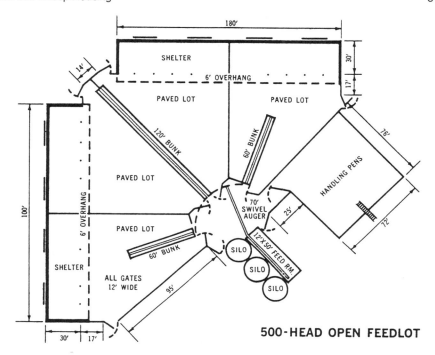

Figure 25.3. Fan-shaped lot design saves on feeding equipment.

Sloping the feed bunk aprons 1:12 will help to keep them clean. Bunks that are oriented approximately north and south allow sunshine to strike the apron on each side for part of the day. Locating the feed center at the north end of the lot also prevents shading the bunks.

In areas of high wind and heavy snowfall, special consideration should be given to building location and orientation, windbreaks, snow fences, and swirl areas. These factors are discussed in chapter 20.

Total Confinement System

Total confinement barns offer more complete protection and more comfortable working conditions in regions where heavy snow, severe winds, and poor drainage make open systems difficult to manage.

A bedded barn can be satisfactorily used for a small herd when bedding is available at low cost. However, labor requirements for handling the bedding and removing the manure tend to be high.

A slotted floor system eliminates the cost of labor associated with bedding, and at the same time animal densities can be increased considerably. Slats may be used over the entire floor area or they may be used in the center 40% of the floor with solid floor area on either side sloped 1:10 to facilitate the movement of manure toward the slotted area.

If the entire floor is slotted, it is common practice to construct the pit deep enough to store manure for up to six months. If only a part of the floor is slotted, it is usually combined with a shallow pit and a mechanical manure scraper which removes the manure daily. Where these systems have been used in cold barns in northern regions, freezing has been a problem with the shallow pit but not with the deep pit.

Water flushing of sloped, solid floors is suitable only in mild climates where it is difficult to justify any type of confinement housing.

Cow-calf Facilities

Beef cows that are bred to calve in the spring may be wintered outdoors. Protection from wind should be available from natural landscape features, plant windbreaks or fences.

Confining the cows to a pasture near the farmstead a short time before calving allows the cows to be observed and helped if necessary. The pasture area should be large enough to allow animals clean surroundings and freedom from interference from other cows and calves. Calf scours is a major problem which can be aggravated by dirty, crowded conditions. Separating cow-calf pairs from cows waiting to calve enhances herd health. The failure of a newborn calf to get the colostrum milk from its mother because another calf nurses the cow considerably reduces its chances for survival.

If calves are born early in the spring, an open-sided shed with several 8 × 12 ft (3.4 × 3.6 m) bedded pens in which the cow and calf may be kept for two or three days is beneficial. A water supply and electrical service are essential. A heat lamp over a protected corner of the pen provides warmth for a newborn calf until it is dry and has nursed. After two or three days, calves are able to tolerate normal weather conditions without difficulty.

Site Selection and Building Design

Any beef cattle housing system should be located on a site that provides good drainage and sufficient space for the facilities as well as easy access for large trucks. It should also be located far enough from the farm home and from neighbors so that odors will not become a problem.

Buildings and equipment should be economical but rugged enough to stand the rigors of housing large animals. Post-frame buildings minimize costs and interior poles can be used for pen dividers, gates, etc. Post-frame barns with trussed roofs to give a clear span are flexible and minimize manure cleaning efforts. Corrugated roofing permits the economy of an open roof deck. Sides may be of metal, wood or plywood. However, metal siding, particularly aluminum, is not rugged enough to withstand the activity of heavy beef animals. For this reason metal siding should be protected where animals are apt to damage it. This can be accomplished with a board wall 4 ft high along the interior perimeter of the building and fencing around the outside. All wood that will come in contact with either the ground or the manure pack should be pressure-preservative treated.

Buildings constructed with a full slotted floor will have a concrete foundation permitting either a frame sidewall and truss construction or rigid frame design.

Environmental Control

Livestock production is more efficient when the animals' environment is within the range of the thermoneutral zone (TNZ). Such factors as solar radiation, wind, humidity, precipitation, animal condition and feed ration all effect the TNZ. The lower limit of the TNZ is called the lower critical temperature. Table 25-1 illustrates the effect of hair coat condition on the TNZ. When environmental temperatures are below the TNZ, animals must use feed energy for keeping warm and thus are less efficient (tables 25-2, 25-3). Other environmental factors such as mud, wind, and rain also affect production efficiency as shown in table 25-4.

In either an open barn or cold confinement building, sufficient air movement is required to remove moisture in winter, heat in summer, and odors from manure throughout the year. Either type of barn may be ventilated without the aid of fans if the following factors are observed:

1. The building should be oriented at right angles to the prevailing wind and on relatively high ground. The winds will then increase air movement through the building.
2. A roof pitched 4:12 or 5:12 and constructed without deep purlins allows free air movement along the underside of the roofing.
3. Openings at the eaves equivalent to one inch for each 10 ft (8.3 mm/m) of building width and an opening at the ridge equal to two inches for each 10 ft (16.7 mm/m) of width are essential for free air movement. No ridge covering is required, but if one is desired, the free distance above the opening should equal half the width of the opening. Animal heat plus the

Table 25-1. Estimated lower critical temperature for cattle
with varying hair coats

		Lower Critical Temperature	
Hair Coat	Feed Level	°F	°C
Summer coat or wet	Maintenance	60	15
Fall coat	Maintenance	45	7
Winter coat	Maintenance	32	0
Heavy winter coat	Maintenance	19	-7

Table 25-2. Predicted performance of an 880 lb (400 kg) steer

Temperature		Daily Gain		
°F	°C	(lb)	(kg)	Feed/Gain Ratio
32	0	2.76	1.25	8.2
24	-4	2.62	1.19	8.9
14	-10	2.44	1.11	9.7
5	-15	2.27	1.03	10.7
-4	-20	2.07	0.94	11.8
-13	-25	1.78	0.80	13.7

Table 25-3. Estimated feed (metabolizable) energy increase
for temperatures below lower critical temperatures

Deviation Below Critical Temperature		1000 lb (455 kg) Pregnant Cow (Mcals)	770 lb (340 kg) Yearling (Mcals)	550 lb (250 kg) Calf (Mcals)
°F	°C			
0	0	0.0	0.0	0.3
5	3	0.9	1.0	0.9
10	6	2.0	1.9	1.7
15	8	3.2	2.8	2.5
20	11	3.6	3.7	3.3
25	14	4.5	4.6	4.2
30	17	5.4	5.5	5.0
35	19	6.4	AIC*	AIC
40	22	7.3	AIC	AIC

* Above intake capacity.

Table 25-4. The effect of rain, wind, and mud on feedlot cattle performance

Treatment	Initial Weight (lb)	Average Daily Gain (lb)	Feed/Gain Ratio
Concrete, wind & rain	648	2.77	8.01
Concrete & wind	634	3.23	6.44
Concrete & shelter	654	3.44	6.44
Mud & shelter	658	2.67	7.49
Mud & wind	625	2.47	7.97

effects of wind will provide enough air movement through these openings to control moisture during the winter months.

4. For summer ventilation, provision should be made for opening at least 25% of the wall area to allow air to circulate freely at animal level.

Feed and Water Systems

Economical beef production requires efficient handling of high quality feed. Feed may be any one or more of the following: loose hay, rectangular bales, big round bales, dry-chopped hay, haylage, silage or grain. Table 25-5 illustrates four feeding systems.

Feeding programs are so varied that it is difficult to establish general storage requirements. Silage storage and grain handling and storage are discussed in other chapters.

Hay storage in humid areas may be in low-cost, pole-type structures. Adjacent feeding facilities will keep labor requirements at a minimum. In dry regions, stacks or large bales may be stored in the open on high, well-drained land. A movable fence allowing the animals access to one stack or bale at a time reduces wastage. However, portable feed racks or the use of equipment that processes the hay for bunk feeding also reduce waste.

Water is an essential ingredient for cattle; about 10 gal (38 L) of water per 100 lb (45 kg)/day is needed, 50 to 100% more in hot weather. Sufficient watering space must be provided so that no animal is prevented from obtaining adequate water. Extreme cold can be a challenge to providing ice-free water and require heaters or

Table 25-5. Feeder alternatives for cattle*

Type of Feeder	Portable Bunk	Fenceline Bunk	Self Feeder	Mechanical Bunk
Cost	Medium	High	Medium	Highest
Loose hay	Some	No	Yes	No
Ground dry hay	Yes	Yes	Yes	Yes
Rectangular bales	Some	Some	Yes	No
Big round bales	—	Grind	Yes	No
Silage, haylage	Yes	Yes	Some	Yes
Grain or pellets	Yes	Yes	Some	Yes
Feed handling system recommended	Hand feed	Front-end loader, unloader wagon	Front-end loader, unloader wagon	Upright silos with conveyors

* Bodman et al. 1987. *Beef Housing and Equipment Handbook.* MWPS-6. Ames IA: MidWest Plan Service.

well insulated waterers which utilize ground heat. It is important that waterers be checked frequently to ensure they have not frozen over. Table 25-6 summarizes space requirements for various beef housing systems.

Manure Management

In managing the manure from a beef cattle enterprise one should strive for:

1. The prevention of pollution of streams, lakes, and groundwater.
2. The conservation of nutrients to provide maximum value to crops.
3. High labor efficiency in handling the wastes.
4. A feasible level of investment in storage facilities and handling equipment.

The methods used to obtain these objectives will be influenced by the type of housing system, the climate of the region, and the ultimate disposal of the manure. Management methods for each of the three housing systems (open lot, barn and lot, and confinement) will be discussed.

Open Lot Systems, and Barn and Lot Systems

At the time of construction, diversion drainage should be installed to intercept surface water so it will not drain onto the feedlot and increase the amount of runoff. In addition, eave troughs should be installed on barns to direct rainwater away from the lot and keep it out of the waste handling system.

The solid waste can be scraped from an unpaved yard periodically and spread on cropland. This is usually done when the moisture level of the manure is low. Paved yards will need much more frequent scraping and storage facilities may be required. A paved storage with a picket dam as described in chapter 19 and shown in figure 19.1 is designed for holding solid manure. Approximately 3/4 ft^3 (0.2 m^3) per animal will be needed each day of the storage period.

All open yards will have liquid runoff from heavy rains or melting snow which contains high levels of pollutants and must be prevented from entering any natural waterway. Therefore, if runoff is not immediately dispersed over adjacent grassland in an acceptable manner, a holding pond is required to store the runoff until conditions are

Table 25-6. Specifications for housing facilities for beef cattle

Space Requirements per Animal	Customary	SI
Open lot (finishing)		
Unpaved — no buildings	250-500 ft²	15-50 m²
Paved — no buildings	50-60 ft²	5-7.5 m²
Sunshade	20-25 ft²	2-2.5 m²
Mounds in yard	30-35 ft²	2.5-2.8 m²
Barn and lot		
Rest area in barn	20-30 ft²	2-3 m²
Unpaved lot	100-300 ft²	9-28 m²
Paved lot	25-35 ft²	2.5-3.2 m²
Mounds in yard	25-30 ft²	2.5-2.8 m²
Total confinement		
Bedded floor	25-40 ft²	2.5-3.5 m²
Slotted floor	18-20 ft²	1.7-1.9 m²
Calving pen 1/12 cows	100 ft²	9 m²
Isolation pen 1/20-40 head	50 ft²	4.5 m²
Feed space per animal		
Once or twice-a-day feeding		
Cows	24-30 in.	600-760 mm
Feeders	22-26 in.	560-660 mm
Calves	18-22 in.	460-560 mm
Continuous feed		
Roughage	6-8 in.	150-200 mm
Grain	4-6 in.	100-150 mm
Number water fountains 50-75 head	1	1
Corrals		
Holding and crowding pens	15-20 ft²	1.4-2 m²
Working chute width		
Under 600 lb	18 in.	460 mm
600-1,200 lb	26 in.	660 mm
Over 1,200 lb	28-30 in.	710-760 mm
Working chute width sloped sides, bottom and top (4 ft)		
Under 600 lb		
600-1,200 lb	13 & 20 in.	330 & 500 mm
Over 1,200 lb	15 & 27 in.	380 & 685 mm
Chute and fence height	19 & 32 in.	480 & 810 mm
Post spacing		
Chute	5 ft	1.5 m
Yard	6 ft	1.8 m
Circular chute radius	8 ft	2.4 m
Feed alley (feedlot)	16.5 ft	5.0 m
	13-33 ft	4-10 m

suitable for disposal on crop or pasture land. The effluent will usually be distributed through an irrigation system. The amount of runoff is estimated on the basis of rainfall records. Local rainfall data is the most satisfactory for design purposes. In addition to the runoff, the size of a holding pond will be influenced by the length of the holding period, the accumulation of solids, and the net effect of rainfall and evaporation.

In the eastern part of the United States and Canada, the rainfall and evaporation are roughly equal and have little effect on the storage capacity of a holding pond. In much of the western part of the United States and Canada, evaporation exceeds rainfall significantly. This increases the effective capacity of a holding pond used for periods of several months. Evaporation is of little significance, however, if the holding pond is emptied frequently.

During an intense storm of short duration, a large volume flow picks up solids and carries them along in the runoff. A settling basin, installed between the lot and the holding pond, greatly reduces the accumulation of these solids. With a detention period of 20 min or more, up to 85% of the solids can be removed from the runoff before it enters the pond. Detention period is defined as the time required for the flow volume to equal the design volume of the basin. In other words, a 20-min detention period is assumed if the drained basin is large enough to hold the expected runoff for a 20-min period. Additional capacity will be required to hold the settled solids. The amount of accumulated solids will be influenced by the area of the lot and the frequency with which the settling basin is cleaned.

A porous dam or a vertical, perforated pipe outlet may be used to restrict the flow to give the required detention time and to drain the basin at the end of the storm. Such dams can be constructed of planks with either horizontal or vertical spacing. A 1/2 in. (12.7 mm) expanded metal screen installed so that it tips away from the top of the dam approximately 30° will help to keep the dam from plugging. The reverse slope produces a self-cleaning action. In addition, periodic scraping of the surface of the dam is necessary for proper operation.

In some areas feedlot runoff may be disposed of by infiltration on an adjacent grassland area. The distribution channel, after a settling basin, must be designed with a very slow slope in order to obtain uniform distribution.

Confinement Housing

If manure is to be stored under a slotted floor, 10 ft of storage depth below the floor will allow up to 180 days of storage time. If a scraper system is used, the storage area is based on 1 ft^3/1,000 lb (454 kg) of animal weight for each day of storage required. Liquid manure storage facilities are discussed in chapter 19.

It is imperative that a building with manure storage below the floor have all ventilation openings wide open before manure is agitated and removed. The noxious gases released when the manure is disturbed can be dangerous, even fatal, to both animals and workers.

Equipment

Every beef farm, regardless of size or type, must have facilities for sorting, treating, weighing, loading, and unloading animals. Designing these facilities for efficiency pays bigger dividends. A well-planned corral saves time and labor and helps to prevent human injuries as well as bruising and more serious injuries to animals.

Facilities which allow producers to handle animals without stress may reduce diseases and increase profit.

The design and layout of handling facilities should consider the following animal psychological characteristics:

- Cattle have panoramic vision; they can see nearly 360° without turning their heads.
- Cattle are motivated by fear and are sensitive to harsh contrast of light and dark. They tend to move toward light and prefer not to enter a darkened area.
- Cattle often balk if they see moving or flapping objects. The sides of crowding pens, loading chutes, etc., should be solid to prevent animals from seeing distracting objects—including handlers.
- Cattle are easily distracted and are sensitive to harsh sounds.
- Cattle can be readily moved by proper control of their flight zone and consideration of their point of balance.
- Cattle will exhibit a natural circling tendency.
- The herd instinct can be utilized to move animals with others; they exhibit natural following behavior.

Veterinarians will be more willing to provide their services where conditions are safe and convenient. Basic facilities required are:

1. A crowding pen where animals are forced into a working chute.
2. A working chute where animals can be treated individually or sorted and directed to a desired location.
3. A squeeze chute where an animal can be immobilized for special treatment.
4. A loading chute for loading or unloading stock trucks and trailers.

The work area should be well-drained and located immediately adjacent to the pens. Rough concrete in the chute and around the headgate is recommended to provide good footing. An all-weather road should provide access to the loading chute.

Round holding pens, diagonal sorting pens, and curved drive lanes and the absences of square corners will make for more efficient cattle handling. A funnel entrance to a chute from a crowding pen should have one straight wall to prevent animals from becoming wedged at the narrow end. A curved chute takes advantage of the natural tendency of cattle to circle and also prevents animals from seeing the squeeze, truck or people. The radius of curvature (inside) should be 12 to 16 ft (3.6 to 4.8 m). Sloping sides are desirable for a working chute. Loading ramps for cattle should use steps with risers of about 3 1/2 in. (90 mm). A 5 ft (1.5 m) level landing should be provided at the top of loading chutes.

A headgate or squeeze chute is needed for restraining animals for health care. Four basic types of headgates are: (1) scissors stanchion, (2) full-opening stanchion, (3) positive control, and (4) self-catcher. Scissors stanchion headgates consist of two biparting halves that pivot at the bottom. The full-opening stanchion has two biparting halves that work like a pair of sliding doors. A positive control headgate locks firmly around the animal's neck and restricts up and down movement. The self-catcher closes automatically in response to forward movement of an entering animal.

For the small herd, a crowd gate in the corner of the yard with an alley leading to a headgate for treating and a chute for loading and unloading is adequate (fig. 25.4).

For larger herds, however, the handling facilities are more complex. A funnel-shaped crowding pen facilitates movement of cattle from a large area to a smaller area. The use of large, curved alleys to direct the flow of cattle recognizes that cattle tend to move more easily if they cannot see where the animals ahead are going. Sorting gates that are well-designed and properly located within the alleys provide for easy sorting and cutting toward a loading chute, scales or a squeeze. Roofing over the handling and treatment areas provides more comfortable working conditions during inclement weather (fig. 25.5). In this plan, weighing animals could be done with portable scales located adjacent to the headgate.

The fences in a corral should be strong, smooth, and high enough so that wild or crowded animals will not be hurt or damage the fence. Yard fences are commonly built with 2 × 6 in. (38 × 140 mm) lumber, although metal is also suitable for fence construction. In the crowding area and working chute, the fence should be 6 ft (2 m) high and have solid walls to prevent balking. However, a single 4 in. (100 mm) slot

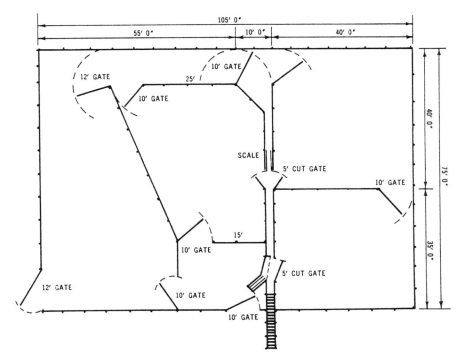

Figure 25.4. Handling pen for a small herd.

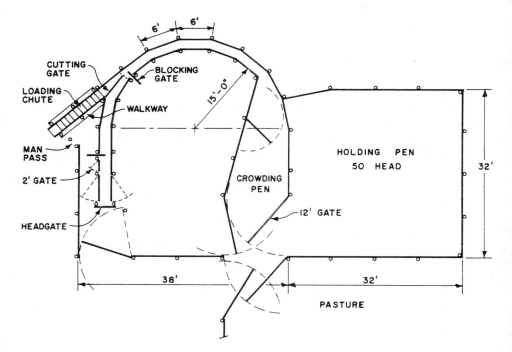

Figure 25.5. Corral for a medium-sized herd.

at the 4 ft (1.2 m) level is thought to keep cattle from jumping. If range animals are being handled, because of their wilder nature, a restraining board running along the top center of the working chute may be necessary to prevent jumping. Jumping is dangerous as an animal is likely to fall, often on its back, and be injured seriously. Even if an animal is uninjured, it is still difficult to get it back on its feet.

If cattle are to be prevented from turning around, the width of the chute is critical and should be constructed to fit the animals most commonly handled. Where both cows and calves will be handled, the sides should be sloped, wide enough at the top to accommodate the cows and narrow enough at the bottom to keep the calves from turning around.

Planning the Beef Cattle System

As with any farm enterprise, it is important to carefully prepare a complete plan for the entire system. The plan should include a topographic layout of the site, the facilities for sheltering and handling the cattle, storage and equipment for feed, and the facilities for storing and handling waste. It is much easier to change a plan than alter a completed structure.

SHEEP HOUSING

Sheep make excellent use of pasture and forage crops and require relatively small amounts of concentrates. Capital investment for housing and equipment for sheep is low in comparison to that for other livestock. Labor needs are modest but unevenly distributed throughout the year, making the enterprise well-suited to a diversified farm operation. Although sheep can be grown successfully over a wide geographic range, overall labor and production costs will be lowest where the grazing season is long and the winter forage requirements are the least.

Sheep can withstand cold temperatures and need shelter only from rain, snow, and wind in the winter and from hot sun in the summer. Warmth is a factor only during lambing and after shearing. Winter lambing schedules and the practice of shearing the ewes prior to lambing increases the importance of having a warm, well-ventilated shelter. During the remainder of the year, an open-front, naturally ventilated building with well-drained yards, securely fenced to keep out predators, will be adequate.

Management Systems

A large majority of sheep producers will try to get their flock to lamb during January and February. This allows them to take advantage of the lush spring pastures to get the lambs off to a good start and be ready for market by the end of the grazing season. These lambs often are marketed at a higher price than the April-May born lambs.

When pasture is not adequate to finish the lambs, they may be sold at about 55 to 65 lb (25 to 30 kg) as feeders to be fed grain and either hay or pasture until they reach market weight of 100 to 120 lb (45 to 55 kg). Shelter for a feeder operation should emphasize labor efficiency and good care since the margin per animal is often quite small.

Some producers will divide their flocks into several groups and try to get three lamb crops from each ewe every 24 months. The facilities are then used on a cycle of three times per year. This accelerated lambing schedule justifies a greater investment in buildings and handling facilities.

Site Selection

A well-drained southerly slope is preferred for a sheep barn and yards. This orientation of the site offers protection from winter winds and exposure to maximum sunshine so that the yards will dry out faster and be easier to maintain. Sheep do not tolerate mud well; therefore, grading and filling should be considered if the natural slope and drainage do not meet the necessary standards. As with all livestock enterprises, the topography should be such that there is no chance of pollution from yard runoff.

While easy access to the barns is important, locating the barns at least 150 ft (45 m) downwind from the farm home will minimize summer barnyard odors in the living area.

Building Design and Layout

Most producers with small flocks will utilize whatever buildings they have available. An open-front, well-ventilated building with a truss roof construction allows a great deal of flexibility in pen arrangements and allows for easy manure removal. If hay and bedding are to be stored in the same building with the sheep, an offset gable roof, with the high side to the back, permits greater height in the area where hay is stored. Facing the open side to the south or southeast provides wind protection and a maximum amount of sunshine.

Although a concrete floor is usually unnecessary, a concrete apron, sloped 1:25, extending from 4 ft (1.2 m) inside to 8 ft (2.4 m) outside, will help maintain firm, clean conditions at the barn entrance. A hard-packed gravel floor with a slope of 1:50 toward the open front is recommended. An eaves trough along the open side that drains the water away from the building is essential. A paved area may be provided for shearing the small flock, while a shearing shed with crowd pens and a raised shearing floor will improve efficiency for large flocks.

Rough lumber, plywood or metal siding are all suitable for exterior walls, and either corrugated roofing on purlins or asphalt roofing on a solid roof deck provide ample protection.

Figure 25.6 shows a plan for a 42 × 72 ft (13 × 22 m) barn that will house a flock of 100 ewes and store the necessary hay and some bedding. By the time lambing starts, an area is available in the hay storage section sufficient to set up the portable lambing pens. Hay racks and panels are movable to allow flexibility in pen arrangement to suit the needs of the seasons. The south side is open to one or more yards. While this figure shows only one of many possible layouts, the flexibility illustrated through the use of movable racks and panels should be part of any plan.

A yard requires a slope of 1:20 to 1:10 and should be of adequate size to remain in good condition; that is, animal density should not be so heavy as to work the yard into a quagmire with every rain storm. Enclosing the yard with a fence at least 4 ft (1.2 m) high is inexpensive insurance against the intrusion of dogs. In range areas where coyotes are a problem, yard fences need to be 6 ft (1.8 m) high and have a buried apron along the outside. The fence is constructed of two 4 ft (1.2 m) wide rolls of woven wire fence. The bottom strip is bent in the middle to a right angle and the 2 ft (0.6 m) apron buried lightly. The closely spaced, horizontal edges of the top and bottom fence strips are joined with wire clips between alternate vertical wires.

The efficiency of handling the flock will be improved with the installation of a permanent crowd gate and sorting chute. For a small flock, one leg of the chute should lead to a loading chute or portable dipping tank (fig. 25.6). In a large operation, a permanent dipping tank or spray yard should be incorporated into the design.

Sheep are prone to infestation by internal parasites. Experience has shown that an effective way to reduce this problem is to confine the flock to slotted floor pens. This can be done on a small scale by mounting a slotted pen on a mobile home trailer frame. Then the entire pen can be shifted to facilitate manure disposal. Large barns can also be constructed with slotted floors over a deep pit. The pit must have a grade access for manure removal with a front end loader. Slotted floors eliminate the need for bedding, require less labor, and allow for greater animal density, all of which help to offset the added cost of construction. Specifications for sheep facilities are summarized in table 25-7.

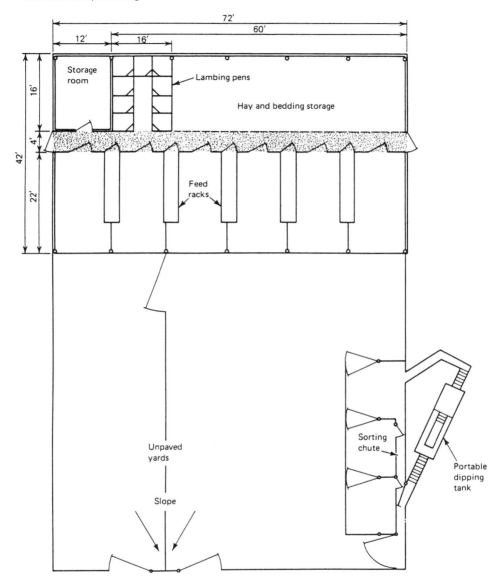

Figure 25.6. Facilities for 100 ewes.

Environmental Control

Throughout most of the year an open-front building provides adequate shelter. To reduce the possibility of condensation under the roof, an open ridge and opening under the eaves at the rear of the building are recommended. One inch (25 mm)/10 ft (3 m) of barn width will suffice at both locations, except that the ridge openings

Table 25-7. Specifications for housing facilities for sheep

	Ewes		Lambs	
Pen space (open to lot)	12-16 ft²	1.1-1.5 m²	6-8 ft²	0.6-0.7 m²
Yard space	25-40 ft²	2.3-3.7 m²	15-20 ft²	1.4-1.9 m²
Solid floor confinement	15-20 ft²	1.4-1.9 m²	8-10 ft²	0.7-0.9 m²
Slotted floor confinement	10-12 ft²	0.9-1.1 m²	4-5 ft²	0.4-0.5 m²
Lambing pens	4 × 4 ft	1.2 × 1.2 m		
Creep space/lamb	2 ft²	0.2 m²		
Feeder space				
Grain — group fed	12-18 in.	300-450 mm	8-12 in.	200-300 mm
Grain — self fed			3-4 in.	75-100 mm
Hay and silage — group fed	12-18 in.	300-450 mm	8-12 in.	200-300 mm
Hay and silage — self fed	6-8 in.	150-200 mm	3-4 in.	75-100 mm
Waterer	1/35	1/35	1/35	1/35
Water/day	2 gal	7.5 L	1 1/2 gal	5.7 L
Feed requirements/day				
Hay	4-5 lb	1.8-2.3 kg	Seasonal	Seasonal
Grain	3/4-1 1/2 lb	0.3-0.7 kg	2-3 lb	0.9-1.4 kg
Silage (only roughage)	12-15 lb	5.5-6.8 kg	4-6 lb	1.8-2.7 kg
(2-3 tons silage = 1 ton hay)				
Bedding requirements/day	1 lb	0.5 kg	1/2 lb	0.2 kg
Manure production/day	6 lb	2.7 kg	3-4 lb	1.4-1.8 kg

should be a minimum of 4 in. (100 mm) to prevent freeze-ups. Summer ventilation is furnished by opening 4 ft (1.2 m) wide doors along the rear wall.

If a warm housing system is desired because of very early shearing or lambing, the building should be insulated to an R of 4 h-ft²-°F/Btu (0.7 m²°K/W) for the wall and an R of 8 h-ft²-°F/Btu (1.4 m²°K/W) for the ceiling. The R-values recommended are based on 0°F (−16°C) and a density of at least one ewe per 20 ft² (2 m²). If density is reduced by 50%, as it probably would be in a separate lambing room, the R-values would need to be doubled.

In a draft-free, insulated building, very little natural ventilation takes place and moisture soon builds up. Failure to remove sufficient moisture results in damp conditions that are conducive to the development of pneumonia and scours. By ventilating with a fan at the minimum continuous rate of 6 cfm (2.8 L/s)/ewe, the temperature should remain above freezing and the moisture balance at a reasonable level. Fan capacity should be at least doubled on mild days, or alternatively, the building should be opened up for natural ventilation. In a reasonably tight building, an air inlet area of 20 in.²/100 cfm (275 mm²/L-s) of fan capacity will produce the recommended air velocity of 700 to 1,000 fpm (3.5 to 5.0 m/s).

Newborn lambs are able to withstand cold temperatures after they are dry and have nursed the ewe. A 250 W heat lamp mounted in an approved frame, suspended with a chain over one corner of the lambing pen, will keep the lamb warm and hasten drying. Use of heat lamps for a maximum of one hour is adequate to get the lambs dry. The outlet into which the lamp is plugged should be above the lamp. The cord should be too short to reach the floor, automatically disconnecting the lamp if it falls.

Feed Management

Hay should be stored as close to the flock as possible for greatest labor efficiency. Grain may be processed and stored in an elevated bulk bin from which it is easily discharged into a feed cart or mixer wagon or augered to self feeders. Feeder lambs are supplied with grain on a continuous basis from self feeders. These may be filled with a conveyor system or from a mixer wagon if the location is suitable.

Young lambs should also be fed grain in a creep on a continuous basis to ensure maximum growth. A lamb creep is a fenced-off area containing a hay rack and a low grain trough. The fence is constructed to allow entrance of lambs while excluding ewes.

If silage is an important part of the ration, one of the following should be considered:

1. Self feeding through a movable fence from a horizontal silo.
2. Feeding from a cart into bunks on either side of a covered alley.
3. Feeding with a mechanical bunk conveyor.
4. Feeding from a mixer wagon, perhaps as a complete ration.

A supply of clean water should be available at all times. Watering tanks may be float-controlled and automatically protected from freezing.

Waste Management

Sheep manure has a moisture content of about 75% which is much lower than that of other livestock. With relatively little bedding, pens stay clean and dry and the manure is easily handled as a solid.

Runoff from yards, however, must be managed so that all environmental regulations are met and no pollution of natural waterways occurs. Surface runoff should be diverted away from the lots so that only the precipitation falling on the lots becomes polluted. In many cases the runoff from yards can be allowed to spread out on a grassed area. If the yards are large and rainfall substantial, it may be necessary to install a settling basin and a holding pond as described in the section on beef cattle. In any case, when planning the waste management system, the local authorities concerned with pollution control should be consulted to assure compliance with state and federal regulations.

Equipment

The equipment required for a sheep enterprise will vary according to size, feeding program, and climatic area, but it need not be elaborate or expensive. Each stage of production requires a somewhat different arrangement and different space needs. Lightweight but rugged portable equipment can help promote the needed flexibility.

Fenceline bunks contribute to efficiency with large flocks but may not be as useful as portable racks for smaller-sized operations. Feeders of all types should be designed to reduce to a minimum the amount of chaff and other trash that works into the wool. Racks and troughs that can be tipped over for cleaning and shifted to form new pen locations are convenient.

Pairs of hinged panels 4 ft (1.2 m) long and 2 1/2 ft (0.75 m) high are useful for lambing pens and for isolating sick animals. Lambing pens for large ewes should be 4 × 5 ft

$(1.2 \times 1.5$ m), while large ewes with triplets need a pen that is 5×5 ft $(1.5 \times 1.5$ m).

Ample lighting in the barn and yards is important, particularly during the lambing season. An electrical service adequate to supply lighting, water heaters, heat lamps, and other equipment is essential.

Well-maintained, woven wire fences not only keep sheep confined to pasture areas, but discourage predators as well. While electric fences can be effective for sheep, it is important to use more than one charged strand of wire alternated with a grounded wire. Sheep must be trained to avoid the fence, since their heavy coat of wool insulates them from shock. Training should be done soon after shearing by placing a little feed behind the wires so that the sheep must touch the wire to reach the feed. Electric fences are also effective in keeping dogs and other predators out of the sheep lots.

Problems

25.1.   Plan an open unpaved feedlot for 200 beef animals. Show the feeding and resting areas and the location of the feed storage facilities. Be sure to indicate the size of the yard.

25.2.   Using the plan developed for problem 25.1, assume that the maximum 1 h rain for a 10-year recurrence period is 11/2 in. (38 mm). Also assume that 4 in. (100 mm) of solids will drain off the yard each year and that a settling basin with a 20-min detention time is to be installed in the drainage channel to a holding pond.

25.3.   What size holding pond will be required to provide for a 6-month storage period? Assume a maximum of 24 in. (600 mm) of precipitation during the period and that evaporation equals precipitation on the pond surface.

25.4.   Design the facilities for feeding 500 lambs, including an open shed and yard with provision for self feeding of grain.

26 Dairy Cattle Housing

Dairy cattle housing systems may be very complex including a number of separately designed structures or areas. Some of these require only simple structures, but combining them into one system requires very careful design. When undertaking new or modified construction, several questions should be addressed:

1. What size herd is planned now and in the future?
2. Will milking be in a stall barn or an elevated parlor?
3. Will the housing provide a warm or cold environment?
4. What type of feeding system will be used?
5. How will manure be handled?
6. How will existing site features impact the operation and how will the planned operation impact the rest of the site?
7. How will existing buildings be utilized?
8. How will replacement animal housing be provided?
9. What type of structure will be used?
10. Can the systems be readily expanded in the future?

There are several basic requirements that planners should attempt to meet. Regardless of the type of system chosen, the following factors should be provided:

• For the cows they include:

1. Adequate shelter from wind, rain, snow, and temperature extremes. Low temperatures are not harmful, if the changes are not too rapid.
2. Adequate space for the cow to rest and feed. Stall, alley, and bunk requirements will be covered later.
3. Layout and equipment that does not subject the animals to undue stress or chance of injury.

• For the operator they include:

1. A design and construction that meets all federal, state, and local requirements relating to building, sanitary, safety, and environmental regulations.
2. A system that is efficient in the handling of the cows, feed, milk, and waste products.

3. A system that uses capital efficiently for an economically sound enterprise.

4. A system that is integrated into the total farm operation in terms of its location in relation to other buildings (including neighbors), feed storage, roads, utilities, and manure disposal.

The manner in which these requirements are met will differ according to climate, farm organization, land values, and markets. For example, farmers in the upper Midwest and southern Ontario may integrate dairying with other farm enterprises, including the production of most of the feed. With a herd size of 30 to 60 cows, a traditional stanchion or tie stall barn seems to best meet the needs. Where severe winters make a warm barn desirable, satisfactory environmental conditions are more easily maintained in a stable barn than in a free-stall barn. Investment per cow for the small- to medium-sized herds is usually less; while this system requires considerable attention to individual animals, it allows for maximum production.

In extreme contrast, the typical operation in the Southwest consists of several hundred cows divided into strings confined to unpaved yards that require scraping only twice a year. Shelter consists of approximately 20 ft^2 (2 m^2) of sunshade per animal. Feeding is in fenceline bunks and milking is done in large milking parlors. Although some cropland may be contiguous with the dairy operation, in many cases all feed is purchased and only enough acreage is included for the yards, buildings, and such pastureland as is necessary for wastewater disposal.

In warm, humid regions, open-side free-stall barns with paved alleys often flush-cleaned are more suitable. Forage may be grown on the adjoining farmland or purchased. Flush cleaning is feasible in areas where the water source is adequate to supply up to 100 gal (380 L)/day for each cow and where that much wastewater can be easily disposed of on the land. The volume of fresh water may be reduced somewhat by recycling wastewater.

In colder areas of the country, as herds have increased in size to 80 cows or more, free-stall barns and milking parlors have become common. The degree of confinement often increases as the climate becomes colder and the snowfall greater. Although there are proponents of warm systems for very cold climates, there is little evidence to indicate that warm barns influence milk production or cow comfort. The only benefit is related to worker comfort. However, the ventilation problems associated with warm systems in cold regions appear to outweigh that advantage.

HOUSING SYSTEMS

The housing system for a dairy enterprise must provide not only for the milking herd but also for dry cows, replacement animals (unbred heifers and springing heifers), calves, and possibly bulls. Table 26-1 illustrates typical herd composition. Facilities must be provided for maternity care, animal treatment, milking, milk handling, grain storage and processing, hay storage, silage storage, manure storage, possibly manure treatment, and utilities. The housing requirements will vary for different animal sizes and thus the number of animals of each size must be known.

Table 26-1. Approximate percentage make-up of a dairy herd

Mature Cows	100	Calves and Heifers	100
Dry cows	17	0-2 months, 150 lbs	8
Transition, first 2 wks	1-5	3-5 months, 250 lbs	12
Next 40 days	11-12	6-8 months, 400 lbs	12
Close-up, 2-3 wks prepartum	3-6	9-12 months, 600 lbs	18
Maternity (pens)	4-6	13-15 months, 800 lbs	12
Fresh cows,		15-24 months, 1050 lbs	38
First 7 days postpartum	1-4		
Two year olds	26-30		
Three years & older	25		
High producers	20-24		
Medium producers	16-20		
Low producers	16-20		
Sick cows	0-5		

Table 26-2. Labor required for dairy cows (manhours)

Year	Per cow	Per 100 kg milk
1930	147	7.2
1940	148	7.0
1950	125	5.2
1960	100	3.1
1970	68	1.5
1975	55	1.2
1980	35	0.7

The make-up of a dairy herd is influenced by a number of factors such as culling and mortality which is 20 to 30% for animals of less than 15 months. An average heifer first calves at 24 months and is used for 8 years. At any given time, about 16% of the mature cows can be expected to be dry and the average dry period is two months. Typically, 5% of calves are born dead and about one half of the live ones are bulls.

The size of a dairy enterprise may be determined in part by the amount of labor available. The annual labor requirement per cow has decreased as shown in table 26-2. Thus, in 1975, one full-time man (40 h/week) could care for about 40 cows (40 h/wk × 52 wk/yr/55 h/cow-yr = 37.8 cows/man-yr); this has now increased to about one man per 60 cows (40 × 52/35 = 59.4 cows/man-yr). Accompanying this has been an increased rate of production by each cow and this has resulted in a ten-fold decrease in the time to produce a unit of milk.

Type of Barn for the Milking Herd

Most cows today are housed in either a restrained-stall barn or a free-stall barn. In restrained-stall barns, cows are restrained in their stalls by tethers or stanchions. The free-stall system allows the cow the freedom to come and go from the stall. Many cows are housed in restrained-stall barns simply because the barn is available and further investment would be required to change. A few new stanchion or tie-stall systems are being constructed where it is desirable to have purebred cows show well or where the farmer wants to give individual attention to his cows in a controlled environment. In some cases, these barns are designed for four rows of cows with either narrow feed alleys and conveyor feeding or wide feed alleys to accommodate a self-unloading wagon. If the system is large enough, a milking parlor may be justified.

The following reasons are given for selecting one of the housing systems: economics, production rate, feed conversion, labor efficiency, sanitation, ability to control animals, operator comfort, and personal desires.

Stable Barns

Popular for herds of 30 to 60 cows, stable barns provide the facilities for feeding, resting, and milking in one location; this generally means less total building area per cow is required. The herdsman moves from cow to cow for milking and must stoop each time to have access to the cow's udder. The high degree of individual animal attention that is required for good herd health and maximum production is easily provided. A warm, well-ventilated stable is a pleasant place to work during the winter and provides an attractive display of breeding stock. For small-sized herds the construction cost is often less than for a free-stall and parlor system.

A minimum number of decisions are required in planning stall barns. Either stanchions or tie stalls may be used to restrain the cows and the arrangement may be face in or face out. Two rows of cows, facing out, will consolidate all cleaning and milking operations in one alley and help to keep barn walls clean (fig. 26.1). In spite of extra labor required to tie cows, tie stalls are chosen over stanchions for most new or modified systems because of the greater freedom of movement that the tie stalls allow for the animals. Of the several styles of tie stalls available, the simple New York stall consisting of a single horizontal pipe 8 in. (200 mm) ahead of the curb and approximately 3 ft (1 m) above the stall floor appears to have the most advantages, particularly in terms of cost. The pipe can double as a water or vacuum line or it may be separate and designed to revolve so that all animals may be unhooked by the herdsman at one time.

Stalls of adequate width and length reduce injuries and keep cows clean (table 26-3). However, when the stall is too long, a cow drops more manure on the platform. Placement of the gutter at an angle to the stall platforms at the time of construction

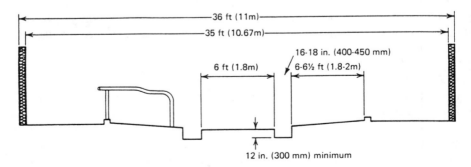

Figure 26.1. Critical dimensions for a dairy stable.

Table 26-3. Dairy stable dimensions

Tie stalls	– width	4.5-5 ft	1.3-1.5 m
	– length	5.75-6.5 ft	1.7-2 m
Platform slope		1:50-1:25	1:50-1:25
Feed alley	– width	6-6.5 ft	1.8-2 m
Service alley	– width	6-6.5 ft	1.8-2 m
Cross alley	– width	4.5 ft	1.4 m
Gutter width		16-18 in.	400-450 mm

provides stalls of varying lengths suitable for all the animals in the herd. German farmers often use 3 ft (1 m) wide gutters combined with gutter grates that can be positioned to adjust the length of each stall.

Various alley and manger designs are used, but the most popular is a simple, flat-feed alley without a raised manger. Stall platforms may be bedded with straw, shavings or sawdust. Rubber mats may be used to minimize the amount of bedding required.

To be competitive with other systems in terms of labor, stable barns must have mechanized materials handling. Milking is most efficient with a clean-in-place pipeline. However, a dumping station that pumps milk to the cooler from a portable receiver is nearly as efficient and considerably less expensive. Feeding can be done with a conveyor system or with a self-propelled cart. Of the two, the conveyor is more labor efficient, but the cart requires less investment and permits individual feed control.

To meet the high standards of cleanliness required in a dairy stable, the walls and ceiling should be smooth, easily cleaned, and moisture resistant. A choice of several materials varying in cost and quality is available. Fiberglass panels are waterproof, durable, and expensive. MDO plywood offers a satisfactory surface at medium to high cost, and painted exterior plywood is the least expensive.

Free Stalls and a Milking Parlor

Free-stall systems were developed by Major Bramley in England in 1958 and first used in the United States by Adolph Oien, Washington, in 1960. These systems are compatible with several methods for feeding, milking, and removing manure, and provide improved labor efficiency compared to a stanchion system. With a herd size of 80 cows or more, the initial investment can be less than for a stall barn. While it is not as easy to give individual attention or to observe the cows closely, milking in an elevated parlor does allow eye-level observation of the cow's udder, and the freedom of animal movement can improve heat detection.

There are at least six variations in the degree of shelter provided by free-stall systems:

1. Enclosed warm systems with heavy insulation and mechanical ventilation prevent extreme temperature fluctuations and the problems of frozen manure and snow. However, the cost of operating the fans is significant, particularly during mild weather. Even with thermostatic control, there are likely to be periods in which condensation will occur in some parts of the barn. This happens because of the extensive, wet floor area and because the cows tend to group together in some places while leaving

other areas unoccupied, resulting in heat deficiency in those areas. As temperature declines and moisture level remains constant, the relative humidity will increase until condensation occurs, either in the air as fog or on inside surfaces of the building. The effect may be minimized by heavy insulation, maintaining maximum animal density, and using a layout designed for uniform animal distribution and heat production during feeding and resting.

2. Modified environment barns maintain indoor winter temperatures higher than outdoors, usually above 32°F (0°C). These barns are usually insulated similar to the enclosed warm barns, but are naturally ventilated. By adjusting closures, ventilation control is critical to prevent large temperature fluctuations and excess moisture buildup. A modified environment barn is more expensive than a cold barn but has fewer freezing problems.

3. Enclosed cold systems have little or no insulation and depend on natural air currents for ventilation. Openings along the eaves and at the ridge provide for ventilation in the cold months, while larger openings along the side walls allow free air movement in mild weather. With the enclosed cold system, most snow problems are eliminated and with the animals completely confined, there is no runoff from a yard to increase disposal problems.

4. Covered cold systems provide a little less protection from drafts and snow, but open on the south, they allow sunshine to enter the building.

5. Partially open systems have perhaps 15 ft² (1.4 m²)/cow less space inside and are used in connection with paved yards. Provision for yard cleaning and yard runoff are necessary.

6. Open systems with covered free stalls, but open feed bunks and exercise areas, are practical in mild climates and are the least expensive. The free-stall barn may be sided or not, depending on local conditions. Water flushing of the alleys may be practical where temperature, water supply, and disposal areas are suitable. Although initial costs will be increased by the flush system, savings in labor will result.

Free-stall Barns

Materials. In order to install the required insulation in a warm barn, frame construction on a concrete foundation is preferred. However pole construction lends itself well to the cold free-stall system. An open roof deck with metal roofing, together with siding of vertical boards, plywood or the same metal as the roof provides for economical construction. A roof pitch of at least 4:12 is desirable for good air movement. While rigid-frame, metal buildings may be used, roof pitches are often rather low and purlins quite deep, restricting free air movement from eave to ridge. This situation can result in ventilation problems and premature corrosion of the frame and roof covering. Stall dividers made of 2 in. (38 mm) wood or metal are satisfactory. Wood that comes in contact with the ground should be pressure-preservative treated. Stall curbing may be made of either concrete or wood. Wood curbing is designed with two pieces, one pressure-preservative treated and fastened securely to the stall posts for permanence, and an untreated member on the alley side that can be easily replaced when it becomes worn.

Concrete is the most durable material for alleys and yards. Because it tends to become slippery, concrete should be given an anti-skid broomed finish when it is placed. In addition, it is common practice to cut 1/2 in. (13 mm) grooves into the surface in a pattern that runs at an angle to the direction of scraping to avoid catching the scraper blade. Coarse, aluminum oxide grit worked into the surface as it sets is another method of reducing both slipping and floor wear. This surface also wears away the cow's hooves enough to reduce the frequency of regular trimming.

Barn layout. In direct contrast to the stable barn where a cow feeds, rests, and is milked in one place, the free-stall housing system allows the cow to move to a different area for each of these activities with free access to feed and water.

The objective in planning the layout for a free-stall system is to meet the requirements of the cow in a minimum suitable area, to allow effective movement of the herd and permit efficient handling of feed and manure. If the layout provides a separate area specifically designed for each function, efficiency will be maximized.

A cow requires a clean, dry place to rest without being bothered by other cows. When she gets up after resting she normally defecates. To keep her resting area clean, a neck rail forces her back as she gets up; thus the manure is dropped into the alley where it collects for mechanical removal by one of several methods. The alley must be wide enough so that cows have no trouble getting into or out of the stall. Feeding is done in a separate area so that the stall will remain clean. Filling the feed bunk is accomplished with a conveyor or a mixer wagon. At milking time the herd is gathered together in one or more groups in a holding area. A mechanical crowd gate may be used to minimize delays. After milking, the cows return to the feed and rest areas.

Although many different floor plans have been used over the years, there has been an evolution to straight rows of stalls and considerably reduced area per cow. However, there are still a number of different designs being used, the choice of which depends on herd size, feeding program, climate, site characteristics, and owner preference. Free-stall barns have been constructed with from one to six rows of stalls; barn widths ranged from 20 to 120 ft (6 to 36 m). Although the feed alley or area may be used for holding cows waiting to enter the milking parlor, it is not recommended that the free-stall area be used for holding as extra stall cleaning will almost certainly result. There are many ways in which stalls, alleys, bunks, etc., may be arranged. Three typical designs are:

1. Two rows of stalls facing each other along one side of the barn, with a silage bunk along the opposite side. Only one side of the bunk is needed. Forty feet (12 m) is an adequate width unless a hay bunk is included which would increase the requirement to 44 to 46 ft (13 to 14 m). This design is suitable for single herds of up to approximately 100 cows.

2. A row of stalls along one side and two rows back-to-back in the center (fig. 26.2). The feed bunk along the opposite side of the barn must be accessible from both sides. A 46 ft (14 m) width with an 8 ft (2.4 m)

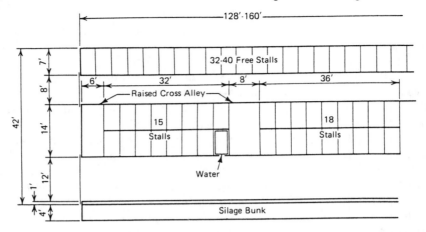

Figure 26.2. Open-side barn, 80 to 104 free stalls.

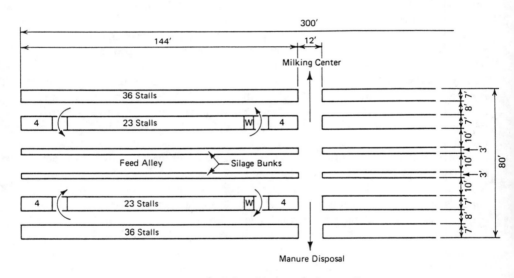

Figure 26.3. Closed barn, 268 free stalls.

overhang on the bunk side is adequate. Both this and the previous design lend themselves to feeding from a self-unloading wagon.

3. Two rows of stalls facing each other on each side of the barn with a central feed alley (fig. 26.3). Seventy-two to 80 ft (22 to 24 m) of width is required with a triple web truss roof design. While this may be designed for feeding with a self-unloading wagon, a conveyor system may be used. Hay is often fed at one end. Divided herd management is easily provided for with this barn layout. An alternative to this arrangement is shown in

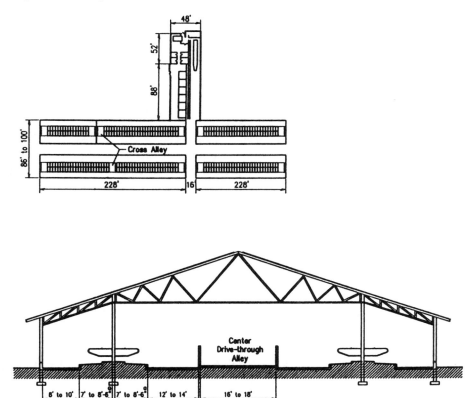

Figure 26.4. A four-row, free-stall barn with drive-through feeding and alleys along outside walls.

figure 26.4 which has the manure alley along the outside wall. This arrangement eliminates the need to attach the free stalls to the outside wall and allows the barn to be open more fully for summer ventilation.

Cows typically rest about 14 h/day, but do so for varying lengths of time over several periods. It is not necessary that each cow have its own stall; some cows may tend to return each time to the same stall and some do not. It is quite satisfactory to overpopulate by 30%, that is house 1.3 cows for every free stall.

Alleys provide for cattle movement and for manure accumulation. They also provide access for distributing bedding to free stalls. Alleys between rows of stalls should be 8 to 10 ft (2.4 to 3.0 m) wide. Narrower alleys may be acceptable where alley scrapers are used and operated frequently; wider alleys may be required for some equipment. Alleys between a row of stalls and a feed bunk should be 12 to 14 ft (3.7 to 4.3 m) to allow passage of cows behind animals eating. Traffic alleys which are only for movement of animals may be only 34 in. (860 mm) wide. Narrow alleys reduce the tendency of animals attempting to turn and block other cows. It is recommended that turns in alleys leading to the milking parlor be avoided. The alleys should have as few corners as possible to facilitate cleaning. Cross alleys should be 10 to 12 ft (3.0 to 3.7 m) wide to allow turning of manure removal equipment. If automatic manure scrapers are considered, it is important that alleys be the same width for the entire length of the barn. Finish the surface of the alleys with a broom to reduce slipperiness. Whatever design is chosen, straight alleys of uniform width are desirable and provision for expansion should be made.

All of the specifications in the following list do not necessarily apply to every barn, but where they do apply, they will contribute to cow comfort and labor efficiency with a minimum of investment. These specifications are for large milk cows. If a barn is being planned for a small breed, some dimensions, i.e., stall size, should be reduced.

1. Free-stall alleys, a minimum of 7 to 8 ft (2 to 2.5 m) wide.

2. Free stall to silage bunk alley, a minimum of 11 ft (3.5 m) wide.

3. Silage bunk to blank wall, a minimum of 10 ft (3 m) wide.

4. Hay rack to silage bunk on opposite side of the alley, a minimum of 13 ft (4 m) wide.

5. Individual free stalls, 3.5 to 4.3 ft (1.1 to 1.3 m) wide, 6.5 to 8 ft (2 to 2.5 m) long including curb, curb height, 10 to 12 in. (250 to 300 mm) depending on length of alley and method of removing manure.

6. Adequate cross alleys, 8 ft (2.4 m) wide and no dead-end alleys, providing ease of animal movement. Cross alleys should be raised to the stall curb level to keep manure in the main alleys during scraping.

7. Approximately 15 ft^2 (1.4 m^2) of holding area per cow, with a slope up to the milking parlor entrance.

8. Provision to divide the herd into groups. Grouping allows feeding in accordance with the level of production. Groups should not exceed 100 cows.

9. No turns in the entrance to the milking alleys.

10. If alleys are necessary, to and from the milking parlor, they should be only 32 to 36 in. (0.8 to 0.9 m) wide to prevent cows from turning.

11. Breeding, hospital, and calving areas adjacent to the milking parlor and arranged so that cows may be easily diverted to them.

12. Access for vehicles into alleys, even in barns with mechanical scrapers and conveyor feeders.

Figure 26.2 shows a relatively small free-stall housing system. If used as an open shed with cows having access to a paved strip at least 10 ft (3 m) wide along the bunk, the area per cow and length of bunk is quite generous. If, however, the plan is used for a closed barn, the floor area and bunk length per cow are probably near the minimum.

Figures 26.3 and 26.4 show plans for barns to house larger herds either with medium or high animal density. If a warm, free-stall system is desired, the high density

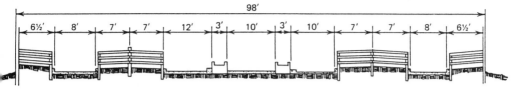

Figure 26.5. Elevation of a high-density, free-stall barn.

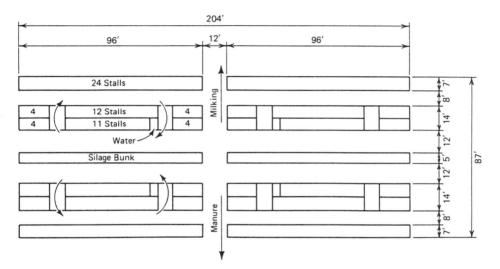

Figure 26.6. High-density closed barn, 252 free stalls.

plan shown in figure 26.4 has a better chance of successful ventilation as there would be only about two-thirds as much wet alley surface per cow. Figure 26.5 shows an elevation through the stalls for the high density plan with a drive-through feed alley. The plan in figure 26.6 is similar to figure 26.5, but it does not have the drive-through feed alley. The plan shown in figure 26.4 has alleys along the outside walls and allows for good natural ventilation.

Designs for free stalls. Free stalls are intended to provide an individual resting place for each cow. The cow is free to enter and leave at will. The purpose of the stall is to provide clean, sanitary conditions and to prevent udder injury. The potential for a cow to injure herself or to be injured by other cows should be minimized. Stalls should be big enough for the cow to lie comfortably, but the partition should prevent her from turning around or getting part of her body through. The cow should be restrained from moving forward far enough to defecate into the stall. Properly designed free stalls provide the cow with a safe comfortable resting place without unduly restricting her freedom including allowing her to rise in a natural manner as illustrated in figure 26.7.

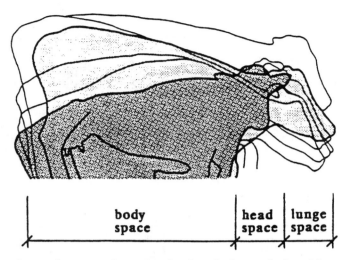

| body | head | lunge |
| space | space | space |

Figure 26.7. A cow thrusts her head as she lunges during rising.

Typical stalls built on-site using wood, and commercial stalls made of steel commonly used in the 1960s and early 1970s are shown in figures 26.8 and 26.9. Most have a sloping rear post set in the concrete curb or just inside the curb. Cantilevered or loop partitions, as shown in figure 26.10, reduce the potential for an animal to become entrapped in the stall and allow easy stall bed maintenance using tractor mounted blade, rake or cantilevered auger. The "Dutch" modified (fig. 26.11) loop partition seems to be an optimum design providing good positioning of the animal in the stall and the maximum comfort.

Because of a cow's biomechanics the natural rising requires a lunge forward. A head room space of 2.3 to 3.3 ft (0.7 to 1.0 m) in front of the fore knee is needed to allow a cow to rise comfortably. A free stall length of 8 ft (2.5 m) will satisfactorily accommodate Holstein cows. Early free stalls were frequently 7 ft (2.2 m) or less to prevent cows from defecating on the stall bed. This problem can be prevented by use of properly placed neck rails and brisket boards. Brisket boards should be 8 to 10 in. (200 to 250 mm) high and angled forward at 45°. A stall length of 7 ft (2 m) is satisfactory if the cow can thrust her head into the adjoining stall while rising, the partition in figure 26.11 allows this motion. Recommended stall sizes are given in table 26-4.

Stall beds may be made of wood planks, concrete, rubber mats, packed clay, limestone or similar material. A porous, firm material is ideal. Mattresses made of 9 oz (2.7 kg/m^2) polypropylene filled with straw or shavings provide good animal comfort and require very little bedding or maintenance (fig. 26.12). Bedding may be sawdust, chopped straw, silt or ground hulls.

Cows prefer to rest with their front slightly elevated and their back downhill. Thus it is recommended that the stall bed be sloped 2 to 6% from front to rear and that a lateral slope of 3% or greater be used. The lateral slope will encourage all animals to lie in the same direction and reduce the potential for udder or teat injury.

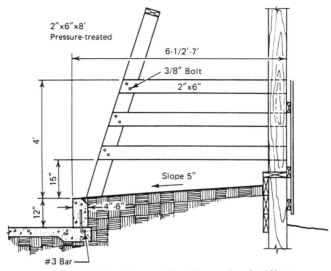

Figure 26.8. Wood free-stall with overhead stiffener.

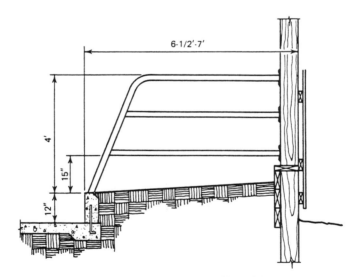

Figure 26.9. Metal free-stall partition.

Curbs are used to separate the manure from the stall. The curb may be either concrete or wood. The height of the curb, limited by the height of the cow's udder, depends
on the length of the alleyway, frequency of manure removal, and width of the alley.
Posts should be pressure-preservative treated, but there is no particular advantage in
using treated wood for the curbing as they are subject to rather rapid wear. Posts must

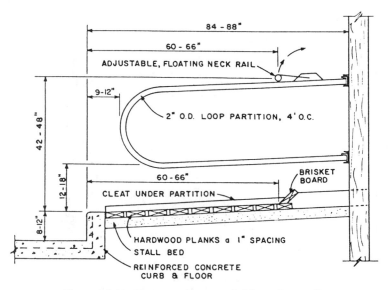

Figure 26.10. Diagram of suspended-loop free stall.

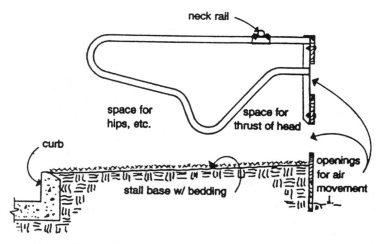

Figure 26.11. A free-stall partition with head space for rising.

be set deep enough to be secure. Alleys and any yard are best paved with concrete.

Curbs need to be 8 to 12 in. high (200 to 300 mm), highest for long alleys to prevent manure from being pushed into the stall. A brisket board at the same level as the curb and 2 ft (0.6 m) from the front of the stall helps to keep the cows from moving too far forward. The bottom side rails should be at least 12 to 15 in. (300 to 380 mm) above the floor and level to keep the cows from catching their legs. Gravel floors are satisfactory in well-drained locations. However, they will need attention to keep them level.

Table 26-4. Free stall dimensions

Animal weight (lb)	780-1,200	1,200-1,500	Over 1,500
Stall width (in.)	42	45	48
Length (Dutch) (ft)	6.5	7.0	7.0
Length (suspended) (ft)	7.5-8.0	8.0-8.5	8.5-9.0
Neck rail height (in.)	37	40	42
Rail distance from alley (in.)	62	66	71

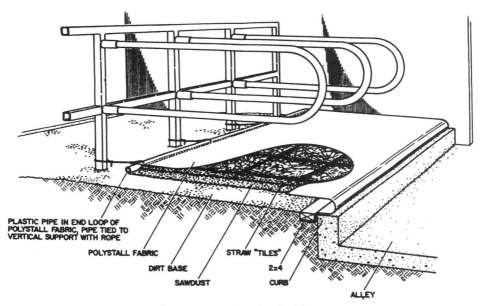

PLASTIC PIPE IN END LOOP OF
POLYSTALL FABRIC, PIPE TIED TO
VERTICAL SUPPORT WITH ROPE

POLYSTALL FABRIC   STRAW "TILES"

DIRT BASE   2x4

SAWDUST   CURB

ALLEY

Figure 26.12. A free stall with a bedding mattress.

Yard or Corral Systems

Open systems of this type are best suited to mild, dry climate zones. Variations include unpaved yards with 500 ft^2 (45 m^2) per cow which are dry scraped twice a year, semi-paved yards with 350 ft^2 (33 m^2) per cow and weekly scraping or complete paving with 125 ft^2 (12 m^2) or less per cow and daily scraping. The choice will depend on rainfall and availability of land both for yards and waste disposal.

Even the earthen yard should have paved areas at the feed bunks and water tanks, along at least one fence and around gates leading to the milking area. The semi-paved yards should have approximately 50 ft^2 (5 m^2) per cow.

Corral arrangement should provide for efficient feeding, good drainage, easy cleaning, and above all, efficient, continuous movement of animals for milking. This can be achieved with either rectangular or pie-shaped layouts.

Rectangular corrals for herds of up to 400 cows have at least four basic arrangements (fig. 26.13).

- Type (a) uses the center lane for feeding and moving cows.
- Type (b) uses the center lane for feeding and adjacent lanes for moving cows.
- Type (c) uses the center lane for feeding and the outside lanes for moving cows.
- Type (d) uses the center lane for cows and the outside lanes for feeding.

Each of these types has advantages and disadvantages that must be weighed and a decision made as to the relative importance for a particular farm. The factors to consider include:

1. Types (a) and (c) with their double cow lanes permit continuous flow of cows for milking. Types (a) and (d) would require a staggered shift to move the cows most effectively.
2. Type (d) has the most convenient feeding arrangement. Hay can be stacked close to where it will be fed and there are no gates to open or close when feeding silage.
3. Types (c) and (d) use the cow lanes as drains. Types (a) and (b) need perimeter drains.
4. Type (b) permits cows to be locked away from feed before milking. The other types require stanchions.

Combinations of rectangular yards with cross alleys are used for herds of 1,000 to 2,000 cows or more.

Pie-shaped corrals (figure 26.14) are suitable for herds of 250 to 500 cows divided into groups of 40 to 60 cows. Thirty-degree divisions keep the area, yard length, and feed bunk length in good proportion. The most significant advantage of the pie-shaped arrangement is that all the corrals are closer to the milking parlor than in a rectangular layout. This permits strings of cows from very large herds to be moved to the milking facilities in a shorter time. A double pie-shaped system, with service facilities between, can handle up to 800 or 1,000 cows. However, expansion beyond that number is difficult.

In either yard system, 20 to 25 ft^2 (2 to 2.3 m^2) of shade area should be provided for each animal. A sun shade with an eave height of 12 to 14 ft (4 m) and double that in width, when oriented north and south, will allow sunshine to strike all parts of the area under the shade at sometime during the day. This helps keep the surface dry and sanitary. If shades are built in the fence line, they must be located on both sides of the yard for all animals throughout the day.

Hospital and Maternity Area

Treatment pens located near the milking center are an essential part of any dairy housing system. One 12 × 14 ft (3.7 × 4.3 m) pen for each 100 milking cows should be adequate. Two or three stanchions in the pen fence allow cows to be restrained for artificial insemination or treatment. Lift equipment, supported on an extra truss or beam, can be useful for elevating animals that get down and can't get up.

One maternity pen of approximately 13 × 13 ft (4 × 4 m) for each 25 cows in the

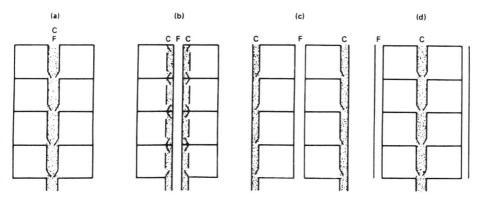

Figure 26.13. Rectangular corrals for up to 400 cows.

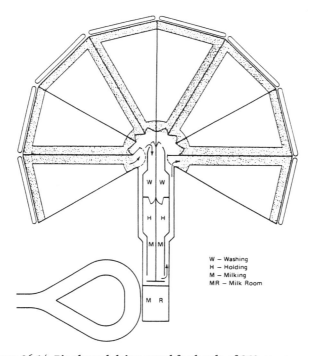

W — Washing
H — Holding
M — Milking
MR — Milk Room

Figure 26.14. Pie-shaped dairy corral for herds of 250 cows or more.

herd is desirable. Designing and locating the pens so they may be cleaned with a tractor will reduce labor. A chute for receiving or shipping cows should be placed adjacent to one of the pens.

Maternity and treatment facilities should allow easy access to the animal, be easy
to clean, and preferably allow one man to safely handle a 1,500 lb cow. They should

also have good environmental control to provide human comfort and minimize stress on sick animals.

MILKING CENTER

More than 50% of the total labor involved in a dairy enterprise is required for the milking operation and labor costs often exceed 75% of the total cost of milking. These factors combine to make the milking center of prime importance in the overall plan. A milking center may include a milking parlor, holding area, treatment area, utility room, milk room, storage room, lounge area, restroom, and office.

The U. S. Public Health Grade A Pasteurized Milk Ordinance requires approval of a plan for each farm before construction or remodeling begins. The milk buyer should be consulted regarding approval procedures before building. Approval agencies usually require an overall plan drawn to scale and showing dimensions, lighting, ventilation, insulation, waste disposal and water supply.

Milking Parlor

While a number of parlor designs have been used, the two most common are the tandem or side opening (fig. 26.15) and the herringbone (fig. 26.16). Side opening stalls allow each cow to be milked at her own pace and to be closely observed. A cow may be easily cut out for treatment. The herringbone parlors are ordinarily less expensive, and because they hold the cows closer together, reduce walking distance to approximately half with fewer gates to open and close.

For large herds of 400 cows or more, other parlor designs may be considered. The polygon herringbone design (fig. 26.17) is one of the most efficient, particularly when

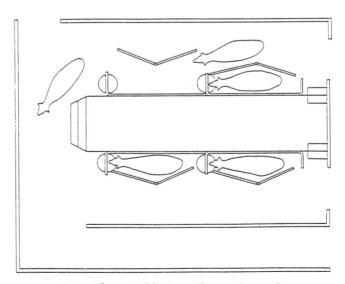

Figure 26.15. Double, two-side opening parlor.

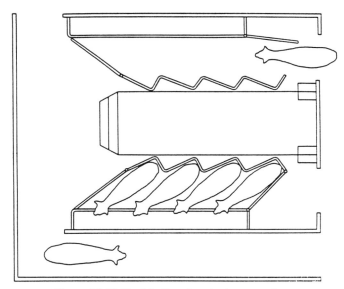

Figure 26.16. Double-four herringbone parlor.

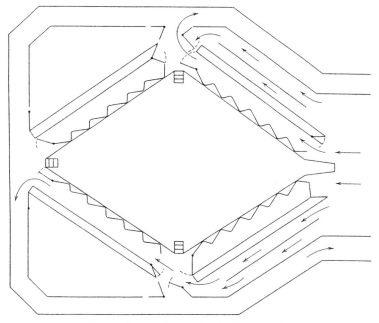

Figure 26.17. Polygon herringbone parlor.

it is fully mechanized. With automatic milk detachers, a throughput of more than 100 cows per hour by one person is possible in a 26-stall unit.

Flat parlors which do not have elevated cow platforms but allow efficient handling of groups of cows have been popular in the southwest (fig. 26.18). In recent years, the parallel parlor has been shown to allow high throughput rates. The parallel parlor (fig. 26.19) positions groups of cows perpendicular to the milking pit for milking from the rear of the animal. Teat cups are attached from the rear by reaching between the hind legs. Milking groups may be 24 to 30 cows.

Although the rate of milking varies more between operators than between systems, generally for similarly equipped systems and herds of equal production, the throughput

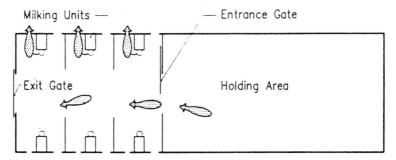

Figure 26.18. Flat milking parlor.

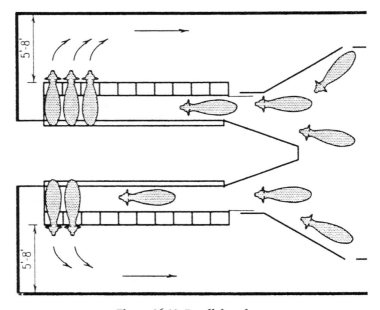

Figure 26.19. Parallel parlor.

of a herringbone will be slightly greater than for a side opening parlor. Automated gates, crowd gates, stimulating sprays in the floor, and detaching units will increase the throughput of all systems but the benefit seems to be greater with the herringbone design.

When relatively little mechanization is available, double-four herringbone parlors for one person or double-eight or ten for two persons are more efficient. Double-three and double-six parlors seem less productive. Where considerable mechanization is installed, including a crowd gate, stimulators, and detachers, one person can work very effectively in a double-eight or double-ten parlor. Smaller parlors hardly justify the initial investment in mechanization.

Rapid exit gates, which may be used with herringbone or parallel parlors, allow all cows in a group to move directly out of the milking stalls via individual gates or by lifting a barrier in front of the cows. Hydraulically operated gates in front of the cow are hoisted to release the entire group after milking is completed.

While early milking parlors were equipped for feeding grain, many parlors are now being constructed with a saving in cost by omitting grain feeding facilities. This follows the trend to feeding a total mixed ration in the feed bunk. Regardless of the type or size of parlor used in a system, there are a number of details common to all that contribute to an efficient, safe, and comfortable operation.

1. A crowd gate to move the cows toward the parlor. Although a separate holding area and crowd gate are investments that can be eliminated by using a part of the feeding area for holding, the efficiency of the milking operation is enhanced by including them in the design. The maximum length of a crowd gate is 30 ft (9 m). The crowd gate should not force cows into the parlor, but provide encouragement. In some cases a simple training signal, e.g., a light, bell or buzzer, may be substituted for a crowd gate.

2. A combined holding area and milking parlor, or a holding area and parlor separated by an overhead door that remains open during milking, can increase the efficiency with which cows move through the parlor. However, the walls and ceiling in the holding area must meet the same sanitary standards as the parlor walls. In contrast, some herdsmen prefer a split entrance door, hinged at either side, that opens toward the holding area. Closing the doors lightly against an entering cow hurries her along and at the same time positively stops the following cow. This system relaxes the requirements for sanitary construction in the holding area.

   The holding pen should provide 14 to 16 ft^2 (1.3 to 1.5 m^2) per cow and hold no more cows than can be milked in 1 1/2 h. The holding pen should be separate from the free stall alley and it is desirable that it slope at 1 to 6% away from the parlor.

3. A straight entrance into the parlor for the cows is recommended; animals turn at the exit instead of the entrance.

4. Minimum steps or ramps for entering and exiting. However, a 5-10% slope upward toward the parlor induces cows to face the entrance.

Table 26-5. Typical dimensions for parlors

Platform width	44-60 in.
Stall length	36-48 in.
Pit width	5-6 ft
Platform height	36-40 in.
Floor slope	1/4 in./ft
Traffic lanes	32+2 in.

5.   A large dispersal area for exiting.

6.   Grates at the rear of cows to reduce splash (should be easily removable for cleaning after milking).

7.   A floor level 3 to 4 in. (75 to 100 mm) above the holding area.

8.   Washable walls with at least 6 in. (150 mm) of concrete at the base.

9.   It is useful to have the pit extend 10 to 12 ft (3 to 3.6 m) into holding area.

10. The holding area floor should be made of high quality (4,000 psi) concrete. Incorporating 1.0 lb ferric oxide aggregate per square foot will reduce the danger of animals slipping. After 7 to 10 years the floor may need to be retreated with epoxy resin and antislip aggregate.

11. Radiant heat above the pit area.

12. Provision to separate exiting cows for special attention without leaving parlor pit.

13. A minimum of 25 ft candles of artificial lighting.

14. Insulation and ventilation sufficient to prevent condensation on walls and ceiling. An insulated concrete foundation.

Typical parlor design dimensions are given in table 26-5.

Milk Room

Details of milk room construction are usually dictated by sanitary codes. Some general characteristics commonly required are:

1. A room with twice the actual area needed for equipment.

2. Floor drains and adequately sloped floors.

3. Insulated walls and ceilings with easily washed surfaces.

4. A self-closing door and high threshold between the parlor and milkroom.

5. A separate utility room.

6. An adjoining lavatory and toilet.

Office

An office is needed for keeping herd health and production records. Records and computer systems that may be housed here need to be protected from dirt and moisture.

Storage Room

A separate storage room is needed for cleaning compounds, medical supplies, bulk materials, replacement milking system rubber components, and similar products. This room should be designed to minimize high temperatures which can accelerate rubber component deterioration. Two refrigerators—one for medical products and a second for replacement rubber products—are desirable.

Materials for Parlor and Milk Room

Sanitation is of paramount importance in milk rooms and milking parlors, requiring construction materials that will withstand moisture and chemicals. Floors should be made of high-quality concrete, and if the building is of frame construction, a concrete curb up to 12 in. (300 mm) high and smoothly coved to the floor facilitates cleaning.

Ceilings and walls should have a smooth, light-colored, water-resistant surface that permits thorough and easy cleaning and improves illumination. In addition, the walls and ceilings need to be well-insulated. In temperature zones above 20°F (–6°C), smooth masonry walls, finished with a waterproof surface, are both durable and easily cleaned. Filled core masonry walls are marginally satisfactory in the 10°F (–12 C) temperature zone. In both cases the ceiling should be insulated. In colder areas, frame walls that can be well-insulated are the most practical.

Of the several surface materials from which to choose, fiberglass-reinforced plastic paneling in sizes large enough to cover a wall without any seams has excellent resistance to moisture and wear and is easily cleaned. Although initially expensive, this is offset by the superior moisture protection and long life. MDO plywood has good overall characteristics at a medium cost. Exterior plywood and tempered hardboard rate a little lower and are also lower in cost. All of these materials, with the exception of fiberglass paneling, need painting with a glossy oil or latex-based enamel. Epoxy may be used if recommended by the manufacturer specifically for these materials. Fiberglass and hardboard need to be backed up with plywood in those areas of the milking parlor with which the cows come in contact. A polyethylene vapor barrier should be installed under all surface materials.

Prefinished metal sheets, either steel or aluminum, rate well for installation as a ceiling. They are easily cleaned and reasonable in price.

VENTILATION REQUIREMENTS

Open Free-stall Sheds

These should have a continuous ridge opening of 2 in. (50 mm) for each 10 ft (3 m) of barn width, while the back eaves should have 1 in. (25 mm) of opening for each 10 ft (3 m) of width. The south side of the building may be left completely open. If problems with blowing snow make it necessary to partially close the open side for a period of time, it is then desirable that the remaining opening be continuous rather than in two or three small openings. This will help prevent drafts. Summer ventilation is augmented by providing a minimum 2 ft (600 mm) opening below the eaves for the length of the building.

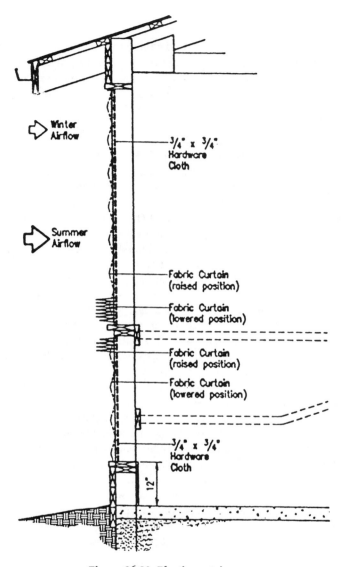

Figure 26.20. Plastic curtains.

Several types of summer vent closures have been used: removable panels, pivot doors, top- or bottom-hinged doors, and plastic or nylon curtains. Curtains readily cover large openings. Maximum summer ventilation may be provided by full-height, sidewall openings. Adjustable curtains can be used to cover the wall during winter (fig. 26.20).

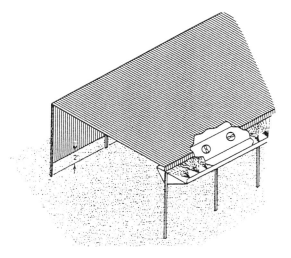

Figure 26.21. Evaporatively cooled sun shade.

Closed Cold Sheds

These may be ventilated similar to the open design, except the eave openings and the drop panels should be on both sides.

Yard or Corral Systems

Even in these systems, dairy cattle respond to modification of the environment. Although it is well known that production losses in the warm climatic zones are substantial during the summer months, in most cases, sunshades represent the only effort to modify environmental conditions. Evaporative coolers (shown in fig. 26.21) have been shown to result in improved conception rates and increased milk production of 8 to 10%. A 4 ft (1.25 m) wide horizontal mat installed above an eave-level plenum is continually sprayed with water. Small fans installed along the back side of the plenum draw air through the wet mats and discharge the cooled air at an angle across the shade area.

Warm Stable and Free-stall Barns

These require insulation and controlled air movement if temperatures and moisture are to be maintained at satisfactory levels. Table 26-6 suggests insulation and ventilation values for both stable and free-stall barns.

All continuously-operating fans should be controlled by low-limit thermostats to insure against freeze-up during periods of very low outside temperatures. Even with the amount of insulation indicated, some condensation may occur on surfaces when the temperature is extremely low. R-values in excess of those shown reduce the chances for surface condensation in severe weather.

Locate all fans in one place except in a very long barn. While the middle of the protected side is ordinarily the recommended location, the fans can be located near an

Table 26-6. Insulation and ventilation values for dairy barns

Design Temperature	15 (-9.4)	10 (-12.2)	5 (-15.0)	0 (-17.8)	-5 (-20.5)	-10 (-23.3)
Ceiling R_1*	6.3	7.6	9.4	15.2	17.1	18.9
R_2	1.1	1.3	1.7	2.7	3.0	3.3
Walls R_1	4.2	5.1	6.3	10.1	11.4	12.6
R_2	0.8	0.9	1.1	1.8	2.0	2.2
Stable barn						
Min. Vent. Rate (cfm)	60	55	52	50	45	40
Min. Vent. Rate (L/s)	28.5	26	24.5	23.5	21	19
Max. Vent. Rate (cfm)	200	200	200	200	150	150
Max. Vent. Rate (L/s)	95	95	95	95	71	71
Free-stall barn						
Min. Vent. Rate (cfm)	70	60	55	50	45	40
Min. Vent. Rate (L/s)	33	28.5	26	23.	21	19
Max. Vent. Rate (cfm)	200	200	200	200	150	150
Max. Vent. Rate (L/s)	95	95	95	95	71	71

* R_1 = ft^2 h °F/Btu; R_2 = m^{2}K/W.

Table 26-7. R-values for milking center walls and ceilings

Design Temperature		R Values			
		Ceiling		Wall	
°F	°C	R_1	R_{si}	R_1	R_{si}
10	-12.2	11.4	2.0	8.0	1.4
0	-17.8	13.6	2.4	10.2	1.8
-10	-23.3	15.9	2.8	13.0	2.3

area such as a silo or manure pit to prevent the spread of odors. In mild weather, the fans should exhaust air from near the ceiling. In the winter there is little difference whether it is drawn from near the floor or the ceiling.

Slot inlets require a range of adjustment sufficient to maintain an inlet velocity of 700 to 1,000 fpm (3.5 to 5 m/s) at all ventilating rates. Twenty square inches of inlet area per 100 cfm of fan capacity will usually produce a velocity within the desired range. (In SI units, 275 mm^2 of inlet area per 1 L/s of fan capacity will produce a similar relationship.)

Locate corrosion resistant thermostats near the center of the barn and about 1 ft (300 mm) from the ceiling. The operating temperature may need to be reduced in mid-winter.

Milking Center

The milk room and milking parlor should be well-insulated to conserve heat and prevent surface condensation. Suggested R-values are given in table 26-7.

Ventilation for the milk room and milking parlor should control moisture and odors while preventing freeze-ups or excessively high temperatures. Approximate recommended rates are 100 cfm (0.05 m^3/s)/stall for winter and 400 cfm (0.2 m^3/s)/stall for summer. A manually controlled exhaust fan may be located in the milking parlor to draw its inlet air through the milk room. Automatic louvers should

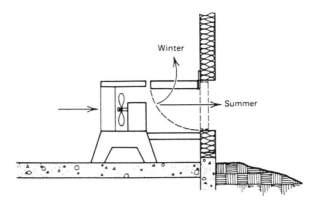

Figure 26.22. Hinged panel directs heat flow for summer and winter.

be installed at both the inlet and outlet of the milk room. The fan capacity should be the equivalent of 6 to 12 air changes of the milk room each hour. Much of the heat needed to maintain comfortable conditions in the milk room can be collected from the milk cooling operation. During the 2-h milking period, 1,000 lb (450 kg) of milk plus the electricity to operate the compressor will produce around 80,000 Btu (84,400 kJ). There will also be some loss from the lights and the water heater. In addition to these sources of heat, it is desirable to have 3 kW of electrical heating capacity in the milk room and up to 15 kW in the parlor. Figure 26.22 shows how one hinged panel in the utility room wall can direct waste heat outside in the summer or conserve it for heating the milk room in the winter.

FEED MANAGEMENT

Feed storage and handling for a dairy enterprise should be set up as an integral part of the overall system.

Hay may be stored above a dairy stable for convenient feeding. However, ground level storages are usually easier to fill and offer some fire protection when they are located an adequate distance from the stable. Hay for free-stall systems is almost always stored in a separate building, although for convenience several days' supply may be placed above the feed racks. Low cost pole or post-frame buildings are very satisfactory for hay storage.

Silage storage is discussed in detail in another chapter. As mentioned, tower silos with mechanical unloaders are generally compatible with conveyor handling and feeding. A single conveyor may collect a complete ration including haylage from a silo, concentrate metered from the storage bin, high-moisture corn which is crushed as it is discharged from an airtight silo, and finally, corn silage from a silo. The complete ration is then conveyed and distributed along the feed bunk.

A horizontal silo, which can be used effectively with a mixer wagon but which is somewhat less efficient to unload, requires considerably less investment than a tower silo.

Conveyor feed systems can be highly automated and require very little attention during operation. Their cost is closely related to the length of the system. The longer the conveyor, the more it costs.

An alternative to the conveyor system is the use of a mixer wagon. With a mixer wagon, the various ingredients may be picked up at several locations, including a horizontal silo. The feed ration is then mechanically mixed and distributed along the feed bunks. A mixer wagon has a fixed cost so that the more animals it serves, the more economical it becomes. However, depending on the layout, a barn may need to be built 10 to 12 ft (3 to 3.7 m) wider if a mixer wagon is used.

For mature dairy cows, feed bunk height should be about 28 in. (710 mm). Two ft (600 mm) of bunk space on one side is adequate for silage, while if hay is fed, 6 to 12 in. (150 to 300 mm) of hay rack is satisfactory.

Electronic technology now provides the opportunity to control and monitor the concentrate intake of individual cows housed and fed in free-stall barns. Computer-controlled feeding stations are used for feeding cows on a selective basis. Each cow wears a device that identifies her to a computer as she approaches the feed dispenser. The computer is programmed to allot a specific quantity to each cow. The allotment may be divided into four or more periods to ensure multiple feedings. Daily feed consumption can be recorded for review by the herdsman. Systems are available that allocate up to three concentrate sources or ingredients to each cow.

One cup-type waterer or 24 in. (600 mm) of access around a tank should be provided for each 20 cows. Waterers should be located for easy access but not in parlor return lanes or narrow cross alleys. They should be positioned to minimize feed deposition into the waterer. If a waterer is located next to a feed bunk or hay rack, a solid barrier should be provided to prevent cows from swinging their heads to the waterer while eating. If the waterer is located in an area that is subjected to freezing temperatures it must be heated or otherwise protected.

Manure Handling

The disposal of manure, wash water, and milk room waste is a major problem that must be dealt with in the overall dairy housing plan. Before planning begins, local and state authorities should be consulted on related health and environmental regulations. Waste management systems are discussed in chapter 19. Once the waste management system has been designed, the proposed plans should be approved by the appropriate authorities before starting construction.

Management decisions such as the amount and type of bedding used will affect the type of waste management system which in turn may affect the housing design. Methods of scraping manure from the free-stall barn may influence management with regard to cow movement to and from milking.

HOUSING FOR CALVES

Newborn calves are particularly susceptible to respiratory and digestive disorders. While the complete management program influences the survival and healthy growth of the young calf, housing is a major factor. The important factors in calf housing are that it be clean, dry, free from drafts, provide adequate space, plenty of bedding, and fresh air. Calves should be separated from older animals to minimize exposure to disease organisms and separated from each other to prevent nose-to-nose contact to reduce disease transfer. Temperature is a relatively unimportant factor. Even in northern states and Canada, the most compelling reasons for warm housing are worker comfort and ease of handling the liquid supplement fed to the calves during the first six weeks.

Placing calves in small groups of 4 or 5 at 3 to 5 months provides an adjustment period before moving into larger groups. Calves may be housed successfully in a variety of shelters including:

• A cold hutch or individual calf shelter.
• A cold barn in which the temperature fluctuates with the weather.
• A warm barn maintained at 50 to 60°F (10 to 15°C) throughout the winter.

Hutches

Calves housed in individual hutches with plenty of bedding do as well or better than those in a warm barn. Hutches should be a minimum of 4 × 4 ft (1.2 × 1.2 m) with a 4 × 8 ft (1.2 × 2.4 m) outdoor run. Each hutch must be thoroughly cleaned and moved to a new location each time a new calf is housed. Deep bedding should be maintained at all times. Hinging the roof at the front edge allows the roof to be lifted so that feed buckets may be placed in racks at the back of the hutch.

Hutches should be sealed tightly except for the front and bottom, to reduce the wind blowing through in winter. For summer, the hutch may have a rear opening or it can be blocked up about 6 in. (150 mm) to allow cross-ventilation.

There are a variety of prefabricated plastic/fiberglass hutches on the market. Hutches made of translucent material require shade in summer. Facing hutches south or east generally provides the best draft protection and sun exposure during winter. Hutches should be located on a well-drained area. Crushed rock or sand provides a good base.

Cold Barns

The most important consideration in a cold barn is good natural ventilation obtained by a roof slope of at least 4:12, a ridge opening of 2 in. (50 mm) per 10 ft (3 m) of barn width, and an eave opening of 1 in. (25 mm)/10 ft (3 m) of barn width. If the barn is open on the south side, the rear eave opening is still required. The use of old dairy stables for housing calves is not satisfactory because it is difficult to provide adequate natural ventilation. In the winter, they tend to be too damp and in the summer they may be too hot.

Warm Barns

A warm barn provides comfortable working conditions and greater labor efficiency, but it is more costly to build and operate. It must be well-insulated and ventilated and have a source of supplemental heat. Old dairy stables may be satisfactory, but only if they are completely renovated and equipped for adequate environmental control. Conditions in the building should be maintained at near 50°F (10°C) with less than 80% relative humidity.

Table 26-8. Estimated supplemental heat required in a warm calf barn*

Wall	R 12 (2.1)†	R 6 (1.1)
Ceiling	R 20 (3.5)	R 15 (2.6)
Outside design temperature		
−10 F (−23°C)	160 W/100 lb (45 kg)	195 W/100 lb (45 kg)
0 F (−18°C)	115 W/100 lb (45 kg)	140 W/100 lb (45 kg)
10 F (−12°C)	70 W/100 lb (45 kg)	90 W/100 lb (45 kg)

* Based on a 1,250 ft² (116 m²) building housing forty 150 lb (68 kg) animals at 50°F (10°C).
† ft² h °F/Btu (m²K/W).

Using the moisture balance techniques discussed in chapter 15, it is shown that for fully occupied housing, approximately 11 cfm (18 m³/h) of ventilation for each 100 lb (45 kg) of animal weight is required to keep the relative humidity at 80% or less. The balance equations will indicate a rate of nearly four air changes per hour. That is, fans should move air at a rate equivalent to four times the volume of the room each hour. This much air movement will supply the necessary fresh air and will keep the relative humidity below 80%. When this much air is introduced, warmed, and exhausted on a 0°F (−10°C) day, it is readily shown that the calves produce only about half the heat required for a heat and moisture balance. It is difficult to determine an exact balance as the heat and moisture produced by calves varies considerably during the first six months after birth. Nevertheless, the animal heat must be supplemented with artificial heat.

Table 26-8 suggests supplementary heat requirements for two levels of insulation and three outside design temperatures. The supplemental heat may be supplied by unit heaters suspended from the ceiling or by electrical heaters installed in metal, fresh-air distribution ducts extending the length of the room. The minimum ventilation should be operated on a continuous basis while the room temperature is maintained at the desired level by the thermostatically controlled heaters.

Heat balances calculated for the moderate temperatures of spring and fall will indicate the need for additional ventilation of up to eight air changes per hour during these seasons. Fans providing this amount of ventilation should be controlled by a thermostat set a few degrees above the heater thermostat to prevent the heaters from operating during periods of increased ventilation. For summer heat removal, total fan capacity should provide an air change every 1 or 2 min.

If inlet distribution ducts are used, they should be adjusted manually each season to produce an inlet velocity of 700 to 1,000 fpm (3.6 to 5 m/s). If unit heaters are used in combination with slot inlets, it is advisable to divide the adjusting baffles into lengths of approximately 6 ft (2 m) so that alternate baffles may be closed tightly in the winter. Even then the remaining baffles will be opened only 1/4 in. (6 mm). Although the complete environmental system just described should maintain good overall conditions within a warm calf barn, zone heating with infrared heat lamps should be provided for young and sick calves.

Stalls and Pens

Calves should be kept in individual stalls or pens, or in a hutch for the first six to eight weeks. This allows for individual attention to feeding and helps to prevent the spread of disease. The stalls or pens may be constructed of wood, plywood, welded wire or sheet metal. To prevent the spread of disease, it is best to design the stall or pen dividers so that the calves cannot lick each other. Stalls should be 2×4 ft (0.6×1.2 m) while pens should be 4 ft (1.2 m) wide and from 4 to 8 ft (1.2 to 2.4 m) long. In each case, a rack to hold two buckets for milk and grain should be installed along a feed alley.

A wide variety of pen and stall designs are used in both the cold and warm barns. Pens are usually bedded with straw, ground corn cobs, shavings or sawdust. Stalls in cold barns are perhaps best located at floor level and bedded. Stalls in warm barns are frequently raised several inches above a rear gutter so that manure may be flushed away. These raised stalls may be completely slotted or the front half solid and bedded. Many operators feel that when the raised, slotted-floor stalls are used in a warm system, the temperature should be a few degrees warmer than is needed with partially or completely bedded stalls.

A 100 cow milking herd would typically require housing for 20 calves under two months of age. Assuming stalls are used, a barn width of 20 to 26 ft (6 to 7.2 m) is adequate for two rows, while 36 to 44 ft (11 to 13 m) are needed for four rows. Walls and ceilings constructed of smooth, easily cleaned materials facilitate the maintenance of sanitary conditions that are essential for successful housing of dairy calves. A feed storage and preparation area should be located near the calf pens. Hot water is important for washing equipment and mixing feed.

HOUSING FOR HEIFERS

Convenience and reasonable cost are prime objectives in planning housing for heifers. Buildings abandoned for other purposes are frequently used for young stock housing. While they may meet the reasonable cost objective, they seldom are very convenient. For this reason, new housing at a higher initial investment is often justified.

At weaning, calves should be grouped together with others of their age. Seven to 10 animals in a group are ideal, but with careful management larger groups are satisfactory. Typical groups might include animals aged 2 to 7, 7 to 12, 12 to 18, and 18 to 24 months. Timid animals may be moved to a lower age group while aggressive animals may be moved up.

A number of successful housing systems are used. They include:

• Loose housing
• Free stalls
• Sloped floor facility
• Warm, slotted floor system
• Dry lot or pasture

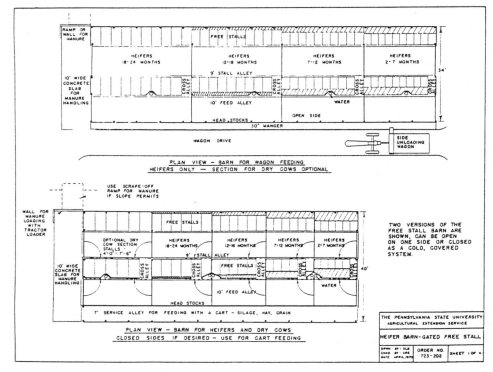

Figure 26.23. Young-stock barn, free-stall system.

Loose Housing

A bedded pack, loose housing system is most satisfactory when plenty of home grown bedding is available and the area is well-drained.

Free Stalls

The free stall system with scraped alleys is a popular choice and works well if the free stalls are sized correctly for the animals in the group. The following sizes of free stalls are suitable:

2 to 7 months, 2.5 × 4.5 ft (0.76 × 1.4 m)
7 to 12 months, 2.8 × 5.0 ft (0.85 × 1.5 m)
12 to 18 months, 3.2 × 6.0 ft (1.00 × 1.8 m)
18 to 24 months, 3.5 × 6.8 ft (1.10 × 2.0 m)

The stalls may be constructed so that the length is adjustable. In that way the operator can make adjustments to improve the cleanliness of the stalls.

Figure 26.23 illustrates how a series of gates may be used to separate the animals into age groups and control their movement for feeding, cleaning the alleys, and handling individual groups.

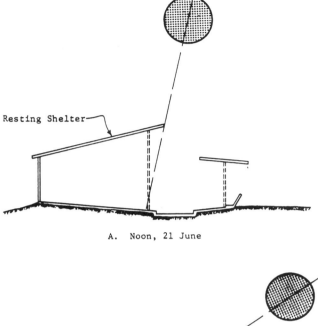

A.   Noon, 21 June

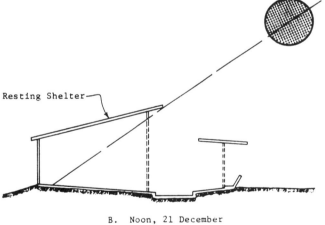

B.   Noon, 21 December

Figure 26.24. Young-stock barn, sloped-floor facility.

Sloped-floor Facility

An open barn with a paved resting area 18 ft (5.5 m) wide, sloped toward the front 1:12 is suitable for milder climates. The action of the animals' hooves moves most of the manure to a litter alley. The balance dries, aided by midwinter sunshine that reaches to the back of the floor area through the open side of the shed roof building. Feeding is done at a covered bunk across the litter alley from the rest area. A 5 ft (1.5 m) wide platform in front of the feed bunk designed with the same slope of 1:12 is also self-cleaning. Only the litter alley must be scraped. Including the 6½ to 9 ft (2 to 2.75 m) litter alley, a total area of 20 to 30 ft^2 (2 to 2.8 m^2)/heifer is available (fig. 26.24).

The resting area is divided into 12 ft (3.7 m) sections to divide the various age groups. Gates extending across the litter alley from the resting-area partitions to the feed bunk complete the pen. Swinging the gates confines the animals to the resting area to allow cleaning the litter alley or handling individual groups.

Warm Slotted-floor Housing System

Slotted-floor housing with no free stalls allows high animal density and improves labor efficiency. A warm, insulated building with mechanical ventilation ensures the effective movement of the manure between the slats. The floor remains dry and clean enough to rear clean animals. Manure may be handled in shallow pits with mechanical scrapers or by storing the manure in deep pits for periodic removal.

Dry Lot or Pasture

In mild climates, heifers may be grown successfully in dry lots or on pasture with open buildings that give protection from storms and offer shade in hot weather.

HOUSING FOR VEAL CALVES

Veal calves, like all calves, are susceptible to respiratory diseases. They are also fed a special diet in order to produce a market carcass with light pink muscle tissue and white fat. These facts coupled with the desire to maximize feed conversion efficiency and rate-of-gain make environmental control of great importance. A temperature of 60 to 65°F (16 to 18°C) and 80% RH are typical recommendations.

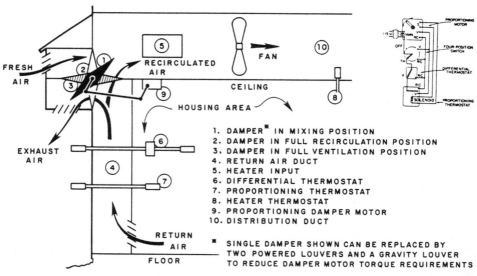

Figure 26.25. Schematic cross-section of positive-pressure, constant airflow ventilation system.

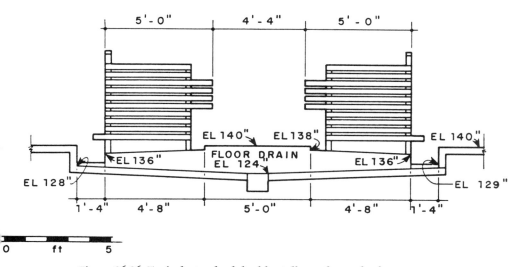

Figure 26.26. Typical, standard double-stall row for veal calves.

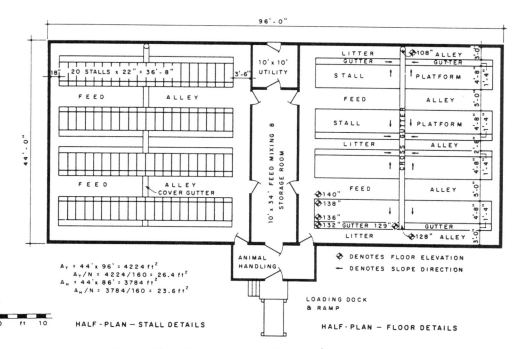

Figure 26.27. Standard, veal calf barn, 160 stalls.

Fresh air circulating throughout the shelter, adequate to maintain uniform conditions, may reduce the humidity to below the desired level. A system designed with a proportioning damper that circulates a mixture of fresh air and room air, allows both adequate air movement and maintenance of the desired humidity. The damper is controlled by a proportioning thermostat which allows more fresh air to enter the system as outside temperatures rise. Air is distributed through plastic or metal ducts running the length of the barn. The number and size of holes in the ducts are based on an air velocity of 800 to 1,000 fpm (4 to 5 m/s). Figure 26.25 shows a cross-section of the proportioning system.

Elevated stalls with slotted floors and either gutters behind the stalls or a flush system under the stalls may be used (fig. 26.26). Plywood or wood, rather than metal, is used for stalls and all bedding is avoided to ensure that iron is unavailable to the calves. Ordinarily, a building width of 44 ft (13.4 m) is required for four rows of stalls including two feed alleys and three litter alleys (fig. 26.27). However, it is possible to reduce the barn width to 36 ft (11 m), including three feed alleys, if water flushing under the stalls is used for manure removal. The barn width may be further reduced to 28 ft (8.5 m) if calves are fed from the back of the stalls. The four rows of stalls would have only two combined feed and litter alleys. Although cost per animal is reduced with the narrower design, it increases the demands for good management. A wash and feed preparation area adjacent to the animal stalls should provide dry feed storage and adequate hot water for washing equipment and preparing the milk supplement.

Problems

26.1.   Draw a scale floor plan for a stable barn equipped with tie stalls for 60 cows. Include space for maternity and hospital pens but not calf pens. In addition make a cross-section drawing showing the alley and stall dimensions and the contour of the floor.

26.2.   Draw a scale floor plan for a high density free-stall barn for 160 milking cows. Include a means for dividing the herd into two milking groups. Show a holding area to be used in conjunction with the milking parlor. Although it may be assumed that they will be located elsewhere, indicate the requirements for maternity and hospital pens.

26.3.   Draw a scale floor plan for a building to house replacement animals for the herd in either problem 26.1 or 26.2. Plan on housing animals from 2 months to 24 months of age.

26.4.   Give recommendations for the housing of calves from birth to 2 months of age for the herd in either problem 26.1 or 26.2.

26.5.   Assume that the 60 cows in problem 26.1 weigh an average of 1,500 lb (680 kg). Suggest ventilation system capacity for each season of the year for an outside design temperature of 10°F (−12°C). Include recommendations for inlet design.

27 Poultry Housing

Rapid, dramatic changes occurred in poultry housing during the 1960s and 1970s. There are many different types of poultry enterprises. Egg production by laying hens and meat production by broiler chickens and turkeys are typically carried out in large, specialized operations. Pullet rearing and poultry breeders are smaller operations. Although ducks and game fowl may also be produced on a commercial scale, this text will only discuss the major poultry enterprises.

CHICKENS

The transition in poultry housing from a place in the barn for a few birds that largely foraged for themselves to a modern environmentally controlled cage house for thousands of birds represents one of the greatest advances ever made in housing for an agricultural enterprise. Automated equipment for feeding, watering, egg collection, ventilating, and manure removal has made egg production one of the most efficient farm operations ever. It is now recognized that good housing also contributes to the overall increase in production efficiencies.

Increased bird densities and improved insulation transformed the poultry house from one of the most difficult buildings to ventilate into one where optimum conditions are readily obtainable. High summer temperature is much more likely to be a problem than is severe winter weather. Higher bird densities also reduce housing costs.

The term bird density relates to two areas. Overall bird density refers to the building floor area per bird, and within the limits of good management, the more birds that can be housed in a building, the lower the cost of housing per bird. The type of cage and number of tiers will affect the bird density in the building as shown in table 27-1.

Density also refers to the area that each bird has in the cage. For example, each of the four birds in a 12 × 18 in. (300 × 450 mm) cage has 54 in.^{2} (33 750 mm^2) of space. The space that the birds have in the cage has an effect on egg production, livability, and feed consumed per dozen eggs produced. If the cost of the hen and the feed were the only considerations, one bird per cage would produce the most eggs with the least feed. However, when all costs, including those for the building, equipment, and labor are considered, either three or four birds per cage show the greatest return on investment. Three birds are best when egg prices are low, while four birds per cage show a greater return with high egg prices. General space requirements are given in table 27-2.

Table 27-1. Cage systems and building densities for layers

Cage Type	Tiers	Cage Size	Rows	House Width, ft (m)	Building Area/bird, ft² (m²)
Flat deck	1	12 × 18*	4	40 (12.2)	0.63 (0.058)
Modified S.S.	2	12 × 18*	4	40 (12.2)	0.63 (0.058)
Modified S.S.	3	12 × 18*	4	40 (12.2)	0.42 (0.039)
Stacked	3	12 × 18*	6	52 (15.9)	0.36 (0.033)
Stacked	4	12 × 18*	6	52 (15.9)	0.27 (0.025)
Reverse	4	18 × 12*	6	42 (12.9)	0.33 (0.031)
Stacked	4	19 × 19†	5	38 (11.6)	0.21 (0.020)

* Four (4) birds/cage and 54 in² (34 838 mm²) per bird.
† Seven (7) birds/cage and 51 in² (33 290 mm²) per bird.

Table 27-2. Poultry housing space and equipment requirements

	LAYING FLOCKS	
	Light Breeds, Customary (SI)	Heavy Breeds, Customary (SI)
Floor space		
Floor	1 1/4-2 1/2 ft² (0.12-0.23 m²)	1 1/2-3 ft² (0.14-0.28 m²)
Cage	0.2-0.7 ft² (0.02-0.07 m²)	0.3-1.0 ft² (0.03-0.09 m²)
Feeders	3 in. (75 mm)	4 in. (100 mm)
Waterers	3/4 in. (19 mm)	1 in. (25 mm)
Nests	4-5/nest	4-5/nest
	BROILER AND REPLACEMENTS	
	0-4 weeks, Customary (SI)	Heavy Breeds, Customary (SI)
Floor space:		
Open house	0.5 ft² (0.05 m²)	1 1/2-3 ft² (0.14-0.28 m²)
Controlled env.	0.5 ft² (0.05 m²)	0.3-1.0 ft² (0.03-0.09 m²)
Feeders	1 in. (25 mm)	4 in. (100 mm)
Waterers	0.2 in. (5 mm)	1 in. (25 mm)
	4-5/nest	4-5/nest

Poultry Housing Requirements

Poultry production is divided into several types of enterprises organized to serve specific egg and meat markets. Breeding flocks supply eggs to hatcheries which in turn produce day-old chicks for broiler and layer replacement needs. Commercial laying flocks produce eggs for the fresh market as well as the egg breaker (liquid egg) market for bakery and processed food industries. Broiler production is a very intensive operation requiring only seven to eight weeks from hatch to market. Five or six flocks of birds are marketed per year.

Each of these enterprises, with housing requirements peculiar to its own needs, will be discussed separately. Birds within the house may be floor-managed or confined in a cage system. Each of these two systems has applications to the various phases of poultry production. Three housing systems are prevalent in various regions of the country.

1. Open housing with little more than a roof and, possibly, roll-up curtains on the sides depending on climate.
2. Naturally ventilated houses that depend primarily on wind and thermal buoyancy ventilation. Building sidewalls are generally 1/2 to 1/3 open and covered with automatically operated curtains. Roofs, and often lower walls and end walls, are insulated depending on climate and density of birds. Usually, some mechanical air circulation is utilized.
3. Environmentally controlled houses are well-ventilated, warm throughout the year, and depend on automatic fan ventilation. These buildings are fully insulated and have no windows. Light control can be readily accomplished, if desired.

Housing for the Breeding Flock

Breeder flocks are floor-managed in either naturally ventilated or environmentally controlled houses. Considerable supervision is required in feeding and disease control in order to produce high-quality, fertile eggs for the hatcheries. Labor efficiency is improved with automatic feeders and waterers which are often located on a slotted-floor area. The floor litter in the balance of the house consequently stays drier and the moisture to be removed by the ventilating system is reduced. Nests are banked in lines along the outside wall or on either side of a center alley for convenient manual egg collection. Labor efficiency is further improved with mechanical egg collection where eggs are delivered to an egg collection table at the end of the building or transferred to a cross-conveyor which travels through a series of buildings to a central handling building. Generally, nests equipped for mechanical egg collection are back-to-back with a common egg-conveying belt eliminating the need for a center access alley, thereby saving building space for additional production.

Breeding flocks are the parent stock for either broiler production or egg production and the genetics and characteristics are completely different and require different feeding regimes. Parent stock for egg production are generally on full feed with males and females on the same feed ration. Parent stock for broiler production are genetically geared to produce meat and are not efficient egg producers. Males are large and feed intake must be severely restricted. Overweight and lazy males tend to do a poor job of fertilizing the females. Females must also be fed special diets and somewhat restricted in feed intake.

Two separate feeding systems are utilized to enhance the objective of producing fertile eggs. The female feeder has a grill with narrowly spaced dividers such that the male cannot comfortably place his head in the openings. The male feeder has wide openings but is raised high enough so that the female cannot comfortably reach the males' food. The most common feeding systems are closed-loop types utilizing either flat-link chain, drag auger cable with plastic buttons or wire link with steel buttons. At higher speeds, these units can deliver a preset quantity of feed evenly distributed in a short period of time. Ample feeder space is required so that all birds can eat simultaneously. Feed is restricted by the number of feedings (usually once or twice) per day.

Water is most commonly supplied from a continuous pipeline with attached nipples or cups suspended from a cable and winch system. Nipples are an increasingly more common method of watering and believed to result in a drier litter. Both watering and feeding systems are usually suspended on a cable and winch system so they can be raised overhead for ease in clean-out.

Housing for Laying Hens

Open houses utilizing cage systems are popular in the South where a mild year-round climate makes insulation and mechanical ventilation unnecessary. The cage system is protected with only a light reflective roof and roll-up curtains on the sides. Emergency cooling systems and rooftop sprinklers may be installed for periods of unusually hot weather. Investment is low and environmental conditions are reasonably uniform.

Most new, commercial laying operations utilize controlled environment buildings using cage systems that permit high bird density. The buildings are well-insulated, windowless structures up to 650 ft (200 m) in length. The width is determined by the type and arrangement of the cages but usually ranges between 40 and 60 ft (12 and 18 m). While the cages are installed on only one floor level, the house may be essentially two stories high to allow space for manure storage for a period of up to 12 months.

Cage Systems

Investment, environment, and labor efficiency are strongly influenced by the cage systems; therefore, it is important to understand the advantages and disadvantages of each type before proceeding with a building design.

A number of different cage and housing systems have been developed (fig. 27.1). Although there are variations in equipment and design, cage systems may be classified by the number of levels of cages and the method of manure elimination from cage area to in-house storage. Most of the early cage systems were flat deck or two-tier, stair-step cages. With the advent of controlled environment housing, cage designs continued to be improved. Three- and four-tier systems, and now five-tier systems have become popular, providing significant increases in bird density within a house.

Manure elimination was simple in the early cage systems. Manure from the flat deck or stair-step cage systems just dropped to the floor or pit. With three or four tiers, the space required and access to the upper cages was unwieldy. The next innovation was the modified stair-step with slanted manure collection boards between levels to prevent manure from entering lower cages causing dirty eggs. Manure was scraped from manure boards from the aisle on a hanging system or with a mechanical scraper on floor stand systems. Manure boards were generally plywood. The plywood boards and the mechanical scrapers required considerable maintenance.

The next innovation was the slant back cage, where the backs of the cages were slanted toward the front of the cage. A plastic curtain on the slant back, extending to within 1 to 2 in. (25 to 50 mm) of the cage above, eliminating the need for a manure board and a mechanical scraper between levels of cages. While this technique does allow a slightly larger window for manure exposure to the cage below, it is not detrimental to the production of table eggs. Table eggs are not allowed to have stains on

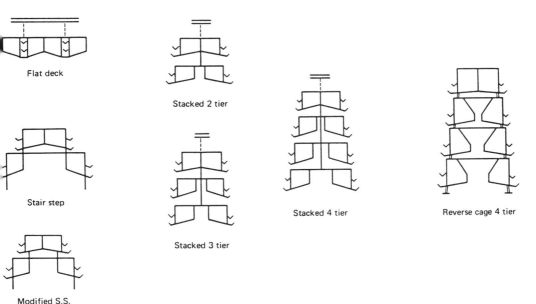

Flat deck

Stacked 2 tier

Stair step

Stacked 3 tier

Stacked 4 tier

Reverse cage 4 tier

Modified S.S.

Figure 27.1. Layer cage designs.

the shells from manure droppings. The slant-back system is most common with four-tier and recently five-tier systems.

Four-tier systems should be equipped with a bump rail located 16 to 24 in. (410 to 610 mm) above the aisle and above the bottom egg tray toward the aisle to protect the bottom egg tray from physical damage. This is helpful in guiding transport carts used to deliver birds to the cages and at removal, and protects the bottom egg tray from damage by the heavy carts. Secondly, the bump rails should be of sufficient strength to support a heavy person to access the top level of cages for routine maintenance and removal of dead birds. The five-tier system should have a second bump-stand rail up one level to provide access to the top level of cages.

In the late 1970s, the European battery style cages started to appear in the U.S. and have captured a significant share of the U.S. market (fig. 27.2). This cage arrangement allows each cage level to be back-to-back and directly above each other, with a manure belt directly under each level of cages. The manure belt acts as a conveyor to move the manure to the end of the building. This system was very common in Europe for quite a number of years prior to introduction to the U.S. However, European applications were in shorter buildings than those common in the U.S and some modifications were necessary for long buildings. The practical limit for systems using a manure belt is about 400 ft (120 m).

Advantages of the battery cage systems (also called stack decks) include higher densities. Because of the narrower overall width of the cage rows, it is often practical to fit in an additional row of cages in the same building width. Other advantages are ease of accessibility to birds and daily removal of manure for better air quality.

Figure 27.2. Three-tier cage laying systems.

Disadvantages are problems related to air movement, light distribution to lower levels, and necessity of handling and storing manure outside of the building on a daily basis. Maintenance requirements are higher, since there are more mechanical parts. Battery cages are available in three, four or six tiers high. Four-tier systems are most popular. Six tiers require special elevated people-movers to manage the top levels.

While in the mid-1970s to mid-1980s, cage bird densities were commonly 48 in.^{2}/bird (310 cm^2), very few commercial producers now use less than 52 in.^{2}/bird (335 cm^2) with up to 58 in.^{2}/bird (374 cm^2) not uncommon. Laws in some areas of Europe, enacted because of pressure from animal rights/welfare groups require up to 80 in.^{2}/bird (516 cm^2). The most common cage sizes are 16 in. (400 mm) or 24 in. (600 mm) across the front and 20 in. (450 mm) deep. The 16×20 in. (410×510 mm) cage will house 6 (53.3 in.^{2}/bird), and the 24×20 in. (610×510 mm) cage will house 9 birds (53.3 in.^{2}/bird). The European battery cage is usually 50×50 cm (19.7×19.7 in.) and will normally house 7 birds (55.4 in.^{2}/bird).

The "reverse" cage was introduced to the industry in the mid-1970s (fig. 27.3). This cage was 18 in. (460 mm) across the front and 12 in. (300 mm) deep (4 birds/cage = 54 in.^{2}/bird [348 cm^2]). This shape allows all four birds to eat at one time, reducing the competition and stress. The advantages of this cage are increased production, fewer cracked eggs, and lower mortality. The disadvantage was the greater initial investment per bird due to greater length of egg belt, feeder trough, and overall building length for a given number of birds. This development did not catch on with the industry, since the increased production did not outweigh the increased investment per bird.

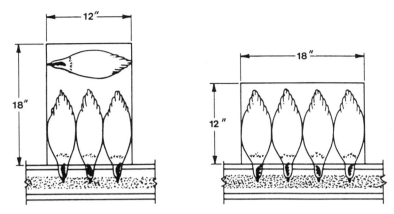

Figure 27.3. Reverse cage design allows all birds to eat at one time.

Feeders

Feed is stored in one or more metal feed bins outside the building from where it is automatically carried by conveyor to the feed hoppers at the end of the each cage row. Several types of automatic feeders can be used effectively in the caged housing system.

Automated closed loop mechanical feeders can be used in any of the cage systems discussed. There are five common types (fig. 27.4):

(a) *Flat-link chain* is a heat-treated steel link with a loop (hook) formed from the center of the link and extending to catch the next link. The connecting loop is nearly closed so that the chain links do not easily disconnect, but can be forced to make splices and repairs. The chain travels at 20 to 100 fpm (100 to 500 mm/s) depending on user preference with 40 to 60 fpm (200 to 300 mm/s) being common. A v-belt drive allows easy adjustment of speed. Ninety degree corners are enclosed with contoured wheels and chain guides. Higher speeds tend to accelerate wear. A 100 ft (30 m) circuit requires a 1 1/2 hp (1.1 kW) motor. The chain operates in a flat bottom trough with one vertical side and one flared side.

(b) *Drag auger* is a hardened spring coil similar to a coil spring except constructed with flat wire instead of a round wire. It operates in a closed loop, and as the name implies, it is dragged around the circuit. The auger is powered by a toothed gear located above the auger and successively engaging each flight of the auger. Ninety degree corners are curved tubes where the auger slides around the curve. Feed helps to act as a lubricant. Auger ends are joined by brazing. A 100 ft (30 m) circuit requires three, 1/3 hp (0.25 kW) gearmotors to power the circuit. The standard speed is 80 fpm. The auger travels in a U-shaped trough with flared sides. The U-shaped trough closes around the top side of the auger just enough to retain the auger yet provide maximum opening for access to the feed.

(a) Flat-link chain.

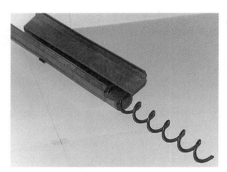

(b) Drag auger.

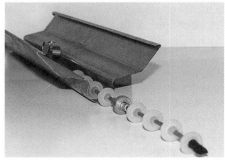

(c) Cable and button.
Figure 27.4. Poultry feeders.

(d) Wire link and button.

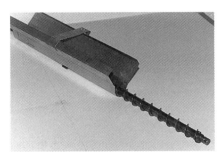

(e) Core-type auger.
Figure 27.4. *continued.*

(c)*Cable and button* system is a stranded flexible steel cable with 1-in. diameter plastic buttons molded in place on two inch intervals. The cable is pulled with a split toothed sprocket which engages the buttons on the cable. Standard corners are 90° with a cast contoured wheel and are enclosed in a pressed steel housing. The cable ends are connected with a swivel fitting which allows the cable to rotate (twist) naturally as the load increases or decreases. Standard speed is 100 fpm (0.5 m/s) and a circuit of 1,000 ft (305 m) requires 1 hp (0.75 kW). The drive unit is arranged with a take-up wheel to take up slack as the cable stretches under load. The trough is U-shaped with flared sides. Hold-downs, usually spaced at 4 ft (1.2 m) intervals, are normally required to keep the cable and button from riding over the feed.

(d)*Wire link and button* system is a pressed steel button shaped to receive a spherical headed wire and washer. The button is constructed with two halves which are welded together. The wires and buttons smoothly articulate around a 9 in. corner wheel or the drive sprocket. The buttons are 1.1 in. (28 mm) diameter and are spaced at 2.8 in. (70 mm) intervals. The wire link and button system is driven from a split tooth sprocket matched to the pitch of the bottoms. The drive unit is arranged with a spring loaded take-up wheel to take up the slack as the wire link and buttons stretch under load. Standard corners are 90° with a contoured wheel enclosed in a pressed steel housing. A 1 hp (0.75 kW) drive is required for a 1,000 ft (305 m) circuit. The wire link and button travels in a U-shaped trough with one or both sides flared. Hold-downs are required to keep the buttons from riding over the feed, and are usually spaced at 10 ft (3 m) intervals.

(e) *Auger, core type* is a small (1.5 in. [38 mm] diameter) auger in an open-top trough. The trough has flared sides with a center U-shaped depression to guide the auger and contain the feed for distribution around the closed circuit. At the end of the row, the feed drops into a cross auger which conveys the feed to the opposite side of the row. Feed is introduced into the circuit from a hopper. This type of auger has a large core relative to the outside diameter and provides a mixing action not common to other types of feeders. Circuit lengths over 600 ft (180 m) should introduce feed at two locations in the circuit to reduce running time. One hp is required to operate 100 ft (30 m) circuit.

Automated dispensing type mechanical feeders have the disadvantage of not being able to mix feed and move old feed to a new location which is believed to stimulate eating.

1. *Traveling hoppers* ride on a track located above the cages or on the floor and dispense feed directly into the trough. Generally speaking, traveling hoppers require enough capacity to dispense feed the entire length of the cage row. Long rows make it increasingly difficult to either carry enough feed or spread it thinly enough to uniformly feed the entire row. Space does not permit a full discussion of various types of dispensing techniques such as floating shoes and metering augers to attempt even distribution. Most troughs are flat bottom with one flared side. Traveling hoppers are easily automated to operate at desired intervals with timers and are automatically refilled between feedings. Generally traveling hoppers are lower initial cost than closed loop feeders.

2. *Dispensing augers*, another variation of augers, is the spring type (coreless) auger enclosed in a small tube within the feeding trough. The small tube has a continuous slot at or near the bottom of the tube. Feed spills out as it is conveyed along to the far end of the trough where a paddle switch stops the feeder. The advantage is that the birds cannot pick out choice morsels before the feed passes on to the next cages as in closed-loop systems. However, the closed-loop systems have been sped up to offset this advantage. A disadvantage of the coreless auger system is that

feed left in front of empty or sparsely populated cages becomes stale and wasted as feed if it is not stirred. Also, vibration can cause feed separation with the fines settling out at the input end as new feed continues to pass over the first dispensed feed.

Manual, dispensing-type, self-propelled feed carts travel on the walkway between rows dispensing feed to 1, 2 or 3 levels at one time. This requires an operator throughout the feeding cycle. The main advantage would be the lowest initial investment cost. Disadvantages are high labor costs, extra management surveillance to see that feed is not spilled and wasted, especially at the ends of the row, and that feed does not get stirred to stimulate eating.

Layers should be encouraged to eat in order to maintain egg production, and the operation of the feeding system has a direct influence on the rate of feed consumption. Providing fresh feed, or merely stirring old feed, stimulates eating (a ploy that can be used with a mechanical feeder controlled by a time clock to operate periodically). When feed is carried slowly along a long trough, chickens tend to "high grade", that is, the first hens to have the feed pass by, pick out the coarse, high energy bits of feed. The fines that are left for the birds at the end of the row contain most of the minerals and other additives. The result is that neither the birds at the beginning nor those at the end get a balanced ration. Uniformity of feed quantity and quality at all points along the cage row can be improved by various means. The traveling hopper and self-propelled feed carts put out the same feed for the length of the trough. Auger feeders are reported to continuously mix the feed. Some chain feeders operate at a high speed so that eating is discouraged until the chain stops moving.

Waterers

Water is critical to egg production and bird comfort. The water system in each house must be adequate, reliable, and free of contamination from feed, manure, and bacterial growth.

The earliest and perhaps the simplest system was a sloping trough that ran the length of the cage row with water flowing past each cage. As building sizes increased and the number of tiers increased from 1 or 2 to 3, 4 or 5 tiers, management of the trough system became impractical. To get the required slope and yet keep the water trough and feed trough parallel, it was necessary to slope the entire building 4 in./100 ft (100 mm/30 m). To save water and reduce disposal problems, the troughs were supplied with water on a limited basis, for example, 30 min, six times a day. Some poultrymen felt that trough systems contributed to feed waste because of the amount that washed off the chickens' beaks and ran down the drain at the end of each trough. With one- or two-tier systems, troughs could be readily checked to see that water was available at each cage; however, with three or more tiers this became a problem. Cleaning and sanitation were difficult and time consuming.

Two more satisfactory methods of supplying water to cages are in common use today. The first is a water cup with a trigger in which the flow is activated by the chicken. Any feed dropped in a cup is picked up again. It also lends itself to medicating birds through the watering system. Depending on the number of birds in each cage, cups are located next to cage dividers or alternating dividers with an access opening through the divider allowing one cup to serve two cages. Generally, one cup will adequately serve up to 12 birds; however when birds have a choice between two cups, frequently one cup will not be used. Typical line pressure is 2 to 4 psi (14 to 28 kPa) for horizontal valve cups and 6 to 8 in. (150 to 200 mm) w.c. for vertical valve cups.

The second method is a nipple waterer mounted overhead in the cage. The bird has to push or peck on the valve to get water. Early designs allowed only vertical trigger motion; later designs allow for 360° trigger action as well as vertical. Generally, one nipple will serve up to 12 birds—8 to 10 birds per nipple work best. Line pressure usually ranges from 4 to 8 in. (100 to 200 mm) w.c. Most designs have some method of limiting flow rate to minimize wasted water. Nipples can be located at a divider with an access opening, usually 4 in.[2], allowing access from adjoining cages. Nipples can be located centrally in a cage; however, the trigger should not extend into the cage. One design has a guard integral with the nipple, and one design has a 45° adapter which allows the line pipe to rest on top of the cage with the trigger still slightly above the top of the cage. Without the above feature, the line pipe should be elevated so that the trigger is just above the cage top.

The two types of watering devices require very low pressure yet require an adequate flow rate to keep birds satisfied on a hot summer day. Care must be exercised in designing an adequate, high-pressure supply to the building as well as proper manifolding and pressure regulation. Standard practice requires one regulator per level for each row. Most manufacturers provide options for quick and efficient flushing of lines bypassing the regulator and applying full pressure and flow. Options include manual and/or automatic discharge devices at the opposite end of the line. Depending on water conditions, the flushing interval should be 1 to 3 weeks.

Egg Collection

Cages contribute to quality egg production by maintaining as closely as possible the characteristics of the egg as laid. The interior quality of the egg is maintained by rapid cooling. In a cage, the eggs immediately roll away from the body heat of the birds to a holding tray or collection belt. With properly designed cages there are very few cracked eggs. In addition, with the absence of manure in the cages, the number of dirty eggs can be drastically reduced.

Eggs roll out the front of the cages either onto an egg tray for hand pickup or onto a collecting belt. Eggs collected by hand are placed on flats carried on a self-guided cart. In the case of four-tier systems, self-propelled elevator carts are used. Mechanical collectors employ belts to carry the eggs to the end of the cage rows where they are raised or lowered to a single level and carried by cross conveyor to the egg packing or processing room.

Cross conveyors are classified as belt or rod type. Rod conveyors provide many advantages over the belt type. Broken eggs filter through the rods and the liquid contents do not transfer to dozens of other eggs. Soft shells drop through the rods and do not slow up automated orienting and packing machinery. Very small pullet eggs may fall between rods, but usually they are of little value. Most dirt and debris that would occur on a belt will fall between the rods which results in a more efficient use of automated packing machinery. Rod-type conveyors can convey eggs at inclines up to 22° and can accommodate variations in levels between buildings and/or packing rooms. Many of the rod conveyor designs can also make turns up to 180° which eliminates some transfer of eggs from one conveyor to another. Each transfer of eggs provides potential for additional cracks and checks. Most rod conveyor designs have intermediate drives which allow very long conveyance distances without transfers. This is especially useful in large modern complexes where one conveyor may travel through a series of 10 buildings to a processing building.

A decision on whether or not to invest in an automated egg collection system should be made in terms of the initial cost versus potential savings in labor. While the hand collection of eggs represents a major portion of the total labor required in an egg production enterprise, the labor saved by the use of a mechanical egg collector is significant only if the eggs are carried directly to a fully automated processing machine.

Egg Handling

Eggs are human food and must be treated accordingly. Periodic outbreaks of salmonella emphasize this point. State agencies are becoming more concerned and have imposed more stringent sanitary requirements. Some currently recommended facilities and conditions are:

1. The building and surroundings shall be free of rubbish, waste, foul odors, insects, rodents, and other vermin.
2. Open windows shall be screened. Doors shall be rodent proof and equipped with self-closing devices.
3. There shall be adequate drains with approved traps and vents.
4. The water shall be ample and potable.
5. Floors, walls, ceilings, etc., shall be easy to clean.
6. Lavatory and toilet facilities shall be available.
7. Facilities for cleaning and sanitizing equipment shall be available.

Egg Cooling Room

Ten cubic feet (0.28 m³) of room volume per 1,000 layers for each day of required holding period should allow adequate space for storage needs. It is advisable to insulate to an R-value of 15 (2.6) and to use specially designed refrigeration equipment for cooling to 55°F (13°C) and 60 to 80% RH. Approximate refrigeration capacity needed for storage rooms is as follows: 5,000 birds, 6,800 Btu/h (2,000 W); 10,000 birds, 11,700 Btu/h (3,400 W). Home air conditioners should not be used. They are inefficient at the required temperature and are designed to remove moisture rather than maintain it.

Manure Handling Systems

The flat deck, full stair-step, and reverse cages with a slant back all allow manure to drop to the floor or the pit below. The modified stair-step cage is also available with a slant back. The stacked cage designs must all be equipped with dropping boards which need to be scraped every one to two days to remove the manure, or be equipped with plastic belts that convey the manure to the end of the cage row. Several types of mechanical scrapers designed to be used with specific cages are available.

The manure which drops from the cages may be handled in one of three ways (fig. 27.5):

1. Manure collects on the floor beneath the cages and is scraped on a two or three week cycle with scraper blades mounted on a small tractor.
2. Manure collects in shallow pits, 12 to 14 in. (300 to 350 mm) deep, which are then scraped with cable-pulled pit scrapers on a daily basis. Stainless steel cables are commonly used to prevent corrosion and frequent replacement. Flushing systems may be used instead of scrapers.
3. Manure collects in a deep pit 8 to 10 ft (2.5 to 3 m) below the cage floor. Cleaning is required not sooner than a year if the ventilation system works well and the watering system is well managed to prevent leaks. Manure may be removed when it is most convenient and advantageous to spread on cropland.

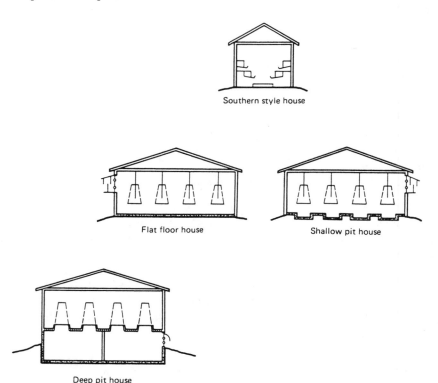

Southern style house

Flat floor house   Shallow pit house

Deep pit house

Figure 27.5. Designs for cage system laying houses.

The manure system dictates much of the building design. For example, if the flat floor, tractor scraping system is used, the cages must be suspended from the building trusses, adding a considerable weight that enters into the truss design and spacing. The deep pit house requires a much different wall construction. Since the pit may be constructed below grade, the importance of good drainage cannot be over emphasized. With dry floor conditions and proper ventilation, the manure will form into ridges and valleys and dry sufficiently for easy handling with mechanical equipment. Reducing the moisture from 90 to 60% will reduce the volume by one-half. Hen manure releases strong odors whenever it is disturbed, but the odor is somewhat less objectionable when the manure is dry. The well-designed, deep pit system would also cut down, but not eliminate, odor problems by holding the manure undisturbed for a long period in a dry condition. On the other hand, high groundwater and wet manure make handling very difficult and increase odor levels considerably. The deep pit storage allows manure to be removed at convenient times while the other two systems require some means of disposing of the manure at frequent intervals throughout the year.

Each of these systems can present problems such as groundwater in the deep pits, cable slippage, wear and breaking with the pit scrapers, and wet spots and scraper breakdowns with the flat floor system. But with good management, any of them will work satisfactorily. A major factor in deciding which system is best for a specific case is the manner and timing of manure disposal once it is out of the house.

The least expensive method of handling the manure is the flat floor, providing the self-propelled scraper can be used in several houses. The deep pit system is the most expensive because of the additional cost of constructing a two-story house.

Housing for Pullet Rearing and Broiler Production

Raising broilers and replacement pullets involves brooding and growing the chicks to either market age or the ready-to-lay stage. Since baby chicks are very susceptible to disease, it is important to thoroughly clean and sanitize the house and equipment before starting the brooding operation. Most chicks for broiler production are started on the floor with either portable or centrally heated brooders.

Gas fired brooders suspended by chains from the ceiling are quite popular. They are preferred by many because of the free air movement on all sides. The brooders are raised to the ceiling level when heat is no longer required. A central, hot water heating system with the boiler located in a separate room will provide maximum fire safety. The heating pipes are located along one wall with a hinged hover that is lowered to confine the heat.

As the chicks grow they are allowed to spread out and use a greater amount of floor area. Compared to the first week, two to three times as much space will be needed by the time they reach seven to eight weeks of age. Since heating and ventilating the entire building is inefficient at the start, "partial room" brooding is recommended. One end of the house is closed off and used for the first two to four weeks. Then the growing birds are allowed to spread out over the whole floor area. Mechanical, flex auger feeders and an automatic water system reduce labor requirements to a minimum. Low pressure watering systems with either cups, or more commonly, nipple waterers are used.

Once the chicks are past the brooding stage of four to five weeks, open housing may be used in mild climates. However, the practice of year-round production and the proven benefits of a uniform temperature of near 70°F (21°C) throughout the growing stage suggests that closed, environmentally controlled houses are advantageous in nearly all geographic areas.

Replacement pullets are commonly grown in cages. The benefits include higher bird density in the house, easier handling of the birds, no litter, less bruising, and fewer disease problems. Chicks are brooded in the upper two of three- or four-level cage systems and spread to all levels after vaccination and debeaking at about two weeks.

Cage brooding systems require a room temperature of 90°F (32°C) at the start. Heat is commonly provided by air make-up heaters.

Experience has shown that pullets grown on the floor can be put into either floor- or cage-managed laying houses. Broiler cage rearing has been plagued with the problems of deformed legs and breast blisters, both of which reduce market quality.

Site Selection and Building Design

Since buildings for all phases of poultry production tend to be the source of considerable odor, the site should be well downwind from neighbors and the farm home. As with all farm buildings, a well-drained site is desirable. This is particularly true for deep-pit laying houses as they may be partially below grade. Foundation drains are essential to protect against wet manure problems. While in mild climates some structures are built without foundations, generally a good foundation not only forms a sound base for the building, but it also allows a tight seal to the floor that prevents rodents and other vermin from entering the house.

Frame construction is popular because of the ease with which insulation can be installed and because rodents cannot penetrate the wall. The size and spacing of the studs are influenced by wall height and truss loads. For example, a house with suspended cages would require 2 × 6 in. (38 × 140 mm) studs, while a brooding and growing house might be adequately framed with 2 × 4 in. (38 × 89 mm) studs.

Trusses that will be supporting cages as well as the usual snow and wind loads must be designed specifically for the job. Bracing between trusses and between the wall and trusses is essential.

There are a number of materials suitable for use as exterior wall covering, and sheet metal, which is reasonable in cost and requires little maintenance, is one of the best. Installing the panels with the pattern horizontal and nailing in the flat will contribute considerable bracing effect. Although many laying houses have been built with plastic foam panels serving as both insulation and interior wall surface, the practice is questionable inasmuch as some of the plastic materials are flammable. While foil covering offers some protection, it may not satisfy insurance underwriters' requirements. Plywood and metal are suitable for interior walls and ceiling but are somewhat expensive. Gypsum board is economical and fire resistant and, although it is subject to deterioration when exposed to high humidity, it should be possible to maintain satisfactory conditions within a high density house so that this would not become a problem. With a suitable interior wall covering, the most economical insulation may be selected for the walls and ceiling. A vapor barrier installed between the interior wall covering and the insulation will prevent moisture from entering the wall.

The installation of reflective roofing will reduce summer attic temperatures and have a small but significant effect on the temperature inside the house.

Environmental Control

Temperature is the most important environmental factor in poultry housing. Young chicks need very warm surroundings just to survive. Older chickens, both layer and meat birds, exhibit their best feed conversion efficiencies at 70 to 75°F (21 to 24°C). However, production drops rapidly as temperatures rise above 80°F (27°C) and temperatures above 100°F (38°C) may be lethal.

Humidity is important in only two circumstances. Very low humidity tends to cause objectionably dusty conditions and high humidity combined with a very high temperature interferes with the bird's natural cooling mechanism and contributes to high mortality.

Brooder and Growing House Operation

Baby chicks are started with a temperature of 90 to 92°F (32 to 33°C) at the edge of the hover. After the first week, the temperature is dropped 5°F (3°C) per week until 70°F (21°C) is reached. A room temperature of 70°F (21°C) is then maintained until broilers are marketed or replacement pullets reach eight weeks of age at which time a small decrease in temperature is acceptable. While birds of more than five weeks of age will gain well at temperatures below 70°F (21°C), feed conversion efficiency will drop significantly.

Table 27-3 suggests insulation and ventilation levels for windowless houses. Only the minimum ventilation rate is required until the heating system is shut off. The thermostatically controlled fan circuits are then activated allowing increasing rates of ventilation as temperatures rise due to animal heat and warm weather.

Fan and motor characteristics have been discussed previously. Fans that are installed high on the wall and spaced along the protected side of the building perform well.

Inlet baffles should be adjusted to give a velocity of 700 to 1,000 fpm (3.6 to 5 m/s). A manometer reading of 0.04 to 0.08 in. (1.0 to 2.0 mm) of water will insure a velocity in this recommended range.

Broiler houses may provide 24 h lighting to encourage maximum feed consumption and rate of gain. In windowless houses, pullets are started on 14 1/2 h of light and decreased 15 min a week to 9 h at 22 weeks. This routine postpones the start of laying but produces larger eggs when production begins. When the pullets are moved to a windowless layer house, a 14 h day length is used throughout the laying period. The light program for pullets to be housed in windowed laying houses requires special planning.

Table 27-3. Insulation and ventilation schedule for
brooding and growing houses

Design Temperature, °F (°C)	Wall R Customary (SI)	Ceiling R Customary (SI)
-10 to 0 (-23 to -18)	12 (2.1)	16 (2.8)
0 to 10 (-18 to -12)	8 (1.4)	12 (2.1)
10 to 20 (-12 to -7)	4 (0.7)	8 (1.4)

Thermostat Set Point °F (°C)	Fan Capacity per Bird cfm (L/s)
90 (heater) (32)	0.2 (0.09)
75 (fan) (24)	0.6 (0.28)
78 (fan) (26)	0.8 (0.38)
85 (fan) (29	1.25* (0.60)

* For pullets over 8 weeks old, add 1.5 cfm (0.7 L/s).

Laying House Operation

Suggested levels of insulation for three temperature zones are given in table 27-4. Thermostat set points and ventilation rates per bird are also provided. These apply to both floor-managed and cage-managed houses. However, due to the much lower bird density in a floor-managed house, the temperature may remain below 60°F (16°C) during periods of low outside temperature. Although a 65 to 70°F (18 to 21°C) set point is listed in the table, if satisfactory air and moisture conditions can be maintained with minimum ventilation, a set temperature of 70 to 75°F (21 to 24°C) will reduce feed consumption. Egg production, egg size, rate of gain, and mortality rates are essentially equal at temperatures between 60 and 75°F (16 and 24°C), but feed consumption is significantly less at the high end of the range.

Exhaust fans for floor-managed houses and for shallow pit or flat-floor cage houses are located high on the wall and installed singly or in groups spaced not more than 100 ft (30 m) apart. Since fans for cage houses are often placed in light trap struc-

Table 27-4. Insulation and ventilation schedule for layer
and breeder houses

Design Temperature, °F (°C)	Wall R Customary (SI)	Ceiling R Customary (SI)
-10 to 0 (-23 to -18)	12 (2.1)	16 (2.8)
0 to 10 (-18 to -12)	8 (1.4)	12 (2.1)
10 to 20 (-12 to -7)	4 (0.7)	8 (1.4)

Thermostat Set Point °F (°C)	Fan Capacity per Bird cfm (L/s)
45 (7)	0.25 (0.12)
60 (16)	0.25 (0.12)
65-70 (18-21)	1.5 (0.71)
75 (24)	3.0 (1.40)

tures, grouping will simplify construction. The light traps allow free air movement, but prevent the entrance of light. This permits the control of "day length" within the house with a timed lighting system.

Exhaust fans for deep pit houses are located in the wall of the pit area. A protective hood will ordinarily be adequate as a light trap. In all types of houses, those fans which will be operating continuously during cold weather should be spaced uniformly along the length of the building.

Inlets determine the distribution of air throughout the house. Slot inlets along the perimeter of the ceiling or along the length of the ceiling over the cages may be equipped with baffles that both direct the flow and control the velocity of the incoming air. The slot inlets at the perimeter of the ceiling allow summer air to be drawn through the soffits where it is usually slightly cooler than in the attic. A velocity of 700 to 1,000 fpm (3.6 to 5 m/s) insures uniform distribution. This velocity range is indicated by a manometer reading of 0.04 to 0.08 in. (1.0 to 2.0 mm). Since ventilation rates vary by a factor of 10 at different times of the year, it is essential that the baffles are easily adjusted. Commercial controls are available that automatically adjust the inlet opening in relation to static pressure differences, thus eliminating the need for manual adjustment. More complete mixing of the cool, inlet air with the warm air of the house takes place when the baffles direct the air along the ceiling (see fig. 15.6).

During heat waves, when outside dewpoint temperatures of 70°F (21°C) or higher are accompanied by dry-bulb temperatures of 104°F (40°C) or higher, ventilation alone will not protect birds against heat prostration and some type of supplemental cooling will be needed.

Fog nozzles that periodically spray water directly on the chickens provide an emergency means of reducing mortality due to heat. Sprinkling the roof of the poultry house is another emergency measure that will lower the inside house temperature a few degrees. This is most effective if the roof happens to be a dark color and if ventilation air is drawn from the attic area.

Evaporative coolers are capable of dropping air temperatures to within 5°F (3°C) of the existing wet-bulb temperature, but in doing so, the relative humidity is raised to about 85%. This high humidity largely offsets the advantage of evaporative cooling for poultry in the eastern United States or Canada. In the western half of the United States, wet-bulb temperatures are low enough so that considerable cooling is possible without reaching unacceptably high relative humidities. Permanent evaporative coolers may be considered feasible under these conditions.

Foggers are used to atomize water and not wet chickens. Some think that wetting chickens is a disease hazard.

Lighting and Miscellaneous Features

Lighting levels need to be just enough for adequate inspection of equipment and birds. One 25 W bulb per 100 ft² (9 m²) is usually considered satisfactory. An exception to this is the bottom level of a four-tier cage system which may be so shaded by the upper tiers that additional lighting is required.

With thousands of birds depending on electricity for light and ventilation as well as feed and water, it is imperative to have an emergency standby generating plant. Capacity should be large enough to operate all of the fans plus part of the balance of the equipment. Feeders and other equipment may be operated in rotation, but if the weather is hot, all of the fans must operate continuously. The generating plant should be located in a dust-free room and equipped with an automatic starter and alarm system.

While dead birds have been disposed of by burying and by placing in septic tanks, burning seems to be the most satisfactory method. Presently approved incinerators have an after burner to keep smoke and odors to a minimum. Smoke emissions must not be greater than the density shown by the standardized "Ringelman no. 2" test.

TURKEYS

The domestic turkeys grown today were developed from birds that descended from native wild turkeys taken from North America to Europe. Wild domesticated turkeys were originally taken from Mexico to Spain as early as 1498 A.D. and spread across Europe by the late 1500s. Domesticated European turkey strains were brought back to North America and bred with wild North American turkeys to produce new strains. Numerous strains were developed with different colored plumage and characteristics. The Broad Breasted Bronze was one of the most important strains in the 1940s and 1950s. In the late 1940s and early 1950s, interest in white turkeys developed. By the mid 1950s, several large white turkey strains were available. In the 1960s and 1970s, the large white strains gradually replaced the Broad Breasted Bronze in popularity. In the mid 1980s, large increases in growth rates, due in large part to genetics, resulted in turkeys that reached market weights 3 to 5 weeks earlier than birds in the early 1980s. These changes in genetics and concurrent changes in nutrition and processing led to significant changes in turkey production and housing.

In the early 1900s, most turkeys were sold live off the farm to individual customers. The birds roamed fields, wooded areas, and farmsteads for food and roosted in trees. Production control increased with increased demand for turkeys, and concurrent improvements in nutrition, disease control, and processing occurred. For many years turkeys were raised seasonally on range. Turkey ranges were fenced pasture land, with feed and water supplied, and shelters to provide some shade and protection from precipitation. In the early 1970s, it became more profitable to raise turkeys in enclosed, environmentally controlled houses because of reduced labor, land, and feed costs, and better environmental, disease, and predator control. Modern turkey production continues to evolve to increase production efficiency.

Current turkey production can be categorized into areas: breeders, hatching, growing, feed production, processing, and marketing. Housing needs for growing turkeys are covered in the following section.

Turkey Housing Requirements

Turkeys are raised in either two- or three-stage systems. Day old poults are brooded in a brooder house and moved and grown to market weight in the remaining stage(s). In two-stage systems, which predominate the industry, the birds are moved at 4 to 8 weeks of age to the grower barn. In three-stage systems, the poults are moved from the brooder to the second-stage grower at 4 to 6 weeks of age and to the finisher or third-stage grower at 10 to 12 weeks of age. Grown turkeys are marketed at different ages and weights to meet processor and consumer demands. Hens are commonly marketed before 14 weeks of age and between 13.5 and 14 lb (6.1 and 6.4 kg). Consumer-sized toms are commonly marketed between 15 and 18 weeks of age at 22 to 26 lb (10 to 12 kg). Larger toms used for further processing are marketed at 28 to 32 lb (13 to 16 kg) with some heavier birds marketed at 35 to 36 lb (16 to 16.3 kg). There are indications in the turkey industry that market weights for both hens and toms may increase further which will affect floor space, equipment, and ventilation requirements.

Turkeys are generally raised on litter on the floor. The litter can be wood chips or shavings, rice hulls or other bedding material depending on local availability. It is important that new bedding be clean and not moldy. Moldspores can cause respiratory problems in poults and older turkeys. Bedding that was not dried properly or became wet during storage or transportation will be moldy.

Biosecurity, disease prevention, and preventing the spread of disease are very important. Foot baths at the entrance to each building will help prevent diseases from spreading. Wild bird and rodent droppings can carry diseases which can be picked up on boots as workers walk between buildings and brought in and spread to the turkeys inside. To reduce disease transmission, most producers do not allow visitors. Employee and vehicle movement is controlled to prevent the spread of disease from one farmstead to another. Pest control is important for disease prevention. Rats, mice, and darkling beetles can be controlled with appropriate use of baits and insecticides, respectively. Larger predators such as skunks, raccoons, and wild birds which can carry and transmit diseases to turkeys are best controlled by preventing access to turkey barns. All openings should be screened and holes patched to prevent predator and bird access.

Turkey housing requirements will depend on the regional climate. In colder climates, well-insulated buildings are needed to reduce building heat loss, prevent condensation, and reduce supplemental heating costs in cold weather. In warmer climates, moderately insulated buildings are used to reduce solar heat gain and reduce heat stress in hot weather. Characteristics commonly considered by producers when adjusting environmental controls in turkey barns are: temperature, litter moisture content, ammonia and dust concentrations, and light.

Brooder Barns

Prior to placing new poults in a brooder barn, the old manure from the previous brooded flock should be removed and the building cleaned and disinfected. Two to four inches (50 to 100 mm) of new bedding should be placed in the barn. Thorough cleaning and new clean bedding is important for disease control for day-old poults that do not have a completely developed immune system.

Brooding barns are well-insulated to provide for the environmental needs of the day-old poults. During brooding, supplemental heat is provided with brooder stoves. The brooder stoves are lowered to within a few feet of the floor and set to provide temperatures around 95°F (35°C) under the stove for the poults. Caution must be exercised to minimize the fire potential with brooders so close to the fresh dry litter. The brooding barn air can be set at 75 to 80°F (24 to 27°C). These very warm temperatures are needed to minimize thermal stress on the young poults. Temperatures are decreased with bird age, approximately 5°F (3°C) per week, until the temperature to be maintained in the grower barn is reached. Insufficient brooder temperatures will cause poults to huddle together for warmth. This bird behavior can be used to detect if brooding temperatures are too low. Poults should be actively moving about eating and drinking.

Poult rings or guards, made of corrugated brooding paper, are usually used to make 10 ft (3 m) diameter rings to confine 300 poults under each brooder stove. Feeders and waterers must be provided within each ring. Usually the feed and water provided within the poult ring is provided manually. Accumulated manure around the feeders and waterers should be removed daily when the poults are in the rings. As the poults grow the rings are enlarged and finally removed after 7 to 10 days. The poults then make a transition and begin using automatic feeders and waterers. During brooding, poults have floor space ranging between 0.5 to 1 ft^2 (0.05 to 0.09 m^2) per bird.

Brooder barns are generally well-insulated and mechanically ventilated. Table 27-5 gives recommended insulation levels for well-insulated buildings. Proper installation of insulation is very important for attaining the desired insulation level. Install a vapor retarder on the warm side to prevent moisture migration into the insulation. Rodent control and building maintenance is also important for maintaining the insulation.

Brooder barn ventilation will depend on outside weather, building size and insulation levels, bird number and weight. A minimum amount of air exchange is needed to provide fresh air and oxygen and to remove moisture and ammonia. Table 27-6 gives recommended mechanical ventilating rates. Brooder ventilating rates need to be adjusted as the poults grow and as the outside temperature changes seasonally. Minimum ventilating rates should be used whenever supplementary heat is being provided. Minimum

Table 27-5. Insulation recommendations for turkey houses

Winter Design Temperatures °F (°C)	Moderately Insulated		Well Insulated	
	Wall R Customary (SI)	Ceiling R Customary (SI)	Wall R Customary (SI)	Ceiling R Customary (SI)
-10 to 0 (-23 to -18)	12 (2.1)	25 (4.4)	20 (3.5)	33 (5.8)
0 to 10 (-18 to -12)	6 (1.1)	17 (3.0)	14 (2.5)	25 (4.4)
10 to 20 (-12 to -7)	6 (1.1)	14 (2.5)	14 (2.5)	22 (3.9)

Customary units = (h-ft^2-F)/Btu.
SI units = (m^2-K)/W.

Table 27-6. Ventilation rates and scheduling for turkeys

Barn	Bird Age (weeks)	Average Tom Weight (lb)	Set Point Temperature (°F)	Ventilating Rate (cfm/bird)
Brooder	1	0.3	80	0.04
	2	0.6	75	0.08
	3	1.0	70	0.16
	4-6	1.7-3.6	65	0.4-0.65
			70	0.6-1.26
			75	1.4-2.9
Grower	7-9	1.9-8.3	60	1.0-1.4
			65	1.7-2.9
			70	3.9-6.6
	10-12	10.1-14.3	60	1.6-1.9
			65	3.5-5.0
			70	NAT
	13-15	16.5-21.0	60	2.2-2.5
			65	5.8-7.4
			70	NAT
	16-18	23.3-27.7	60	2.5-2.7
			65	8.2-9.7
			70	NAT
	19-21	29.9-34.2	60	2.8-2.9
			65	10-12
			70	NAT
	22-24	36.3-40.1	60	3.0-3.2
			65	12-14
			70	NAT
Breeder		35	60	1.75
			65	5.25
			70	17.5

ventilating rates are usually based on the minimum amount of air exchange needed to remove moisture generated by poult respiration, drying feces, and spilled water. Most growers adjust the minimum ventilating rate to maintain good litter conditions.

It is important to prevent exposing poults to cold drafts that can chill them. Two potentially important sources of drafts are poorly designed and adjusted inlets and infiltration. Poorly maintained barns that are leaky will experience a great deal of infiltration (uncontrolled air exchange) depending on wind speed and direction. This uncontrolled air exchange can produce cold drafts that move past the poults and chill them. Poult rings provide minimal protection from drafts.

Ventilating air should enter a barn through properly designed and adjusted inlets. Some brooder barns in cold climates bring cold outdoor air through a heated entry-way to temper the cold air before bringing it into the brooding area. Inlets need to be sized and regularly adjusted to handle both the minimum and maximum ventilating rates. Guidelines for inlet sizing and adjustment were discussed earlier.

The small amount of ventilating air exchanged in brooder barns, especially when the poults are first placed, makes it difficult to maintain uniform thermal conditions throughout the building. Many brooder barns have mixing fans to help distribute fresh

Table 27-7. Turkey barn space and equipment requirements per bird

Turkey Barn	Floor Customary (SI)	Feeder Customary (SI)	Waterer Customary (SI)
Brooding	0.5 to 1 ft² (0.05 to 0.09 m²)	0.75 in. * (190 mm)	0.5 in.† (127 mm)
Growing hens	2 to 2.5 ft² (0.18 to 0.23 m²)	0.75 in. (190 mm)	0.5 in. (127 mm)
Growing toms	3 to 4 ft² (0.28 to 0.37 m²)	1.5 in. (381 mm)	0.75 in. (190 mm)
Heavy toms	4 to 5 ft² (0.37 to 0.46 m²)	1.5 to 2 in. (381 to 508 mm)	1 to 1.25 in. (254 to 318 mm)
Breeders	5 to 8 ft² (0.46 to 0.74 m2)	1.5 to 2 in. (381 to 508 mm)	1 to 1.25 in. (254 to 318 mm)

* 1.5 in. (381 mm) per poult during manual feeding in poult ring.
† One jug waterer per 100 birds during manual feeding in poult ring.

air and break up the thermal gradients that naturally develop. Mixing can be achieved using either axial fans strategically located around the brooder barn or paddle fans. Care must be exercised to prevent the mixing fans from creating drafts across the poults.

Lighting intensity, duration, and timing affect poult growth. Poults can be started with as little as 0.4 foot candle of light. Intermittent lighting, 2 h on followed by 4 h off repeated 4 times each day, has been found to be very effective and energy efficient compared to continuous light.

Sufficient feeder and waterer space is critical for efficient production. Good quality and adequate supplies of feed and water are very important for achieving good rates of gain. Table 27-7 gives feeder and waterer space recommendations. If water jugs are used during the initial weeks of brooding, one jug per 100 birds should be provided.

Grower Barns

Grower barns are prepared to receive turkeys from a brooder barn after the previous flock was marketed. Wet, feces-laden litter under the feeders and waterers is removed and replaced with fresh, mold-free bedding. Dry litter away from feeders and waterers might not be removed until after several flocks or unless there are disease problems. The building interior can be cleaned and pressure-washed. Feeding, watering, heating, and ventilating equipment should be checked and either repaired or replaced if necessary. In cold weather the heaters should be turned on in time to warm the building before the birds are moved into the barn. In grower barns, hens are given 2 to 2.5 ft² (0.18 to 2.3 m²) of floor space per bird while the toms are given 3 to 4 ft² (0.28 to 0.37 m²) per bird. Very heavy toms may require 4 to 5 ft² (0.37 to 0.47 m²) per bird.

In cold climates, grower barns are well-insulated because the buildings are heated in cold weather to maintain temperatures for good feed conversion. Table 27-5 gives recommended insulation levels for well-insulated and moderately insulated turkey grower barns.

Grower barns can be either mechanically or naturally ventilated. Good environmental control is needed in both types of buildings to maintain environmental conditions for efficient production. Integrated controllers that control both heating and air exchange are commonly used.

Turkeys grow efficiently at temperatures (indoor) between 70 to 79°F (21 to 26°C). At temperatures above 79°F (26°C) there is a decrease in feed efficiency because feed consumption decreases because of the heat. At temperatures above 95°F (35°C), heat prostration begins to have an impact with the larger birds being more susceptible. At temperatures between 50 to 70°F (10 to 20°C), there is a decrease in feed efficiency because feed energy is needed to maintain thermal equilibrium. Supplemental heat is used to keep indoor temperatures above 50 to 60°F (10 to 15°C). Minimum air exchange, which maintains litter moisture conditions, should be used whenever supplemental heat is added to minimize heating costs.

Litter management is very important in turkey grower barns. Proper litter conditions are maintained by providing sufficient air exchange to remove moisture, adding new bedding, and tilling or mixing the litter. Litter tilling or mixing releases ammonia into the air. Increased ventilation is needed for several hours to control ammonia concentrations. Excessive litter moisture content can contribute to increased ammonia generation and foot/leg problems. Exposure to high levels of ammonia and dust have been associated with detrimental effects on turkey respiratory health.

Ventilation rates for moisture control during cold weather will depend on the number and size of the turkeys housed in the building, outdoor air humidity ratio, and the amount of spilled water. Excessive air exchange can create excessively dry dusty conditions. Table 27-6 lists recommended ventilation rates for mechanically ventilated turkey grower barns. Naturally ventilated barns must also provide sufficient air exchange. During moderate weather, ventilation rates need to be increased to remove heat and prevent indoor temperatures from increasing too much. Almost all turkey grower barns have curtains or large doors in the sidewalls for natural ventilation during warm weather. Large sidewall openings with even moderate winds can provide adequate air exchange in the summer. Table 27-6 indicates that natural ventilation is used when inside temperatures begin to reach 70°F (20°C) regularly. During hot weather, sprinkler systems can be used to provide cooling. Excessive sprinkling that creates wet litter should be avoided.

Intermittent lighting has been found to increase productivity and be energy efficient. More efficient fluorescent or sodium vapor lights are being used replacing incandescent lights. Light levels for growing market hens should be around 1 ft candle. Market toms need more light than hens. Light levels can be as high as 5 ft candle. Lower light levels should be used if the toms exhibit aggressive behaviors.

Sufficient feeder and waterer space is critical for efficient production. Feed wastage and water spillage should be avoided by properly adjusting feeders and waterers. Water is very important during hot weather when respiratory system cooling is most important. Table 27-7 gives recommended feeder and waterer capacities for growing hens and toms.

Breeders

Breeder facilities house the toms and hens needed to produce fertilized eggs for hatching poults raised by growers. Year-round egg production is accomplished using environmentally controlled enclosed houses. Mature toms and hens are housed in breeder facilities. Toms are sometimes housed separately and hens impregnated by artificial insemination. Light control, including the use of light traps at ventilation air inlets and exhausts, is used to maintain year-round egg production.

Problems

27.1.   A poultryman wishes to construct a deep pit house in which to install "reverse" cages 8 rows wide, 4 tiers high. Using this configuration, determine the width and length of the building necessary to house 30,000 layers.

27.2.   Design a schedule showing the thermostat set-point, number of fans, fan capacity, and fan location for each step in the ventilation capacity required for the 30,000 layers in problem 27.1. Suitable fan models are available to the poultryman which deliver either 7,500 cfm or 12,000 cfm at 1/8 in. S.P. (3450 and 5665 L/s).

27.3.   What is the total inlet area required to match the maximum fan capacity operating at 70°F (21°C) or lower? What is the total inlet area required when all fans are operating?

27.4.   Investigate the cost of insulating materials and materials suitable for interior walls and ceilings for cage layer houses. Taking into consideration economy, insulating value, ease of installation, fire safety, and durability, recommend a wall and ceiling construction for a cage house.

28 Housing for Horses and Alternative Livestock Enterprises

The rising popularity of pleasure horse riding has increased the interest in and the need for both horse barns and riding facilities. Well-designed stables contribute to the ease and pleasure of caring for horses, and an attractive, well-constructed building adds to the pride of ownership. Because horses are large and spirited animals, and because individuals are generally more intimately involved with them than with other farm animals, prime consideration in planning a horse barn and related facilities must be given to the health and safety of both the animals and the people who will come in contact with them.

Horse Barns

The barn, whether it be large or small, should be well-planned, durable, and attractive. It must provide shelter from wind, rain, and snow, be adequately ventilated, and be located in a well-drained area. A slope 1:20 away from the entrance and soil that is naturally well-drained help maintain firm surface conditions. This is particularly important if the horse is allowed to run in a paddock adjacent to the barn. If natural conditions are not adequate, gravel fill may be necessary. As with other livestock housing, it is desirable to locate a horse barn downwind from the home. A distance of 150 ft (45 m) is usually sufficient.

Barn Layout

Many pleasure horse barns house one to three horses and are designed to be aesthetically pleasing in appearance, using such features as gambrel roofs, cupolas, and window shutters (fig. 28.1 and 28.2). Vertical boards and battens, novelty siding, or Texture 1-11 plywood are practical and attractive for siding materials. Barns are often designed for outside service with a roof overhang for weather protection.

Large barns with either box stalls or tie stalls may be designed with a central alley and inside service for maximum convenience and protection from the weather. The width of the barn is typically 36 ft (11 m) and the length in increments of 12 ft (3.6 m) as required. With tie stalls the barn can be somewhat narrower. Figure 28.3 illustrates a typical layout for a box stall barn with stalls on each side of a central alley.

An alternative design places two rows of box stalls back to back with outside service on both sides of the barn. Eight foot (2.4 m) roof overhangs provide protection.

Figure 28.1. Two-stall horse barn with Dutch doors.

The overall width is typically 40 ft (12 m) with the length in increments of 12 ft (3.6 m). While this design does not offer as much convenience or protection, the outside doors somewhat improve fire safety.

Single-story gable roof designs employing either stud wall or post frame construction are suitable for either small or large barns and are adaptable to either inside or outside service plans.

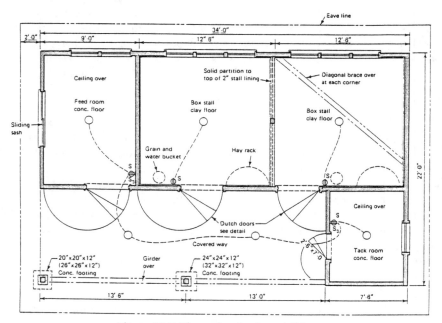

Figure 28.2. Floor plan for two-stall barn.

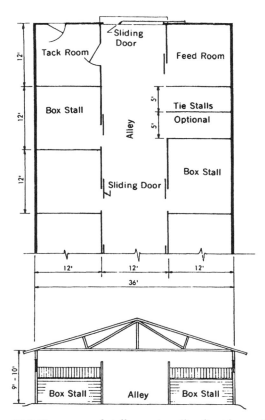

Figure 28.3. Two rows of stalls, center alley (inside service).

Stalls and Alleys

Horses may be confined in either tie stalls or box stalls. Although box stalls require approximately twice as much space, they are recommended because pleasure horses often fail to receive adequate and regular outdoor exercise, and a box stall permits limited exercise inside. On the other hand, tie stalls require less bedding and are easier to clean. They can often be constructed in buildings that are not suitable for box stalls. The width of a horse barn is determined by the size of the box stall or the length of a tie stall plus the width of the alley. Table 28-1 lists the recommended sizes for alleys, stalls, and stall equipment. It should be emphasized that young animals require generous-sized stalls just as older horses do.

Alleys of adequate width for easy handling of the horses are not only more convenient, they are also safer. A minimum door and alley height of 8 ft (2.4 m) is acceptable if a horse is never mounted inside. However, if animals will be mounted within the building, a minimum height of 12 ft (3.7 m) is essential.

Full-length, sliding doors, with a bottom guide to prevent them from being pushed

Table 28-1. Specifications for housing facilities for horses

	Customary	SI
Box stall size		
Foals to 2 years	10 × 10 ft	3 × 3 m
Mature mares and geldings	12 × 12 ft	3.7 × 3.7 m
Stallions	14 × 14 ft	4.3 × 4.3 m
Tie stall size		
Foals to 2 years	5 × 9 ft	1.5 × 2.7 m
Mature animal	5 × 9-12 ft	1.5 × 2.7-3.7 m
Stallions	Not recommended	
Ceiling height		
Horse alone	9 ft	2.4 m
Horse and rider	12 ft	3.7 m
Doors		
Stalls	4 × 8 ft	1.3 × 2.4 m
Barn alley, horse & rider	12 × 12 ft	3.7 × 3.7 m
Alleys	8 ft minimum, 12 ft is best	2.4 minimum, 3.7 m is best
Hay mangers	(L × W × D × H)	(L × W × D × H)
Foals to 2 years	30 × 18 × 20 × 34 in.	760 × 450 × 500 × 860 mm
Mature animals	36 × 24 × 24 × 40 in.	900 × 600 × 600 × 1000 mm
Grain box		
Foals to 2 years	18 × 12 × 6 × 34 in.	450 × 300 × 150 × 860 mm
Mature animals	24 × 12 × 8 × 40 in.	600 × 300 × 200 × 1000 mm
Water requirements per day	8-12 gal	30-45 L

out, are convenient for box stalls opening onto an inside alley. Swinging doors are sometimes used, but they are not as satisfactory because of the space required to swing open. When box stalls open to the outside, Dutch doors, with 4 ft (1.2 m) high lower sections, allow for light and ventilation. Latches must be strong and easy to operate from both inside and outside the stall but not so simple that the horse can open the door. A 4 to 8 ft (1.2 to 2.4 m) roof overhang offers weather protection and shade for both horse and attendant.

Stall and Alley Construction

Sturdy construction is imperative for all facilities. Stall walls should be constructed of 2 in. (38 mm) lumber, preferably tongue and groove, which is bolted together. Stall posts may be made of 6 × 6 in. (140 × 140 mm) wood or 5 in. (125 mm) steel with welded channels to hold the partitions. Box stalls should have 5 ft (1.5 m) high, solid walls topped with a 2 ft (0.6 m) open metal or wood stall guard to allow free air movement. The guard may be constructed pipe, steel bars, expanded steel, welded steel or wood. Whatever material is used, it must be spaced to keep the horses from reaching one another. A height of 6 ft (1.8 m) for the front half and 4 ft (1.2 m) for the rear half is adequate for tie stalls.

Flooring materials may be brick, concrete, asphalt, packed clay, treated planks or wood blocks in concrete. Table 28-2 provides a summary of flooring considerations for stalls and alleyways used in horse facilities.

Sloping tie-stall floors 1:50 toward a 2 × 14 in. (50 × 350 mm) concrete gutter

Table 28-2. Flooring types and considerations for stalls and alleyways

Floor Type	Usage	Comments
Packed clay	Stalls and alleyways	Good resiliency, poor cleaning, can pit
Rubber mat	Stalls, breeding and foaling areas	Good resiliency, cleans well, expensive
Wood shavings or chips	Alleyways and breeding areas	Good exercise surface, frequent maintenance, hard to clean and disinfect
Treated wood planks	Stalls and alleyways	Fair resiliency, hard to disinfect
Wood blocks in concrete	Stalls and alleyways	Fair resiliency, can be uneven if poorly installed
Asphalt	Stalls and alleyways	Good resiliency, cleans well, should be finished with a rough, slip-resistant surface
Brick in sand	Stalls and alleyways	Fair resiliency, easily repaired
Concrete	Stalls and alleyways	Poor resiliency, can be slick, easy maintenance, requires deeper bedding

makes them easier to keep clean and dry. Concrete feed alleys are easiest to keep clean. Concrete floors are also preferable in the wash area and feed and tack rooms.

Tack Room

Although horses do not require or benefit from a warm environment, horse owners usually enjoy a warm tack room. A simple, dust-free storage for tack is adequate, but frequently tack rooms are equipped with a desk, chairs, water and toilet facilities, and thermostatically controlled heat. It's a matter of personal choice.

Feed and Bedding

The feed area should be kept as dust free as possible, and the stored grain should be in vermin-proof bins. For small quantities, garbage cans or wooden bins with tight covers are satisfactory. For large enterprises, commercial or home built bins or hopper bottom bins with mechanical unloading are used.

A limited amount of hay and bedding storage should be located in the same building as the horses. This may be in either a stall or a separate room dedicated for that purpose. Hay can be stored overhead in a loft, but lofts limit ventilation and a large amount of stored hay can be a fire hazard. An open front or wide door access to the storage location provides convenient unloading from trucks and easy distribution to mangers. Danger from fire can be reduced by having a separate storage area in a nearby barn or building for the bulk of hay and bedding to be used.

The hay and bedding storage space required will depend on the number and size of animals and the length of the storage period. Each horse will consume about 10 ft^3

(0.3 m^3) of hay per week and an equal amount of straw or other bedding is likely to be used. Grain consumption will range up to about 2 ft^3 (0.6 m^3) per week.

An adequate supply of clean, fresh water is essential for a healthy horse. Inasmuch as up to 12 gal (45 L) of water are required daily for each horse, a frost-free hydrant or a waterline and faucet protected with heat tape is convenient. An electrically heated water bowl can be located in a box stall partition to serve two horses. Where several horses are released from tie stalls at the same time, a frost-free watering tank is desirable.

Manure Handling

Stall waste includes the solid and liquid portions of horse manure and the soiled stall bedding. Horse manure is about 80% solids and 20% urine. A horse produces about 45 lb of manure per day (0.75 ft^3, or 5.63 gal) per 1,000 lb of body weight. The volume of soiled bedding is about twice the volume of the manure removed daily.

In most stables, the waste is removed daily and temporarily stockpiled in an accessible deposition area, such as a concrete slab with a wood backstop. Waste is then either spread on fields or removed by a contract hauler. Composting manure is an alternative, particularly for larger operations, but requires more management.

Any on-site storage should not contribute to water pollution. An acceptable grassed waterway or liquid runoff containment pit or tank should be provided to prevent contamination of surface and groundwater. Leachate can also be directed to a seepage field. Additionally, make sure that field application of waste is done such that runoff will be minimized.

Early Warning Devices and Fire Protection

Because of the value of horses and the number of combustible materials located in horse barns or stables, early warning devices and fire protection systems may be desirable. Early warning devices include smoke detectors and heat detectors. Smoke detectors should be installed in office areas or in small equipment storage areas, such as tack rooms. The dust and other contaminants in the air in the stable area can trigger false alarms for most smoke detectors. Fixed temperature or rate-of-rise heat detectors have been used successfully in most agricultural environments. The heat detectors are not subject to the dust or environment problems. More elaborate control panels, monitoring systems, and telephone dialers can be incorporated with warning devices to alert the owner or manager of problems if they should occur.

Fire protection devices include manual suppression using appropriate fire extinguishers, stored water supplies, and automatic sprinkler systems. The National Fire Protection Association (NFPA) has developed a series of consensus standards that govern the design, installation, and maintenance of automatic sprinkler systems. Several types of sprinkler systems are available, including both wet-pipe systems where water is always present under pressure, and dry-pipe systems using pressurized air in the delivery pipes until the sprinklers are activated.

Ventilation and Lighting

Horses do not require warm surroundings, but they do not easily tolerate drafts, dampness, and high humidity. Like all animals, they produce heat and moisture. The moisture must be removed from the barn to prevent condensation and damp conditions and to reduce odors. The most effective method of moisture and odor control is through proper ventilation.

If the barn is always open, a 4 in. (100 mm) ridge ventilator or gable end louvers should be adequate. If the doors are closed tightly at night, 4 in. (100 mm) eave openings are also necessary.

Completely enclosed stables will need to be well-insulated and ventilated. Since the animal density is usually low in a horse barn, particularly one with box stalls, additional heat in the range of 4,000 to 5,000 Btu/h (1200 to 1500 W) per stall will be needed to supplement animal heat. A minimum of 50 cfm (25 L/s) per stall continuous ventilation should be provided plus at least 100 cfm (50 L/s) per stall additional capacity which is thermostatically controlled. An allowance of approximately 20 in.^{2} of inlet area is required for each 100 cfm of fan capacity (275 mm^2/L-s).

A small, adjustable window for each stall provides both light and warm weather ventilation. Any windows within reach of horses must be protected with wire mesh. Each stall should have a protected lamp; a 100 to 150 W bulb is adequate in most cases. Two lamps with a total of 300 W are desirable for foaling stalls. A duplex outlet should be provided for each two stalls and an alley light provided every 12 ft (3.6 m).

Riding Rings

The great increase in pleasure horse riding has led to more horse shows and competition of all types. While outdoor rings are relatively inexpensive, there is a growing demand for all-weather riding that can be satisfied only with indoor riding rings.

The National Horse Show Association's recommendation on dimensions for outdoor rings is 120 × 240 ft (36.6 × 73.2 m) and for indoor rings 110 × 220 ft (33.5 × 67 m). Perhaps the first factor to consider in planning an indoor facility is that the recommended size will cost well into six figures. Smaller-sized rings may be satisfactory in many cases. Eighty to 100 ft (24 to 30 m) in width has been recommended as a minimum for horse shows, while equitation classes may be conducted in a ring as small as 50 × 60 ft (15 × 30 m).

Structural design of trusses, sidewalls, and foundations for the wide, clear span structures require careful engineering. Snow loads on a 100 × 220 ft (33.5 × 67 m) ring might accumulate a 360 ton (330 t) snow load.

Regardless of the size, a 16 to 18 ft (5 to 5.5 m) ceiling height is recommended for safety in jumping events. The design of the lighting system must take into account the prevention of shadows as well as the level of lighting. Fluorescent lights cast fewer shadows and are less expensive to operate than incandescent lamps. Transparent panels in the roof provide some natural light during the day.

Sandy loam on a firm, well-drained base makes an excellent floor. A sub-base of packed clay with a 9 in. (230 mm) base of crushed limestone or "dense grade" rock is often used. The top layer can then be a finer grade material, such as sandy loam, or for indoor tracks, a mixture of cedar shavings and sand can be used. Non-screened sand or other dusty materials are not suitable for the top layer of an area or exercise area.

A safety feature that is strongly recommended is a knee board installed around the inside perimeter of the ring. It consists of a solid 2 in. (38 mm) wall sloping from a point 18 in. (450 mm) from the base of the wall to a point 5 ft (1.5 m) up on the wall. This will help to prevent rider injuries.

An adequate spectator section can be provided with a lean-to addition along one or more sides of the ring. While stalls may be located around the perimeter of the ring at minimal cost, a stall barn perpendicular to the ring will be more efficient. When stalls are located around the ring, it is best to provide outside doors and a roof over-hang so that horses may be moved while the ring is in use.

Fences

Horses, particularly young ones, often run, play, and kick their feet into the air. Woven wire and barbed wire fences represent a risk of causing cuts, muscle strain or pulling off a shoe. Proper fence design and maintenance is important to reduce the threat of injury. Mesh wire and board fences are excellent choices for confining any farm animal, but are particularly suitable for leisure and high-value horses. Fencing designs are summarized in table 28-3.

Wood fences have been traditional for horse paddocks and, when well-maintained, are attractive enclosures on the rural landscape. However, they are expensive to con-struct and require considerable maintenance. Nevertheless, wood fences are the safest type of fencing for horses and are a necessity for small enclosures such as show rings, training rings, corrals, and stallion pens. Wood fences are commonly painted either white or black, with the black-painted fences requiring less maintenance. Commonly used black paints include oil-based or oil mixed with coal tar, and do not normally contain creosote. Table 28-4 provides suggested heights and board spacings for fences used with horses.

A 1 × 6 in. (18 × 140 mm) board along the top of a wire fence reduces potential injury. Woven wire fence with a board top is less expensive than an all wood fence and provides good visibility while at the same time preventing horses from "riding down" on the fence. Chain link, welded pipe, and cable fences are also satisfactory for hors-es. High-tensile fences are used for horses but are less visible compared to the other fences listed, unless a top rail or other means is used to make them more visible. Barbed wire should never be used. Electric fences can be used with appropriate pre-cautions or modifications. Horses have to be trained to an electric fence and some never learn to respect its action. A problem with many electric fences or non-electric high-tensile fences is the low visibility associated with such fences. Addition of a top rail or use of PVC pipe as a top rail are techniques used to improve visibility. Electric fences using steel-braided polyethylene wires and tapes, which are available in light or bright colors, are more visible and are used successfully for horses. For division fences in rotational grazing, two wires are suggested with the top wire 36 to 40 in. (1 m) high.

Table 28-3. Summary of fencing for horses

Lumber	Height: 4.5 to 6 ft
	Lumber: 1 or 2 in. × 6 to 8 in.
	Posts: 8 ft o.c. × 7 to 9 ft long
	Straight and diamond panel designs
	* High cost, maintenance required, decay, breakage, splitting and cribbing
Mesh wire	Height: 4.5 to 6 ft
	Designs, diamond mesh, square knot or chain link
	Top board or extra barbless twisted wire required for visual barrier
	* High initial cost, low maintenance
Woven wire	Height: 26 in. to 4 ft
	Light and heavy gages available
	Top board or barbed wire restrainer required for visual barrier
	Tension must be maintained
	* Horses susceptible to leg injury, less control of unwanted animals
Barbed wire	Height: 4.5 to 6 ft
	12 1/2 gage — 4 to 6 strands
	Standard or suspension types
	Posts spaced 10 to 16 ft
	* Horses susceptible to leg injury, no control of unwanted animals
High-tensile wire	Height: 5 to 6 ft
	12 1/2 gage smooth
	Tension maintained with in line springs
	Posts spaced 12 to 16 ft
	Can be electrified if desired
	Sight board desirable
	* Must be properly braced, limited control of unwanted animals
High-tensile, electric	Provides good control
	Less pressure on fence and posts
	Good quality charger required
	Allows easy use of temporary fencing for strip grazing, limited confinement
	* Proper fence charger must be used

Pressure-preservative-treated posts, 5 in. (125 mm) in diameter, set 8 ft (2.4 m) on centers, and 3 ft (1 m) into the ground will give adequate support for any type of fence.

If fences cut across bridal paths, consideration should be given to gates that can be opened without dismounting. Plans for gates and many other items of equipment used with horses are described in the Midwest Plan Service Horse Handbook (Midwest Plan Service, 1971).

Alternative Enterprises

Farmers and ranchers are frequently looking for alternative sources of income. Livestock management skills can be utilized in raising buffalo, angora goats, deer, elk, and rabbits. Most of the alternative operations are relatively small and utilize simple structures. Standard housing systems have not been developed but the management requirements provide guidance as to the housing needs.

Table 28-4. Board fence designs for horses

Fence Height (ft)	Lumber Sizes				
	Pastures			Rings and Paddocks	
	Line Posts	Corner Post	Boards	Posts	Boards
4 1/2	4 in. × 4 in. × 7 ft	6 in. × 6 in. × 7 1/2	1 in. × 6 in. × 16 ft	-	-
5	4 in. × 4 in. × 8 ft	6 in. × 6 in. × 8 ft	1 in. × 6 in. × 16 ft	6 in. × 6 in. × 8 ft	2 in. × 6 in. × 12 ft
6	5 in. × 5 in. × 9 ft	6 in. × 6 in. × 9 ft	1 in. × 8 in. × 16 ft	6 in. × 6 in. × 16 ft	2 in. × 8 in. × 12 ft

Fence Height (ft)	Board Spacings (in.)										
	3 Boards			4 Boards				5 Boards				
	a	b	c	a	b	c	d	a	b	c	d	e
4 1/2	12	12	12	8	8	7	7	-	-	-	-	-
5 -	-	-	-	9	9	9	9	6	6	6	6	6
6 -	-	-	-	7*	7	7	7	6*	6	6	6	6

* 2 × 6 in

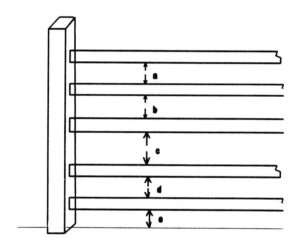

Buffalo

Bull calves which weigh 45 to 55 lb (20 to 25 kg) at birth may be marketed at 1,100 to 1,200 lb (500 to 545 kg) in about 2 1/2 years. Buffalo are bred in June and the gestation is 287 days. Corrals and working fences for handling buffalo should be 7 to 8 ft (2.1 to 2.4 m) high. All gates must be heavy-duty. Spring-loaded, locking slam-gates are recommended. A 5 to 6 strand barbed wire fence with wood or steel posts which are set 12 to 14 ft (3.7 to 4.3 m) apart will keep buffalo in pasture as long as they have plenty to eat. Buildings or calving sheds are not necessary for efficient buffalo production. In 1993, the equipment and facilities costs for a 50-cow buffalo herd was estimated at $60,000.

Angora Goats

Angora goats reach sexual maturity at seven months or more. Fall and early winter is the breeding season which is triggered by declining daylight hours. The gestation period is 148 days. Kid crops can be expected to be 115% to 140%. Kids weighing about 4 lb (1.8 kg) at birth reach 55 to 65 lb (25 to 30 kg) by 18 months. Mature does (nannies) weigh 75 to 100 lb (35 to 45 kg); bulls (billies) weigh 85 to 125 lb (40 to 55 kg). Suitable facilities for mature goats would be about 20 ft^2 of indoor housing and 25 ft^2 (2.3 m^2) of open lot during the winter and inclement weather. Angora goat herds can be managed in total confinement, but that generally is not economical. Feeding and handling facilities required are similar to sheep. Building, facilities, and equipment costs for 125 head goat herd in 1993 was estimated at $24,000.

Elk

Most cows first calve at about three years of age and mature at four to five years. Mature cows weigh 600 to 800 lb (270 to 360 kg) and bulls 800 to 1,000 lb (360 to 450 kg). Calves weigh 30 to 40 lb (14 to 18 kg) at birth and are weaned at about six months weighing 225 to 275 lb (100 to 125 kg). Cows typically are bred in late September and gestation is 250 days. Woven wire fences 7 ft (2.1 m) high are recommended around pastures. Handling facilities and corrals should be 8 ft (2.4 m) high. Wintering sheds are not required, but wind protection should be provided.

Red and Fallow Deer

Fallow does are small (about 100 lb [45 kg]), while red deer are about twice as large. Deer normally breed in October and gestation is about 230 days. Normal birth weights are 8.5 to 10 lb (3.9 to 4.5 kg) for fallow deer and 16 to 24 lb (7 to 11 kg) for red deer. A deer farm requires a building, fenced grazing land, year-round access to water, supplementary winter feed, and handling facilities.

Rabbit

Rabbits are grown worldwide for various reasons and there is a broad range of sizes. Small rabbits are 3 to 4 lb (1.4 to 1.8 kg) at maturity, mediums are 9 to 12 lb (4.1 to 5.4 kg), and large breeds are 14 to 16 lb (6.4 to 7.3 kg). Self-cleaning, wire cages elevated about 2 to 3 ft (0.6 to 0.9 m) above the ground are commonly used. Each cage should have a 12 in. w × 12 in. h × 18 in. l (305 × 305 × 455 mm) nest box with ample straw. Feeders should be 2 1/2 to 3 1/2 in. (64 to 89 mm) above the floor. Low pressure automatic waterers are recommended. Recommended space requirements are given in table 28-5.

Rabbits may be marketed at about 8 weeks weighing 4 1/2 to 5 lb (2.0 to 2.3 kg). Typical building investment is $40 to $60 per cage. Estimated 1992 annual cost for a

Table 28-5. Recommended space requirements for rabbits

Animal Size, lb (kg)		Space, General, in.^{2} (mm^2)		Space, Nursing Does (in.^{2})	
3-5	(1.4-2.3)	180	(116 000)	576	(372 000)
6-8	(2.7-3.6)	360	(232 000)	720	(465 000)
9-11	(4.1-5.0)	540	(348 000)	864	(557 000)
> 12	(5.4)	720	(465 000)	1080	(700 000)

50-doe rabbitry in North Dakota was: equipment and cages, \$0.96/doe; building and land, \$3.20; depreciation of fixed assets, \$10.40/doe.

Rabbits can tolerate a wide range of temperatures, if kept dry and draft free. A totally enclosed, insulated building with a mechanical ventilation system is needed to provide this environment in the northern climate of the U.S. Breeding rabbits in the summer is difficult as fertility decreases dramatically at temperatures above about 85°F (30°C). During hot summer days, rabbits require a sun shade and some type of cooling is desired. Blocks of ice can be used for short periods or the air can be cooled using an evaporative cooler.

Buildings for rabbits should be easily cleaned and allow for efficient manure handling. If suspended cages are used, the support trusses must be designed for the additional weight. A design load for the cages and rabbits is about 10 psf. Framing and cladding for rabbit buildings can be any common material such as steel or wood. Concrete floors are generally preferred.

While rabbits tolerate a wide temperature range, optimum performance can be expected at about 55°F (13°C). At lower temperatures, the rabbits will consume more feed to keep warm. The rate-of-gain will not decrease much as long as the temperature is above freezing. If the building is kept below 55°F (13°C), newborn kits may need to be placed in a warmer room except during feeding periods.

Temperatures above 55°F (13°C) may result in decreased rate-of-gain because the animals reduce feed intake. Feed efficiency remains fairly high until heat exhaustion occurs. Fertility, especially of males, decreases rapidly above 95°F (30°C). Males exposed to high temperatures for several days in a row may require four to six weeks to regain normal fertility. Maintaining a 35 and 50% RH will result in a dry manure pack. Lower relative humidities may result in respiratory problems. Ammonia levels, which are a common problem in rabbit facilities, will be elevated when relative humidity is above about 50%. During cold periods relative humidity may be allowed to increase as high as 80% for short periods by reducing ventilation rates. This will save some on heating costs, but will cause an increase in odor levels. It is desirable to keep ammonia levels below 10 ppm. Levels above 25 ppm may affect both workers and rabbits.

Ventilation which controls moisture and ammonia will normally be sufficient to control other gases such as carbon dioxide and hydrogen sulphide. A good ventilation system will bring air into a building through planned openings. The fresh air is mixed with the air inside the building and exhausted. During summer, a natural ventilation system is generally used. For winter conditions, a mechanical system provides more accurate control. Minimum winter ventilation rate should be about 0.1 cfm/lb (0.1 L/s-kg) of rabbit. Summer rates are 10 times (1.0 cfm/lb [1.0 L/s-kg]) the winter rate.

A 40 × 100 ft (12 × 30 m) building with 8 ft (2.4 m) sidewalls with 4,000 lb (1820 kg) of rabbits would require a winter ventilation rate of 400 cfm (200 L/s). Inlet velocities of about 800 fpm (4 m/s) are needed to get good air mixing within the space. For the above building, an inlet area of 0.5 ft^2 (0.05 m^3) would give an inlet velocity of 800 fpm (4 m/s). If the inlet length is 100 ft (30 m), the width should be only 1/16 in. (1.6 mm). An alternative would be to make the length only 16 ft (5 m) by spacing four slots, 4 ft (1.2 m) long, every 16 ft (5 m) along the 100 ft (30 m) wall. With 16 ft (5 m) of slot length, the width needed would be 1/2 in. (13 mm).

The above building could have 25% of the walls open for summer ventilation. A 5 mph wind will provide an air exchange about every 30 s(120 air changes/h). This provides about 30 cfm/lb (30 L/s-kg) of rabbit.

Problems

28.1. Plan a barn for eight horses, including a central alley, tack room, and feed room.

28.2. Draw a layout for a small show ring, including stalls for 40 horses and spectator stands for 200 people.

References

Chapter 1

Arthur, E. and D. Witney. 1972. *The Barn*. Greenwich, Conn.: New York Graphic Society, Ltd.

Fitchen, J. 1968. *The New World Dutch Barn*. Syracuse, N.Y.: Syracuse University Press.

Gray, H. E. 1955. *Farm Service Buildings*. New York: McGraw-Hill.

Janik, C. 1990. *The Barn Book*. New York: W. H. Smith.

Sloane, E. 1966. *An Age of Barns*. New York: Funk & Wagnalls.

Welsch, R. L. 1968. *Sod Walls, The Story of the Nebraska Sod House*. Broken Bow, Nebr.: Purcells, Inc.

Chapter 2

American Plywood Association. 1984. Grades & specifications, *APA Product Guide*. Tacoma, Wash.: APA.

_____. 1977. *Plywood Siding*. Tacoma, Wash.: APA.

_____. 1993. *Residential & Commercial, APA Design/Construction Guide*. Tacoma, Wash.: APA.

_____. 1981. *Applications Summary, APA Industrial Guide*. Tacoma, Wash.: APA.

_____. 1982. *Pressure Preserved Plywood*. Tacoma, Wash.: APA.

_____. 1984. *Performance Standards and Policies for Structural-use Panels*. Tacoma, Wash.: APA.

_____. 1976. *Plywood Agricultural Construction Guide*. Tacoma, Wash.: APA.

Anderson, L. O. 1967. *Selection and Use of Wood Products for Home and Farm Building*. Agricultural Information Bulletin 311. Madison, Wis.: USDA Forest Service.

Engineered lumber demands respect. 1992. *Rural Builder* 26(2): 34-35.

Engineered lumber coming of age. 1992. *Rural Builder* 26(2): 18-19.

Forest Products Laboratory. 1987. *Wood Handbook*. Handbook No. 72. Washington, D.C.: USDA.

Hornbostel, C. 1978. *Construction Materials*. New York: John Wiley & Sons.

Janowiak, J. J. 1993. Evolution of Structural Lumber Composite. *Frame Building News*. 5(6):32, 33, 36, 38, 40.

Markwardt, L. J. 1943. Wood as an engineering material. Edgar Marburg Lecture, American Society for Testing Materials, Vol. 43. Presented at 46th Annual Meeting of ASTM.

Midwest Plan Service. 1987. *Structures and Environment Handbook*. MWPS-1, 11th Ed. (rev). Ames, Iowa: Midwest Plan Service.

Moody, R. and M. P. Collet. 1992. Market forces will drive new engineered wood products. *Rural Builder* 26(2): 30-31.

National Bureau of Standards, Products Standards Section. 1983. U. S. Product Standard PS 1-83 for Construction and Industrial Plywood with Typical Grade-Trademarks. Reprinted by American Plywood Association, Tacoma, Wash.

National Forest Products Association. 1991. *National Design Specification for Wood Construction*. Washington, D.C.: NFPA.

Shull, L. R. 1977. Wood preservatives should be used with caution. *Hoard's Dairyman* 122(17).

The switch is on to engineered substitutes. 1992. *Rural Builder* 26(2): 20, 22-25.

U. S. Department of Agriculture. 1977. *Gardening for Food and Fun*. Yearbook of Agriculture. Washington, D.C.: USDA.

Chapter 3

A contractors' guide to air-entraining chemical admixtures. 1990. *Concrete Construction* 35(3): 279-286.

For reinforcing shotcrete Canadians prefer steel fibers. 1987. *Concrete Construction* 32(Sept.): 775-776.

Giese, H. A. 1948. *A Practical Course in Concrete.* Chicago, Ill.: Portland Cement Assoc.

Haynes, B. C. Jr. and J. W. Simons. 1974. *Construction with Surface Bonding.* Information Bulletin 373. Washington D.C.: USDA Research Service.

Kosnatha, S. H. and W. C. Panarese. 1992. *Design and Control of Concrete Mixtures,* 13th Ed. (rev). Skokie, Ill.: Portland Cement Association.

Lee, M. 1989. Economical cooling of hot weather concrete. *Concrete Construction* 34(9): 971-796.

Making concrete stronger. 1984. *Compressed Air Magazine* (Jan.): 19-23.

Owens-Corning Fiberglas Corp. 1977. *BlocBond Construction Techniques.* Toledo, Ohio: Owens-Corning Fiberglas Corp.

Plastic-based rebar meets special demands. 1987. *Concrete Construction* 32(Sept.): 783-784.

Polypropylene fibers in concrete. 1986. *Concrete Construction* 31(April): 363-368.

Portland Cement Association. 1974. *Concrete Construction Practices.* Skokie, Ill.: PCA.

_____. 1963. *Concrete Improvements on Farm and Ranch.* Skokie, Ill.: PCA.

_____. 1967. *Control Test for Quality Concrete.* Skokie, Ill.: PCA.

_____. 1980. *Concrete for Small Jobs.* Skokie, Ill.: PCA.

_____. 1986. *High-Strength Concrete.* Skokie, Ill.: PCA.

_____. 1986. *Concrete Paved Feedlots.* Skokie, Ill.: PCA.

Runestad, J. A. and J. H. Pederson. 1986. *Farm and Home Concrete.* AED-26. Ames, Iowa: Midwest Plan Service (Feb.).

_____. 1987. *Cast-in-place Concrete Walls for Farm and Home.* AED-28. Ames, Iowa: Midwest Plan Service (Sept.).

Scalon, J. M. and R. J. Ryan. 1990. Accelerating admixtures for cold weather concreting. *Concrete Construction* 35(3): 287-294.

Chapter 4

American Plywood Association. 1974. *Plywood Siding.* Tacoma, Wash.: APA.

Asphalt Roofing Manufacturers' Association. 1974. *Manufacture, Selection and Application of Asphalt Roofing and Siding Products.* New York: ARMA.

Callender, J. H. 1966. *Time-Saver Standards, A Handbook of Architectural Design.* New York: McGraw-Hill.

Gypsum Association. 1974. *Gypsum in the Age of Man.* Evanston, Ill.: Gypsum Association.

_____. 1977. *Using Gypsum for Walls and Ceilings.* Evanston, Ill.: Gypsum Association.

Onduline U.S.A., Inc. 1977. *Installation Instructions—Performance Data—Specifications.* Fredericksburg, Va.: Onduline U.S.A., Inc.

Chapter 5

American Society for Testing and Materials. 1971. Standard methods of testing metal fasteners in wood, Part 16. Philadelphia, Pa.: ASTM.

Forest Products Laboratory. 1987. *Wood Handbook.* Handbook No. 72. Washington, D.C.: USDA.

Independent Nail Corporation. 1977. Advertising brochure. Bridgewater, Mass.
Midwest Plan Service. 1987. *Structures and Environment Handbook.* MWPS-1, 11th Ed. (rev). Ames, Iowa: Midwest Plan Service.
National Forest Products Association. 1991. *National Design Specification for Wood Construction.* Washington, D.C.: NFPA.
Timber Engineering Co. 1976. *Structural Wood Fasteners.* Washington, D.C.: Timber Engineering Co.

Chapter 6

ASAE Standards, 39th Ed. 1992. EP288.3. Agricultural building snow and wind loads. St. Joseph, Mich.: ASAE.
_____. 1992. EP378.1. Floor and suspended loads on farm structures due to use. St. Joseph, Mich.: ASAE.
_____. 39th Ed. 1992. D240. Grain storage loads, pressures, and capacities. St. Joseph, Mich.: ASAE.
_____. 39th Ed. 1992. D241.2. Density, specific gravity, and weight-moisture relationships of grain for storage. St. Joseph, Mich.: ASAE.
American Society of Civil Engineers. 1988. Minimum design loads for buildings and other structures. ASCE Standard 7-88. New York: ASCE.
_____. 1994. Minimum design loads for buildings and other structures (Draft). ASCE Standard 7-95. New York: ASCE.
Irish, W. W. et al. 1984. *Pole and Post Buildings: Design and Construction Handbook.* NRAES-1. Ithaca, N.Y.: Northeast Regional Agricultural Engineering Service.
Nelson, G. L., H. B. Manbeck and N. F. Meador. 1988. *Light Agricultural and Industrial Structures.* New York: Van Nostrand Reinhold Co.

Chapter 7

Baumeister, T., ed. 1967. *Marks' Standard Handbook for Mechanical Engineers,* 7th Ed. New York: McGraw-Hill.
Callender, J. H., ed. 1966. *Time-Saver Standards, A Handbook of Architectural Design.* New York: McGraw-Hill.
Gray, H. E. 1955. *Farm Service Buildings.* New York: McGraw-Hill.
Lytle, R. J. 1978. *Farm Builder's Handbook,* 3rd Ed. Farmington, Mich.: Structures Publishing Co.
Portland Cement Association. 1963. *Concrete Improvements on Farm and Ranch.* Skokie, Ill.: PCA.
Walker, J. N. and F. E. Woeste, eds. 1992. *Post-Frame Building Design.* St. Joseph, Mich.: ASAE.

Chapter 8

American Plywood Association. 1962. *Plywood Rigid Frame Design Manual.* Tacoma, Wash.: APA.
Armco Steel Corp. 1977. Armco Building Systems. Middletown, Ohio: Armco Steel Corp.
Hausmann, C. T. and M. L. Esmay. 1975. Pole barn wind resistance design using diaphragm action. ASAE Paper No. 75-4035. St Joseph, Mich.: ASAE.

Irish, W. W. et al. 1984. *Pole and Post Buildings*. NRAES-1. Ithaca, N.Y.: Northeast Regional
   Agricultural Engineering Service.
Midwest Plan Service. 1987. *Structures and Environment Handbook*. MWPS-1, 11th Ed. (rev).
   Ames, Iowa: Midwest Plan Service.
National Forest Products Association. 1961. *Manual for Home Framing*. Washington, D.C.:
   NFPA.

Chapter 9

Gang-Nail Systems. 1981. *The Wood Truss Handbook*. Miami, Fla.: Gang-Nail Systems, Inc.
Melaragno, M. 1981. *Simplified Truss Design*. New York: Van Nostrand Reinhold Co.
Midwest Plan Service. 1987. *Structures and Environment Handbook*. MWPS-1, 11th Ed. (rev).
   Ames, Iowa: Midwest Plan Service.
National Lumber Manufacturers' Association. 1978. *Wood Structural Design Data*. Vol. 1,
   3rd Ed. Washington, D.C.: NLMA.
Senft, J. F. 1973. Further studies in combined bending and tension strength of structural 2 by 4
   lumber. *Forest Products Journal* (Oct.): 36.

Chapter 10

American Institute of Timber Construction. 1994. *Timber Construction Manual*, 4th Ed.
   New York: John Wiley & Sons, Inc.
Faherty, K. F. and T. G. Williamson. 1995. *Wood Engineering and Construction Handbook*,
   2nd Ed. New York: McGraw-Hill, Inc.
Gray, Harold E. 1955. *Farm Service Buildings*. New York: McGraw-Hill.
National Forest Products Association. 1991. *National Design Specification for Wood
   Construction*. Washington, D.C.: NFPA.
National Lumber Manufacturers' Association. 1978. *Wood Structural Design Data*. Vol. 1,
   3rd Ed. Washington D.C.: NLMA.
Parker, H. and J. Ambrose. 1993. *Simplified Engineering for Architects and Builders*, 8th Ed.
   New York: John Wiley & Sons, Inc.
Walker, J. N. and F. E. Woeste. 1992. *Post-Frame Building Design*. St. Joseph, Mich.: ASAE.

Chapter 11

Boyd, J. S. and C. L. Reynolds. 1993. *Practical Farm Buildings*, 3rd Ed. Danville, Ill.:
   The Interstate Printers and Publishers, Inc.
Lewis, J. R. 1983. *Basic Construction Estimating*. Englewood Cliffs, N.J.: Prentice-Hall, Inc.
Lytle, R. J. 1978. *Farm Builder's Handbook,* 3rd Ed. Farmington, Mich.: Structures Publishing
   Co.

Chapter 12

Midwest Plan Service. 1987. *Structures and Environment Handbook*. MWPS-1, 11th Ed. (rev).
   Ames, Iowa: Midwest Plan Service.

Chapter 13

Esmay, M. L. and J. E.Dixon. 1986. *Environmental Control for Agricultural Buildings*.
   Westport Conn.: AVI Publishing Co.

Chapter 14

Albright, L. A. 1990. *Environment Control for Animals and Plants*. St. Joseph, Mich.: ASAE.

Barre, H. J., L. L. Sammet and G. L. Nelson. 1988. *Environmental and Functional Engineering of Agricultural Buildings*. New York: Van Nostrand Reinhold Co.

Hellickson, M. A. and J. N. Walker, eds. 1988. *Ventilation of Agricultural Structures*. St. Joseph, Mich.: ASAE.

Chapter 15

ASHRAE Handbook of Fundamentals. 1993. Atlanta, Ga.: American Society of Heating, Refrigeration and Air-Conditioning Engineers, Inc.

Colega J. J. and E. Palmer. *Temperature Guide for New England*. Agricultural Experiment Station, Technical Bulletin No. 105. Durham: University of New Hampshire.

Midwest Plan Service. 1987. *Structures and Environment Handbook*. MWPS-1, 11th Ed. (rev). Ames, Iowa: Midwest Plan Service.

_____. 1989. *Natural Ventilation Systems for Livestock Housing*, MWPS-33. Ames, Iowa: Midwest Plan Service.

_____. 1990. *Mechanical Ventilating Systems for Livestock Housing*, MWPS-32. Ames, Iowa: Midwest Plan Service.

_____. 1990. *Heating, Cooling and Tempering Systems for Livestock Housing*, MWPS-34. Ames, Iowa: Midwest Plan Service.

Chapter 16

Bartsch, J. A. and G. D. Blanplied. 1984. *Refrigeration and Controlled Atmosphere Storage for Horticultural Crops*. NRAES-22. Ithaca, N.Y.: Northeast Regional Agricultural Engineering Service.

Goetsch, W. D., D. P. Stombaugh and A. J. Muehling. 1984. *Earth Tube Heat Exchange Systems*, AED-25. Ames, Iowa: Midwest Plan Service.

Goetsch, W. and A. J. Muehling. 1981. Earth-tube heat exchangers for swine buildings. *Energy Tips*. Dept. of Agric. Engr. Urbana, Ill.: University of Illinois.

Midwest Plan Service. 1990. *Heating, Cooling, and Tempering Air for Livestock Housing*, MWPS-34. Ames, Iowa: Midwest Plan Service.

Phillips, R.E. 1981. *Farm Buildings: From Planning to Completion*. St. Louis, Mo.: Doane-Western, Inc.

Chapter 17

Meinel, A. B. and M. P. Meinel. 1976. *Applied Solar Energy*. Reading, Mass.: Addison-Wesley Publishing Co.

Midwest Plan Service. 1983. *Solar Livestock Housing Handbook*, MWPS-28. Ames, Iowa: Midwest Plan Service.

Williams, J. R. 1974. *Solar Energy, Technology and Application*. Ann Arbor, Mich.: Ann Arbor Science Publishers, Inc.

Chapter 18

Bartsch, J. A. and G. D. Blanpied. 1990. *Refrigeration and Controlled Atmosphere Storage for Horticultural Crops*. NRAES-22. Ithaca, N.Y.: Northeast Regional Agricultural Engineering Service.

The ASHRAE Handbook of Refrigeration Systems. n.d. Atlanta, Ga.: American Society of Heating Refrigeration and Air-Conditioning Engineers, Inc.

USDA. 1986. *The Commercial Storage of Fruits, Vegetables and Florist and Nursery Stocks.* Agricultural Handbook No. 66. Washington, D.C.: U.S. GPO.

Chapter 19

Graves, R.E. 1976. *Earthen Storage Basins for Liquid Manure.* Madison: University of Wisconsin Cooperative Extension Service.

Louden, T. L. 1978. Picket dams provide drainage for semi-solid stack. *Dairy Herd Management.*

Chapter 20

Canada Department of Agriculture. n.d. *Snow and wind control for farmstead and feedlot.* Bulletin No. 1461. Ottawa, Canada: Canada Department of Agriculture

Midwest Plan Service. 1977. *Farmstead Planning Handbook.* MWPS-2. Ames, Iowa: Midwest Plan Service.

_____. 1987. Structures and Environment Handbook. MWPS-1, 11th Ed. (rev). Ames, Iowa: Midwest Plan Service.

Chapter 21

ASAE Standards, 41st Ed. 1994. EP250.2. Specifications for farm fence construction. St. Joseph, Mich.: ASAE.

Bartok, J. W. and J. J. Maisano. 1992. Pesticide storage. *Connecticut Dairy Pipeline* (April). Storrs: University of Connecticut Cooperative Extension Service.

Friday, W. H. et al. 1985. *Farm Shop—Plans Book,* MWPS-26. Ames, Iowa: Midwest Plan Service.

Hofman, V. L. and C. W. Moilanen. 1980. Farm service centers, Farmstead engineering. In *Proc. of the ASAE Farmstead Engineering Conf.* St. Joseph, Mich. ASAE.

Kammel, D. W., R. T. Noyes, G. L. Riskowski and V. L. Hofman. 1991. *Designing Facilities for Pesticide and Fertilizer Containment.* MWPS-37. Ames, Iowa: Midwest Plan Service.

Lechner, F. G., R. T. Lorenzen and F. P. Steinhardt. 1981. *Planning Farm Shops,* NRAES-16. Ithaca, N.Y.: Northeast Regional Agricultural Engineering Service.

Meador, N. F. 1980. Machinery storage—Why and how, Farmstead engineering. In *Proc. of the ASAE Farmstead Engineering Conf.* St. Joseph, Mich.: ASAE.

Chapter 22

Loewer, O. J. et al. 1974. *Layout of Grain Storage and Handling Facilities.* AEN-1. Lexington: University of Kentucky Cooperative Extension Service.

Midwest Plan Service. 1988. *Grain Drying, Handling and Storage Handbook.* MWPS-13. Ames, Iowa: Midwest Plan Service.

National Silo Association, Inc. 1974. *Design Standards for Concrete Stave Silos.* Cedar Falls, Iowa: NSA.

Portland Cement Association. 1954. *Concrete Horizontal Silos.* Skokie, Ill.: PCA.

Silage and Silos. n.d. S.C. 80. University Park: Pennsylvania State University Cooperative Extension Service.

Chapter 23

Aldrich, R. A. and J. W. Bartok Jr. 1994. *Greenhouse Engineering*. Ithaca, N.Y.: Northeast Regional Agricultural Engineering Service.

Roberts, W. J. et al. 1989. *Energy Conservation for Commercial Greenhouses*. Ithaca, N.Y.: Northeast Regional Agricultural Engineering Service.

Chapter 24

Granite City Steel Division of National Steel Corporation. 1977. *Farmstead Planning Swine Manual*. Granite City, Ill.: Granite City Steel Division of National Steel Corporation.

Midwest Plan Service. 1983. *Swine Housing and Equipment Handbook*. MWPS-8. Ames, Iowa: Midwest Plan Service.

_____. 1987. *Structures and Environment Handbook*. MWPS-1, 11th Ed. (rev). Ames, Iowa: Midwest Plan Service.

Chapter 25

Bodman, G. R. et al. 1987. *Beef Housing and Equipment Handbook*, MWPS-6. Ames, Iowa: Midwest Plan Service.

Brownson, R. and D. Ames. 1975. *Winter Stress in Beef Cattle*. Great Plains Beef Cattle Handbook, GPE 1900. Fargo, N. Dak.: North Dakota State University/USDA Cooperative Extension Service.

Grandin, T. n.d. *Design of Ranch Corrals and Squeeze Chutes for Cattle*, Great Plains Beef Cattle Handbook. Fargo, N. Dak.: North Dakota State University/USDA Cooperative Extension Service.

_____. n.d. *Livestock Psychology and Handling—Facility Design*, Great Plains Beef Cattle Handbook. Fargo, N. Dak.: North Dakota State University/USDA Cooperative Extension Service.

Hirning, H. J. 1990. *Minimum Facilities for Beef Cattle Production*. AE-986. Fargo, N.Dak.: NDSU Extension Service.

Huhnke, R. L. and S. Harp. n.d. *Corral and Working Facilities for Beef Cattle*, Great Plains Beef Cattle Handbook.

Midwest Plan Service. 1987. *Structures and Environment Handbook*. MWPS-1, 11th Ed. (rev). Ames, Iowa: Midwest Plan Service.

_____. 1986. *Beef Housing and Equipment Handbook*. MWPS-6. Ames, Iowa: Midwest Plan Service.

Munroe, J. A. (Technical Adviser). 1988. *Canadian Farm Buildings Handbook*. Publ. 1822E. Ottawa, Ontario: Agriculture Canada.

Myer, D. J. 1976. *Cattle Handling Corral Design*. Madison: University of Wisconsin Cooperative Extension Service.

Chapter 26

Bodman, G. R. 1976. *Non-mechanical Ventilation of Animal Housing Facilities*. University Park: Pennsylvania State University Cooperative Extension Service.

Brevik, T. J. and A. N. Bringe. 1974. Controlled environment housing for dairy calves. Fact Sheet A2578. Madison: University of Wisconsin Cooperative Extension Service.

Collins, W. H. and W. R. Murley. 1975. Replacement and dry cow facilities. ASAE Paper No. 75-4561. St. Joseph, Mich.: ASAE.

Fehr, R. L. (Planning Comm. Chr.). 1983. Dairy housing II. In *Proc. of 2nd National Dairy Housing Conf.* St. Joseph, Mich.: ASAE.

Gaunt, S. N. and R. M. Harrington, eds. 1975. *Raising Veal Calves.* Amherst: University of Massachusetts Cooperative Extension Service.

Graves, R. E. et al. 1986. *Dairy Free Stall Housing*, NRAES-24. Ithaca, N.Y.: Northeast Regional Agricultural Engineering Service.

Hahn, L. 1976. Cows' response to cooling. *Confinement* 1(3).

Light, R. G. et al. 1980. *Milking Center Design Manual*, NRAES-12. Ithaca, N.Y.: Northeast Regional Agricultural Engineering Service.

Pohl, S. H. et al. 1995. *Dairy Housing and Equipment Handbook,* MWPS-7, 5th Ed. Ames, Iowa: Midwest Plan Service,.

The way cows will be managed on your dairy tomorrow. 1993. *Dairy Illustrated* (Winter)25(4).

Chapter 27

Building the Connecticut Panel Poultry House. Publ. No. 66-29. Storrs: University of Connecticut Extension.

Midwest Plan Service. 1987. *Structures and Environment Handbook.* MWPS-1, 11th Ed. (rev). Ames, Iowa: Midwest Plan Service.

Chapter 28

Turner, L. W., S. G. Jackson, R. S. Gates and C. H. Wood. 1987. Horse housing in Kentucky— An evaluation from the viewpoint of the engineer and the horseman. ASAE Paper No. 87-4009. St. Joseph, Mich.: ASAE.

Appendix A
Conversion Factors

Appendix Table 1. Conversion factors

Quantity	From Customary	Multiple by	To SI Units	Name
Length	ft	0.305	m	meter
	in.	25.4	mm	millimeter
Area	ft^2	0.093	m^2	square meter
	in.^{2}	645.16	mm^2	square millimeter
	acre	0.405	ha	hectare
Volume	cu ft	0.028	m^3	cubic meter
	cu in.	16 387	mm^3	cubic millimeter
Fluid volume	oz	29.574	mL	milliliter
	gal (U.S.)	3.785	L	liter
	gal (U.K.)	4.542	L	
	cu ft	28.317	L	
Velocity	ft/min	0.005	m/s	meter per second
	mph	1.609	km/h	kilometer per hour
Acceleration	ft/s^2	0.305	m/s^2	meter/second squared
	32.15 ft/s^2		9.8 m/s^2	acceleration of gravity
Mass	lb	0.454	kg	kilogram
	oz	28.35	g	gram
	grain	0.065	g	
	ton	0.907	t	tonne
Mass/Area	psf	4.882	kg/m^2	kilogram/square meter
Force	lb	4.448	N	newton
	kip	4.448	kN	kilonewton
Pressure	lb/sq ft	47.88	Pa	pascal
	lb/sq in.	6.895	kPa	kilopascal
	kip/sq in.	6.895	MPa	megapascal
Heat, energy	Btu	1.055	kJ	kilojoule
	kWh	3.6	MJ	megajoule
	kilocalorie	4.187	kJ	kilojoule
	Btu/h	0.293	W	watt
Power	hp	0.746	kW	kilowatt
Temperature	°F	0.556	C	Celsius
	°F	0.556	K	kelvin
Thermal capacity	Btu/(lb-°F)	4.187	kJ/(kg-K)	
Illuminance	ft candle	10.764	lx	lux

Temperature may be converted from scale to scale as follows:

°C = (°F − 32) × (5/9).

°F = (°C × 9/5) + 32.

°K = °C + 273.15.

°R = °F + 459.9.

Appendix Table 2. Conversion factors for multiple units

Quantity	From Customary	Multiply by	To SI Units
Thermal conductivity	Btu-in./(h-ft^2-°F)	0.144	Wm/(m^2-K)
Thermal conductance	Btu/(h-ft^2-°F)	5.678	W/(m^2-K)
Thermal resistance	(h-ft^2-°F)/Btu	0.176	m^2-K/W
Heat flow	Btu/(h-ft^2)	3.155	W/m^2
Permeability	grain-in./(h-ft^2-in.Hg)	0.017	g-m/(24h-m^2-mmHg)
Permeance	grain/(h-ft^2-in.Hg)	0.66	g/(24h-m^2-mmHg)
Vapor flow	grains/(h-ft^2)	16.73	g/(24h-m^2)
Fluid flow	ft^3/min	0.472	L/s

Appendix Table 3. Preferred multiples, submultiples, and prefixes

Multiplication Factor	Name	Symbol
10^{18}	exa	E
10^{15}	peta	P
10^{12}	tera	T
10^9	giga	G
10^6	mega	M
10^3	kilo	k
10^{-3}	milli	m
10^{-6}	micro	μ
10^{-9}	nano	n
10^{-12}	pico	p

Appendix Table 4. SI derived units with special names

Quantity	Unit Name	Symbol	Formula
Frequency	hertz	Hz	cycles/s
Force	newton	N	kg-m/s^2
Gravitational force	newton	N	9.8 m-kg/s^2
Pressure	pascal	Pa	N/m^2
Energy, Heat	joule	J	Nm
Power	watt	W	J/s
Torque	newton meter	Nm	Nm

Appendix Table 5. Weather bin data for selected stations

Temperature Range (°C)		Anchorage	Tuscon	Denver	Orlando	Bismarck	Des Moines
∞	-34.4	1	0	0	0	3	0
-34.4	-28.9	9	0	1	0	34	0
-28.9	-23.3	68	0	8	0	147	16
-23.3	-17.8	271	0	35	0	352	114
-17.8	-12.2	554	0	137	0	550	273
-12.2	-6.7	921	1	380	0	686	506
-6.7	-1.1	1361	25	948	3	990	929
-1.1	4.4	1528	296	1427	82	1246	1343
4.4	10.0	1431	1042	1481	413	1065	993
10.0	15.6	1932	1589	1513	1011	1213	1139
15.6	21.1	629	1584	1411	1949	1165	1475
21.1	26.7	53	1830	876	3435	804	1273
26.7	32.2	2	1452	465	1667	404	593
32.2	37.8	0	829	78	200	97	104
37.8	∞	0	112	0	0	4	2

Temperature Range (°C)		Orleans	New Syracuse	Isle	Presque Bend	South Atlanta	Columbia
∞	-34.4	0	0	0	0	0	0
-34.4	-28.9	0	0	3	0	0	0
-28.9	-23.3	0	1	65	3	0	0
-23.3	-17.8	0	31	257	38	0	25
-17.8	-12.2	0	171	530	141	2	102
-12.2	-6.7	3	492	829	405	32	292
-6.7	-1.1	36	954	1151	1025	185	702
-1.1	4.4	301	1536	1488	1572	775	1260
4.4	10.0	808	1362	1268	1148	1274	1155
10.0	15.6	1326	1376	1413	1199	1483	1184
15.6	21.1	1703	1450	1208	1479	1832	1515
21.1	26.7	2851	1070	464	1211	2041	1497
26.7	32.2	1583	386	83	483	979	810
32.2	37.8	149	31	1	56	156	209
37.8	∞	0	0	0	0	1	9

Appendix Table 6. Heating degree days (base 18.3 °C)

	Anchorage	Tuscon	Denver	Orlando	Bismarck	Des Moines
Jul	136	0	3	0	19	0
Aug	162	0	5	0	16	5
Sep	287	0	65	0	123	55
Oct	517	14	238	0	321	202
Nov	713	128	455	40	602	465
Dec	873	226	575	110	813	684
Jan	906	262	629	122	949	777
Feb	731	191	521	92	801	646
Mar	718	134	493	58	668	537
Apr	488	42	310	3	358	272
May	329	3	160	0	183	117
Jun	175	0	37	0	65	22
Total	6035	1000	3491	425	4918	3782

	New Orleans	Syracuse	Winnipeg	South Bend	Atlanta	Columbia
Jul	0	3	21	0	0	0
Aug	0	16	39	0	0	0
Sep	0	73	179	62	10	30
Oct	11	231	379	207	71	139
Nov	107	413	695	432	230	362
Dec	179	641	976	625	348	537
Jan	202	706	1116	678	355	598
Feb	143	633	955	594	294	486
Mar	107	558	814	518	243	398
Apr	22	317	452	292	93	180
May	0	138	225	133	14	67
Jun	0	25	82	33	0	7
Total	771	3754	5933	3577	1658	2804

Appendix Table 7. Fan test results (from University of Illinois)

Fan Diameter (in.)	0.04 in. S.P.		0.10 in. S.P.	
	(cfm)	(cfm/W)	(cfm)	(cfm/W)
24	5990	15.8	5500	14.0
24	6210	15.2	5680	13.4
24	4810	14.0	4420	12.6
24	6750	13.4	6320	12.3
24	5320	13.0	4870	11.7
24	5960	11.6	5580	10.9
24	4900	11.7	4470	10.4
24	6180	10.4	5850	9.8
24	5410	9.5	5000	8.6
24	6120	8.7	5840	8.2
36	10600	19.8	9500	17.4
36	9700	19.2	8900	16.6
36	10900	18.2	9700	15.7
36	8500	18.0	7500	15.1
36	9700	17.3	8900	15.0
36	8300	17.5	7200	14.6
36	9800	17.3	8800	14.6
36	10200	17.4	8800	14.4
36	6400	15.8	8600	14.0
36	10100	15.9	8900	13.7
36	9100	15.2	8300	13.2
36	11000	15.1	9800	13.0
36	8700	14.8	7100	11.8
36	11000	12.4	9800	11.3
36	7800	12.4	6500	10.4
36	11000	9.4	9900	8.4
36	8400	9.5	7600	8.3
48	23900	23.4	21900	19.9
48	22900	22.2	20900	19.0
48	19000	19.5	17400	17.4
48	22200	19.6	20200	17.1
48	17100	18.9	15600	16.9
48	25000	19.0	23000	16.9
48	18800	19.9	16700	16.5
48	20300	18.1	18900	16.4
48	17500	18.6	15500	16.1
48	18600	17.6	16900	15.7
48	19000	17.3	17300	15.1
48	16100	17.7	13300	14.5
48	19600	15.1	18300	13.7
48	16200	15.7	13200	13.3
48	23000	14.6	21100	12.8
48	12900	14.8	11600	12.4
48	20800	12.6	19100	11.3
48	17700	12.4	15500	11.0
48	22600	10.5	20600	9.6
48	9100	10.7	4100	4.6

Appendix Table 8. Ventilation troubleshooting checklist

---

1. Building too cold
   A.   Thermostat — location, setting, faulty
   B.   Insulation inadequate, wet, deteriorated
   C.   Low animal occupancy (number or time)
   D.   Excess infiltration, inlets open too wide
   E.   Fan/furnace design, operation

2. Building too warm
   A.   Fans dirty, belts slipping, shutter not operating
   B.   Inlets inadequate or clogged
   C.   Short circuiting
   D.   Also 1A or 1B

3. High relative humidity
   A.   Waterer or plumbing leaks
   B.   Disease outbreak
   C.   Excessive evaporation of urine
   D.   Also 1C

4. Condensation on building surfaces
   A.   Extreme, extended low outside temperature
   B.   Single glazed windows
   C.   Also 1B & all of 3

Appendix B
List of Tables

Appendix C
List of Figures

Index